JOHN I. JOHNSON, JR.
BIOPHYSICS DEPARTMENT
MICHIGAN STATE UNIVERSITY
EAST LANSING, MICHIGAN 48823

The Comparative Anatomy and Histology of the Cerebellum from Myxinoids through Birds

The Comparative Anatomy and Histology of the

CEREBELLUM

from Myxinoids through Birds

by

OLOF LARSELL, Ph.D.

edited by JAN JANSEN, M.D.

with a Foreword by Robert S. Dow, M.D.

THE UNIVERSITY OF MINNESOTA PRESS, MINNEAPOLIS

*Publication of this book was aided by a grant from the
National Institute of Neurological Diseases and Blindness of the
United States Public Health Service (grant NB 06794-01).*

Printed in the United States of America at the Lund Press, Inc., Minneapolis

Library of Congress Catalog Card Number: 67-19421

PUBLISHED IN GREAT BRITAIN, INDIA, AND PAKISTAN BY THE OXFORD UNIVERSITY PRESS, LONDON, BOMBAY,
AND KARACHI, AND IN CANADA BY THE COPP CLARK PUBLISHING CO. LIMITED, TORONTO

FOREWORD

IT IS with a genuine feeling of thankfulness that I am privileged to write a foreword to this volume. For more than forty-five years Olof Larsell was occupied with the cerebellum, and during at least half of that time he dreamed of seeing his life's work presented in monographic form. I had the rare good fortune of being more or less intimately associated with this effort in one way or another from the time I was a medical and graduate student under Professor Larsell's tutelage over thirty years ago. One seldom sees the singleness of purpose which will keep an investigator devoted to one subject for almost half a century. Such, however, was Larsell's record.

In 1950 Professor Larsell asked me to write a chapter or two dealing with cerebellar physiology and pathology to be included in a volume he was already beginning to prepare on cerebellar anatomy. This stimulus resulted, with the invaluable collaboration of Professor Giuseppe Moruzzi, a friend of now almost thirty years, in the publication by the University of Minnesota Press of *The Physiology and Pathology of the Cerebellum* in 1958.

When this latter work was initiated in 1952 we fully expected that its appearance would follow by a year or two the publication of Larsell's volume on the anatomy of the cerebellum. Because of the perfectionistic attitude with which this scientist approached his life's work, however, repeated revisions were undertaken in an effort to make the volume more complete and up to date. Fortunately, the University of Minnesota Press continued to maintain an active interest in its completion. In 1955, after two years at the University of Minnesota as professor of neuroanatomy, Dr. Larsell spent a full year in Oslo, Norway, as a Fulbright research scholar at the Anatomical Institute, where he was made welcome by Professor Jan Jansen, a cerebellar morphologist of renown who also had been a former pupil of C. Judson Herrick.

After Larsell's return to Portland, Oregon, in 1956, his work continued steadfastly, but in the rather uninspiring environment of a small study in his home. Then, with the establishment of the Laboratory of Neurophysiology at Good Samaritan Hospital in 1960 and through the generosity of the hospital staff and his former students, a more suitable place for his work was provided and some funds for the necessary secretarial and artistic help were raised to permit him to complete this volume.

Death claimed him, though, before his work in fact was completed. What a tragedy it would have been if his work could not have been made available to future anatomists and physiologists. Happily, this was sensed by the National Institute of Neurological Diseases and Blindness of the United States Public Health Service, which provided a grant (NB 05838-01) to permit Professor Jan Jansen to complete the work.

A better choice could not have been found: a loyal friend of many years whose knowledge of cerebellar morphology combined with his devotion to Professor Larsell to make his acceptance of the task a source of gratification and pleasure both to Professor Larsell's family and to his scientific offspring as well.

Professor Jansen's less than six months' sojourn in Portland was time enough for him to assemble and place in the hands of the publisher the manuscript of this volume, and to finish almost all of a second volume dealing exclusively with the mammalian cerebellum. He unselfishly refused to permit the publication of these volumes with himself listed as joint author, even though that had been part of the original plan in bringing him to Portland. Without his help the work would never have been completed, and I personally feel an indebtedness to Professor Jansen that I can never repay for his willingness to drop his own research to come to the United States and complete this monumental work.

Thanks should be expressed also to Clarice Ashworth Francone, a devoted friend who worked with Professor Larsell during most of his many years at the University of Oregon Medical School and whose skill and patience in helping to prepare or repair the over seven hundred illustrations for the two volumes have been invaluable. Secretarial assistance was provided by Maybelle Romig, a lifelong friend of Professor and Mrs. Larsell who worked very closely with the manuscript for almost ten years.

It is a real gratification to see the first volume of this work in final published form and to have had a small part in helping to see it completed at long last. The small part I have played in this cannot begin to repay my own personal debt to Professor Larsell, who is chiefly responsible for introducing me to neurological investigation.

ROBERT S. DOW
Laboratory of Neurophysiology
Good Samaritan Hospital, Portland, Oregon

PREFACE

INSPIRED by Dr. C. Judson Herrick, then professor at the University of Chicago, Olof Larsell's research interest was directed to the broad field of comparative neurology early in his scientific career and quite particularly to the comparative anatomy of the cerebellum, a subject which for more than forty years remained his primary field of research.

At the suggestion of Professor Herrick, Larsell's comparative studies of the cerebellum began with its description in a generalized amphibian brain. In 1920 his paper on "The Cerebellum of Amblystoma" was published in Herrick's distinguished *Journal of Comparative Neurology*. This was the first of a long series of papers published over the following four decades, dealing with the development and morphology of the cerebellum from cyclostomes to man.

Out of these comprehensive and extensive studies grew the plan for a monographic presentation of present knowledge of the comparative anatomy of the cerebellum, including ontogenetic and phylogenetic development.

The last ten years of his life Olof Larsell devoted to this truly magnificent task. Because of his long-continued investigations of nearly all orders of vertebrates, pursued with a true scientist's insatiable curiosity, no one could have been better qualified to write this monograph.

In addition to these special qualifications, Olof Larsell was endowed with another, more general qualification, no less important for the author of a monograph on present-day knowledge of a subject. He had a genuine and profound interest in history, combined with a deeply felt desire to acknowledge the contributions of fellow scientists and to do justice to those who had laid the foundation on which our present knowledge rests.

It is sad, but not surprising, that Larsell did not live to see the monograph finished. With his uncompromising demand for quality and completeness the book could hardly ever be finished. Whether Larsell realized that himself I do not know. It was incompatible with his sense of quality and scientific standards to make concessions in order to see his lifework finished.

At his death in 1964 the third full draft of the text was well advanced and more than a thousand illustrations were in various stages of completion—some finished, others merely sketched.

While the work was in progress Dr. Larsell spent one year in the Anatomical Institute of Oslo University, and I had the privilege of his daily company, thus becoming familiar with the preparations for this unique contribution to comparative neuroanatomical literature. No doubt this monograph in years to come will serve as the leading source of reference for all who are interested in the comparative anatomy of the nervous system.

The editing of Dr. Larsell's monograph is the consequence of collaboration by many, all inspired by admiration for the author and his work. No single person deserves more credit in this connection than does Dr. Larsell's former student and collaborator in many investigations, Dr. Robert S. Dow. Dr. Dow, with the benevolent support of the Good Samaritan Hospital in Portland, Oregon, arranged for Dr. Larsell to have laboratory facilities and favorable working conditions. Subsequently Dr. Dow was able to obtain a grant from the National Institute of Neurological Diseases and Blindness of the United States Public Health Service to permit preparation of the manuscript. In so doing Dr. Dow indeed rendered neurological science a great service.

When entrusted with the responsibility for the publication of the book, I was most fortunate, during a five months' sojourn in Portland, to be able to draw on the good will of those who in one way or another had assisted Dr. Larsell. I am especially indebted to Mrs. Clarice Ashworth Francone, who with expert skill, made most of the illustrations, and to Mrs. Maybelle Romig for excellent secretarial assistance.

My secretary, Mrs. Agnes Holter, has materially eased my work by reading proofs, by preparing the index, and by assisting in various other ways. Her help is acknowledged with deep gratitude.

It gives me a great pleasure to express, furthermore, my appreciation to the entire staff of the University of Minnesota Press. I am particularly grateful to Miss Marcia Strout and Miss Jane McCarthy for their wholehearted cooperation and skillful handling of all technical and typographical matters.

In concluding I wish to extend my warm thanks to Mrs. Olof Larsell and her son Robert for placing at my disposal so liberally and unconditionally all material related to this monograph, and for the confidence bestowed on me.

JAN JANSEN
Anatomical Institute
University of Oslo, Norway

Oslo, October 1966

CONTENTS

*The Comparative Anatomy and Histology of the
Cerebellum from Myxinoids through Birds*

INTRODUCTION

HEROPHILUS (335–280 B.C.) is usually credited with recognition of the human cerebellum as a distinct division of the brain. Aristotle (384–322 B.C.), however, calls it parencephalis, indicating that he did not regard it as part of the principal mass of the brain. The great Galen (A.D. 131–200) designated the vermis cerebelli "the worm-like outgrowth" (epiphysis scolexoides). The arbor vitae was described by Thomas Willis (1664) in his *Cerebri Anatome* as a "ramificatio cerebelli ad foramen arboris." The latter author also suggested that the cerebellum presides over the involuntary movement of the body, the cerebrum controlling those movements brought about by volition. The first good drawing of the vermis was published by Heister (1717), but Vesalius (1543) had included in his *Fabrica* rather crude illustrations of the entire cerebellum which are in striking contrast to his beautiful figures of muscles, bones, and other structures. Haller (1777) described the cerebellar hemispheres under the name lobi, and Malacarne (1780) gave a detailed description of the entire organ. Many of the terms which Malacarne introduced are still in use. He also described the surface folia or "laminette," giving their total number as 500 to 780. In the cerebellum of an idiot he found only 340 folia, leading him to conclude that intelligence depends on the number of cerebellar folds.

Analysis of the lobes and fissures was undertaken by a number of investigators. Gordon (1815) introduced the term "mons cerebelli" for the upper portion of the organ. A sharper differentiation was first made by Meckel (1817), who gave the name "monticulus" to the dorsal projection. Schwalbe (1881) attempted to limit the term monticulus to the culmen, which Burdach (1822) had described as the highest elevation of the superior surface of the vermis. Burdach also named the declive, or downward slope, of the monticulus.

The lingula was first described by Malacarne, who designated it "linguetta laminosa." Reil (1807–08) published the first drawing, and a more complete description was given by Stilling (1864). Because it is very rudimentary in development, Malacarne believed it might be absent altogether. Ziehen (1903, p. 454), however, found a layer of gray substance at least 0.5 mm thick on the anterior medullary velum, in the most extreme cases of atrophy of the lingula. He states that it is never entirely absent.

The lobulus centralis was named by Malacarne (1776), and Stilling described an occasional doubling of this lobule. The latter investigator also divided the monticulus of Meckel into six "Wände," the caudal two of which correspond to the declive.

The folium vermis was called "chorda laminosa transversalis s. commissura cerebelli" by Malacarne (1780). Reil, Burdach (folium cacuminis), Arnold (1838), and Schwalbe (1881) all described it under different names. The designation "folium vermis" was applied by the Commission on Nomenclature in Basel in 1895. The tuber vermis, called the tuber valvulae by Burdach, corresponds to the "short or visible and long or covered transverse bands" of Reil. Arnold speaks of "laminae transversales inferiores."

The pyramis was designated pyramis laminosa by Malacarne (1780), who also named the uvula; and called the nodulus the "tuberculum laminosum." Reil (1807) used the term "Knötchen," subsequently latinized into nodulus.

The nodulus of the vermis have been variously grouped by different investigators. Henle included lingula, lobulus centralis, and monticulus in his vermis superior (Oberwurm); the folium vermis and tuber vermis he grouped together as vermis posterior, the pyramis, uvula, and nodulus as vermis inferior. Arnold (1851) included the lobules from lingula to folium vermis as the Oberwurm, and those from tuber vermis to nodulus as Unterwurm. Subsequently, Flatau and Jacobsohn (1899) divided the vermis at the sulcus superior anterior into anterior and posterior vermis.

The medullary body of the cerebellum, called the nucleus by Malacarne and metullium cerebelli by Burdach, gives ray-like branches to the cortical subdivisions. Many students of the cerebellum have made the principal medullary rays the basis of the vermian lobules. On the basis of the rays leading to them, Ziehen (1903) distinguishes seven lobules: (1) lingula, (2) lobulus centralis, (3) culmen, (4) declive–folium–tuber vermis, (5) pyramis, (6) uvula, (7) nodulus. Schwalbe (1881) included declive, folium, and tuber in a posterior vermis lobule not identical with the Hinterwurm of Henle. Ziehen holds that the developmental history of the cerebellum favors the seven divisions he recognizes.

There is, however, no agreement as to the number of principal medullary rays of the vermis. Usually two are recognized as rising from the central mass, the anterior or vertical branch ("stehender Ast" of Reil) and the posterior or horizontal branch ("liegender Ast" of Reil). Ziehen recognizes seven branches corresponding to his seven vermian lobules.

The vinculae lingulae were usually designated by Stilling, who first described them, as "frenula lingulae." The alae lobuli centralis were first clearly described by Reil, and the lobulus quadrangularis was described by Meckel (1817), although Malacarne (1780) had recognized it under the name "lobus superior anterior s. quadrilaterus." Koelliker designated as lobus lunatus anterior the part of the lobulus quadrangularis which continues medially with the culmen, and as lobus lunatus posterior that portion which is continuous with the declive of the monticulus.

The lobulus semilunaris superior of Meckel (1817) was called lobus superior posterior by Malacarne. The lobulus semilunaris inferior, in whole or in part, has been described under various names. Malacarne described the posterior portion, adjoining the lobulus semilunaris superior, as the lobus inferior posterior and the anterior portion as lobus subtilis. Burdach included both parts in his lobus inferior posterior, and Meckel combined them as lobus posterior inferior sive semilunaris. Arnold used the designation lobus inferior posterior again in the narrower sense of Malacarne for the posterior part, and also limited Meckel's lobus semilunaris inferior to the caudal part; the forward part, the lobus subtilis of Malacarne, he regarded as the lobus inferior medius s. gracilis. Henle included both portions, as above stated, with the lobus semilunaris, as lobus posterior. Schwalbe returned to

Burdach's nomenclature, whereas the Commission on Nomenclature (1895) followed by Ziehen, returned to Meckel's terminology.

The lobus semilunaris inferior in its further course is divided into three sublobules. The most caudal, i.e., that lying next to the lobus semilunaris superior, corresponds essentially to the enlarged gyri of the tuber vermis in the sulcus horizontalis, the middle sublobule from the surface folia of the tuber vermis, and the most rostral from the folia of the tuber vermis projecting into the sulcus inferior posterior. This third lobule as a rule is especially well developed; it corresponds most nearly to what the older authors designated as lobus subtilis s. gracilis. Ziehen designates the three sublobules briefly as posterior, middle, and anterior. Schäfer (1893) designates the entire lobulus semilunaris inferior as lobus posteroinferior and the three sublobules as lobus semilunaris inferior, lobulus gracilis posterior, and lobulus gracilis anterior.

The lobulus biventer of Malacarne, the hemispheral representative of the pyramis in part, was called lobus anterior inferior s. cuneiformis s. biventer by Meckel. The tonsilla, also named by Malacarne, was called lobulus medullae oblongatae by Vicq d' Azyr, and lobus inferior internus or monticulus by Meckel. The flocculus, which represents the nodulus laterally, was known to Thomas Bartholin (1655), although he did not sharply distinguish it from the tonsilla; this distinction was made by Tarin (1750), who called the two flocculi the tubercula minima cerebelli. The term flocculus is derived from Malacarne's flossi laminosi, converted by Meckel to flocculus. The accessory flocculus or Nebenflocke of Henle is usually regarded as rudimentary, but according to Ziehen it is seldom entirely lacking.

The nucleus dentatus appears to have been described by Vieussens (1685); he called it substantia rhomboidea s. corpus rhomboideum. Vicq d' Azyr (1786–90) named it corps festome ou dentele, and Rolando (1825) called it corpus denticulatum. The nucleus fastigii was first described and illustrated by Stilling, as was the nucleus globosus, although Meynert (1872) had perhaps seen the latter. The emboliform nucleus was described clearly for the first time by Stilling, who called it Propf or Embolus. It probably was known to Meynert.

Schäfer (1893) recognized that the flocculus and nodulus are distinct from the main mass of the cerebellum, applying to these two subdivisions the term nodulofloccular lobe. No indication of the functional significance of this lobe could be given at that time. These authors also described the other lobules and principal fissures in considerable detail, as already indicated. Many terms introduced by various authors have proved confusing to the experimental investigator of the cerebellum and to the comparative anatomist because the terms were based on the orientation of the adult human cerebellum rather than on morphological considerations of embryonic and phylogenetic origins. Ziehen (1899) and Dejerine (1901) have provided the most complete and thorough descriptive analysis of the macroscopic anatomy of the human cerebellum. Thirty-five years later Ziehen followed this by an exhaustive account of the microscopic anatomy of the organ, as shown by sections stained by the Weigert method and by the silver methods of Golgi and Cajal.

Malacarne had classified the folds of the cerebellar cortex as lobi, lobetti, and foglietta. Reil had distinguished four orders of subdivision of the organ: lobe, lobuli, ramuli, and folia. Subsequent investigators varied these terms in greater or less degree. The Commission on Nomenclature recognized only lobuli and gyri, a terminology which Ziehen did not regard as sufficient to meet the needs of factual presentation. He therefore divided the organ, according to the depth of the delimiting furrows, into lobules, gyri, and gyruli, but recognized as sublobules the subdivisions which are formed by the fusion of two or three gyri. The lobules and fissures of Ziehen are summarized in the accompanying tabulation.

Vermis Lobules	Delimiting Furrows	Hemispheral Lobules
Lingula		Vinculum lingulae
	Sulcus postlingualis	
Lobulus centralis		Ala lobuli centralis
	Sulcus postcentralis	
Monticulus		Lobulus quadrangularis
(a) Culmen		(a) Pars anterior
	Sulcus sup. ant.	
(b) Declive		(b) Pars posterior
	Sulcus sup. post.	
Folium vermis		Lobulus semilunaris sup.
	Sulcus horizontalis	
Tuber vermis		Lobulus semilunaris inf.
	Sulcus inf. post.	
Pyramis		Lobulus biventer
	Sulcus inf. ant.	
Uvula		Tonsilla
	Sulcus praeuvularis	
Nodulus		Flocculus

The earlier studies of the cerebellum in animals were largely experimental in execution. Rolando (1809) removed the cerebellum in fishes, reptiles, and mammals, described the disturbances of voluntary movement that resulted, and pointed out that cerebellar ablation does not affect sensation. Flourens (1844) confirmed and extended Rolando's observations, emphasizing the exaggeration of tendon and antigravity reflexes and the curious stiff-legged locomotion, with retraction of the head, that follows ablation of the cerebellum in birds. Ferrier (1876) reported his observations on the responses of the

eyes, head, and neck to electrical stimulation of the cerebellum in dogs. Luciani (1891) described the results in the dog of complete removal of the organ, and Sherrington (1900) defined the cerebellum as the "head ganglion of the proprioceptive system," holding that it functions as a whole because it deals with the musculature of the body as a whole rather than with individual muscles. This concept was the dominating influence in cerebellar physiology for more than forty years.

During the last decade of the nineteenth century a new approach toward an understanding of the organ was begun by studies on its comparative anatomy and its embryonic development. The first article to appear in the *Journal of Comparative Neurology* was a comparative paper on the cerebellum by C. L. Herrick (1891). Kuithan (1895) described stages of development of the organ in sheep and human embryos; he recognized and named as sulcus primarius the deep fissure which divides the principal mass of the organ into anterior and posterior lobes. The same year saw publication by Stroud (1895) of a comparative study of the development of the cerebellum in cat and human embryos. This author homologized the accessory paraflocculus (Henle's Nebenflocke) with the paraflocculus of mammals. Whereas this interpretation has proved correct only to the extent that the Nebenflocke is a small and rudimentary subdivision of the entire complex of the paraflocculus, it gave a great impetus to closer comparison of other subdivisions of the mammalian cerebellum with that of man.

Elliot Smith (1902, 1903a, 1903b, 1903c), in a series of papers based on a wide range of mammals from marsupials to man, divided the cerebellum into anterior, medial, posterior, and floccular lobes. He emphasized the fissura prima (the sulcus primarius of Kuithan) as the deepest and most important, but recognized in his later papers that the postnodular (uvulonodular) fissure appears earlier in the embryo. He further subdivided the lobes into various lobules and areas.

During the same period Bradley (1903, 1904, 1905) reported an extensive study of the development of the cerebellar lobes and fissures in mammalian embryos, and an analysis of the fully developed cerebella of a large number of species of mammals. In order to avoid anthropomorphic implications he used Roman numerals and letters of the alphabet to designate the fissures, lobes, and lobules.

Bolk (1906) published an analysis of the adult mammalian and fetal human cerebellum. This was based on an investigation of a large number of species which have wide variations in the development of different regions of the body. Bolk held that the sulcus primarius of Kuithan divides the cerebellum into anterior and posterior lobes.

He defined and named the subdivisions of the cerebellar hemispheres and the lobules of the vermis using Arabic numerals and letters of the alphabet for the latter. On the basis of the degree of development of the various subdivisions, in correlation with the size and therefore the muscle masses of the subdivisions of the body, Bolk attempted to assign to the various lobules a functional relationship with body regions. His concepts appeared at first to be largely confirmed by van Rijnberk (1908), using physiological methods. Discrepancies gradually came to the fore, so that the functional localization of Bolk and van Rijnberk is no longer tenable. Bolk's descriptive terminology of the cerebellar lobules, however, has remained in use, except for his formatio vermicularis. This complex part of the cerebellum Bolk failed entirely to analyze correctly, as soon was recognized.

Edinger (1909), on the basis of comparative studies of the cerebellum of mammals and birds and other lower vertebrates, drew a distinction between the vermis, or paleocerebellum, and the hemispheres or neocerebellum, the latter representing the portion of the cerebellum having functional relations to the cerebral cortex. Langelaan (1919) showed, however, in human embryos that the vermian segments are continuous with hemispheral subdivisions on either side. Riley (1929) confirmed the conclusions of Langelaan in a large series of adult mammals and man and gave names to each of the vermian-hemispheral "lobuli," basing his terminology, with some modifications, on that of Bolk.

Bolk had compared the human fetal cerebellum at various stages of development with the pattern demonstrated in adult mammals. Reference will be made in subsequent pages to his comparisons of individual lobules. A more comprehensive embryological investigation, complemented by comparative anatomical and experimental studies, was undertaken by Ingvar (1918). Studying the early embryonic development of the organ largely in chick embryos, Ingvar concluded that there are three principal lobes of the avian and the mammalian cerebellum: anterior, medial, and posterior. The anterior lobe of Ingvar is identical with that of Elliot Smith, Bolk, and all others who have recognized such a division. His medial lobe, however, differs from that of Elliot Smith in being bounded caudally by the prepyramidal fissure, instead of the fissura secunda. Ingvar's posterior lobe, as a result, is bounded rostrally by the prepyramidal fissure, instead of by the fissura secunda; the posterior lobe, as defined by Elliot Smith, differs accordingly from that of Ingvar. Unfortunately Ingvar had interpreted as prepyramidal fissure in the chick embryo and, as a result, in the numerous species of adult birds he described, the furrow that corresponds to the fissura secunda of mammals.

It has since become clear that Ingvar's fissure z, which, he says in a footnote, probably corresponds to the fissura secunda of Elliot Smith, is in reality a secondary furrow of the uvula; Ingvar's sulcus y, which in the same footnote he regards as the prepyramidal fissure, corresponds, both in embryonic and adult birds, to the fissura secunda of mammals rather than to the prepyramidal fissure. Ingvar's medial lobule and that of Elliot Smith, therefore, are morphologically identical.

Basing his morphological interpretations on Ingvar's concepts of three cerebellar lobes, Jakob (1928) presented a comprehensive study of the human cerebellum, embryonic and adult. Hochstetter (1919, 1929) had given an account of the development of the human cerebellum in terms of the classical terminology but with no attempt at interpretation in relation to the cerebellum of other mammals. A wealth of exact observation on carefully preserved and prepared human embryonic material had been gathered by Jakob and Hochstetter, but the correlation of most of the cerebellar subdivisions with those of other mammalian species remained unaccomplished. The human cerebellum, with its many peculiarities, was still largely uninterpreted in terms of comparative neurology. The application of experimental results on animals to an understanding of cerebellar function in man, except with respect to general areas, remained uncertain.

In the meantime, studies of the simpler cerebellum of lower forms had begun to establish a fundamental basis for an understanding of the morphology of the organ. Johnston (1901) showed in the lamprey that the cerebellum is a dorsomedial extension of the somatic sensory column, as he had, many years earlier, shown in the human embryo that the cerebellum is a derivative of the alar plate. Johnston traced into the primitive cerebellum of the lamprey the lateral-line and vestibular fiber tracts, and showed the primitive Purkinje cells and other cerebellar elements as modifications of cells of the acousticolateral area. Numerous papers on the cerebellum of many species of fishes by other authors provided a wealth of detail about fiber tracts and connections, but added little to an understanding of the organ's function, despite the fact that the fishes provide the greatest variations of this organ to be found within any class of the vertebrates.

C. J. Herrick's paper (1914a) on the cerebellum in Necturus and certain other urodeles again opened the door to a simpler approach to morphological and functional analysis of this organ. I began that same year to continue this approach by studying the cerebellum of the salamander, Amblystoma. This was followed by studies of other amphibians, of reptiles, and of primitive mammals. In these investigations it became apparent that the primitive predominantly vestibular and lateral-line organ cerebellum of the lampreys is continued in the urodeles and higher forms as a laterally situated vestibular and lateral-line subdivision, medial to which develops a corpus cerebelli whose fiber tract connections are quite different. The corpus cerebelli receives proprioceptive and other sensory impulses and becomes the predominant feature of the cerebellum in the vertebrates above the sluggish urodeles, as well as in the active types of fishes such as selachians and teleosts.

Experimental studies have in recent years attracted more attention than the morphological studies with which this volume is concerned. The extensive review of these matters (Dow and Moruzzi, 1958), which was planned as a companion to this work, unavoidably preceded the present volume. Ablation experiments, stimulation experiments, and, more recently, electrophysiological studies have all been of value in testing the validity of these morphological concepts. More detailed investigation is largely dependent on more detailed and adequate knowledge of the anatomy of the cerebellum in experimental animals and a better understanding of its fundamental morphology.

To provide such a basis for morphology and anatomy is the subject of this monograph. The cerebellum is followed through all stages of phylogenetic and ontogenetic development. For practical purposes the monograph is published in two volumes.

This first volume deals with the cerebellum of cyclostomes, fishes, amphibia, reptiles and birds. The second volume will be devoted to the cerebellum of mammals.

It is my purpose to present the study of the development and adult structure of the organ in a comprehensive manner, that, it is hoped, will be sufficiently detailed to clarify the principal morphological problems and questions involved in its analysis.

MYXINIDAE

THE most primitive living vertebrates, namely the myx-inoids, have a peculiar brain whose subdivisions long baffled attempts to establish homologies with those of the typical vertebrate encephalon. The brain of Myxine glutinosa was described by A. Retzius (1822) and Müller (1837, 1838). Subsequent studies on the brains of Myxine or Bdellostoma were made by G. Retzius (1893), Sanders (1894), von Kupffer (1899, 1906), Holm (1901), Julia Worthington (1905), Edinger (1906), Sterzi (1907), and Holmgren (1919) but there was little agreement in the interpretations of some of the subdivisions of the organ. Not until the brain of Bdellestoma stouti was elucidated by Conel (1929, 1931) by study of its development, and the brain of adult Myxine glutinosa was reinterpreted by Jansen (1930) on the basis of a thorough study of its fiber tracts did the subdivisions of the myxinoid brain become understandable in terms of those of other vertebrates.

The dorsal view of the brain of Bdellostoma stouti, illustrated in figure 1, shows four pairs of lobes that correspond to those in Myxine, the brain of which is similar but more foreshortened, as illustrated by Retzius (1893). The studies of Jansen (1930) in Myxine demonstrated that the most anterior pair, which receives the olfactory nerve bundles, constitute the olfactory lobes; the second pair represents the telencephalon; the third pair the diencephalon; and the fourth and smallest pair forms the mesencephalon. The medulla oblongata is the largest subdivision of the brain. It divides rostrally into two large horns which lie lateral and caudal of the mesencephalon, one on either side. A deep cleft, the fissura rhombomesencephalica of Conel or fissura isthmi of Jansen, delimits the medulla oblongata from the midbrain.

With respect to the cerebellum, Retzius (1822) believed that no trace exists in Myxine. Müller (1838) regarded the fourth pair of lobes as corresponding to the

cerebellum of higher vertebrates. Retzius (1893) named the four pairs of lobes Riechhirn, Vorderhirn, Mittelhirn, and Hinterhirn, corresponding respectively to Jansen's olfactory lobes, telencephalon, diencephalon, and mesencephalon. Uncertainty regarding the homology of the fourth pair was expressed by Retzius, who recognized the need for developmental studies, but he added that un-

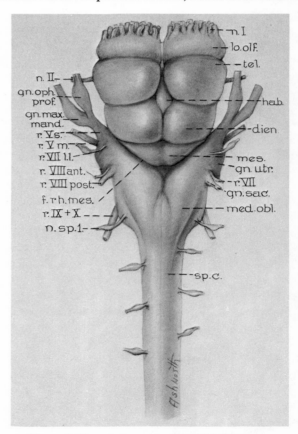

Figure 1. Dorsal view of brain of Bdellostoma stouti. ×7.5. (Larsell, 1947a.)

8

til further evidence became available it could only be regarded as the metencephalon. The fourth pair of lobes had been interpreted as cerebellum by Müller (1838) and, subsequent to the contribution of G. Retzius, by Sanders (1894) and Holmgren (1919) in Myxine, and by Worthington (1905) in Bdellostoma. Holm (1901), Edinger (1906), and Sterzi (1907) all regarded the cerebellum as lacking in Myxine, as did Stefanelli (1935, 1939). A study of embryos of Bdellostoma led von Kupffer (1899) to conclude that a cerebellum is present at the rostral end of the posterior division of the brain, which he called the rhombencephalon.

Holmgren (1919) describes a fascicle of fibers which he calls commissura cerebellaris and marshals his reasons for regarding as cerebellum the fourth brain division of G. Retzius and others. The evidence adduced by Holmgren was analyzed point by point by Jansen (1930), who concluded that this part of the brain is not cerebellum but represents a small mesencephalon. The Mittelhirn of G. Retzius and others was shown by Jansen, and by Conel (1929, 1931) on embryological grounds, to be the diencephalon. Jansen believed that Holmgren's commissura cerebellaris is the posterior commissure of the tectum, but conceded that it may include a few fibers of a rudimentary cerebellar commissure that interconnect the two horns of the medulla oblongata. Such connections Jansen was unable to establish; he concluded that a cerebellum cannot be recognized with certainty in Myxine.

Conel (1931) decided that the cerebellum, if there is one in embryos of Bdellostoma, is situated in the anteromedial part of the roof of the rhombencephalon which forms the posterior wall of the rhombomesencephalic fold. In some stages of the embryos fibers were seen that could be interpreted as a cerebellar commissure. A ridge of cells at the base of the rhombomesencephalic fold, connected by these fibers, was also described, but Conel concluded that the evidence was too limited to justify the interpretation that this ridge constitutes a cerebellum. A commissure, interpreted as cerebellar, was described in two embryos of Myxine by Holmgren (1946). It included fibers that enter the midbrain and fray out within it. In the larger of the two embryos the commissure is described as surrounded by nerve cells. Holmgren inclined to the belief that a not insignificant portion of the midbrain rostral to this commissure is related to the cerebellum.

Clarification of the morphology of the brain of myxinoids and of homologies of its subdivisions with those of other vertebrates by Conel (1929, 1931) and Jansen (1930) makes possible a closer comparison of the region in which the cerebellum would be found with the simple cerebellum of petromyzonts. In 1947 I described a fascicle of fine fibers in Bdellostoma, which was designated the acousticolateral commissure, and also a chain of cells from the ventromedial part of the acousticolateral area of either side extending toward the ventricular canal. The commissure and the cellular extensions together were regarded as the incipient cerebellum. Further study of hagfish and lamprey brains has confirmed these interpretations. Before considering the cerebellum of myxinoids further, however, it is important to describe briefly the acousticolateral area and the nerves and sensory organs related with this area.

THE LATERAL-LINE ORGANS AND NERVES

The lateral-line organs of Bdellostoma, according to Ayers and Worthington (1907), are small and difficult to find but form two groups. An anterior group comprising three to five, but usually four short series, is situated on the side of the head in front of the eye. Ayers and Worthington (1908) found that these are served by lateral-line components in the buccal, trigeminal, and probably also the facial nerves. A posterior group of organs lies on the dorsal surface of the head and is divided into medial and lateral subgroups. The medial subgroup comprises two or three rows of organs which extend lateralward. The rows of the lateral subgroup extend at a slight angle with the longitudinal axis of the body. The entire posterior group is served by the posterior lateral-line nerve; this nerve is said to have an individual trunk instead of being associated with the vagus nerve as in higher Ichthyopsida. Ayers and Worthington (1908) found no trace of lateral-line organs or nerves on the trunk of Bdellostoma. In Myxine, according to Lindström (1949), the buccal nerve has a lateral-line component, and Holmgren (1919) mentions such a component in the VII nerve. Lindström, however, found no branches to the skin from the facial nerve and questions a lateral-line component in this as well as the ophthalmic division of the V nerve. A bundle of fibers in the IX–X nerve complex, which are coarser than others, was regarded by Jansen (1930) as the posterior lateral-line nerve.

The lateral-line organs of myxinoids are embryonic in appearance, compared with those of higher Ichthyopsida, and Ayers and Worthington (1907) state that the sensory epithelium is poorly differentiated. In a strict sense the terms lateral-line organs and lateral-line nerves are inappropriate as applied to the cephalic representations of the system in myxinoids as well as other Ichthyopsida. They are so called because of their resemblance to the lateral-line series of the trunks of petromyzonts and fishes in general.

The anterior lateral-line nerve, in Myxine, enters the dorsolateral surface of the medulla oblongata, according to Jansen (1930), and divides into two parts. One part passes into the acousticolateral area, the fibers bifurcating into ascending and descending branches which end in an acousticolateral nucleus. The other part descends with the descending root of the V nerve to the level of the nucleus of the X nerve. Jansen was unable to follow the posterior lateral-line root into the medulla oblongata, but according to Ayers and Worthington (1908) this root in Bdellostoma passes directly to the medial border of the acousticolateral nucleus, taking a rostromedial and ventral course, and then goes forward to the anterior end of the nucleus. The fascicle divides into dorsal and ventral branches which distribute in the dorsal rostromedial part of the nucleus. A few fibers bifurcate and, as seen in Golgi material, occasional fibers turn caudalwards.

THE MEMBRANOUS LABYRINTH AND THE ACOUSTIC NERVE

The sensory organ of the labyrinth is primitive in Myxinidae. It comprises a saccus communis, from the ends of which arises a single arch with a small ampulla at each of its two bases (Retzius, 1881–84). According to de Burlet (1934), this arch represents the anterior and posterior semicircular canals, the two being confluent and forming a dorsolaterally directed ring.

The acoustic nerve divides into anterior and posterior branches which terminate along the saccus communis. Ayers and Worthington (1908) describe the two branches in Bdellostoma as ramus acusticus utricularis (anterior branch) and ramus acusticus saccularis (posterior branch), each having its own ganglion. As described by Jansen (1930) in Myxine, the utricular ganglion is the larger and is formed principally of large bipolar cells, but small cells occur in its posterior part.

Several bundles of rather coarse fibers from the dorsal border of the ganglion enter the medulla oblongata and cross the descending bundle of V root fibers at right angles, retaining a superficial position. They then turn ventrally and enter the acousticolateral area, in which their fibers bifurcate into ascending and descending rami. Many of the fibers from the utricular ganglion, however, enter the descending V bundle from the medial surface of the ganglion and form a large fascicle in the ventral part of this bundle. Most of these fibers also bifurcate, the ascending rami, which are the larger as a rule, apparently emerging from the medulla oblongata with the V nerve in large numbers. Presumably these are general cutaneous fibers. According to Ayers and Worthington (1908) the utricular nerve in Bdellostoma has a large general cutaneous component which innervates the membrane lining the labyrinth. The descending rami of the bifurcated utricular fibers in the ventral part of the trigeminal fascicle extend to the posterior end of the medulla oblongata, according to Jansen.

The root fibers from the smaller saccular ganglion, whose cells are much smaller than those in the utricular ganglion, follow the dorsal utricular roots into the acousticolateral area. Here they bifurcate and end.

THE TRIGEMINAL NERVE

The trigeminus is relatively very large in Bdellostoma and Myxine. It enters the anterior tip of the horn of the medulla oblongata. For a detailed description of its ganglia and branches in Myxine reference is made to Lindström (1949). The sensory fibers from the ophthalmic and maxillo-mandibular ganglia, after entering the medulla oblongata, form three large descending fascicles of fibers, most of which are coarse. As they descend toward the spinal cord the fibers branch and also give off collaterals in all directions. Some of the branches and collaterals enter the acousticolateral area. The number decreases rapidly toward the posterior end of the medulla oblongata, but a distinct fascicle continues in the dorsolateral funiculus of the cord beyond the level of the second spinal nerve (Jansen, 1930).

THE ACOUSTICOLATERAL AREA

The acousticolateral area of the medulla oblongata of Bdellostoma and Myxine is small and is much less differentiated than in petromyzonts. Ayers and Worthington (1908) describe an "acusticus nucleus" in Bdellostoma, and Jansen (1930) calls an elongated zone of lateral-line and acoustic root fibers and related cells in Myxine the acousticolateral area. It is situated medially in the horns of the medulla oblongata, the lateral part of these being formed chiefly by the general cutaneous system.

The root fibers of the lateral-line and acoustic nerve which constitute the principal afferents to the acousticolateral area already have been described in general. According to Jansen (1930), the fibers are coarse and frequently divide, also giving off collaterals to neighboring areas. Some primary fibers appear to end in relation to large reticular neurons beneath the acousticolateral area or to enter the bulbar commissure, but the evidence is uncertain. The ascending rami of the bifurcated fibers extend toward the anterior end of the horn of the medulla oblongata, many turning into the general cutaneous nucleus before terminating. Fibers also pass into the fasciculus solitarius. The descending rami take a caudomedial course and then turn caudalward to end in a group of large cells which Jansen calls the nucleus acusticolateralis magnocellularis.

10

The nucleus of the acousticolateral area is formed predominantly of small bipolar or multipolar cells, usually more or less spindle-shaped and with long dendrites which may extend into adjacent areas. Larger scattered cells occur throughout the length of the area, and near its posterior end large multipolar cells of motor type constitute the magnocellular acousticolateral nucleus of Jansen. The root fibers of the acoustic and lateral-line nerves are distributed among the cells, and collaterals from general cutaneous fibers also reach the nucleus. It therefore appears to be a correlating center for lateral-line, vestibular, and cutaneous impulses.

Cells of the acousticolateral nucleus give rise to axons that enter the internal arcuate system of fibers. According to Jansen these fibers, for the most part, enter the ventral commissure of the medulla oblongata, but some enter the ipsilateral reticular formation, and others form an ipsilateral correlation tract. Crossed fibers enter the bulbar lemniscus, some ending in the motor V and motor VII nuclei, others reaching the midbrain. Descending branches of the fibers that end in the motor nuclei and midbrain join others that descend from the acousticolateral area in a crossed bulbo-spinal tract. Ipsilateral descending fibers from the same group also are shown in Jansen's diagram (fig. 58, 1930).

The Cerebellum

The brain of Bdellostoma during development has a generalized structure very similar to that of the urodele, Necturus, according to Conel (1931). All the ventricles are well defined, including a recessus lateralis of the fourth ventricle. As the brain grows and its walls thicken the ventricles gradually close. The recessus lateralis disappears, commencing laterally, but the median part of the fourth ventricle, the cerebral aqueduct, and the preoptic and infundibular recesses remain open in the adult brain. The rhombencephalic or fourth ventricle is a narrow canal until it approaches the anterior end of the medulla oblongata. Here it divides into a small dorsal and a larger ventral canal (fig. 2), the latter widening into an expanded space which is continuous with the mesencephalic ventricle. The dorsal canal was called the anterior diverticulum of the rhombencephalic ventricle by Sterzi (1907) and the isthmic canal by Nicholls (1912b). It is not present in some of my series of Bdellostoma, possibly owing to differences in age of the specimens, since Conel (1931) does not mention it in embryonic stages of this species.

A cellular ridge is described by Conel in the position occupied by the cerebellum in petromyzonts, fishes, and amphibians, and as closely resembling the embryonic cerebellum of Amphibia. It extends into the anterior roof of the rhombencephalon and is said to cross the midline. Some of Conel's illustrations suggest that only the layer of ependymal cells crosses the median sagittal plane, as is true in embryonic stages of Amphibia and in adults as well as embryos of petromyzonts and elasmobranchs. A fascicle of fibers accompanies the cellular ridge, crossing the midline and forming a commissure between the bilateral halves of the rhombencephalon, which Conel regards as a possible cerebellar commissure. He states, however, that the evidence is insufficient to permit definite interpretation of the cellular ridge as the cerebellum. In adult Myxine Jansen (1930) found some cells and fibers that are possibly cerebellar, but he was uncertain of their relations.

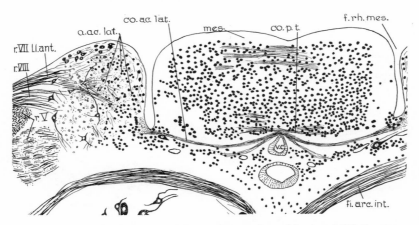

Figure 2. Dorsomedian part of transverse section of brain of Bdellostoma stouti, approximately at the level of label "mes" in figure 1. The usual acousticolateral and posterior tectal commissures and the median extensions of cells from acousticolateral areas are seen.
Cajal method. ×51. (Larsell, 1947a.)

In adult Bdellostoma a medial extension of cells from the ventromedial part of the acousticolateral area continues to the ventricular canal (fig. 2). The cells, in Cajal preparations, are similar to the small elements of the acousticolateral nucleus. Occasional larger cells occur near the acousticolateral area (fig. 2). These medially directed cell chains appear to correspond to the ridges of cells described by Conel in embryonic stages, but they have been submerged by caudal growth above them of the posterior part of the mesencephalon. Fine fibers from the acousticolateral area are distributed among the cells, some also coming from the ventral part of the cutaneous area. The latter may be cutaneous fibers from the utricular ganglion, but whether any of the fibers are continuations of root fibers or derive from other sources could not be determined with any certainty.

A fascicle of fine fibers is assembled at the ventromedial margin of the acousticolateral area and continues medially above the cellular extension. It decussates dorsal of the anterior diverticulum of the rhombencephalic ventricle (fig. 2), or, when that is absent, dorsal of the junction of the thin roof of the ventricular canal with the mesencephalon. The fibers derive in part from small cells of the acousticolateral nucleus, but fine continuations of lateral-line and acoustic root fibers cannot be excluded. Slender branches of such fibers extend toward the beginning of the fascicle, but could not be followed into it with any certainty. A small fascicle also arises in the medial extension of cells and joins the one from the acousticolateral areas immediately dorsolateral of the ventricular canal, decussating with it (fig. 2).

The decussation dorsal of the ventricular canal or its anterior diverticulum, and the fascicles leading to it, appear to correspond to the commissural bundle of Conel already mentioned in embryos. In my earlier (1947a)

description of this region in Bdellostoma I called it the acousticolateral commissure. Near the midline it is situated immediately above the ependymal layer, just before this layer detaches from the midbrain (fig. 3), and it is somewhat intermingled with the posterior tectal commissure. Its fibers are thinner, however, and have a more brownish color in Cajal preparations than those of the tectal commissure. Also they arch lateroventrally instead of laterodorsally, as do the posterior tectal fibers which can readily be followed in the midbrain (fig. 2). The commissural fibers can be followed into the two fascicles above described which, in my earlier description (1947a), I included as parts of the acousticolateral commissure.

Restudy of my material has confirmed the earlier observations, and more extensive comparison with the cerebellum and commissures of petromyzonts and other Ichthyopsida makes it clear that the medial cellular extension should be regarded as a cerebellar structure. It appears to correspond to the rostral part of the cell column which, in petromyzonts, is enlarged in the cerebellum as the cellular part of the lateral lobule, described below. The component of the commissure which arises from these cells therefore represents a more strictly cerebellar commissure that corresponds to fibers interconnecting the bilateral halves of the vestibulolateral division of the cerebellum of petromyzonts and fishes, described in the following sections.

In addition to the lateral-line and acoustic impulses to the acousticolateral area, the cutaneous impulses reaching it through the fibers and collaterals of the trigeminal nerve, above noted, constitute a factor in the correlating function of this area in hagfishes. A corpus cerebelli, which in all other Ichthyopsida receives cutaneous and

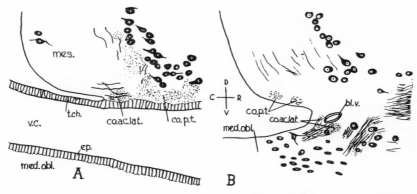

Figure 3. Sagittal sections through lower caudal region of the midbrain of Bdellostoma, showing acousticolateral and posterior tectal commissures. A. Midsagittal section. B. Section lateral to A. Cajal method. ×260. (Larsell, 1947a.)

other fibers not represented in the acousticolateral area, except as noted below, and having a distinct commissure, appears to be entirely lacking in Bdellostoma. The acousticolateral area presumably correlates lateral-line, acoustic, and cutaneous impulses ipsilaterally, and the commissure interrelates the bilateral acousticolateral areas and their medial extensions.

The medial extensions of cells and the commissural connection between them, together with the more strictly acousticolateral commissure, constitute the precursor of a cerebellum of the petromyzont type, which is principally vestibulolateral in its relations. The cerebellum of lampreys, however, has in addition a rudimentary corpus cerebelli.

PETROMYZONTIDAE

THE cerebellum of lampreys was recognized by Robin (1849) and was included by Ahlborn (1883) in his description of the brain of these animals. Jeleneff (1879) and Schaper (1899) described it as consisting of an outer fibrous and an inner cellular layer, Schaper adding a description of the cellular elements from Golgi preparations. The cell types were further described by Johnston (1902), who also demonstrated the intimate relations of the cerebellum to the acousticolateral area and included a description of the fiber connections of both. Clark (1906), in Petromyzon fluviatilis, and Stefanelli (1935, 1937), in P. marinus, described the cerebellum and its connections, and Pearson (1936a) paid special attention to the relations of cerebellum and acousticolateral area in several species of lampreys. Saito (1930) includes a brief account of the cerebellum of Entosphenus japonicus in a description of the brain of this species and Heier (1948) describes the cerebellum and acousticolateral area in his comprehensive study of the brain of Petromyzon fluviatilis. Tretjakoff (1909) made important contributions to an understanding of the cerebellum in ammocoete stages of Petromyzon fluviatilis.

In 1947 I published the results of a study of the development of the cerebellum and acousticolateral area in larval stage of Lampetra planeri,[1] and of the adult structure and the connections of these two parts of the brain in Entosphenus tridentatus, E. appendix, Petromyzon fluviatilis, P. marinus, and Ichthyomyzon concolor. Subsequently I have reviewed much of this earlier material, including Johnston's Golgi preparations, and also have had opportunity to study Heier's excellent Bodian preparations at the Anatomical Institute in Oslo.

[1] The embryos and ammocoetes described in my 1947 contribution were called Entosphenus tridentatus. It has since appeared that they probably were developmental stages of Lampetra planeri.

Some of my earlier conclusions have been modified and others expanded.

There are variations in different species but in general the petromyzont cerebellum appears superficially as a nearly transverse plate which arches above the anterior end of the fourth ventricle immediately behind the optic tectum of the midbrain (fig. 4). The plate expands on either side, forming a slight eminence dorsomedial to the entrance of the root of the V nerve into the medulla oblongata. This enlargement, which I shall call the lobulus

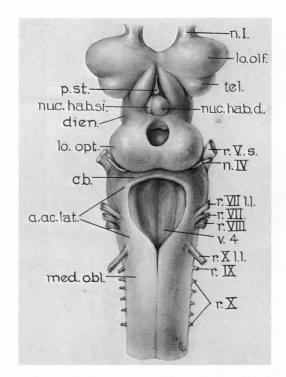

Figure 4. Dorsal view of brain of Entosphenus tridentatus (Gairdner). ×7.5. (Larsell, 1947a.)

14

lateralis of the cerebellum, is more prominent, superficially, in Entosphenus tridentatus than in Petromyzon. It merges medially with the arch above the fourth ventricle and caudally is continuous with the acousticolateral area of the medulla oblongata. The cerebellar arch comprises only the dorsocaudal margin and a short medial segment of the superficial part of the organ. The cerebellum also includes part of the massive anterior and lateral walls of the rostral portion of the fourth ventricle. The middle part of the arch represents a fibrous and molecular connection between the more massive bilateral halves of the organ, but includes fascicles of fibers from the acousticolateral area. The cerebellum is delimited from the midbrain by a deep transverse mesencephalo-cerebellar fissure.

A submerged mass of rather compactly arranged cells is situated ventromedial of the lateral lobule. Usually called the granular layer of the cerebellum, this mass is the primitive corpus cerebelli, described below. It is relatively smaller than its homologue in urodeles (p. 138), but its morphological relations and fiber tract connections correspond, except that the latter are much reduced in lampreys.

Herrick (1914a) made it clear that the "auricle" of Necturus is part of the cerebellum, but is also intimately related with the acousticolateral area. As will appear, Herrick's "auricle" in Necturus and other urodeles is homologous with the lobulus lateralis of petromyzonts. The relation between the acousticolateral area and the cerebellum of lampreys is especially well shown in larval stages. A basis for an understanding of the adult structure of the petromyzont cerebellum can best be established by a description of the nerves and root fibers related to the acousticolateral area, the development of the acousticolateral area, and the adult structure of this area.

THE LATERAL-LINE ORGANS AND NERVES

Petromyzonts have lateral-line organs on the head and sides of the body. These occur as pit organs in grooves of the skin, the free ends of the organs extending to the level of the surface epidermis or slightly short of this level. Each pit organ consists of a number of short pear-shaped, ciliated neuro-epithelial cells which are arranged between the outer parts of more elongated sustentacular cells. Terminal twigs of lateral-line nerve fibers form basket-like synaptic endings on the bases and bodies of the sensory neuro-epithelial cells.

The distribution of the lateral-line organs and the nerves serving them has been described by Alcock (1899), Johnston (1905, 1908), Tretjakoff (1927), Lindström (1949), and others. The lateral-line organs of the head, according to Johnston, are arranged in supra-orbital, infraorbital, and hyomandibular series. These are served by anterior lateral-line components in corresponding branches of the VII nerve. Other neuromasts occur along a recurrent branch of the VII nerve which joins the posterior lateral-line nerve. Some are distributed to the ventral part of the head region by lateral-line branches of the IX nerve, and pit organs also occur in the posterior region of the mandibular nerve.

Pit organs in the branchial region are served by lateral-line components of the epibranchial trunk of the X nerve. Behind the last gill cleft this trunk swings ventrally and forward, its lateral-line component serving pit organs ventral of the gill clefts. A dorsally situated continuation of the posterior lateral-line nerve serves the pit organs of the trunk. Lindström's description of the lateral-line nerves differs in some details but is in general agreement with that of Johnston.

The anterior lateral-line nerve enters the medulla oblongata dorsally and slightly rostrally of the roots of the acoustic or VIII nerve by a dorsal and a ventral root (fig. 4). The posterior lateral-line nerve has a single root which includes lateral-line fibers distributed by branches of the IX nerve. This root enters the medulla oblongata slightly rostral and dorsal of the sensory root of the IX nerve (fig. 4).

THE MEMBRANOUS LABYRINTH AND THE ACOUSTIC NERVE

The membranous labyrinth, with which is associated the acoustic or VIII nerve, is more complex in petromyzonts than in myxinoids. Compared with the lateral-line organs it is much more elaborate and its sensory epithelium occurs as patches. These consist of neuro-epithelial and sustentacular cells of the same types as those in the pit organs.

Detailed descriptions of the petromyzont labyrinth we owe to Retzius (1881–84), de Burlet (1934), and Heier (1948). Two vertical semicircular canals, corresponding to the anterior and posterior canals of higher vertebrates, unite in a short crus commune. Each canal has an ampulla that opens into the anterior and posterior ends, respectively, of an elongated utriculus. The floor of the utricle has two pouches. The rostral pouch is small and probably corresponds to the sacculus of higher vertebrates; the much larger caudal pouch forms a blind sac which is the lagena (de Burlet, 1934). The sensory patches correspond to the maculae utriculi, sacculi, and lagenae; the macula or papilla neglecta; and the cristae anterior and posterior of higher vertebrates. Except for the two cristae, these patches are connected by narrow bridges of epithelium. In addition, de Burlet describes a small sensory area at the end of the endolymphatic duct which, with the corresponding twig of the VIII nerve, ap-

15

pears to be unique in petromyzonts (Ariens Kappers, 1947).

The VIII nerve has two principal branches, an anterior and a posterior. The anterior branch, according to de Burlet, serves the crista anterior, macula utriculi, and the sensory patch of the endolymphatic duct. The posterior branch innervates the maculae of the sacculus and lagena, the macula or papilla neglecta and the crista posterior. The two branches include both large and small fibers. The small fibers are distributed to the macula or papilla neglecta and the maculae of the sacculus, lagena, and utriculus, the latter also receiving large fibers. The anterior and posterior roots of the nerve correspond, respectively, to its two principal peripheral branches.

Heier's (1948) description of the organ of the labyrinth and its nerve in Petromyzon differs somewhat from that above presented. According to Heier the labyrinth is divided into a rostral and a caudal arcus (utriculus), each having an ampulla. Between the two subdivisions of the arcus are situated a rostral and a caudal saccus. A ganglion utriculare, consisting of large bipolar cells that give rise to coarse processes, is described as corresponding to each arcus. Rostral and caudal saccular ganglia, composed of small cells with fine processes, are situated between the two utricular ganglia. From these four ganglionic masses corresponding groups of fibers enter the medulla oblongata in the same succession as the position of their ganglia. Heier describes four components of the VIII nerve: rostral and caudal utricular roots of large fibers, and rostral and caudal saccular roots of small fibers.

My own observations on sagittal and horizontal serial sections of the heads, with the brains in situ, of Lampetra larvae 125 mm to 127 mm in length, are in general agreement with the description of Ariens Kappers (1947). Coarse fibers, arising from the large ganglionic cells, pass to the cristae of the two ampullae. These cells are found at the anterior and posterior borders of the ganglionic mass and are the largest, as pointed out by Weston (1939c). Cells of somewhat smaller size, intermingled with quite small ones, occur along the entire medial wall of the utricle. The centrally directed fibers from the ganglion are gathered into a rostrocaudally elongated sheet which is cut transversely in horizontal sections. The coarsest fibers are found at the anterior and posterior borders of this sheet but many large ones are intermingled with fine fibers throughout the remainder of the nerve root.

The Development of the Acousticolateral Area and the Cerebellum

According to the studies of Bergquist and Källén (1953) and Hugosson (1957) the wall of the newly formed neural tube of vertebrates consists of an inner layer of ependyma and a number of cell rows that form a matrix layer. The wall is derived from an earlier single layer of columnar neuro-epithelium. Gradual migration of cells from the matrix layer, from stage to stage of the embryo, results in the formation of a new layer in the wall of the tube, called the migration layer (fig. 5). This is the mantle layer or zone of differentiation. In some species the mass of migrated cells remains continuous with the ventricular gray layer, no distinct migration layer being apparent. The cells of the migration layer subsequently become grouped into nuclei and other centers.

The migration layer is not uniform in thickness. In the rhombencephalon it presents four longitudinal ridges which extend throughout the length of this subdivision of the brain. These ridges do not appear simultaneously but develop in a definite order. They were called columna dorsalis, columna ventralis, columna dorsolateralis, and columna ventrolateralis by Bergquist and Källén (1953). We shall return to these columns in other vertebrates, in which they have been described more fully than in petromyzonts. The close relation of the acousticolateral area to the cerebellum in the lampreys is most clearly shown, however, by following the development of the rhombencephalon and the dorsal and dorsolateral cell columns in larval stages.

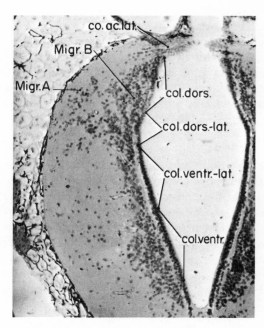

Figure 5. Transverse section of cerebellar rudiment of Petromyzon fluviatilis, 80 mm long, showing the four longitudinal zones of the brain stem and cell migrations, "Migr. A" and "Migr. B" from the dorsal column (col. dors.). (Courtesy S.-I. Rüdeberg.)

According to Hugosson (1957) the dorsal and ventral embryonic cell columns appear at about the same time in Lampetra fluviatilis. They are recognizable in embryos 4.5 mm long. At this stage the region between them is a single bulge of ventricular gray, forming a columna intermedia. In the 7.5 mm embryo this column is divided into columna ventrolateralis and columna dorsolateralis. From this stage onward in development the four columns become increasingly distinct.

The descriptions of the columna dorsalis in lamprey embryos are very brief. According to Hugosson (1957) its cells are widely scattered and no distinct nuclei have been formed, but lateral-line fibers end in it. Rüdeberg (1961) describes the columna dorsalis only in the cerebellar region. The matrix layer here is thin in the 6.5 mm Petromyzon embryo and a well-developed migration layer occupies the greater part of the brain wall. A demarcation between the two layers is faintly visible but is more distinct in the 7.5 mm embryo. Lateral of the migration layer, in the 7.5 mm stage, a zone nearly free of cells constitutes the stratum zonale or marginal layer. Ascending lateral-line and VIII root fibers are included in the dorsal column, according to Rüdeberg, and the rostral limit of the cerebellar region is marked by an acousticolateral commissure. Rüdeberg confirmed the differentiation of the columna dorsolateralis from the intermediate cell column at the 7.5 mm stage.

In embryos of Lampetra planeri, at the 7 mm stage (fig. 6), the cell mass of the dorsal part of the rostralmost level of the rhombencephalon is expanded lateralward, corresponding to the columna dorsalis of Rüdeberg's Petromyzon embryos, and a more ventrally situated migration appears to correspond to the columna dorsolateralis. Scattered cells with short processes in both

columns represent early neuroblasts. Ascending root fibers of the V, lateral-line VII, and VIII nerves occupy the marginal layer.

In 26–38 mm larval stages of Petromyzon fluviatilis, according to Rüdeberg (1961), the columna dorsalis, in the cerebellar region, is differentiated into a lateral more diffuse cell mass, called "migration A," and a denser medial cell mass called "migration B." Caudal of the cerebellar rudiment, at about the level of the entrance of the posterior root fascicles of the V nerve, a number of larger cells occur which differ from those surrounding them. These cells, which belong to the vestibular area, are believed by Rüdeberg to have derived from the ventral part of the columna dorsolateralis. In later stages these large cells form the nucleus octavomotorius anterior.

In the 42 mm Lampetra ammocoete (fig. 7) the cerebellar part of "migration A" is continuous caudally with a column of scattered cells which evidently represents a migration from the acousticolateral part of the columna dorsalis. The nucleus dorsalis and nucleus medialis of the acousticolateral area presumably differentiate from the columna dorsalis, as in Torpedo ocellata (Hugosson, 1957), but no details have been provided in petromyzonts. In a 55 mm Lampetra larva (fig. 8) two indistinct groups of scattered cells appear to represent the nucleus dorsalis and nucleus medialis, while a ventral group in the path of the VIII root fibers is the nucleus ventralis or incipient area vestibularis. The nucleus dorsalis is well defined in the 64 mm larva. It has no relation to the part of the rhombencephalon which becomes included in the cerebellum, except by a small fascicle of fibers. The longer column of the nucleus medialis is continuous, however, with the posterior part of Rüdeberg's "migration A." In subsequent development this posterior part en-

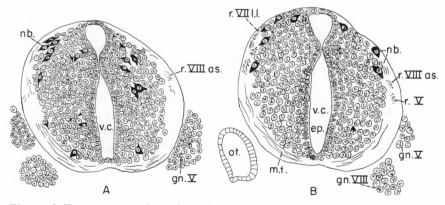

Figure 6. Transverse sections through brain of larval Entosphenus tridentatus, 7 mm long. Mantle layer composed of closely crowded nuclei among which a few early neuroblasts are recognizable. A. Rostralmost level of medulla oblongata. B. Level of rostral part of otocyst, on left side. Iron-hematoxylin stain. ×205. (Larsell, 1947a.)

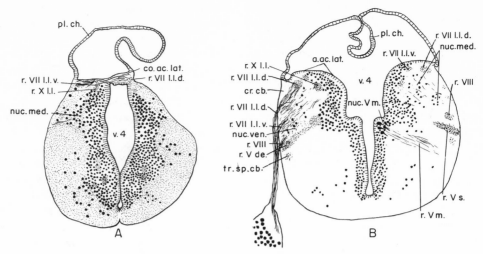

Figure 7. Transverse sections through brain of Entosphenus ammocoete, 42 mm long, total length. A. Level of acousticolateral commissure. B. Level of entrance of lateral-line VII and VIII nerve roots. Iron-hematoxylin stain. ×100. (Larsell, 1947a.)

larges as the cerebellum differentiates, and turns toward the midline. The cerebellar part of "migration A" apparently gives rise to the cellular part of the lobulus lateralis and part of the nucleus cerebelli, described below. The continuation of the same cell column into the acousticolateral area differentiates into the nucleus dorsalis and nucleus medialis.

The columna dorsolateralis, according to Hugosson, has no distinct nuclei in early stages of Petromyzon but it receives fibers from the VIII, IX, and X nerve roots. In Torpedo and other higher vertebrates Hugosson derives the vestibular (ventral) nucleus from this column.

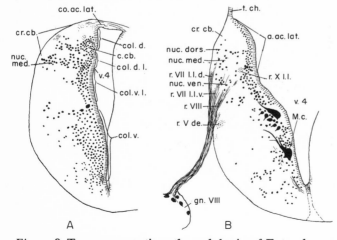

Figure 8. Transverse sections through brain of Entosphenus ammocoete, 55 mm long. A. Level of acousticolateral commissure. B. Level of entrance of lateral-line VII and VIII roots. Borax-carmine and Lyons blue stain. ×102.5. (Larsell, 1947a.)

In 42 mm Lampetra larvae the acousticolateral area forms a broad rounded zone, in transverse section, which constitutes the floor of the fourth ventricle at the level of entrance of the anterior lateral-line and VIII roots (fig. 7B). The cells of the nucleus dorsalis, nucleus medialis, and vestibular area of this level and rostralward are scattered among the ascending fascicles of the lateral-line and VIII nerve roots. The dorsal part of the rhomboidal fossa is broad, as is the roof plate. Toward the isthmus, however, the ventricle narrows and its walls are nearly vertical (fig. 7A). The acousticolateral area tapers medially toward a thin plate which crosses the midline and also is attached to the posterior border of the optic tectum. Fibers from the anterior and posterior lateral-line roots, constituting the acousticolateral commissure, decussate through this plate. I have been unable to follow ascending fibers of the VIII root into the commissure in the 42 mm larva. The dorsoventral level of the commissure is the same as that of the two principal fascicles from which the commissural fibers are derived.

In larvae of 55 mm length the acousticolateral area is thickened rostrally and the nuclear cell groups are more prominent. At the level of the VIII roots the area is tilted dorsalward in such a manner that the rounded surface which constitutes the floor of the lateral part of the fourth ventricle at the 42 mm stage now forms the dorsal portion of the lateral ventricular wall (fig. 8B). The contour of the ventricular walls varies from stage to stage, probably owing to growth factors. The ventricle as a whole has widened rostrally in the 55 mm stage, but at the level of the VIII roots the distance between the taeniae of the

18

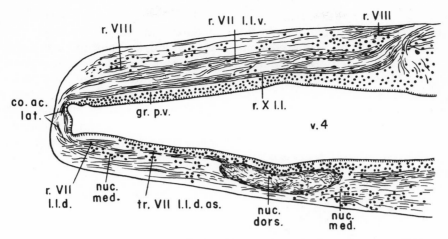

Figure 9. Horizontal section through rostral part of medulla oblongata of Entosphenus ammocoete, 64 mm long. Iron-hematoxylin stain. ×102.5. (Larsell, 1947a.)

two sides is relatively less than in smaller larvae. Beneath the commissure it remains narrow.

The rhombencephalon retains the form of a deep trough in the 64 mm larva. The anterior part of the rhomboidal fossa is narrow and the commissure in the roof of its anterior end is a short fibrous arch which is continuous on either side with fascicles of fibers in the acousticolateral area. These fascicles and the commissure are shown in figure 9, illustrating a section through the head of a 64 mm larva cut in a slightly oblique horizontal plane, the right hand side of the figure representing the more ventral level. The two sides together show all the components of the acousticolateral commissure. These are ascending branches of bifurcated ventral anterior and posterior lateral-line root fibers and similar branches of the VIII root. Branches of dorsal anterior lateral-line root fibers emerge from the rostral end of the nucleus dorsalis, forming a compact fascicle which appears to reach the commissure at this stage of the larva but in later stages they do not seem to do so. The ventral anterior and posterior lateral-line root fibers can be followed through the nucleus medialis to the commissure. The ascending VIII root fibers, superficially situated and of smaller size, also reach it.

The fossa gradually widens caudally for some distance before tapering toward the posterior end of the rhombencephalon. In the 120 mm ammocoete the anterior part of the acousticolateral area has tilted medialward so that the dorsal part of the fossa is narrow; between the ventral part of the acousticolateral area and the eminence of the motor V nucleus, however, it is wide from side to side (fig. 10B).

The three nuclei of the acousticolateral area are well-defined aggregations of cells and fibers in the 120 mm ammocoete. Beginning at a level slightly rostral of the anterior end of the nucleus dorsalis the acousticolateral area, including the nucleus medialis and the ascending fascicles of fibers, but not the nucleus dorsalis and vestibular area, begins to turn medialward, from either side, toward the commissural bridge above the anterior end of the ventricular cavity. The hitherto lateral walls of the anterior part of the cavity now begin to become an anterolateral wall on each side. In the 127 mm ammocoete the medial deflection of the acousticolateral area is so pronounced that a wide ventricular space separates the bilateral angles of the deflections and is limited rostrolaterally by the medially turned continuation of the acousticolateral area and, rostrally, by the cerebellar arch which connects the bilateral deflections (fig. 11B).

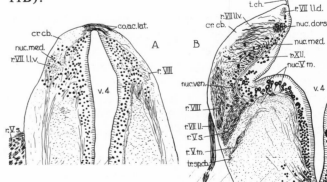

Figure 10. Transverse sections through brain of Entosphenus ammocoete, 120 mm long. A. Level of acousticolateral commissure. B. Section slightly rostral to entrance of lateral-line VII and VIII roots. Protargol stain. ×70.
(Larsell, 1947a.)

19

The deflected middle cell column enlarges in subsequent development and becomes the primordium of the eminentia granularis, described below. This is continuous, ventrolaterally, with the vestibular area as well as with the nucleus medialis of the acousticolateral area. We shall return to this cell mass in the adult lamprey, in which it is considerably enlarged and also has many fibers among the cells, in addition to the commissural fibers that traverse it. Because, as will appear, it is the expanded terminus of lateral-line and vestibular fibers this cell mass

11A). One layer turns rostralward and attaches to the anterodorsal margin of the optic tectum; the other turns caudalward, attaching to the dorsocaudally directed part of the anterior wall of the fourth ventricle. The median part of this wall I have called the cerebellovelar plate (1947a). As seen in median sagittal section, it forms the posterior limb of a V, the anterior limb of which is the median part of the optic tectum and includes the posttectal commissure at the caudoventral margin of the tectum (fig. 11A).

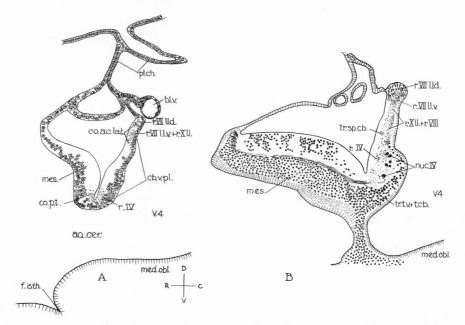

Figure 11. A. Midsagittal section through cerebellovelar plate and midbrain of Entosphenus ammocoete, 65 mm long. Borax-carmine and Lyons blue stain. ×164. B. Sagittal section, slightly to one side of the midplane, showing cerebellovelar plate and midbrain of Entosphenus ammocoete, 127 mm long. Protargol stain. ×104. (Larsell, 1947a.)

probably should be regarded as a modified derivative of "migration A" of Rüdeberg, from which the nucleus medialis appears to be derived.

The corpus cerebelli, described below, differentiates ventromedial of the lateral lobule. This division of the cerebellum adds another element to the massive wall of the anterior part of the fourth ventricle and, as the corpus cerebelli expands, to the cerebellar arch.

CEREBELLOVELAR PLATE

The choroid part of the roof of the fourth ventricle lies well above the dorsal margins of the rhombencephalon, to which it is attached on either side. It is continuous rostrally with the choroid roof of the optocoele but at a level just caudal of the fovea isthmi the membrane loops downward as a sheet consisting of two cell layers (fig.

The ventral part of the cerebellovelar plate is relatively massive and is continuous with the caudoventral margin of the optic tectum. It includes fibers of the IV nerve root and in the 65 mm ammocoete, a narrow zone of cells. At the 127 mm stage it is much thicker and includes migrated cells of the IV nucleus (fig. 11B). The layer of smaller cells is continuous with the deep cell layer of the optic tectum. The thinner dorsal part of the cerebellovelar plate is entirely fibrous. In the 65 mm larva only the components of the acousticolateral commissure are recognizable; at the 127 mm stage spino-cerebellar fibers, described below, have been added to these. In adult Entosphenus and Petromyzon trigeminal fibers can be distinguished. The entire plate becomes tilted dorsalward by the increasingly higher walls of the fourth ventricle with which it is continuous on either side. This strongly tilted condition prevails until the ventricle broadens rostrally and the acousticolateral areas are spread farther apart, their margins assuming a relatively more ventral position. Only the thin dorsal portion of the cerebellovelar plate has any relation to the cerebellum or the acousticolateral area. The ventral or velar part is closely related with the optic tectum.

Because of the intimate relations of the IV nerve and nucleus to the cerebellum in adult lampreys the fibers of the nerve roots appear to cross in the ventral part of the cerebellum and the cells of the nucleus to lie within it. Consideration of the development of this nerve and its nucleus in larval stages (Larsell, 1947b) makes it clear that both nucleus and nerve roots are situated ventro-rostral of specific cerebellar territory. In the earlier larval stages the nerve fibers emerge ipsilaterally from their cells of origin, which are situated in the rhombencephalon ventrolateral of the acousticolateral commissure. As the rostral end of the rhombencephalon is turned medialward by the widening of the fourth ventricle and other factors, above mentioned, the point of emergence of the IV roots assumes a more medial and dorsal position with reference to the lateral margin of the hindbrain. The cells of the nucleus also migrate dorsomedially, many of them crossing the midline to the opposite side, so accounting for the decussation of the nerve roots (Larsell, 1947b). Cells and root fibers, however, are confined to the velar portion of the cerebellovelar plate and the nerve emerges from this, not from the cerebellum, in later larval and adult stages of development (fig. 11B).

The cerebellar gray substance does not reach the midline in ammocoetes or, as also noted by Pearson (1936a), in the adult lamprey. There also is a gap between the velar cell mass and that of the lobulus lateralis. The periventricular gray of the lateral wall of the narrow cerebral aqueduct is continuous dorsally with the deep cellular layer of the optic tectum and the velar part of the cerebellovelar plate; ventrally it is continuous with the periventricular gray of the medulla oblongata.

THE CORPUS CEREBELLI

A rather closely packed cell mass, situated lateral of the ependymal layer of the rostral part of the columna dorsalis in the 42 mm Lampetra larva, is the primordium of the corpus cerebelli. The corresponding cell mass in the 55 mm ammocoete lies ventromedial of the acousticolateral area and tapers rostromedially toward the isthmus. Since the fourth ventricle still is a narrow vertical cleft at this level in this stage of development, the medial surface of the rudimentary corpus cerebelli is directed rostrocaudally, and parallel with the surface of the ventricular wall (fig. 8A). As the cell mass increases in later

stages and the ventricle widens, the corpus cerebelli projects into the cavity and becomes deflected medialward in the same manner as the rostral part of the nucleus medialis but less sharply. Growth of the rudiment results in the inclusion of the rostral part of the corpus cerebelli in the ventral part of the cerebellar arch.

We shall return to the corpus cerebelli in adult lampreys. Here it need be said further only that the early primordium of this division of the cerebellum appears to correspond to "migration B" of Rüdeberg in Petromyzon embryos. This migration, according to Rüdeberg (1961), develops into the stratum granulosum of the cerebellum. In my earlier contribution (1947a) I regarded a zone in the base of the cerebellar arch of adult lampreys as the primordium of the corpus cerebelli. The deep layer of cells which extends into the lateral ventral part of the arch itself, however, I considered part of the general granular layer of the cerebellum. Heier's (1948) independent identification of the corpus cerebelli in Petromyzon includes this layer, as my subsequent studies of larval and adult cerebella confirm.

The origin of this so-called granular layer from "migration B" corresponds to the origin of the granular layer of Squalus acanthias, an elasmobranch, and Esox lucius, a teleost, as described by Rüdeberg. In these two species, the cerebellum of which is typical of their respective classes, the granular layer is part of a large division of the organ which I call the corpus cerebelli, *sensu strictiori* (pp. 45, 104), and which includes also a layer derived from "migration A." Unless it be by large cells described below, "migration A" does not appear to be represented in the corpus cerebelli of petromyzonts.

A small tract, apparently of bulbar and spinal origin, is recognizable in the 42 mm Lampetra larva immediately ventral of the descending tract of the V nerve root (fig. 7B). There is no indication of a bulbo- or spino-cerebellar component of the commissural complex in the anterior end of the rhombencephalon at this stage. In later stages a small fascicle occupies the position of the spino-tectal and spino-cerebellar tracts of adult lampreys. In well-stained sagittal and horizontal sections collaterals from this fascicle pass into the cerebellar region, as Herrick (1914b) found from the spino-tectal tract in Ambystoma. In the ammocoetes such fibers are given off at right angles to spino-tectal fibers in the region rostral to the sensory roots of the V nerve; they enter the rudiment of the corpus cerebelli. Farther caudally similar fibers curve rostrodorsally toward the cerebellum, accompanied by a few fibers that are not collaterals. These more caudal fibers interdigitate to some extent with V root fascicles. In the 127 mm ammocoete a small fascicle of about ten fibers crosses the midline in the lower cerebellar part of the cerebellovelar plate (fig. 11B). This represents the spinal component of the commissura cerebelli.

A small trigemino-cerebellar tract, in the 120 mm and later larval stages, is formed by the rostral branches of a small fascicle of fine V root fibers that bifurcate on entering the medulla oblongata. Tretjakoff (1909) also described trigemino-cerebellar fibers in the ammocoete and sometimes is incorrectly cited as describing a trigeminal commissure in the cerebellum. I have been unable to follow trigeminal fibers into the commissural complex in larval stages, although in adult lampreys such fibers form part of the commissura cerebelli.

The nucleus cerebelli. According to Rüdeberg (1961, p. 124) the nucleus cerebelli, which I described in adult Entosphenus, is derived from all or part of "migration A" of the early Petromyzon embryo, with some possible contribution from "migration B." I have not followed this nucleus in larval stages but we shall return to it in adult lampreys. In these the nucleus appears related to only part of the cell mass which Rüdeberg derives from "migration A," but a continuity of cells between it and the derivative of "migration B" appears definitely to indicate a contribution from this migration.

Adult Lampreys
THE ACOUSTICOLATERAL AREA

The acousticolateral area of lampreys has been variously subdivided by different authors. Three elongated zones of cells and fibers and a crista cerebelli were recognized by Johnston (1902), Ariens Kappers (1920), Pearson (1936a), Ariens Kappers, Huber, and Crosby (1936), and Stefanelli (1937, 1939). These were variously named and defined. Ariens Kappers (1947) divides the area into anterior lateral-line lobe or dorsal static region, medial or intermediate static region, posterior static region and ventral static region. The entire complex is called the static or vestibulolateral area by Heier (1948), who divides it into a ventral area vestibularis and a dorsal area lineae lateralis. The latter he subdivides into lobus lineae and a zone beneath this lobe which he calls the tractus lineae, this tract including the ascending and descending fibers of the ventral anterior lateral-line root.

The nuclei of the acousticolateral area. On the basis of my own studies the terms nucleus dorsalis, nucleus medialis, and area vestibularis, the latter subdivided into several distinct nuclei, seem most suitable for the principal subdivisions of the acousticolateral area. These studies were made on many series of sections, cut in the three conventional planes, and stained by the iron-hematoxylin, pyridine-silver, Cajal, Golgi, Nissl, and Bodian methods. The series included adult brains of several

species and larval stages of Lampetra planeri. The terms nucleus dorsalis, nucleus medialis, and area vestibularis also are applied to the respective homologous subdivisions of the acousticolateral area in other Ichthyopsida, described in subsequent sections, further justifying their use in petromyzonts.

The nucleus dorsalis (figs. 12 and 13) of adult petromyzonts in fiber-stained preparations presents, as its most obvious feature, a mass of bifurcated fibers of the dorsal anterior lateral-line root (fig. 15). Small cells, however, are scattered among the fibers, and neurons of medium to large size are arranged along its medial border. At the ends of the nucleus large rounded cells are numerous.

The nucleus medialis (figs. 12, 13) consists of ascending and descending fibers of the ventral anterior and posterior lateral-line roots and interspersed cells. It is continuous anteriorly with the principal cell mass of the lobulus lateralis of the cerebellum. It is not clear whether the anterior and deep lateral nuclei of Stefanelli (1935) in Petromyzon marinus represent portions of this cell mass. Pearson (1936a), however, calls it the stratum griseum superficialis cerebelli and Heier (1948) uses the term lobus auricularis. For reasons that will appear (p. 29) I shall refer to it as the primordium of the eminentia granularis. The cells within the nucleus medialis are small, but larger elements along its medial border send their dendrites among the fascicles of fibers that traverse the nucleus.

The area vestibularis extends from the region behind the entering roots of the VIII nerve to the nucleus octavomotorius anterior. The area includes ascending and descending fascicles of VIII root fibers and large, medium-sized, and small cells. The largest cells are gathered into three groups: the nucleus octavomotorius anterior, already mentioned; the nucleus octavomotorius medius; and the nucleus octavomotorius posterior.

The nucleus octavomotorius anterior of Schilling (1907), Tretjakoff (1909), van Hoevell (1916), Ariens Kappers (1920, 1947), and Ariens Kappers, Huber, and Crosby (1936) is situated immediately dorsomedial of the entrance of the root of the V nerve and ventrolateral of the lobulus lateralis of the cerebellum (figs. 14, 19). As Ariens Kappers (1947) points out, it is subcerebellar. The nucleus octavomotorius medius lies just caudal of the entrance of the VIII roots. Dorsocaudal of this nucleus and more or less continuous with it is found the nucleus octavomotorius posterior. Ariens Kappers (1947) includes these two nuclei in a single nucleus octavomotorius posterior which he subdivides into medial and lateral parts. The two principal groups of cells are situated so far apart, however, that Heier's recognition of them as distinct nuclei seems preferable. Cells of somewhat small-

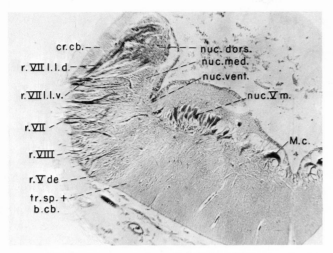

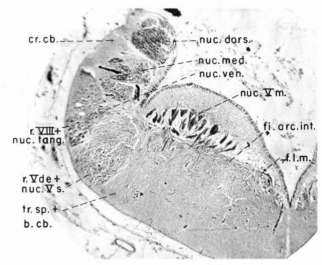

Figure 12. Transverse section of medulla oblongata of adult Entosphenus tridentatus at the level of entrance of lateral-line VII and VIII roots. Iron-hematoxylin stain. (Larsell, 1947a.)

Figure 13. Transverse section of medulla oblongata of adult Entosphenus tridentatus rostral to entrance of lateral-line VII and VIII roots, showing acousticolateral area. Iron-hematoxylin stain. (Larsell, 1947a.)

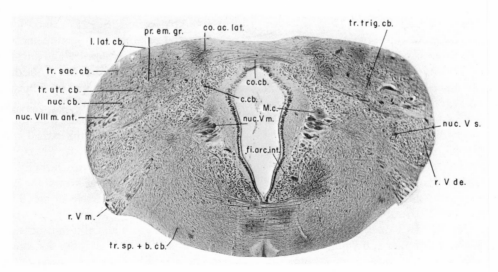

Figure 14. Transverse section of medulla oblongata of Petromyzon fluviatilis (?) at the level of cerebellar commissure. Bodian method.

23

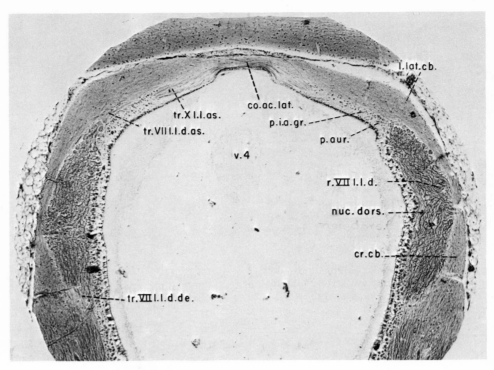

Figure 15. Horizontal section of rostral part of medulla
oblongata of Petromyzon.

er size occur among the entering fibers of the posterior VIII root. These were identified by Stefanelli (1937) with the tangential vestibular nucleus of teleosts, reptiles, and birds. Between the three octavomotor nuclei occur neurons of small and medium size, the latter having slender transversely directed dendrites that branch among the VIII root fibers. The small and medium-sized cells are most numerous near the groups of large cells and many are intermingled with the large neurons.

The large cells of these nuclei correspond to a peculiar type of spindle cells described by Johnston (1902), in Lampetra, as found only in the vestibular area. Coarse VIII root fibers terminate on these cells by spoon-like synaptic endings. According to Stefanelli (1937) all the large cells of the nuclei, with which the large utricular and ampullary fibers are related, have an oval form. Ariens Kappers (1947) found oval cells only in the anterior octavomotor and tangential nuclei, those of his posterior octavomotor nucleus being described as multipolar and resembling the cells of Deiters's nucleus in higher Ichthyopsida. In larval stages of Lampetra planeri, by my own observation, the cells of all three octavomotor nuclei are elongated. In adult Entosphenus elongated neurons occur in the anterior octavomotor nucleus but many cells have oval or pear-shaped cell bodies (figs. 19, 20). Spoon-like synaptic terminals could be identified on the

cells of lightly stained iron-hematoxylin preparations but not in the more heavily stained series or in Golgi material. Dendritic processes extend into the surrounding region, some reaching the lateral lobule of the cerebellum. Spoon-like synaptic terminals also occur on the large cells of the medial and posterior octavomotor nuclei, as also noted by Stefanelli (1937) and Heier (1948), and on the smaller cells of the tangential nucleus.

The lateral-line nerve roots. The dorsal root of the anterior lateral-line nerve is formed of coarser fibers than the ventral root, as also noted by Johnston (1902) and Tretjakoff (1909). This probably indicates a more rapid conduction rate and possibly also differences in the peripheral end organs related to the dorsal root fibers. After entering the dorsal nucleus the fibers dichotomize into ascending and descending branches (fig. 15). These take a somewhat tortuous course within the nucleus, in which most of them end. A fascicle of small fibers, however, emerges from the rostral end of the nucleus, accompanied by a chain of small cells, and passes to the cerebellum. It terminates ipsilaterally, for the most part, but some fibers seem to enter the acousticolateral commissure. Some dorsal root fibers end in the nucleus medialis, according to Johnston (1902) and Pearson (1936a).

The ventral root of the anterior lateral-line nerve enters the nucleus medialis, its fibers bifurcating into as-

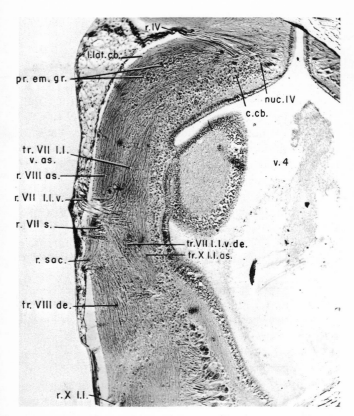

Figure 16. Horizontal section of left half of cerebellum of Petromyzon with adjacent part of medulla oblongata. Bodian method.

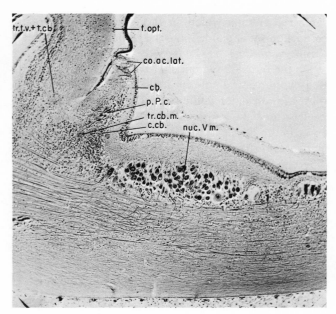

Figure 17. Sagittal section of cerebellum of Petromyzon fluviatilis, with adjacent parts of mesencephalon and medulla oblongata. Bodian method. (Courtesy P. Heier.)

cending and descending branches (fig. 16). Some of the fibers appear to end in the nucleus, but a continuation of the ascending fascicle reaches the primordium of the eminentia granularis and many of its fibers cross in the acousticolateral commissure (figs. 17, 18). The descending fascicle (tractus lineo-spinalis of Heier) extends toward the commissura infima at the caudal end of the medulla oblongata. According to Heier they reach this commissure and its nucleus. Herrick (1908) found various proportions of somatic and visceral sensory fibers in the nucleus and commissura infima of different types of teleosts but specific lateral-line fibers are not mentioned. My observations in petromyzonts are inconclusive regarding lateral-line fibers. Ventral anterior root fibers to the nucleus dorsalis are described by Pearson (1936a) and Heier (1948).

The posterior lateral-line root also enters the nucleus medialis (fig. 16), branching into ascending and descending fascicles. The fibers are larger than those of the ventral anterior lateral-line root. Some bifurcate but others turn rostralward or caudalward without apparent branching. The ascending fibers form a fascicle whose fibers end among the cells of the nucleus medialis and an-

other which continues to the cerebellum (fig. 15). The latter ends among the cells of the primordium of the eminentia granularis in part, but also contributes to the acousticolateral commissure. The descending fascicle extends to the posterior part of the medulla oblongata, fibers ending in the caudal part of the nucleus medialis, in which some descending fibers of the ventral anterior lateral-line root also may terminate. Descending ventral anterior, and ascending posterior lateral-line root fibers, accordingly, overlap in the region of the nucleus medialis, which lies between the anterior and posterior lateral-line roots. In front of the anterior roots the ascending fascicles of both terminate in the rostral continuation of the

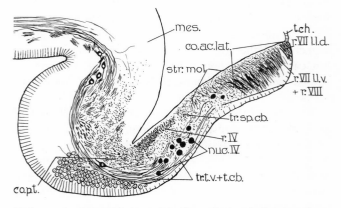

Figure 18. Midsagittal section through cerebellum and anterior medullary velum of Petromyzon marinus. Pyridine-silver method. ×130. (Larsell, 1947a.)

25

same cell column which, in the lobulus lateralis of the cerebellum, is expanded into the primordium of the eminentia granularis.

On the basis of anatomical relations the impulses carried by the ventral anterior and the posterior lateral-line roots are correlated in the cell column represented by the nucleus medialis and its cerebellar continuation. Differences in the size of the fibers of the two roots and experimental evidence in other Ichthyopsida (p. 125) point to differences between these impulses.

The acoustic nerve roots. The VIII nerve root fibers, with some exceptions, bifurcate on entering the medulla oblongata. The ascending and descending branches collect into fascicles in the vestibular area (fig. 16). The descriptions of the connections of these fascicles by Stefanelli (1937), Ariens Kappers (1947), and Heier (1948) vary somewhat in detail but are in general accord. I can confirm most of them but must modify some others.

Ariens Kappers describes the coarsest root fibers as connected peripherally with the crista of the ampullae and the macula of the utricle. Those from the anterior crista are said to terminate centrally as spoon-like or calyciform endings on large cells of the nucleus octavomotorius anterior. According to Heier coarse ascending fibers from the "ganglia utriculares" form spoon-like synaptic connections with the cells of this nucleus. They are said to continue, as smaller fibers branching from the margins of the synaptic enlargements, to the nucleus of the IV nerve and the acousticolateral commissure, decussating on the dorsal surface of the IV nucleus. Whether these branches alone constitute Heier's tractus utriculo-cerebellaris or are included with others to form this tract is not clear from Heier's description.

In Entosphenus numerous fibers of smaller size than the coarse ascending root fibers, but apparently utricular in origin, pass rostrally in company with the coarse fibers as far as the anterior octavomotor nucleus. They then turn dorsomedially into the lobulus lateralis and acousticolateral commissure (fig. 20). I have failed to find fine branches of the coarse fibers near the synaptic calyces but cannot deny their existence. Possibly they are included with the utriculo-cerebellar fibers, above described.

The cells of the IV nucleus of lampreys lie, in part, in the path of the acousticolateral commissure and, in part, in the velar portion of the cerebellovelar plate (Larsell, 1947a, 1947b). They send dendritic branches into the commissural fascicle. It is possible that there is an ampullary component of this fascicle which is related to the velar part of the cerebellovelar plate and so to the nucleus of the IV nerve. Further studies, especially of fortunate Golgi preparations, are needed to unravel more completely the relations between the IV nucleus and the acousticolateral commissure.

Large fibers from the utriculus are said by Ariens Kappers (1947) to end as calyces on cells of his medial posterior and lateral posterior nuclei. According to Heier coarse descending fibers, identified only as arising from the utricular ganglion end as calyces on cells of the nucleus octavomotorius medius and continue as collaterals to the posterior octavomotor nucleus. The latter nucleus is also related with descending lateral-line and saccular fibers, Heier says.

Large fibers from the posterior ampullary crista and some from the papilla neglecta terminate by calyx-like synaptic endings on cells of the nucleus tangentialis (Stefanelli, 1937). Some large fibers from the utricular ganglion are described by Ariens Kappers (1947) as joining the descending V root fascicle. These probably are comparable with similar fibers found by Jansen (1930) in Myxine.

The small fibers of the VIII root that come from the maculae of the utriculus and sacculus and the papillae lagenae bifurcate into ascending branches from utriculo-cerebellar and sacculo-cerebellar fascicles. The descending branches pass to the small and medium-sized cells in the region of the medial and posterior octavomotor nuclei. Many of the fibers come into synaptic relations with cells whose axons pass into the fasciculus longitudinalis lateralis. Heier, who regards all the small fibers as saccular, believes that descending branches also continue to the nucleus commissurae infimae.

In addition to the lateral-line and VIII root fibers, Johnston (1902) followed coarse fibers of the ophthalmic division of the V nerve into the medial part of the acousticolateral area in Golgi material of Lampetra, tracing them to the caudal end of the area and some to the posterior part of the medulla oblongata.

According to Pearson (1936a) small collections of fibers from the spino-acousticolateral cerebellar system (p. 31) enter the acousticolateral area, a few at a time, throughout most of its extent. These trigeminal and spinal connections indicate that impulses of cutaneous and, perhaps, proprioceptive origin, in addition to those from the lateral-line organs and the labyrinth, reach the acousticolateral area of petromyzonts.

Müller cells, defined by Tretjakoff (1909) in ammocoetes as all cells that send axons from the midbrain and medulla oblongata along the fasciculus longitudinalis into the spinal cord, are described in adult lampreys by Johnston (1902), Heier (1948), and others. In Lampetra Johnston describes a pair of Müller cells larger than all others, situated immediately behind the level of the motor VII roots. He regarded them as possibly homologous with Mauthner's cells of higher Ichthyopsida. These cells I can confirm in adult lampreys. Occasionally a laterally directed dendrite was seen to divide into terminal branches among the entering fibers of the VIII root, corresponding to the lateral dendrite of Mauthner's cell in elasmobranchs and other fishes described in subsequent sections. There seems little question that these large Müller cells in lampreys are homologous with Mauthner's cells, as Bartelmez (1915) also believed.

The crista cerebelli. In the younger ammocoete stages a small zone, in which fibers are not recognizable in iron-hematoxylin preparations, is situated dorsal of the ventral anterior lateral-line root, and dorsolateral of the ascending fascicle of root fibers. This represents the incipient cerebellar crest (fig. 8). By the 120 mm stage of Lampetra this zone is quite distinct from the lateral-line nuclei but only a few stained fibers appear in it in the most favorable preparations (fig. 10). Golgi series of adult lampreys show that the crista is composed, in part, of fine fibers from small cells of the dorsal and medial nuclei and fine terminal fibers of lateral-line origin. To these are added dendritic processes and their terminal twigs from the larger cells of the lateral-line nuclei. So far as observed few, if any, cells of the vestibular area send dendrites into the cerebellar crest, although dendrites from medium-sized cells extend into the nucleus medialis and branch among its fibers.

The crista is related to the lateral-line tracts and nuclei but not to the vestibular area. It ends caudally anterior of the entrance of the posterior lateral-line nerve. Rostrally it is continuous with the molecular layer of the cerebellum.

The efferent fibers of the acousticolateral area. The efferent fibers of the acousticolateral area comprise a system of internal arcuate fibers from the lateral-line nuclei and the vestibular area, and tracts of larger fibers that represent axons of the large cells of the three octavomotor nuclei. Internal arcuate fibers from neurons of the nucleus dorsalis and nucleus medialis pass ventralward, turn ventromedially at the lateral angle of the fourth ventricle, and continue toward the midline of the medulla oblongata (fig. 23A, B). According to Pearson (1936a) they are grouped into a small periventricular division which passes into a fiber layer separating the motor column from the ependymal layer, and a ventral division which continues medially beneath the motor column. Small cells of the vestibular area, according to Heier (1948), give rise to finer internal arcuate fibers. Medium-sized spindle-shaped cells, in the medial part of the vestibular area, whose dendrites branch among the vestibular fibers, give rise to axons that take a ventromedial course, decussate in the floor of the ventricle, and enter

the lemniscus lateralis of Ariens Kappers and others. These neurons are found especially at the level of the motor V nucleus (Heier).

Some of the internal arcuate fibers enter the ipsilateral fasciculus longitudinalis medialis, others decussate and enter the corresponding contralateral fascicle. Many internal arcuate fibers, originating both in the lateral-line nuclei and in the vestibular area, form a more ventral decussation and assemble in the lateral lemniscus of Ariens Kappers. Heier says these more ventrally decussating fibers are collaterals of those first mentioned.

The lateral lemniscus of petromyzonts, according to Stefanelli (1937), includes also some secondary vestibular fibers and fibers from the gray substance related to the descending sensory root of the V nerve. Herrick (1948) pointed out that the lemniscus lateralis, as the term is used by many authors in Ichthyopsida, has none of the distinguishing features of the lemniscus lateralis of mammals, although probably including its primordium. He regarded the term fasciculus longitudinalis lateralis as more appropriate, as it also appears to me. This fascicle, according to Heier (1948), who called it the lemniscus vestibulolateralis, includes a tract of secondary vestibular fibers to the cerebellum and secondary fibers to part of the tectum opticum and the torus semicircularis of the midbrain, the nucleus of the posterior commissure, and the primordium of the posterior geniculate body. Some fibers may decussate in the posterior tectal commissure and the commissura posterior.

The large cells of the three octavomotor nuclei give origin to coarse axons that form anterior, medial and posterior octavomotor tracts. The tract from the anterior octavomotor nucleus (figs. 20, 22), passes rostroventrally and medially, decussating in the rostral end of the ventral commissure of the medulla oblongata. It then continues rostralward through part of the intermediate oculomotor nucleus and turns dorsorostrally to end in the torus semicircularis, the nucleus of the posterior commissure, and the primordium of the posterior geniculate body. Pearson (1936a) describes some of its fibers as entering the ipsilateral and contralateral medial longitudinal fascicles and others as ending in the oculomotor nuclei. In larval stages of Lampetra I have observed collaterals from some fibers of this fascicle extending to these nuclei (1947a). Ariens Kappers (1947) regarded the anterior octavomotor nucleus, with its crossed anterior octavomotor tract, as resembling the nucleus of Bechterew of higher vertebrates, but with the difference that the ascending fascicle from the latter is uncrossed.

The fibers taking origin in the medial and posterior octavomotor nuclei bifurcate ventral of the nuclei and form ascending and descending fascicles. Ariens Kappers believes that the posterior nucleus gives rise to a direct vesti-bulo-spinal tract; the medial nucleus gives rise to crossed (and uncrossed?) fibers that ascend and descend in the medial longitudinal fascicle. The posterior octavomotor nucleus was regarded by Stefanelli as homologous with the nucleus of Schwalbe. Some fibers of both nuclei de-cussate in the ventral commissure of the medulla oblon-gata and enter the fasciculus longitudinalis lateralis. As-cending fibers reach the torus semicircularis, the nucleus of the posterior commissure, and the primordium of the posterior geniculate body. Descending fibers of both ap-pear to reach the spinal cord. According to Heier (1948), the ascending fibers of the posterior octavomotor nucleus traverse the superficial and intermediate oculomotor nu-clei before reaching the same terminations in the mesen-cephalon and diencephalon as those from the other two nuclei.

Heier (1948), in his comprehensive account of the brain of Petromyzon fluviatilis, describes the torus semi-circularis as situated between the lateral recess of the tec-tum and the sulcus limitans of His, dorsoventrally, and between the posterior and posterior tectal commissures, anteroposteriorly. It is continuous with the tectum and gradually merges into the nucleus of the posterior com-missure. Structurally and functionally it is similar to the tectum but receives fewer optic fibers and more fibers from the fasciculus longitudinalis lateralis.

The nucleus of the posterior commissure includes the sensory areas of the mesencephalon and diencephalon situated in the adjacent borders of these divisions of the brain. It is formed of fibers and migrated cells. Some of the cells are large and some of the fibers coarse. The rudi-ment of the corpus geniculatum posterius is described as formed of cells that have migrated toward the optic tract in the pars dorsalis thalami. These make up a nucleus, behind the fasciculus retroflexus, composed of cells of varying size with large cells scattered among them.

The fasciculus longitudinalis medialis is a complex tract. In addition to the ascending secondary fibers of the lateral-line and vestibular systems, already mentioned, it includes efferent fibers from the tectum and torus semi-circularis, fibers from the motor tegmentum and other gray substance of the midbrain, fibers of Müller cells, and other fibers (Heier). The fascicle is said to form the principal path for descending impulses to motor regions.

The Adult Cerebellum

The acousticolateral area extends rostralward and slightly laterally, in adult Entosphenus, to merge with the lobulus lateralis of the cerebellum (fig. 4). The cere-bellar arch is a nearly transverse, dorsally tilted plate be-tween the two lobules, the medial deflections beginning at the transition zone from the acousticolateral area to the lobule on either side. The cerebellum of Ichthyomy-zon concolor, as illustrated by Herrick and Obenchain (1913), also comprises a pair of slight lateral swellings and an arch in line with them. In the more elongated brain of Petromyzon marinus the anterior part of the acousticolateral area begins to turn rostromedially at the level of entrance of the anterior lateral-line and VIII roots. The bilateral areas converge toward a relatively short transverse bridge. There is little external evidence of a lateral lobule in Petromyzon marinus but internally the cell mass which produces this swelling in Entosphe-nus is recognizable also in this and other species of lam-preys (fig. 14). In Petromyzon fluviatilis the deflection toward the cerebellar arch is most prominent immediate-ly rostral of the anterior end of the nucleus dorsalis.

THE VESTIBULOLATERAL LOBE

The swelling which constitutes the lobulus lateralis of the adult cerebellum is owing to increase in the aggrega-tion of somewhat scattered cells that form its principal histological feature. This aggregation was called cellulae cerebellares by van Hoevell (1916), stratum griseum su-perficialis cerebelli by Pearson (1936a), and lobus auri-cularis by Heier (1949). In the larval stages, already de-scribed, I have referred to it as the primordium of the eminentia granularis. The reasons for this must now be presented.

The eminentia granularis of Franz (1911b) in teleosts is a mass of granules and other cells which forms a prom-inent enlargement in the lateral part of the cerebellum. It is directly continuous with the nucleus medialis of the acousticolateral area, as is clearly seen in Ictalurus (p. 107), young and adult salmon (p. 107), and other spe-cies. The afferent paths to the granular eminence com-prise primary and secondary lateral-line and acoustic fi-bers, and the bilateral eminentiae are interconnected by commissural fibers. A primitive eminentia granularis, with similar connections, is found in elasmobranchs (p. 52), and successive stages of differentiation toward the teleostean type are represented in chondrosteans, holos-teans, and other Ichthyopsida described in subsequent sections of this book. The afferent connections in all these types have a common pattern.

In larval Lampetra, as already set forth, the cell col-umn, which in the acousticolateral area of adult lam-preys is represented by the nucleus medialis, continues directly into the part of the rhombencephalon that be-comes the cerebellum. There may be a slightly increased number of cells at its anterior end which in later develop-ment becomes deflected medially. In adult lampreys the anterior part of this cell column has enlarged into the cell mass of the lateral lobule which I regard as the primordium of the eminentia granularis. The cells are more scattered than those of the deeper corpus cerebelli (fig. 14), described below, which correspond to Pearson's (1936a) stratum griseum profundum cerebelli.

This expanded and medially deflected cell mass has the same relations to the nucleus medialis of the acousticolateral area as does the eminentia granularis of teleosts. Its morphological relations to the primitive corpus cerebelli, described below, also correspond to those of the teleostean eminentia granularis. In petromyzonts, however, the cell mass is relatively so small that it has little resemblance to the eminentia of other Ichthyopsida so far as its form is concerned.

The afferent connections of the primordium of the eminentia granularis are entirely similar to those of the eminentia granularis of teleosts although the fibers are much fewer. There also are indications of connections between the bilateral cell masses by fibers that pass through the acousticolateral commissure. The fiber connections and the relations to the nucleus medialis are also similar in other Ichthyopsida.

An analysis of the recent contribution of Rüdeberg (1961) on cell migrations provides additional evidence apparently favoring the concept that the external zone of more scattered cells in the petromyzont cerebellum corresponds to the eminentia granularis of fishes. Rüdeberg

says these cells are derived from his "migration A" which, as above described, also gives rise to the nucleus medialis and nucleus dorsalis of the acousticolateral area. The nucleus dorsalis, however, ends short of the cerebellum, only the cell column representing the nucleus medialis continuing forward.

In an 11 mm embryo of the teleost Esox lucius, Rüdeberg describes a "ventral cell cluster of migration A" which subsequently differentiates into "migration A_1" and "A_2". Part of "migration A_1" is regarded as developing into the eminentia granularis which, in Esox, is typical of the teleostean granular eminence. "Migration A_2" appears to combine with part of "migration B" to form the lateral part of the granular layer. In embryos of Squalus acanthias "migration A" is said to divide into A_1 and A_2, the latter being joined by cells from "migration B" to form the nucleus cerebelli (the nucleus lateralis cerebelli of Edinger). No nucleus cerebelli could be identified by Rüdeberg in Esox or Salmo.

Distinct migrations A_1 and A_2 or A_2B are not formed in Petromyzon embryos but the cellulae cerebellares of van Hoevell, according to Rüdeberg, are clearly derived from "migration A," with possibly a contribution from "migration B." All or part of "migration A," Rüdeberg adds, should be regarded as the nucleus cerebelli in Petromyzon.

The nucleus cerebelli of Entosphenus tridentatus, as

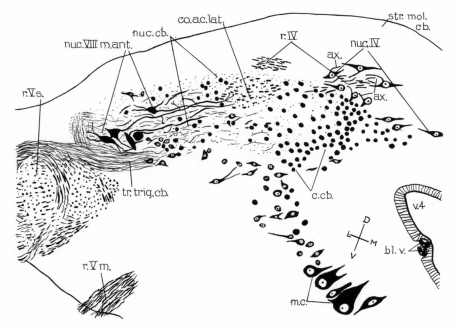

Figure 19. Transverse section showing anterior motor VIII nucleus and adjacent structures in adult Entosphenus tridentatus. Iron-hematoxylin stain. ×102.5. (Larsell, 1947a.)

I described it (1947a), comprises small and medium-sized cells scattered above and medial to the anterior octavomotor nucleus (fig. 19). The ill-defined dorsomedial limit of the nucleus cerebelli is not sharply differentiated from the cell mass which I formerly considered part of the general granular layer of the cerebellum, but now regard more specifically as the primordium of the eminentia granularis. A zone more sparse in cells intervenes between the nucleus cerebelli and this primordium, the two cell groups corresponding respectively to the so-called nucleus medialis pars dorsalis and the stratum griseum superficialis cerebelli of Pearson (1936a) in Petromyzon marinus. The nucleus cerebelli is connected by a chain of cells also with the corpus cerebelli, as described below. The deep granular layer which is the rudiment of the corpus cerebelli is derived from "migration B," according to Rüdeberg. The chain of cells connecting the corpus with the nucleus cerebelli presumably is derived from the same migration. If the ventrolateral part of "migration A" which contributes to the nucleus cerebelli be considered a derivative of an incipient "migration A_2," the dorsomedial mass of cells (primordium of eminentia granularis) could be regarded as developed from a rudimentary "migration A_1." It would then correspond in origin to the eminentia granularis of teleosts. We shall return to the nucleus cerebelli.

These interpretations are based on incomplete evidence and must be regarded as tentative. They are presented because, so far as they are valid, they clarify some difficult questions of homology and illuminate the petromyzont cerebellum.

There is no auricle, as defined in other Ichthyopsida (p. 137), in the petromyzont cerebellum but, in addition to the precursor of the eminentia granularis, a quite separate chain of small cells extends from the anterior end of the nucleus dorsalis into the posterior part of the lobulus lateralis. These cells follow the fascicle of ascending dorsal anterior lateral-line root fibers, already mentioned, and are situated between this fascicle and the ependymal lining of the fourth ventricle. A slight indentation in the ventricular wall suggests an incipient recessus lateralis of the ventricle. The position of the chain of small cells and its relation to this indentation and to the nucleus dorsalis lead one to think of this chain as a possible rudimentary auricle, *sensu strictiori*, as defined in fishes.

The two lobuli laterales, together with the acousticolateral commissure, interconnecting them and also the bilateral acousticolateral areas, evidently constitute a unit in which lateral-line and VIII nerve impulses are correlated at a higher level than in the acousticolateral area. In addition to impulses of ipsilateral origin, those resulting from contralateral stimuli reach both lobules through the acousticolateral commissure. This unit I shall call the vestibulolateral lobe of the cerebellum, employing the term vestibulolateral to differentiate it more sharply from the related acousticolateral area.

THE CORPUS CEREBELLI

The corpus cerebelli in adult petromyzonts is represented by a rostromedially directed mass of rather compactly arranged cells situated ventromedial of the incipient eminentia granularis and continuous caudally with the periventricular gray substance (figs. 14, 16). It is entirely submerged, forming the deep part of the dorsolateral wall of the fourth ventricle and extending forward and medially beneath the fibrous and molecular part of the cerebellar arch but not reaching the midline. In my earlier study (1947a) of the lamprey cerebellum I regarded cells in the rostral part of the medulla oblongata and ventral of what I now call the primordium of the eminentia granularis as foreshadowing the corpus cerebelli. Spinal, bulbar, and trigeminal fibers were described as terminating among these cells, and spinal and trigeminal fibers form the commissura cerebelli. Heier (1948) described the corpus cerebelli as a much larger mass of cells which includes a portion of the cerebellar arch, which I had designated only as part of the granular layer of the organ and which represents a portion of Pearson's (1936a) stratum griseum profundum cerebelli. Heier speaks of the corpus cerebelli as a continuation of the periventricular cells in the "area linea-lateralis." I have confirmed his observations in the adult cerebellum and have followed the principal steps of development of the corpus cerebelli in larval stages, as above described, but am led to the conclusion that there is no relation of this division of the cerebellum to the acousticolateral area. Saito (1930) employs the term corpus cerebelli for the paired "Platten" and their bridge of connection above the fourth ventricle which apparently correspond to the lobuli laterales and cerebellar arch.

The corpus cerebelli, *sensu strictiori*, extends farther both rostrally and medially than the primordium of the eminentia granularis beneath which it is situated. A layer of fibers incompletely separates the two cell masses, scattered cells occurring in this layer (figs. 14, 16). The cells of the corpus cerebelli are more compactly arranged than those of the primordium of the eminentia, as already noted, and in general they are smaller. Neurons of medium and fairly large size, however, also are included. Some of the cells send their axons into the commissura cerebelli, described below, while the axons of others take a ventrolateral course. Granule-like cells send fine axons into the molecular layer (fig. 23).

The molecular layer. The molecular layer of the cerebellum is a continuation of the crista cerebelli, as already noted. It accompanies the commissures across the midline, forming a thin rostral zone of very fine fibers but blending deeply with the commissures. The fine fibers are axonic processes of small cells of the lateral lobules and corpus cerebelli, apparently supplemented by fine collaterals and terminal branches of the commissural fibers.

Because of the convergence of lateral-line and VIII root fibers into the lateral lobule, and the presence of trigeminal and other bulbar, and of spinal fibers in the corpus cerebelli, the molecular layer receives a different complex of impulses than the cerebellar crest. Tecto-, probable toro-, and lobo-cerebellar tracts bring additional impulses, entirely unrepresented in the crista, which probably are relayed through granules of the corpus cerebelli to the molecular layer. Dendritic branches of large cells of the cerebellum, described below, end among the fine fibers. Histologically there appears to be no difference between the molecular layer and the crista, but functionally the molecular layer must be regarded as a much more complex neuropil.

The nucleus cerebelli. The nucleus octavomotorius anterior of petromyzonts often is considered the precursor of the cerebellar nuclei of higher vertebrates. Ariens Kappers (1920) believed that a phylogenic migration of cells has occurred from this nucleus or its immediate vicinity into the cerebellum. According to Stefanelli (1937, 1939) the anterior octavomotor nucleus of lampreys, which he called the anterior vestibular nucleus, is entirely vestibular. On the basis of its development and fiber tract connections I came to the same conclusion (1947a). The cells are derived from the ventral part of the columna dorsalis or the dorsal part of the columna dorsolateralis, as shown by Rüdeberg (1961).

The zone of diffuse cells above called the nucleus cerebelli is closely related in position to the anterior octavomotor nucleus (figs. 14, 20). In origin it is related to the cell migrations that give rise also to the primordium of the eminentia granularis and the rudimentary corpus cerebelli. A chain of cells, in adult Entosphenus, extends toward the nucleus from the corpus cerebelli, evidently corresponding to the possible contributions from "migration B" mentioned by Rüdeberg. The relations of the nucleus to "migration A" and to the ventrolateral part of the stratum griseum superficialis of Pearson and the cellulae cerebellaris of van Hoevell have been sufficiently considered.

Although there is no sharp demarcation between the nucleus cerebelli and the primordium of the eminentia granularis in the adult cerebellum, there is a greater aggregation of nuclear cells rostral of the lateral level of the

primordial eminentia and dorsomedial of the anterior octavomotor nucleus. The cells, in Cajal preparations, tend to be spindle-shaped. Their axons collect into a fairly compact fascicle of fine fibers directed ventrorostrally (fig. 20). Scattered fibers or small fascicles pass ventrally or ventrocaudally. No clear picture of afferent fibers to the nucleus could be found. One gains the impression that ascending VIII root fascicles that appear unrelated

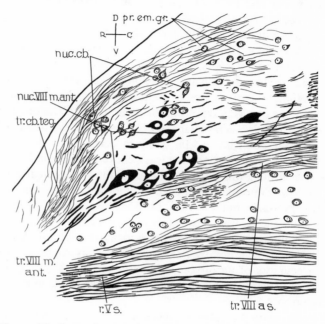

Figure 20. Rostral part of medulla oblongata of adult Entosphenus tridentatus, showing anterior motor VIII nucleus and scattered cells of primitive nucleus cerebelli. Oblique horizontal series. Cajal method. ×205. (Larsell, 1947a.)

to the anterior octavomotor nucleus but reach the primordium of the eminentia granularis send fibers or collaterals into the nucleus cerebelli. Ascending trigeminal and spinal fibers also may do so, but there is no conclusive evidence of either group. Presumably the nucleus receives fibers or collaterals of fibers originating in the cerebellum, probably as axons of the primitive Purkinje cells, but positive evidence is lacking.

The afferent tracts. In addition to the afferent tracts of the acousticolateral area, already described, to the lobulus lateralis and acousticolateral commissure a number of other tracts end in the corpus cerebelli. One of these, the spino-cerebellar tract, is part of the spino-acousticolateral-cerebellar system of Pearson, already mentioned. This system is a collection of fibers at the posterior end of the medulla oblongata, ventral of the descending tract of the V nerve (figs. 12, 13), which ascends from the lateral funiculus of the spinal cord. As the fascicle is followed rostralward it gives off small groups of fibers to the acousticolateral area and continues into the cerebellum.

The spino-cerebellar component of this fascicle comprises small bundles of fibers that arch dorsalward, on approaching the roots of the V nerve (fig. 14), and interdigitate between the root fascicles. They enter the base of the cerebellum, distributing in the corpus cerebelli, some of the fibers decussating in a deep commissura cerebelli (fig. 18). The relations of the tract are similar to those in urodeles but fewer fibers decussate. This fascicle is accompanied by the spino-tectal tract as far as the level of the V roots. Beyond this level the spino-tectal tract arches dorsalward more gradually into the optic tectum. In Golgi series of adult Lampetra there are suggestions of collaterals from the spino-tectal fibers passing into the spino-cerebellar tract but the apparent branches could not be followed far with any certainty.

A spino-cerebellar tract was believed present in Petromyzon fluviatilis by Clark (1906) but he was unable to follow it into the spinal cord. Stefanelli (1937) doubted its presence but Pearson (1936a) and Heier (1948) found such a tract essentially as above described.

Bulbo-cerebellar fibers accompany the spino-cerebellar tract, as noted by Pearson. These may represent the precursors of an olivo-cerebellar tract but Ariens Kappers (1947) doubts that an inferior olive exists in petromyzonts.

Trigemino-cerebellar fibers were found in adult lampreys by Johnston (1902), Stefanelli (1935), Woodburne (1936), and Pearson (1936a). In my 1947 paper I described trigeminal fibers in the commissura cerebelli and Heier (1948) found them ending in the corpus cerebelli. They form a larger fascicle in the adult cerebellum than in ammocoetes, above described. Small fascicles also take origin from the sensory trigeminal nucleus and form a secondary trigemino-cerebellar tract (fig. 14). A small fascicle of these and, apparently, of trigeminal root fibers crosses in the loose aggregation of fibers immediately caudal to the spino-cerebellar decussation as a trigeminal component of the commissura cerebelli.

A tecto-cerebellar tract was described by Clark (1906) and by Pearson (1936a) in adult lampreys but Johnston (1902) found no fibers from tectum to cerebellum in Golgi preparations. Heier (1948) says such fibers may be represented among the fine fibers that decussate in the post-tectal commissure. In Petromyzon marinus a tract of fibers arising from cells in the optic tectum passes into the cerebellovelar plate, some of the fibers apparently terminating among the cells of the IV nucleus and others continuing into the cerebellum (fig. 18). A similar tract occurs in the 127 mm Lampetra larva (fig. 11B).

A mesencephalo-cerebellar (Pearson) or toro-cerebellar tract (Heier) is apparent in later larval and adult stages. It arises in the portion of the midbrain which Heier (1948) identifies as the torus semicircularis, and distributes to the ventral region of corpus cerebelli.

A lobo-cerebellar tract, passing between the inferior lobes of the hypothalamus and the cerebellum, was described from Golgi material by Johnston (1902). This tract was also observed by Clark (1906) and Pearson (1936a) in adult lampreys, and Tretjakoff (1909) found it in ammocoetes, but Heier (1948) was unable to trace it with certainty. I have confirmed it in ammocoete stages and in Cajal, pyridine-silver, and iron-hematoxylin series of adult lampreys (1947a). The fibers are scattered and the cells of origin were not determined, the direction of conduction being assumed from a degeneration experiment on the corresponding tract in bony fishes reported by Wallenberg (1907), and from my own observations on the corresponding fibers in teleosts (p. 116). The lobo-cerebellar tract is intermingled with the anterior fibers of the cerebello-motor system, as described by Johnston and by Pearson, and ends in the corpus cerebelli.

The cerebellar commissures. The commissural system of the cerebellum of petromyzonts has been variously described by different authors. According to Johnston (1902) it consists of a dorsal and a ventral commissure. Tretjakoff (1909), Addens (1928), and Pearson (1936a) include decussating fibers of the IV nerve, and Tretjakoff and Pearson differentiate vestibular and anterior lateral-line root fibers as components. Pearson also includes posterior lateral-line and bulbo-, spino-, and tecto-cerebellar fibers, designating the entire complex the commissura cerebelli. Under the name commissura cerebello-lateralis, which he defines as the rostral commissure of the sensory zone of the rhombencephalon, Heier (1948) includes his lineo-cerebellar (ascending anterior and posterior lateral-line root fibers), utriculo-cerebellar, sacculo-cerebellar, spino-cerebellar, trigemino-cerebellar, and cerebello-tectal tracts, and fibers from the sensory nucleus of the V nerve. He adds that the commissural fibers arising in the cerebellum itself and possibly in the area lineo-lateralis (nucleus medialis) are included. These fibers are differentiated from the decussating root fibers of the VIII nerve. I can confirm these components of the commissural system (fig. 18) but would add secondary fibers from the vestibular area that terminate in the primordium of the eminentia granularis.

The functionally different origins and terminations of the fibers, the fact that the acousticolateral fibers appear at a much earlier larval stage than the spinal and trigeminal components, and the arrangement of acousticolateral fibers as a large posterodorsal group and of the spinal and trigeminal as a smaller anteroventral group, makes it necessary to recognize two commissures instead of one only (fig. 14). The acousticolateral commissure corresponds closely to the vestibulolateral commissure of urodeles, as named by myself, and by Herrick (1948). The commissura cerebelli, in the narrow sense, is relatively much larger in urodeles and is more widely separated from the acousticolateral commissure.

The cerebellar crest and the molecular layer in relation to the afferent tracts. In urodeles, which have no cerebellar crest except rostrally in some higher species, a neuropil is formed among the fibers of the fascicles of the acousticolateral area. It consists of collaterals of these fibers, interlacing among them and the terminal dendritic processes of neurons situated in the gray layer (Herrick, 1948, and p. 130). The fine fibers of lateral-line origin mentioned above in petromyzonts apparently represent similar collaterals which, in these animals, extend beyond the limits of the fiber tracts and, with other elements, form the crista cerebelli. At any rate a neuropil within the fiber tracts has not been demonstrated. The rostrocaudal extent of individual fine fibers in the crista is unknown but probably is limited, as it appears to be in teleosts (p. 100). It also is probable that the fibers entering the crista at successive levels, beginning posteriorly, overlap those at more anterior levels to a greater or lesser extent. There is no evidence that branches of VIII root fibers enter the cerebellar crest, as in teleosts, but ascending saccular and utricular fibers enter the molecular layer of the cerebellum and decussate, as already noted.

These considerations and the afferent connections of the acousticolateral area and cerebellum point to increasing functional complexity of successively more anterior segments of the cerebellar crest and of the molecular layer of the cerebellum as compared with the cerebellar crest.

Spinal fibers enter the acousticolateral area throughout most of its length. Their specific distribution within the area is unknown, but their impulses probably contribute an element to the complex that reaches the cerebellar crest. The caudal part of the crista, related with the caudal region of the nucleus medialis whose principal afferents are the posterior lateral-line root fibers, appears to be functionally the simplest. The region of crista extending forward to the primordium of the eminentia granularis covers the part of the nucleus medialis which receives ascending fibers of the posterior lateral-line root, and ascending and descending fibers of the ventral anterior lateral-line root. Rostrally the crista also covers the nucleus dorsalis. This rostral part of the crista accordingly receives a greater variety as well as a greater concentration of impulses than the caudal part.

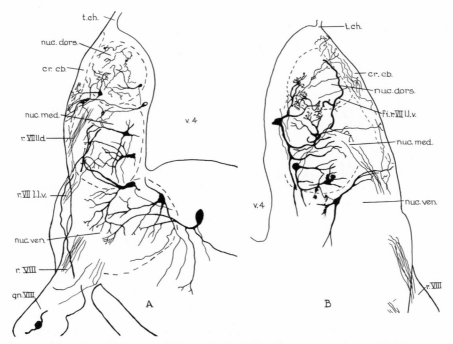

Figure 21. Transverse sections through acousticolateral area of Lampetra wilderi. A. Level of entrance of lateral-line VII and VIII roots, showing types of cells in the dorsal, medial and ventral nuclei. ×52. **B.** Same level on opposite side of brain. ×82. Golgi method. (Larsell, 1947a.)

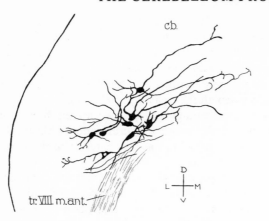

Figure 22. Cells of the anterior motor VIII nucleus, with dendrites extending dorsomedially into the lateral part of acousticolateral commissure. Lampetra. Golgi method. ×130. (Larsell, 1947a.)

The molecular layer of the cerebellum, in addition to impulses through VIII root fibers, receives correlated lateral-line and vestibular impulses through fine axons of granule-like cells in the primordium of the eminentia granularis. Also, correlated spinal, trigeminal, and other bulbar impulses reach the molecular layer from the corpus cerebelli. Furthermore the acousticolateral and cerebellar commissures provide pathways for bilateral impulses to each of the two divisions of the cerebellum. The molecular layer, accordingly, represents a much more complex neuropil than the cerebellar crest.

The neurons of the acousticolateral area and cerebellum. The cells of the acousticolateral area range from small to large. The bodies of those related to the nucleus dorsalis are situated near the periphery of the nucleus, some of them immediately adjacent to the ependymal layer (fig. 21A, B). Large rounded cells, already men-

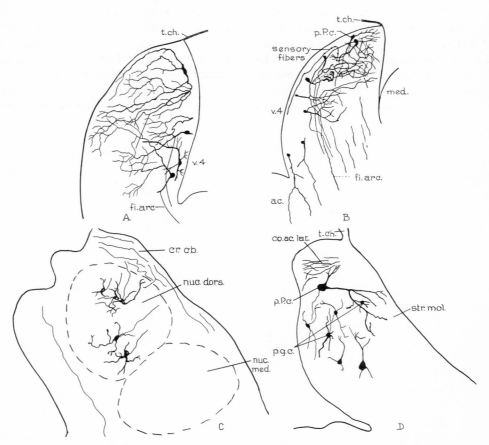

Figure 23. Types of cells in cerebellum and acousticolateral area of Lampetra. A. Transverse section of acousticolateral area. (Johnston, 1906.) B. Sagittal section of cerebellum. Golgi method. (Johnston, 1906.) C. Transverse section at the level of entrance of VIII root, showing small cells in dorsal nucleus whose axons pass into the cerebellar crest. ×102.5. D. Sagittal section of cerebellum showing Purkinje cells. (Larsell, 1947a.)

tioned, occur at the ends of the nucleus. The dendrites of these cells, probably including those of the polar cells which have not been seen in Golgi preparations, pass into the nucleus and branch among its fibers. Dendritic branches from some of the cells also enter the cerebellar crest (fig. 21A). Fairly large cells situated near the ependyma send dendrites into both the nucleus dorsalis and the nucleus medialis (fig. 21B). The cell bodies of medium-sized neurons that are related to the nucleus medialis tend to lie within this nucleus, their dendrites branching among its fiber tracts. Cells deeply situated at the borders of the nucleus medialis and vestibular area send dendrites into the latter area as well as the nucleus medialis (fig. 21A). The axons of the large and medium-sized cells form internal arcuate fibers.

The neurons of the vestibular area, at the level of entrance of the VIII root (fig. 21), are relatively large but much smaller than those of the three octavomotor nuclei. Their dendrites spread toward the entrance of the VIII root fibers, some entering the nucleus medialis or the territory medial of the vestibular area. Small and medium-sized cells are numerous both within and near the octavomotor nuclei but sparse between them. These neurons give rise to arcuate fibers that collect as secondary ascending paths. The cells of the octavomotor nuclei, already partly described, are rarely impregnated in Golgi preparations. Many of them are spindle-shaped, but multipolar neurons also occur in these nuclei. Their axons already have been described as forming specific fiber tracts (figs. 20, 22).

The neurons of the cerebellum comprise large, medium-sized, and small cells, both in the primordium of the eminentia granularis and in the corpus cerebelli (figs. 23, 25). The large cells of both divisions are similar to those of the octavomotor nuclear cells. Some of their dendrites, however, branch into the molecular layer, whereas others branch among the cells of the primordial eminentia and corpus cerebelli. Small terminal tufts of dendrites from the corpus cerebelli, seen in the molecular layer, may indicate a slightly greater differentiation of the large cells of this division. The large cells of both corpus cerebelli and primordial eminentia correspond to the primitive Purkinje cells of Johnston. Their axons enter the anterior part of the internal arcuate fiber system. These primitive Purkinje cells have no resemblance in form to the embryonic Purkinje cells of mammals, contrary to what is sometimes asserted.

Cells of medium size spread their dendrites in the cellular layers, such processes from the corpus cerebelli extending also into the primordial eminentia. Axons of such cells in the corpus are directed ventrolaterally in

many instances, but medially many of the axons can be seen to enter the commissura cerebelli and cross the midline (fig. 24).

Small cells of both divisions of the cerebellum appear to be primitive granules. Not many were encountered, possibly owing to failure of these elements to become impregnated in Golgi preparations. The fine axons extend toward the molecular layer, a few being seen to enter it. The dendrites usually are short but vary in length and also lack the terminal enlargements characteristic of granule cells in higher vertebrates (fig. 23D).

The efferent fibers. The axons of the primitive Purkinje cells of the cerebellum form a system of internal arcuate fibers which is a rostral continuation of that having its origin in the acousticolateral area. The fibers radiate caudoventrally and rostrally from the basal part of the cerebellum (fig. 17). The caudal part of the radiation comprises crossed and uncrossed fibers that descend into the medulla oblongata and, apparently, the cord. Heier

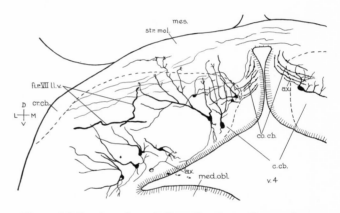

Figure 24. Section of cerebellum showing cell types. Lampetra wilderi. Golgi method. ×82. (Larsell, 1947a.)

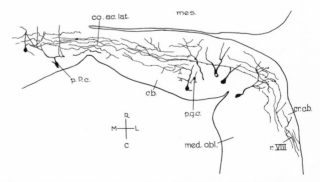

Figure 25. Horizontal section showing primitive Purkinje cells, a primitive granule cell and fibers of VIII root in acousticolateral commissure. Lampetra. Golgi method. ×65. (Larsell, 1947a.)

(1948) includes these fibers in a tractus cerebello-bulbaris et spinalis, describing them as entering the fasciculus longitudinalis medialis.

A cerebello-tegmental tract, which is augmented by fibers from the nucleus cerebelli, accompanies the anterior octavomotor fascicle for some distance and then fans into the tegmentum of the midbrain. Heier believed that fibers of a cerebello-thalamic tract probably are intermingled in a fascicle of fine fibers that appear to correspond with the cerebello-tegmental tract, and that some fibers reach the torus semicircularis. A cerebello-tectal tract is described by Pearson (1936a) and is mentioned by Heier as passing through the commissural system of the cerebellum.

Pearson also describes fibers of cerebellar origin as intermingled with those of the lobo-cerebellar tract and reaching the gray substance of the hypothalamus. The axons of the large cells of the corpus cerebelli I have been able to follow only a short distance ventrolaterally. They probably join the internal arcuate system.

ELASMOBRANCHII

THE cerebellum of elasmobranchs has been described by Burckhardt (1897), Haller (1898), Edinger (1901, 1908), Ariens Kappers (1906, 1921, 1947), Sterzi (1908), van Hoevell (1916), Voorhoeve (1917), and Ariens Kappers, Huber, and Crosby (1936) with reference to structure, fiber tracts, and histological features. Sterzi (1912) and Palmgren (1921) studied its development, and the cell types were described from Golgi preparations by Schaper (1898), Houser (1901), and Sterzi (1909). Experimental demonstration that the dorsal part of the cerebellum of Squalus acanthias is physiologically independent of the vestibular apparatus was made by Tilney (1923), and Stefanelli (1939) compared the selachian cerebellum with that of petromyzonts with reference to their respective functional divisions.

The present account is based on a study of the development of the cerebellum and acousticolateral area in shark and ray embryos and pup stages, stained by the Bodian method, and a review of older stages of several species of sharks and of Raja clavata stained by the Weigert or pyridine-silver methods, supplemented by dissections of the cerebellum of Squalus acanthias. The results have clarified the morphology of the organ and its functional organization.

The most conspicuous feature of the adult elasmobranch cerebellum is a dorsally situated loaf-shaped median division which Sterzi calls the corpus cerebelli (fig. 26). A constricted ventral continuation of the corpus, the cerebellar peduncle of Sterzi, attaches to the anterior medullary velum, the medulla oblongata and a transverse plate which extends above the fourth ventricle from one lateral wall to the other (fig. 27). This plate, the "Unterlippe" of Edinger (1901) and Voorhoeve (1917), valvola cerebellare of Sterzi (1909), pars medialis auriculi of Palmgren (1921) and labium inferius posterior of Ariens Kappers (1934, 1947), is divided by Sterzi into pars horizontalis and pars verticalis. The latter is separated from the corpus cerebelli by a prominent cleft, the myelometencephalic fissure of Sterzi or sulcus postremus of Voorhoeve. On the basis of embryonic development, described below, the peduncle and pars horizontalis of Sterzi both belong to a topographic subdivision which I shall call the pars ventralis of the corpus cerebelli to distinguish it from the loaf-shaped pars dorsalis of the corpus (fig. 28).

The pars verticalis of Sterzi forms the anterior wall of the rhomboidal fossa, arching above the narrower caudal part of the ventricular space which continues forward to the mesencephalic ventricle. Behind the pars verticalis or pars medialis of the vestibulolateral lobe, as I shall call it, the rhomboidal fossa is broad (fig. 27); its anterior part extends rostrolaterally, on either side, as a recessus lateralis. Beginning at the level of entrance of the anterior lateral-line roots the margin of the rhomboidal fossa and its lateral recess is folded rostrolaterally, on either side, into expanded ear-like projections, the Rautenohren of Burckhardt or orechiette romboidale of Sterzi, usually called the auricles (fig. 28). This anterior part of the rhombic lip differs in structure from that behind the level of entrance of the anterior lateral-line roots, as Burckhardt pointed out.

Each auricle comprises an inferior or posterolateral fold, which is continuous caudally with the acousticolateral area, and a superior or anteromedial fold, continuous with the pars medialis. As will appear, the deep part of this median division also is continuous, laterocaudally, with the principal cell column of the acousticolateral area of the medulla oblongata through an expanded cell mass in the floor of the recessus lateralis. The afferent connections of this expansion, as well as of the auricle and the pars medialis, are derived from the acousticolateral area and its related nerves, whereas the corpus cerebelli receives spinal, olivary and other bulbar, and mesencephalic fibers almost exclusively.

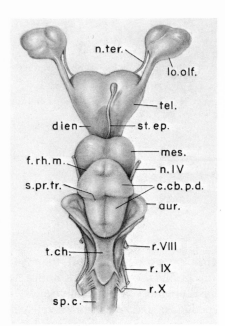

Figure 26. Dorsal view of brain of Acanthias vulgaris, 1 m long. ×1.2. (Modified from Sterzi, 1909.)

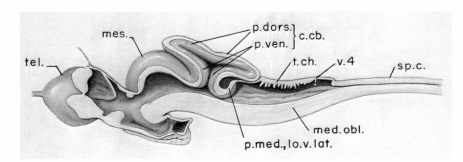

Figure 27. Midsagittal section of brain of Acanthias vulgaris, 1 m long. ×1.5. (Modified from Sterzi, 1909.)

Figure 28. Dorsal view of rhombencephalon of Acanthias vulgaris, 90 cm long, after removal of the caudal part of corpus cerebelli and tela choroidea myelencephali. ×3. (Modified from Sterzi, 1909.)

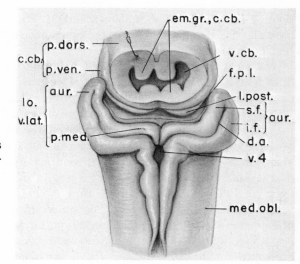

The auricles, the floor of the recessus lateralis, and the pars medialis are so distinct from the corpus cerebelli in their functional connections as well as in morphogeny and adult relations that they constitute a unit, the bilateral halves of which are interconnected by commissural fibers, which I shall call the vestibulolateral lobe of the cerebellum (fig. 28). The pars medialis corresponds to the pars medialis auriculi of Palmgren (1921) in selachian embryos. The sulcus postremus of Voorhoeve corresponds to the posterolateral fissure of other Ichthyopsida.

As in all large vertebrate groups that are diversified with respect to body size and habits, the cerebellum of elasmobranchs varies in the relative size of its subdivisions in different species. This is true of the corpus cerebelli and vestibulolateral lobe and also of the subdivisions of these primary divisions. A basic pattern, common to all, may be recognized, however, in the many species of small, medium-sized, and large sharks and rays described and illustrated by Sterzi (1909) and Voorhoeve (1917), when compared with the more limited number of species on which my own studies have been based.

The form of the elasmobranch cerebellum differs in many respects from that of the numerous variations found in other Ichthyopsida. These differences have presented difficulties in establishing homologies, but the embryonic development of the organ in Squalus, Apristiurus, and Raja, described below, has clarified these problems.

The subdivisions of the vestibulolateral lobe are so clearly associated with the acousticolateral area, both in embryonic development and in adult relations, that this area must also be considered with reference to development and adult structure. In order to give functional significance to the anatomical subdivisions of both the acousticolateral area and the vestibulolateral lobe the acousticolateral system of sensory organs and nerves will first be described. A brief description of the cutaneous and proprioceptor end organs is also included. Impulses from these organs reach the corpus cerebelli by way of the spinal nerves and the spinal cord or, in the head region, by trigeminal connections with the cerebellum.

THE LATERAL-LINE ORGANS AND NERVES

The lateral-line organs and nerves of elasmobranchs have been studied by Ewart (1889, 1892), Strong (1903), Hawkes (1906), Johnson (1917, 1918), Norris and Hughes (1920), and others. In Squalus acanthias, according to Norris and Hughes, four types of sensory organs are associated with the lateral-line system. These are canal organs, pit organs, ampullae of Lorenzini, and tubular organs regarded as modified ampullae. Vesicles of Savi represent an additional type in the electric rays or

Torpedinae. The canal organs are found in bilaterally represented supraorbital, infraorbital, mandibular, and hyomandibular canals of the head and in the lateral canals of the body. The latter lie within the dermis but those of the head, for the most part, are more deeply situated. The two lateral canals in Squalus and Mustelus, according to Johnson, are connected by a transverse supratemporal commissural canal which is situated immediately behind the openings of the endolymphatic ducts. The lateral canals extend from the ends of the commissural canal to the caudal end of the body. The supraorbital and infraorbital canals merge, medial and slightly rostral of the spiracle, on either side, forming a short canal which is continuous with the ends of the commissural canal.

Pit organs occur in two series in adults. A dorsal series, situated above the lateral canal, extends from a point slightly behind the eye to the caudal end of the body in Mustelus; in Squalus this series reaches only to the region of the first dorsal fin. A mandibular series begins at the posterior margin of the spiracle and curves around the end of the hyomandibular canal and then forward almost to the midline of the ventral surface behind the mouth. In embryos two additional lines of pit organs are found anterior of the attachment of the yolk sac. An accessory series, apparently developing from the superior margin of the epithelial cord that gives rise to the lateral canal rather than as individual pits, was found in Squalus. The ampullae of Lorenzini occur in cavities of the skull along the principal canals of the head. Tubular organs, or modified ampullae of Lorenzini, occur on the mandible and in the anterior wall of the spiracle of Squalus. The vesicles of Savi are small isolated sacs beneath the epidermis of the lips and near the mouth of Torpedo.

The end organs of the lateral-line systems of Ichthyopsida basically comprise groups of pear-shaped, ciliated sensory cells, called neuromasts, situated among the epithelial cells of the outer layer of epidermis, as described by Löwenstein (1957). The organs may take the form of free sensory hillocks, projecting above the ectodermal epithelium, or they may be sunk beneath the surface as pit organs, elongated furrows, or canals. Several types can co-exist in the same individual.

In the free sensory hillocks, according to Löwenstein, the hair processes protrude above the ectodermal epithelium and are enclosed in an elongated gelatinous cupula which is freely movable in the surrounding water. Motion of the water past a stationary fish, or locomotion, deflects the cupula from its resting position, resulting in stimulation of the hair cells. Pit organs, those occurring in grooves or furrows, and also the canal organs are protected from overstimulation. The same individual may have several types of these end organs.

The pit organs, the simplest type in elasmobranchs, are characterized by a depression the walls of which are formed of thickened epithelium; the sensory organ is situated in the bottom of the pit. This is formed of tall columnar epithelial cells and shorter pear-shaped sensory cells. The tall cells extend from the basement membrane to the surface and serve as supporting elements, the sensory cells being arranged among them. Cuticular hairs from the free ends of the sensory cells project beyond the epithelial surface. Fine terminal branches of the lateral-line nerve fibers surround the body of each sensory cell.

The canal organs are formed of groups of sensory and supporting cells arranged in a continuous series in the canals, which themselves are lined with low epithelium. The more elevated epithelium of the canal organs forms a continuous column, usually on the dorsal wall of the canal. The lateral-line nerves accompany the canals and give rise to a continuous series of twigs which end as terminal filaments on the successive groups of hair cells. The canals open to the surface, at approximately regular intervals, by tubules that take a short ventral course and then turn lateralward to penetrate the epidermis, forming a pore.

The ampullae of Lorenzini are flask-shaped bodies, containing a jelly-like substance, which are connected by slender canals with pits that open on the surface. The expanded deep part of each ampulla has sensory organs of the same general type as the pit organs but more complex. Developmentally the ampullae begin as pits which extend inward to their final positions, Johnston (1906) states. The vesicles of Savi have sensory organs histologically similar to those of the pits and canals; they are served by nerves that also reach the pit and canal organs.

The functions of the lateral-line system have been studied experimentally by many authors. Parker (1904, 1908b, 1918) concluded that in teleosts the system is stimulated by vibrations of low frequency in the water, in the range of low sound tones. Hofer (1908) first demonstrated conclusively that the lateral-line system is a receptor for water currents. It was also postulated by Hofer (1908), Steinmann (1914), Hoagland (1935), and Sand (1937) that these organs serve as accessory proprioceptors, indicating the progression and magnitude of body flexion during swimming. The only effect on locomotion in blind fishes, when the lateral-line system is eliminated, according to Löwenstein (1957), is a "reluctance" to move. Movement resulted in frequent collisions with the wall of the aquarium and with other solid objects. No lack of muscle coordination affecting the swimming movements themselves was detectable. Dijkgraaf (1934) demonstrated that the lateral-line organs are not concerned chiefly with rheotactic behavior, since tactile stimuli also are of importance in rheotactic responses. Analysis by oscillographic methods, in Ameiurus and other teleosts demonstrated a spontaneous activity of the lateral-line end organs, with discharge of impulses during rest (Hoagland, 1933a), and Sand (1937), in elasmobranchs, also found a vigorous resting discharge. According to Sand (1937) the effective stimulus for the canal organs is a slow movement of the fluid in the canal. No evidence was found for the existence of rapidly adapting receptors in the canals, but the system is exceedingly sensitive to vibrations of low frequency, according to Sand. Hoagland (1933a,b, 1935), who studied the lateral-line system by oscillographic methods, suggested that the lateral-line receptors of the head may have a different function than those of the body. He found evidence that the fibers of the posterior lateral-line nerve serve at least two types of receptors. One type responds to touch, pressure, and compression of surrounding tissues; its nerve fibers give evidence of activity only when the receptors are stimulated. The other is continuously active, but the frequency of impulses is dependent on the activity of the receptors and is affected by changes of temperature. Vigorous spontaneous discharges of impulses in the acusticolateral area and cerebellum were recorded when the lateral-line nerves were intact. According to Hoagland (1935) the lateral-line organs respond to certain vibratory stimuli by getting into phase so that their cilia beat synchronously. A volley of impulses was produced by concave flexing of the trunk, the speed and degree of movements modifying the frequency of these discharges. Since neuromuscular spindles have not been demonstrated in fishes, the receptors of the lateral-line system are suggested as playing a role in the control of equilibrium and swimming. Rubin (1935) found evidence of thermic fibers in the lateral-line nerve. According to Murray (1956) the lateral-line organs of the South American frog Xenopus have a threshold for temperature changes of $1–2°C$, whereas in similar preparations of cutaneous nerves the threshold was $5–10°C$.

Dijkgraaf (1947a, 1952) emphasizes the role of the lateral-line system in perception of limited water currents in the neighborhood of solid bodies. He says that fishes are able to detect and locate moving bodies, and even obstacles at some distance, by a distance-touch sense (Ferntastsinne) of very great sensitivity, the receptors of which are the lateral-line organs. Local damming phenomena (increase of water resistance) produced by the moving body itself and modified by obstacles in its environment give rise to displacements of the water that also are detected by the lateral-line organs. According to Wunder (1950) the lateral-line organs of fishes register the direction of feeble currents and repercussions in the water. Blind predatory fish find and catch their prey by means of these organs. Even fish which nose about at the bottom of streams and other bodies of water may find small larvae of insects through stimuli supplied by this sensory system. The lateral-line organs of the head in larval urodeles also play a part in the detection of food (Scharrer, 1932; Detwiler, 1945). Hoagland (1935) found no evidence that all the fibers of different functional significance, mentioned by him in fishes, are related to the lateral-line organs. The observations of the various authors above cited indicate, however, that these organs may respond to several types of stimuli.

Löwenstein (1957) says that the lateral-line organs chiefly are the receptors for the Ferntastsinne of Dijkgraaf, serving distance-touch orientation. This sense compensates for poor vision in the water, helping to localize moving objects at a distance as well as stationary objects by echo location. This author regards it unlikely that the lateral-line system plays any significant role in hearing.

The special modifications of lateral-line organs in elasmobranchs appear to have specific functions. The ampullae of Lorenzini are temperature receptors, according to Sand (1938) and Hensel (1955). They are very sensitive to changes of temperature and behave like the cold receptors of the human tongue (Hensel). A specific mechanoreceptor function is suggested by Murray (1957), who (1959), by oscillographic methods, observed increased frequency of response after temperature change. About the functions of the corpuscles of Savi little is known.

The lateral-line nerves. The nerves of the lateral-line system of elasmobranchs are similar in general to those of petromyzonts but are much larger and branch more freely. As described by Norris and Hughes (1920) in Squalus the anterior lateral-line ganglion gives rise to a large superficial ophthalmic VII nerve which is closely accompanied by fascicles of the superficial ophthalmic V nerve. The lateral-line component of the combined nerve serves the supraorbital canal and the supraorbital group of ampullae of Lorenzini. The ramus buccalis VII becomes closely associated with ramus maxillaris V to form the infraorbital trunk. The buccal component is distributed to the infraorbital canal and the associated ampullae of Lorenzini; some of the branches pass to ampullae only but most of them distribute to canal organs and ampullae. A ramus oticus VII serves the posterior continuation of the supraorbital canal, which connects with the canal of the trunk; it also serves the tubular organ in the anterior wall of the spiracle. The ramus mandibularis externus VII, which is a large branch from the hyomandibular trunk, serves the hyomandibular and mandibular canals, the tubular organs anteroventral to the mandibular canal

and near the line of junction of the mucous membrane with the epidermis at the angle of the mouth, also a hyoidean group of ampullae of Lorenzini and the series of pit organs extending from the spiracle toward the median ventral line.

The anterior part of the trunk canal and possibly some pit organs above it are served by a lateral-line component of the IX nerve in Squalus, according to Norris and Hughes (1920). The remainder of the trunk canal and perhaps some pit organs are served by the lateral-line X nerve. In the rays a dorsal lateral-line branch appears to be lacking. Variations of detail are found in other species of elasmobranch but the general pattern shown in Squalus prevails.

The membranous labyrinth. The membranous labyrinth, described by Retzius (1881) and de Burlet (1934), varies in different groups of elasmobranchs. In all species there are three semicircular canals, in contrast with the two of petromyzonts. The additional canal, the horizontal or lateral, is closely related to the anterior canal, both ends opening into the latter as a rule (de Burlet). Each canal has an ampulla and a crista ampullaris. An otosaccus, into which the semicircular canal opens, is differentiated into utriculus, sacculus, a small lagena which is poorly demarcated from the sacculus, and a papilla or macula neglecta. The endolymphatic duct opens on the surface of the head. The maculae utriculi, sacculi, lagenae, and neglecta and the cristae ampullares are patches of epithelium formed of hair cells and supporting elements similar to those of the lateral-line organs. The maculae utriculi and sacculi differ from the lateral-line organs by possessing a covering otolithic membrane. The remaining sensory patches have no distinct covering membrane or otoconia. Whether the sacculus of elasmobranchs has any indication of an auditory function, as in teleosts (p. 96) appears to be unknown. Aside from this possibility the membranous labyrinth is vestibular in function.

The acoustic nerve. The acoustic or VIII nerve is divided into anterior and posterior branches. The anterior branch distributes to the crista of the anterior and lateral ampullae and to the macula utriculi. The posterior branch sends rami to the maculae of the sacculus and lagena, the papilla or macula neglecta, and the crista of the posterior ampulla. The root fibers of the nerve enter the vestibular area of the medulla oblongata by what appears in the adult as a single large and broad root, the dorsal fibers of which are so intermingled with ventral anterior lateral-line root fibers that a line of distinction between the two nerve roots cannot be drawn, as also found by Norris and Hughes (1920). In embryonic stages these two roots are quite separate and the root of the anterior branch of the

VIII nerve clearly enters at a more ventral level than the root of the posterior branch. The anterior root fibers are separated by the visceral sensory root of the VII nerve, and the anterior acoustic root fibers behind the VII nerve root are intermingled with posterior acoustic root fibers to such an extent that the central courses of the two acoustic roots are difficult to differentiate. Both roots include small and large fibers, but the anterior root has a greater number of coarse fibers. All the fibers bifurcate in the vestibular area. My observations on developmental stages are in accord with the description of Ariens Kappers (1947) of the adult. We shall return to the distribution of the root fibers in connection with consideration of the acousticolateral area of the adult (p. 51).

PROPRIOCEPTORS AND THE CUTANEOUS SENSORY SYSTEM

Nerve endings of proprioceptive type were found in the muscles, aponeuroses, and at the ends of muscle fibers in sharks and rays by Pansini (1889), Giacomini (1898a), and others. Terminaisons en paniere, at the ends of muscle fibers, are basket-like terminals that frequently surround several muscle fibers but have no capsule. Brush-like terminals (en pinceau), which somewhat resemble muscle spindles have also been described. These are surrounded by nuclei, and the muscle fibers in such areas are somewhat modified (Byrnes, 1929). A complex nerve plexus which divides into terminal fibers was found by Pansini (1889) on the aponeurotic layers of the dorsal musculature of Torpedo. Some of the terminal fibers, after losing their myelin sheath, divide into three or more branches having nucleated plaques at their ends. On the tendons of the fin muscles Pansini describes true Golgi organs, in the form of numerous terminal plaques, on a limited portion of the tendon. The great mass of segmental musculature and its attachments in elasmobranchs must contain very large numbers of the several types of proprioceptors above described.

The innervation of the skin of Squalus acanthias, according to Weddell (1941), is by a cutaneous nerve plexus comprising two principal layers. Single fibers from deep nerve trunks enter the cutaneous plexus and dichotomize repeatedly the terminal fibers ending beneath and between the cells of the basal layer of the epidermis.

The Development of the Acousticolateral Area and the Cerebellum

In vertebrate embryos, in general, a matrix of several layers of cells develops in the neural tube by proliferation of elements of the neural epithelium. Gradual migration of cells from the matrix results in a more peripheral mantle or migration layer. In urodeles, however, the cell bodies of nearly all neurons of the brain, even of the adult, are crowded into a dense layer near the ventricle, with but little migration of cells away from this layer. Precursors of many of the nuclei characteristics of higher vertebrates can be recognized in local specialization of cells in the gray layer or by connections of related nerve fibers, as described in detail by Herrick (1948). Early differentiation of the nervous system in Ambystoma larvae advances by acceleration of first one, then another functionally defined region of the even more primitive neural tube, according to Coghill (1924). On the basis of Coghill's observations on these zones of accelerated growth, as indicated by mitotic figures, and of the experimental results of others, Herrick (1933a) points out that this differentiation is partly intrinsic, and can advance to a certain point before any connections are developed between parts of the brain. A stage is reached sooner or later, however, when continuation of differentiation is dependent on some formative influence excited by the characteristic nervous connections of the part. Later stages of growth and differentiation continue during functional activity, and seem more or less dependent on it. Coghill, in a series of studies, and Herrick (1933a,b,c, 1948) have analyzed the differentiation and development of the subdivisions of the neural tube in terms of their functional significance. Kuhlenbeck (1956) has emphasized a theoretical "Bauplan" or common pattern of the neural tube in all vertebrates. Holmgren (1922, 1925) and his school have approached the problem by attempting to trace the cell masses of the brain from the earliest possible stages of embryonic development and following their embryonic history. We shall give further consideration only to the medulla oblongata and cerebellum.

According to Bergquist and Källén (1953, 1954, 1955) migration areas of the mantle layer form several transitory series of transverse bands in early embryos: the proneuromeres, neuromeres, and postneuromeres. When the postneuromeres begin to disappear, four longitudinal cell ridges begin to form on the mantle layer. These extend throughout the length of the rhombencephalon and are identifiable, in modified form, in the remainder of the brain. They were named the columna dorsalis, columna dorsolateralis, columna ventrolateralis, and columna ventralis and were regarded as corresponding in principle respectively, to the somatic sensory, visceral sensory, visceral motor, and somatic motor columns of Herrick and Johnston in adult brains. Further studies, however, led Hugosson (1957) to conclude that the boundaries between the early cell columns gradually disappear and a new generation of four columns is formed by differentiation of the nuclei of the cranial nerves which are related to the medulla oblongata. The nuclei of the four functional columns develop, in general, from the earlier embryonic columns, the somatic nuclei from the dorsal column, and so on; but because of certain exceptions Hugosson concluded that the functional columns of Herrick and Johnston are formed from the new generation of cell columns, for the development of which the earlier columns provided the building material.

The dorsal column ends rostrally at the isthmic fold. According to Bengmark, Hugosson, and Källén (1953), specifically in the mouse, its most rostral part gives rise to the cortex of the cerebellum. The sensory trigeminal and cochlear nuclei were derived by Vraa-Jensen (1956) from the area immediately ventral of the rhombic lip in the chick. The vestibular nuclei, except the lateral nucleus of Deiters, were believed by Vraa-Jensen to derive from the dorsal part of the alar lamina, corresponding to the columna dorsalis. Deiters's nucleus, the cells of which are described as motor in type and as forming a link in the motor pathway, migrate from the medial part of the basal lamina, Vraa-Jensen states. The basal lamina also gives origin to somatic and special visceral efferent neurons. Hugosson (1957), however, derives the vestibular nuclei of the chick, electric ray (Torpedo ocellata), frog, mouse, and man from the dorsolateral cell column which also gives rise to visceral sensory nuclei. The dorsal and medial nuclei of the acousticolateral area in Torpedo (lacking in the other species mentioned) have their origin from the columna dorsalis, according to Hugosson. It has already been noted that the cerebellum of all species is a development of the columna dorsalis.

THE ACOUSTICOLATERAL AREA

The columna dorsalis of Torpedo ocellata, according to Hugosson (1957), is formed of diffusely arranged cells up to stages 24 mm in length. In the 29 mm embryo the cells are grouped in two masses and at the 33 mm stage the dorsal and ventral anterior lateral-line nuclei are distinctly represented. I find early indications of the two nuclear masses in 25 mm Apristiurus embryos; in 40 mm Squalus embryos, and probably earlier, the nuclei are well differentiated.

The dorsal and ventral roots of the anterior lateral-line nerve which enter the dorsal and medial nuclei, respectively, at an early stage of differentiation are well developed and bifurcated in the 60 mm Squalus embryo. Both nuclei have enlarged to such an extent that a groove has appeared between their ventricular surfaces (fig. 32A,B). In the rostral part of the acousticolateral area, which flares outward at this stage, the groove is shallow (fig. 32C). At the level where the ventral anterior lateral-line root enters the medulla oblongata the marginal part of the area, which includes the nucleus dorsalis, has folded me-

dialward so that it forms the lateral wall of the fourth ventricle (fig. 32A). The ventricular groove is deep between the elevation formed by the nucleus dorsalis and that produced by the medial and vestibular nuclei which form its floor. This groove continues beyond the caudal extremity of the nucleus dorsalis as a deep furrow between the medially tilted rhombic lip and the nucleus medialis.

The choroid tela is attached at the dorsolateral margin of the nucleus dorsalis (fig. 32A) as far rostralward as the level of the roots of the VIII nerve. From this level forward, however, a zone of closely arranged cells, evidently derived from proliferative elements of the tenial attachment, forms a dorsolateral cap, as seen in transverse sections, which covers the nucleus proper (fig. 32). This cap is a continuous band which increases in prominence rostralward and merges directly with a more enlarged granular ridge that constitutes the inferior fold of the incipient auricle. Owing to further growth and folding the projection of the nucleus dorsalis into the ventricular space in the pup stages of development is so pronounced that the dorsal part of this space is much narrower than the floor of the fourth ventricle. The nucleus dorsalis is connected with the nucleus medialis only by a thin zone of arcuate fibers situated between the ventricular groove, above described, and a fairly thick cerebellar crest which has developed by these stages. The band of granules covers the large anterior part of the nucleus dorsolaterally, but the bluntly ending anterior extremity of the nucleus is entirely separated from the granular ridge. The boundary between this ridge and the nucleus is fairly distinct since the latter consists of cells of different type and appearance, scattered among the fibers of the dorsal root of the anterior lateral-line nerve. Caudally the nucleus dorsalis tapers in the margin of the rhombic lip, disappearing at about the level of the root of the IX nerve.

The nucleus medialis of the 60 mm Squalus embryo extends throughout the length of the acousticolateral area (fig. 32). It receives the ventral root of the anterior lateral-line nerve and the root of the posterior lateral-line nerve; these root fibers also bifurcate. The nucleus is a distinct nearly uniform mass of scattered cells from the level of the ventral anterior lateral-line root to a level caudal of the posterior lateral-line root. Rostral of the ventral anterior root it gradually enlarges, merging with a similar cell mass in the floor of the recessus lateralis of the fourth ventricle. In the pup stages the volume of the nucleus is increased and its cells are more crowded, especially in front of the ventral anterior lateral-line root. Caudally it gradually diminishes beyond the level of the posterior lateral-line root but is covered by a thin layer of cerebellar crest.

The nucleus ventralis or vestibular area is quite distinct from the nucleus medialis at the level of the roots of the VIII nerve in the 60 mm Squalus embryo. At a point opposite the entrance of the root fibers many large and somewhat scattered multipolar cells represent a primitive Deiters's nucleus. Farther rostrally the cells are smaller and the nuclear mass is small but distinctly separated from the nucleus medialis. A collection of small cells also extends caudalward a short distance. In the pup stages the large cells, now increased in size, are less scattered. Small cells are much more numerous and merge anteriorly with those of the nucleus medialis, no boundary between the two nuclei being discernible. The fascicles of ascending branches of both the ventral anterior lateral-line roots and those of the VIII nerve pass forward into the floor of the recessus lateralis in the cell mass which extends rostralward from the level of the ventral anterior lateral-line and VIII roots.

At the entrance of the larger fibers of the anterior VIII root oval cells, smaller and differing in appearance from the multipolar cells of Deiters's nucleus, probably correspond to the tangential nucleus of Ramon y Cajal (1908b) in teleosts, but I have been unable to identify the spoon-like synaptic terminals characteristic of this nucleus in bony fishes and certain other vertebrates. Ariens Kappers (1947) states that such terminals are lacking on cells in elasmobranchs that he also believed correspond to the tangential nucleus.

A pair of giant cells situated in the lateral part of the motor tegmentum, opposite the entrance of the roots of the VIII nerve, was found in several 40 mm Squalus embryos. A large lateral dendrite extends into the nerve roots, in one instance terminal twigs reaching a short distance into the extramedullary part of the root. A large ventral dendrite, a number of smaller radiating dendrites, and a dorsomedially directed axon that enters the fasciculus longitudinalis medialis give these cells the characteristics of Mauthner's cells of teleosts and other Ichthyopsida. Another embryo of 40 mm length but much earlier stage of brain differentiation showed no indication of similar large cells. All series of 60 mm embryos examined had more elongated giant cells in a similar position and with similar characteristic processes. In the most favorably stained series terminal boutons of acoustic root fibers were found on the large part of the lateral dendrite. Müller cells, smaller than the Mauthner cells and with shorter dendritic processes, were situated more ventrally in the motor tegmentum of the 60 mm Squalus embryos, as also described in Ameiurus by Bartelmez (1915). In the pup stages only Müller cells were found except in

one specimen, 170 mm long, which showed a pair of somewhat shrunken elements that resembled Mauthner's cells. Embryos of Raja binoculata 40 mm, 55 mm, and 130 mm long showed no unmistakable Mauthner's cells, but the largest specimen had many Müller cells and a pair of larger cells that were somewhat similar to Mauthner's cells of Squalus in position and general appearance but lacked a large lateral dendrite. A 65 mm embryo of Apristiurus brunneus showed large cells of reticular type in the motor tegmentum but none that could be identified as Mauthner's cells. The large axon of Mauthner's cell in Squalus appears to accompany those of the neighboring Müller cells through the medulla oblongata.

Mauthner's cell does not appear to have been described hitherto in elasmobranchs. Johnston (1902) found a pair of large cells in Petromyzon, immediately behind the roots of the VIII nerve, that probably are homologous. These I also have seen. Bartelmez (1915) describes Mauthner's cells, in larval and adult Ameiurus, as having connections through their dendrites with acoustic root fibers and fibers from the lateral-line and many other centers, including the cerebellum and tectum. The large Mauthner's fiber is said to continue into the tail.

According to Stefanelli (1953), who studied Mauthner's cell in teleosts, urodeles, and anuran larvae, it forms a connecting link between the lateral-line organs and the spinal motor centers of the tail. He concluded that Mauthner's cells are essentially larval organs. They are found in adult fish only in species that retain the larval manner of swimming, and in sluggish swimmers. Atrophy of Mauthner's cells occurs in species in which the tail is reduced as a swimming organ and also in strong swimmers such as predatory species of the open sea. In the latter species it is replaced by a stronger system related to the fasciculus longitudinalis medialis.

The Mauthner's cell in the embryo of the viviparous Squalus acanthias and its subsequent functional replacement by a group of cells that give rise to the medial fascicle of Stieda (p. 53) of the adult apparently corresponds in principle to the history of this cell in strong-swimming teleosts. The newborn Squalus is capable of swimming, strong movements of the tail playing an important part as in the adult. Locomotion in the Rajidae is largely accomplished by undulatory movements of the pectoral fins, the small tail being insignificant in this function. The apparent absence of Mauthner's cell from both embryos and adults of the oviparous Rajidae must be compared with the situation in species of dogfish that are oviparous instead of viviparous, as in Squalus, and other comparisons must be made before valid deductions can be drawn about this cell in elasmobranchs generally. The meager information at hand appears to suggest that in correlation with the insignificant locomotor function of the tail in rays, Mauthner's cell does not appear at any stage, although it is present in young stages of teleosts and throughout life in some species, as above related. The connections of Mauthner's cell with the roots of the VIII and anterior lateral-line roots and with the cerebellum, described in teleosts, have been only partially confirmed in Squalus, but the cell appears to have a transitory function related to impulses from these nerves and possibly from the cerebellum.

THE CEREBELLUM

The first indication of the cerebellum in elasmobranch embryos, according to Sterzi (1912) is a thickened area on either side of the midline in the roof of the rhombencephalon and immediately behind the isthmic fold (fig. 29). Such thickenings are described in embryos of Rajidae 6–7 mm in length and in selachian embryos of 7–8 mm length. A narrow thinner zone of the roof of the rhomboidal fossa connects the bilateral halves of the rudimentary cerebellum across the midline. The thickened area in each half of the cerebellar rudiment undoubtedly is the matrix layer, formed by proliferation of neural epithelial cells lining the ventricular cavity. In a 9.5 mm Squalus embryo, according to Rüdeberg (1961), the

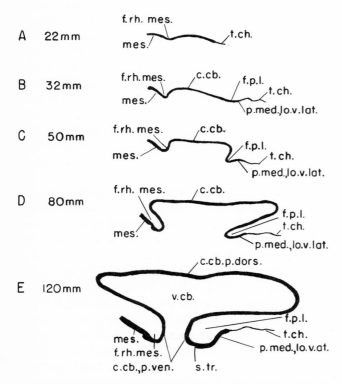

Figure 29. Paramèdian sagittal sections of cerebellum of embryos of Acanthias vulgaris. ×4.7.
(Modified from Sterzi, 1912.)

neural epithelium is thick and forms the entire brain wall except for a thin stratum zonale.

The stratum zonale widens and cells migrate into it from the neural epithelium, with the result that a distinct layer of loosely arranged cells, called "migration A" by Rüdeberg, has appeared in the 18 mm Squalus embryo. A second migration is differentiated within the neural epithelium at the 20 mm stage. The cells of this "migration B" are compactly arranged and the epithelium becomes separated as a thin layer. The dorsal part of "migration A" remains thin but the ventral part thickens and gives rise to secondary "migrations A_1 and A_2." These migrations all are included in the cerebellar part of the columna dorsalis of Bergquist and Källén. According to Rüdeberg, "migration A_2" gradually loses its continuity with the dorsal part of "migration A" and is joined by cells from "migration B," forming "migration A_2B." The thin dorsal part of "migration A" apparently differentiates into the Purkinje cell layer of the cerebellar cortex. The dorsal part of "migration B" is thick and becomes the granular layer. The caudal part of "migration A_2B" gives rise to the nucleus cerebelli (p. 55).

The youngest stage of development in elasmobranchs which I have studied is a 25 mm embryo of Apristiurus. At this stage continuity of the cerebellar with the rhombencephalic part of the columna dorsalis is quite evident. Individual cell migrations, however, have not been analyzed. Larger embryos of Apristiurus, Squalus, and Raja, in which the recessus lateralis has been formed, show continuity through the walls and floor of this recess. The cerebellar rudiment enlarges rapidly and becomes an elongated tube, the caudal margin of which flares out and continues as the anterodorsal and ventrolateral walls of the recess on either side (figs. 30, 31).

A shallow furrow appears in front of the flared-out part of the anterodorsal wall in the 20 mm Squalus embryo, says Sterzi (1912). It gradually extends dorsomedially, parallel with the cerebellar margin which it delimits from the larger anterior part of the cerebellar rudiment. This furrow, the myelometencephalic sulcus of Sterzi, corresponds to the posterolateral fissure of other vertebrates and I shall so call it. In the 32 mm Squalus embryo it is represented at the midline only by a slight depression on the dorsal surface of the posterior part of the cerebellar tube (fig. 30). It gradually deepens medially as well as laterally and divides the cerebellum into the rudiments of the corpus cerebelli and vestibulolateral lobe (fig. 31). The latter comprises the posterior cerebellar margin and the walls and floor of the recessus lateralis in the 60 mm embryo. The corpus cerebelli develops precociously, in anticipation of the large size it eventually attains, and will be described before we return to the further differentiation of the vestibulolateral lobe. For convenience of description, however, the posterior margin of the median part of the cerebellar rudiment will be identified as the pars medialis of the vestibulolateral lobe.

The corpus cerebelli. A dorsal arching of the cerebellar plate between the faint posterolateral fissure and the rhombomesencephalic fold, as illustrated by Sterzi (1912) in the 32 mm Squalus embryo, indicates the in-

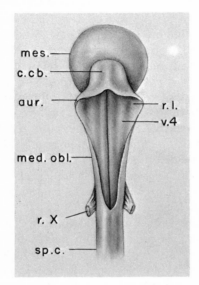

Figure 30. Dorsal view of rhombencephalon of 32 mm long embryo of Acanthias vulgaris. ×11. (Modified from Sterzi, 1912.)

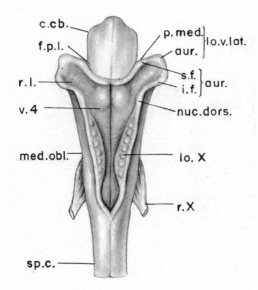

Figure 31. Dorsal view of rhombencephalon of 60 mm long embryo of Acanthias vulgaris. ×11. (Modified from Sterzi, 1912.)

ception of rapid enlargement of the corpus cerebelli (fig. 29). At the 50 mm stage an elongated bursa has appeared, from the lower caudal margin of which the pars medialis continues almost horizontally caudalward. The cavity of the bursa is continuous with the fourth ventricle. In the 80 mm embryo further enlargement of the corpus cerebelli has resulted in the submerging of the pars medialis beneath a caudal projection of the corpus. The enlarged bursal cavity is continuous with the fourth ventricle by a relatively constricted opening. The 120 mm embryo shows the dorsal part of the corpus cerebelli as expanded both rostrally and caudally to such an extent that its connection with the medulla oblongata, anterior medullary velum, pars medialis, and the posterior part of the cerebellar base on either side of the fourth ventricle, is reduced to a peduncle-like constriction. Because of further modifications that result in the adult relations, described below, I shall call this constricted portion the pars ventralis, and the anteroposteriorly elongated portion the pars dorsalis of the corpus cerebelli (fig. 29). The lateral walls of the pars dorsalis expand less rapidly than the anterior and posterior walls, resulting in an ellipsoidal form of the principal cerebellar mass, as viewed from above. A large cerebellar ventricle in the pars dorsalis is now connected with the fourth ventricle by a vertically directed space in the pars ventralis. This part of the cerebellar ventricle is broad from one side to the other but narrow anteroposteriorly.

The pars dorsalis is gradually divided into the rudiments of anterior and posterior lobes by a transverse furrow, the sulcus primus transversus cerebelli of Voorhoeve in the the adult cerebellum (fig. 26). This is faint in the 120 mm Squalus embryo, but eventually becomes a prominent fissure. The pars ventralis of the corpus cerebelli remains constricted in the pup stages. In the 165 mm Squalus pup its anterior part, which is the anterior wall of the vertical part of the cerebellar ventricle, descends nearly vertically before turning rostralward to become continuous with a short anterior medullary velum. The posterior part also descends vertically, near the midline, and then turns sharply caudalward as the horizontal plate, already mentioned, which is continuous with the pars medialis of the vestibulolateral lobe. As the pars dorsalis expands and the walls of the entire corpus cerebelli thicken the pars ventralis loses its peduncle-like aspect but remains as a constricted part of the corpus cerebelli which attaches to the deeper structures.

As the roof of the pars dorsalis folds inward, with deepening of the transverse fissure, the dorsal part of the cerebellar ventricle becomes divided into a cavity of the anterior lobe and one of the posterior lobe, both communicating with the vertical part of the cerebellar ventricle (fig. 27). An internal median fissure, recognizable in early stages of the embryo, extends to the ependymal plate which connects the bilateral halves of the corpus cerebelli (fig. 32D). Increased proliferative activity of the matrix layer on either side of this furrow results in a thickening of the medial part of the developing granular layer into bilateral longitudinal ridges that project into the ventricular space and deepen the internal median fissure. In the 60 mm Squalus embryo these ridges, formed of closely arranged granule-like cells, are fairly prominent (fig. 32D). They follow the contours of the ventricular walls from the anterior medullary velum to the pars horizontalis of the inferior part of the corpus cerebelli and then to the posterior surface of the pars medialis of the vestibulolateral lobe. As they increase in volume these ridges reduce the cerebellar ventricle to a narrow space in the median part of the corpus cerebelli; lateral to the ridges, however, the ventricle expands rapidly into a large thin-walled cavity.

The lateral and posterior walls of the pars ventralis are continuous ventrally with a swelling, the eminentia ventralis cerebellaris, which reduces the width of the posterior ventral part of the cerebellar ventricle. This eminence is formed chiefly by the nucleus cerebelli (nucleus lateralis cerebelli of Edinger in the adult), already mentioned as derived from cell migration A_2B of the columna dorsalis, according to Rüdeberg (1961).

The vestibulolateral lobe. The anterior part of the acousticolateral area, the transition zone, and the pars medialis are intimately related in their development. The transition zone flares laterally, as the lateral part of the posterolateral fissure deepens, forming an expansion into which extends a lateral recess of the rhomboidal fossa. The anteroventral wall of this recess is a continuation of the cellular sheet of the pars medialis; laterocaudally it is continuous with the acousticolateral area.

The expanded transition zone has assumed an ear-like form in the 60 mm Squalus embryo and the earlier anteroventral wall of the recessus lateralis has become its broad floor (fig. 31). The margin of the recess, which in the 32 mm embryo is a thin tenial attachment of the choroid tela, is a rounded ridge of closely arranged cells in the 60 mm stage, with a narrow tenial border. The ridge (fig. 31) is continuous medially with a similar but less prominent ridge in the dorsal margin of the pars medialis. This, in turn, is continuous with the longitudinal ridge which reaches the medial margin of the pars medialis from the corpus cerebelli. The ridge bordering the recessus lateralis is continuous caudally with a similar one in the rhombic lip of the anterior part of the acousticolateral area which, as seen in sections, ends lateral of the anterior part of the nucleus dorsalis. Sections also show that the cellular layer of the floor of the recessus lateralis is continuous, in the 60 mm embryo, more spe-

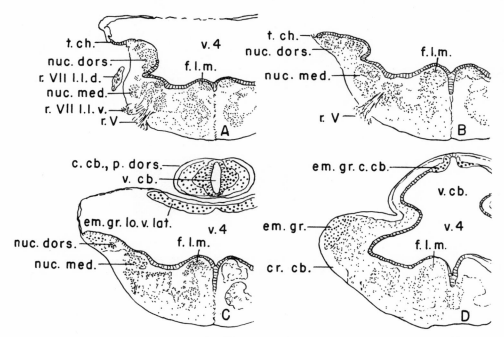

Figure 32. Transverse sections of rhombencephalon of 60 mm long embryo of Squalus acanthias. A. Level of entrance of VIII nerve. B. Level of entrance of V nerve. C. Level of caudal part of corpus cerebelli. D. Level of rostral part of corpus cerebelli. Bodian stain. ×30.

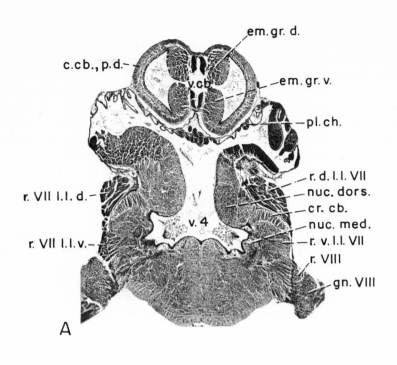

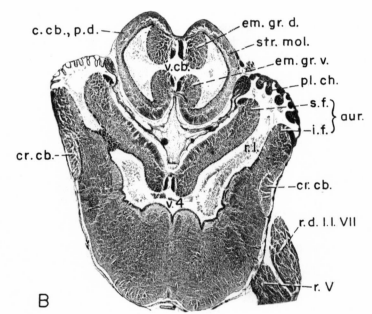

Figure 33. Transverse sections of rhombencephalon of 170 mm long embryo of
Squalus acanthias. A. Level of entrance of VIII nerve. B. Level rostral
to entrance of V nerve. Bodian stain. ×20.

cifically with the deep zone of scattered cells of the pars medialis and with the nucleus medialis of the acoustico-lateral area. Rostrally it is continuous, beneath the posterolateral fissure, with the pars ventralis of the corpus cerebelli and the incipient ventral cerebellar eminence.

The cells beneath the floor of the recessus lateralis are similar to those of the nucleus medialis but are somewhat more crowded and there is a gradual increase, rostral-ward, of small cells which become so numerous anteriorly that the floor merges with the anterior granular ridge. This merging probably is the result of the overlapping of the deep border of the granular ridge and the border of the layer of more scattered cells, and of fusion between the two borders. The expanded cellular column of the floor of the recessus lateralis I shall call the primitive eminentia granularis. Van der Horst (1925) also regarded as eminentia granularis, in selachian embryos, a cellular mass described as continuous caudally with the "lobus liniae lateralis ventralis" (nucleus medialis), but losing its identity in the rostral part of the auricle.

The rounded ear-like expansion of the 60 mm Squalus embryo elongates rostrolaterally in subsequent growth and the marginal granular ridge which nearly circumscribes it becomes the rudiment of the superior and inferior folds of the auricle. These folds increase greatly in volume, with the result that the recessus lateralis becomes a slit, superficially, between them. The floor of the recess remains broad medially but tapers toward the forward tilted apex of the projection as this elongates in the pup stages. In embryos of Raja binoculata the ear-like expansion does not tilt forward, the early anterior wall of the recessus lateralis remaining more nearly vertical. The marginal granular ridge forms a semicircle around the recessus lateralis which has a broad medial continuity with the fourth ventricle. In the 130 mm embryo of Raja the marginal lip is thickened but is still semicircular and now has a dorsomedial tilt. Both in Squalus and in Raja embryos it is continuous, by less prominent marginal ridges of granules, with the dorsal margin of the pars medialis and with the dorsal or lateral surface of the anterior part of the nucleus dorsalis of the acousticolateral area. Restricting the term "auricle" to the enlarged part of the granular ridge which forms the lips of the recessus lateralis, the continuation in the dorsal margin of the pars medialis may be called the interauricular granular band; it appears to correspond to the "granular cell string" of Palmgren (1921) in Squalus embryos. The continuity with the granular ridge of the anterior region of the acousticolateral area is considered further below.

The auricular folds have enlarged to such an extent in the pup stages that the floor of the recessus lateralis is hidden from view except in sections, in which it still is

relatively broad. The continuities of the primitive eminentia granularis with the pars medialis, the base of the corpus cerebelli and, caudally, with the nucleus medialis of the acousticolateral area are readily seen. In the 130 mm stage of Raja the continuity with the pars medialis is almost horizontal (fig. 34); in the less flattened cerebellum of Squalus pups and adults it is obliquely ventromedial from either side, the enlarged posterior lobe of the corpus cerebelli covering and depressing the pars medialis (fig. 33).

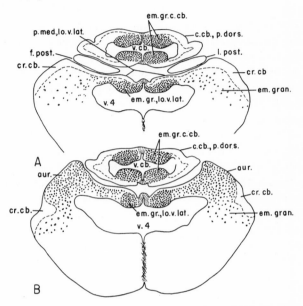

Figure 34. Transverse sections of rhombencephalon of 130 mm long embryo of Raja binoculata. A. Level of lateral recess of fourth ventricle. B. Level a little rostral of A. ×17.

In the 150 mm to 170 mm Squalus pups the pars medialis is strongly tilted dorsalward from the posterior end of the pars horizontalis and the auricles extend dorsalward on either side of the pars dorsalis of the corpus cerebelli (fig. 33). The adult pattern of auricles, primitive eminentiae granulares, and marginal granular ridges is fully established in these stages but as the brain elongates the auricles tilt forward, their longitudinal axes becoming more nearly horizontal.

The developmental relations and structure of the primitive eminentia granularis show that it corresponds morphologically to the more differentiated but still primitive eminentia of Acipenseriformes (p. 74). The primitive eminentia granularis and the auricle together form an anatomical unit which corresponds to the lateral lobe of Johnston (1901) in Acipenser and to the auricle of Hocke Hoogenboom (1929) in Polyodon. In the light of a reanalysis of these divisions in these fishes I call them the lateral lobule in both species (pp. 73, 76).

The developmental history of the rostrolateral and somewhat dorsal projection of the medulla oblongata on either side of the corpus cerebelli in elasmobranch embryos clearly shows that this projection comprises two parts, namely, an early-appearing rudiment of a primitive eminentia granularis and a later granular ridge which becomes the auricle. The two together correspond to the lateral lobule of Acipenser (p. 73) and Polyodon (p. 76). Except for the differences in relative size of the auricle and eminentia granularis of elasmobranchs, as compared with Acipenseriformes, the lateral lobules of the two groups are very similar in structure. In elasmobranchs the auricles constitute the predominant feature, whereas in chondrosteans the primitive eminentia granularis is most conspicuous. If one envisages the adult elasmobranch lateral lobule as tilted dorsomedially and the auricle facing caudally, the similarity to the chondrostean lateral lobule, as described below, is quite apparent.

The medial continuation of the eminentia granularis with the deep part of the pars medialis, and the medial continuation of the dorsal or anteromedial fold of the auricle as the interauricular granular band, together with commissural fibers across the midline, correspond to similar structures in Acipenseriformes described below. The lateral lobules and pars medialis together make up the rudiment of the vestibulolateral lobe.

The Adult Brain
THE ACOUSTICOLATERAL AREA

The outflared lip of the rostral part of the acousticolateral area in the 60 mm Squalus embryo folds dorsally and medially in subsequent development. The nucleus dorsalis is shifted from its dorsolateral position, with respect to the nucleus medialis, to a dorsal or dorsomedial position in the pup stages and to a dorsomedial to partly medial situation in adult Squalus and most other sharks. Hexanchus, a primitive species, however, retains the outward-flaring embryonic aspect of the anterior part of the acousticolateral area (Ariens Kappers, 1906) and the nucleus dorsalis has a dorsolateral position. In Raja the nucleus dorsalis lies above the nucleus medialis. The two nuclei have individual cerebellar crests separated by an external groove; in Raja this is very deep. A thin fibrous layer beneath the ventricular surface connects the two nuclei in both sharks and rays.

In the pup stages of Squalus a mass of closely packed granules, evidently corresponding to the granular ridge of the adult, but short and thick, forms a layer dorsal of the anterior part of the nucleus dorsalis and continues rostrolaterally with the posterolateral fold of the auricle (fig. 33B). Caudomedially it is partially divided by a shallow superficial groove into lateral and medial parts. Between the lateral part and the nucleus dorsalis there is a well-defined line of demarcation, but the medial part is continuous with the dorsal nucleus, forming a dorsal, anterior, and medial layer of granules. The cells are closely arranged near the surface but become more scattered in the deep part of the nucleus (fig. 33). Behind approximately the middle level of the entering dorsal root of the anterior lateral-line nerve no such layer exists and small cells, probably granules, are diffusely scattered among the larger elements.

Numerous fascicles of dorsal lateral-line root fibers ascend in the nucleus dorsalis. In sagittal sections, stained by the Bodian method, many of the fibers may be seen to end among the cells of the granular part of the nucleus; others terminate among the larger cells. Fascicles of fibers also accompany the granular ridge at the dorsal border of the nucleus. Farther rostrally these fascicles, diminished in number to two or three, lie in the deep part of the cerebellar crest and continue to the more expanded auricle. Fibers from these fascicles enter the caudal part of the granular ridge and, probably, also farther rostrally. Their course, however, is too confusing for detailed analysis without selective Golgi impregnations.

The ventral anterior lateral-line fascicle, mentioned above as entering the nucleus dorsalis, also continues forward.

The nucleus dorsalis evidently is related functionally to the auricle proper in somewhat the same manner as is the nucleus medialis to the primitive eminentia granularis. The embryonic tenial ridges give rise to the auricle and its related caudal ridge and, by migration of some of their elements, to the granules of the anterior part of the nucleus dorsalis and of the eminentia granularis.

Beginning caudally at the middle level of the entering dorsal root of the anterior lateral-line nerve, a granular ridge, elongated in adult Squalus, covers the dorsal surface of the anterior part of the nucleus dorsalis and continues rostrally or rostrolaterally to merge with the posterolateral fold of the auricle. In embryonic stages the precursor of this ridge is distinct from the nucleus dorsalis, whose cells are more scattered. The granular ridge is derived from proliferative cells at the tenial border, whereas the nucleus dorsalis is differentiated from the columna dorsalis as already mentioned.

In the pup stages the caudal part of the well-developed ridge lies in close apposition to the nucleus dorsalis, but a sharp boundary delimits most of the granular mass from the collection of more scattered cells of the nucleus proper. A thin cap of granules, evidently migrated from the ridge, covers the anteromedial part of the nucleus, and some granular extensions also penetrate into it. Posterior of the entrance of the nerve roots no granular ridge occurs.

This granular ridge, which is considerably more elongated in the adult than in pup stages, represents the caudal segment of the continuous marginal granular enlargement which constitutes the folds of the auricle and, medially, the interauricular granular band. This band, in turn, is continuous with the medial longitudinal granular ridge of the pars medialis and corpus cerebelli. The caudal segment perhaps should be regarded as cerebellar, as are the other subdivisions of the elongated and tortuous ridge. It disappears, however, in teleosts with the disappearance or reduction of the nucleus dorsalis, although the auricles remain in reduced form in most species and the interauricular granular band is often relatively large. Although there is no distinct boundary, in elasmobranchs, between the vestibulolateral lobe and the rostral part of the acousticolateral area, the caudal segment of the granular ridge appears to be more closely related to the anterior region of this area.

The ventral part of the nucleus medialis of the adult is merged with the vestibular area in the region of the entrance of the ventral anterior lateral-line and VIII nerve roots. The fibers of the lateral-line roots are so intermingled with those of the posterior VIII root that the two roots are difficult to differentiate. In embryonic and pup stages, as already noted, the individual roots and also the nuclei to which they distribute are more distinctly separated. The root fibers, however, appear to have reached their terminal zones of distribution in the pup stages.

The cerebellar crest is prominent in elasmobranchs. Beginning as a thin molecular layer a little anterior to the level of entrance of the posterior lateral-line root, it continues anteriorly as a cap, first on the nucleus medialis and, from the posterior part of the nucleus dorsalis and forward, on both these nuclei. In some species a pial septum extends inward, from the bulbar surface, between the part of the crista which covers the nucleus medialis and the part covering the nucleus dorsalis. The two parts are separated at some levels in the rays by a deep external furrow into which the dorsal root of the anterior lateral-line nerve enters and penetrates the crista in the roof of the furrow to reach the nucleus dorsalis. The two parts of the crista unite farther rostrally and are continuous with the molecular layer of the cerebellum.

THE CENTRAL CONNECTIONS OF THE LATERAL-LINE AND ACOUSTIC ROOTS

The dorsal root of the anterior lateral-line nerve, in Squalus, passes medially through a deep longitudinal fold between the flared-out caudal continuation of the inferior posterolateral auricular fold and the nucleus medialis before entering the nucleus dorsalis. In Raja it enters the ventrolateral surface of the more dorsally situated nucleus dorsalis. The fibers bifurcate into descending and ascending branches within the nucleus, but those of the more ventral root fascicles, in Squalus pups, bifurcate before entering the nuclear mass. The descending branches give off slender twigs that end as terminal boutons among or on the cells of the nucleus. Some caudally directed fibers from the nucleus enter the cerebellar crest but their relations to branches of the root fibers are obscure. The ascending branches of fibers that bifurcate before the nucleus is reached, and also ascending branches from within the nucleus, pass forward to a fascicle, to which we shall return, which lies beneath the granular ridge. Large numbers of ascending branches, however, end in the rostral part of the nucleus, dividing into slender twigs with terminal boutons. It appears fairly certain that no dorsal root fibers end in the primitive eminentia granularis.

The fibers of the ventral anterior lateral-line root all bifurcate within the nucleus medialis. The descending branches end, in part, in the zone of fusion of this nucleus with the vestibular area, which Ariens Kappers calls the medial static area. The majority, however, continue into the region of the nucleus medialis which lies between the entering ventral anterior and the posterior lateral-line roots. Here the fibers are gathered into elongated anastomosing fascicles from which terminal fibers distribute among the cells. Some reach the crista cerebelli. The ascending fascicles, probably including secondary fibers, extend to the primitive eminentia granularis.

The posterior lateral-line root gives rise to ascending fibers that form fascicles in the nucleus medialis ventral and medial to the descending ventral anterior root fibers. Part distribute in the nucleus and part continue to the primitive eminentia granularis. Norris and Hughes (1920) found only ascending fibers of the posterior lateral-line root in adult Squalus but descending branches are also present in small numbers, according to Ariens Kappers (1947). A few are identifiable in Bodian series of pup stages. Some fine fibers, apparently of different origin, also enter the posterior end of the nucleus medialis. Possibly these are collaterals of spinal fibers. Johnston (1902) and Pearson (1936a) found spinal fibers to the acousticolateral area of petromyzonts, as already noted, but corresponding connections have not been described in elasmobranchs. Such a connection is possibly represented in the posterior end of the nucleus medialis.

The longitudinal cell column which ends anteriorly as the expanded primitive eminentia granularis is characterized by regional differences in its functional connections. These differences and some variations in the proportions of cell types appear to justify dividing it into four regions, beginning posteriorly. The small caudal region, receiving only descending posterior lateral-line fibers and possibly collaterals of spinal fibers, is the least complex. The region between the posterior and the ventral anterior lateral-line roots is the principal zone of distribution of ascending posterior root fibers, but the descending ventral anterior root fibers add to its functional complexity. This part of the cell column also is enlarged in the adult and includes many small cells, most of the small cells immediately beneath the cerebellar crest representing granules. Numerous polymorphic cells of small to large size are scattered throughout the nucleus. The term posterior lateral-line lobe, applied to it by some authors, is misleading, however, because of the two sources of fibers distributing in it. The term is also unsatisfactory in a topographic sense since the so-called anterior lateral-line lobe of many authors receives only the dorsal root of the anterior lateral-line nerve. I shall call the portion of the cell column which extends from the posterior to the ventral anterior lateral-line roots the intermediate region of the nucleus medialis.

The zone of entrance of the ventral anterior lateral-line root fibers and the more or less intermingled posterior VIII root fibers, together with the cellular and fibrous zone continuing rostralward, was called the tuberculum acusticum by the earlier students of elasmobranch and other fish brains. Since it does not correspond to the tubercle so named in mammals and man the term has been discontinued in Ichthyopsida, and Ariens Kappers (1947) substituted medial static region. Although there is no visible boundary between the part of this region related to the lateral-line roots and the part related to the roots of the VIII nerve, it will be recalled that in embryonic stages the respective nerve roots and cell groups are distinct from each other, as in the adult stage of some other Ichthyopsida. Clarity of anatomical analysis will be served by describing the merged cell mass in adult elasmobranchs in terms of the embryonic cell groups contributing to it. Lacking any other boundary in the cell column to differentiate the nucleus medialis from the eminentia granularis, the level at which considerable expansion begins may arbitrarily be regarded as the rostral end of the nucleus medialis. The portion of the nucleus between this level and the ventral anterior lateral-line root I shall call the anterior region. Ascending posterior and ventral anterior lateral-line roots pass through it and ascending branches of the anterior and posterior VIII roots also do so, all probably giving off collaterals, since innumerable terminal twigs are evident in Bodian preparations. These ascending fibers terminate in the primitive eminentia granularis which is the fourth region of the sensory column.

The nucleus dorsalis and nucleus medialis both give rise to internal arcuate fibers that cross the raphe of the medulla oblongata and ascend as the acousticolateral lemniscus. This is the principal efferent tract of the acousticolateral areas. It terminates in the lateral subtectal part of the midbrain, which is called the torus semicircularis by Ariens Kappers, but is much less distinctly differentiated than the torus of teleosts. Some fibers end in the optic tectum; others reach the nucleus isthmi. Fibers from both nuclei also enter the fasciculus longitudinalis medialis, according to Sterzi (1909) and Ariens Kappers (1947).

Wallenberg (1907), on the basis of Marchi experiments, describes fibers from the nucleus dorsalis and nucleus medialis that enter the arcuate system, cross the raphe, and terminate in the contralateral nuclei, thus forming a tegmental commissure between the lateral-line and vestibular nuclei of the two sides. Sterzi also describes ipsilateral fibers from one nucleus to the other, evidence of which I also find in pup stages.

Beginning immediately behind the granular ridge which ends on the nucleus dorsalis, a rounded longitudinally directed fascicle is found beneath the tenial border. As it approaches the caudal end of the nucleus, small fascicles branch off, some entering the nucleus medialis and others intermingling with arcuate fibers. The fascicle continues in reduced form in the tenial margin of the nucleus medialis. I am unable to determine either the cells of origin or the terminations of any of the fibers that appear related to this fascicle. Sterzi (1909) calls an apparently corresponding bundle the dorsal fascicle of the anterior lobe. The general relations of the fascicle in Squalus pup stages suggest that it may correspond to tract *a* of urodeles (p. 131), which appears to include, among others, descending fibers that have their origin in the acousticolateral nuclei and the lateral lobule of the vestibulolateral lobe.

Acoustic nerve connections. The peripheral and central connections of the VIII nerve have been summarized by Ariens Kappers (1947). Coarse fibers of the anterior root come from the anterior and lateral cristae ampullares and perhaps, in part, from the macula utriculi. They turn caudalward after entering the medulla oblongata, some passing dorsally to cross the midline at the level of the VI nerve and disappearing in the reticular formation. Perhaps they reach the VI nucleus. Others form an ipsilateral ventral descending tract which continues into the ventrolateral part of the spinal cord. Many root fibers end on the cells of the tangential nucleus. The greater part of the anterior root of the VIII nerve consists of utricular fibers that terminate in the nucleus of Deiters.

Ascending branches enter the "auricle," according to Ariens Kappers.

The posterior root of the VIII nerve, according to Ariens Kappers (1947), consists chiefly of fibers from the sacculus and lagena, some utricular fibers possibly being included. The posterior root fibers are smaller than most in the anterior root. After entering the bulb they pass to a more dorsal and medial level. In sagittal series of pup stages numerous fibers can be followed from the root fascicles into the cell mass formed by the fusion of the vestibular area and the anterior part of the nucleus medialis. Many of the fibers continue to the eminentia granularis. According to Ariens Kappers ascending posterior root fibers reach the nucleus cerebelli ("nucleus of the ventral cerebellar eminence"). Most of the ascending posterior root fibers probably correspond to saccular fibers in Petromyzon, described by Heier (1948) and on page 16, that reach the cerebellum. Other posterior root fibers come into relation with a group of large cells opposite the entrance of the root, and some descend among numerous small polygonal cells. Terminal branches to the lateral dendrite of Mauthner's cell in Squalus embryos already have been mentioned.

Secondary connections from the vestibular area comprise both ascending and descending fibers. A large ipsilateral vestibulo-spinal tract arises from Deiters's nucleus. The large cells at the entrance of the anterior VIII root give rise to a crossed vestibulo-spinal tract, according to Ariens Kappers (1947). The fasciculus longitudinalis medialis receives fibers from Deiters's nucleus and from the descending fibers of the posterior VIII root. The large cells which are related to posterior VIII root fibers are the origin of the medial fascicle of Stieda, which is situated lateral of the medial longitudinal fasciculus and enters the dorsal funiculus of the spinal cord. This fascicle, according to Ariens Kappers (1947), probably serves the reflexes of the tail in a manner analogous to Mauthner's fiber in teleosts.

THE VESTIBULOLATERAL LOBE

The predominance of the large auricular folds in the vestibulolateral lobe of adult elasmobranchs obscures other features of this primary division of the cerebellum. The rostrolateral elongation of the auricle of sharks has transformed the floor of the recessus lateralis into a rostrolaterally and somewhat dorsally tapering space largely hidden by the thick folds of the auricle (figs. 26, 28). In the more foreshortened brain of rays, the auricles are tilted dorsalward to a greater degree and the two auricular folds are more widely separated, exposing a larger part of the floor of the recessus lateralis, which is somewhat rounded. The medial continuation of the eminentia

granularis with the deep part of the pars medialis is also nearly horizontal, as in the embryo, and therefore more apparent than in most sharks, in which the pars medialis is deeply submerged (fig. 27).

The pars medialis (the Unterlippe of Edinger, 1901; the vertical part of the valvola cerebellare of Sterzi, 1909) comprises a deep zone of cells, similar to those of the primitive eminentia granularis; a marginal zone of granules called the interauricular granular band; and a medial granular ridge, continued from the pars horizontalis of the corpus cerebelli. A molecular layer is continuous, beneath the floor of the posterolateral fissure, with that of the pars horizontalis.

The pars medialis, which Ariens Kappers (1934) recognized as continuous with the anteromedial fold of the auricle, is delimited from the pars horizontalis by the floor of the posterolateral fissure and, on the ventricular surface, by a shallow transverse sulcus described by Palmgren (1921) in Squalus embryos but also shown in some of Edinger's (1901) figures of adult Scyllium. This sulcus may be situated directly ventral of the floor of the posterolateral fissure or in the lower surface of the anterior wall of the principal expansion of the fourth ventricle.

THE CORPUS CEREBELLI

The pattern of the corpus cerebelli of the pup stages of Squalus becomes modified in the adult by the enlargement of the anterior and posterior lobes, the thickening of their walls, and the deepening of the transverse fissure. The pars ventralis loses its peduncle-like aspect, though remaining constricted. As seen in median sagittal section, its anterior wall in the adult may descend almost vertically before turning forward to become continuous with the anterior medullary velum (fig. 27), or the ventral wall of the anterior lobe of the pars dorsalis may turn sharply forward into the velum. The posterior wall of the pars ventralis may also descend nearly vertically and then turn posteriorly as a horizontal plate (fig. 35), or it

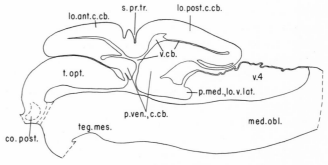

Figure 35. Midsagittal section of brain stem of Scyllium, 24 cm long.

53

may descend obliquely caudalward to continue, beneath the posterolateral fissure, with the pars medialis of the vestibulolateral lobe. The variations are possibly related to the size and age of individual specimens, the vertical wall and horizontal plate pattern apparently being characteristic of smaller individuals or species, as in the specimen of Scyllium (fig. 36).

lobules closely corresponding to those of Mustelus, but all the furrows are deeper and the secondary and tertiary folds of cortex are more prominent. In Lamna the same pattern of secondary and tertiary folds prevails in the deeply separated anterior and posterior lobes as in Mustelus and Carcharias, but the tertiary folds are more numerous. In a 24 cm specimen of Scyllium the anterior and

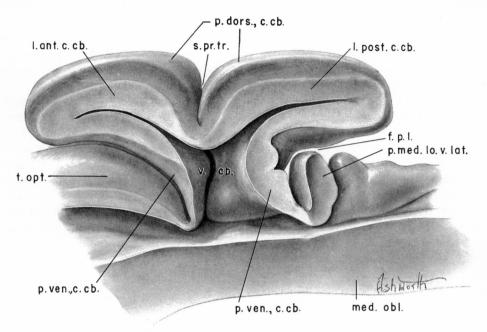

Figure 36. Midsagittal section of cerebellum of Squalus acanthias.

The primary transverse fissure is lacking in Heptanchus, Hexanchus, and Scymnus, representing the most primitive elasmobranchs, and in Spinax, representing one of the smallest neoselachians, Ariens Kappers, Huber, and Crosby (1936) state. It deepens in larger species. In Lamna the fissure extends almost to the roof of the fourth ventricle, dividing the corpus cerebelli into anterior and posterior lobes that have individual cerebellar ventricles. The anterior and posterior lobes vary in relative size in different species. In Rajidae, Voorhoeve (1917) found the anterior lobe to be smaller than the posterior, in Torpedinae the two lobes are approximately equal, and in Trygonidae and Myliobatidae the posterior lobe is smaller.

Some species, especially the larger ones, have additional transverse furrows in both anterior and posterior lobes. Sterzi (1909) shows the cerebellum of a specimen of Mustelus laevis, 80 cm long, in which the anterior lobe is divided by a deep furrow into two lobules, each of which is subdivided by shallower furrows. The posterior lobe is also subdivided. Carcharias, illustrated by Sterzi and also by Voorhoeve, shows transverse furrows and

posterior lobes are undivided but a small fold is present in the floor of the primary transverse fissure (fig. 36). The specimens of Squalus that I have examined, and those illustrated by Sterzi (1909), show a fairly deep primary fissura transversa but no secondary folding of the two lobes. Johnston (1906), however, illustrates a brain of Squalus sectioned in the median sagittal plane in which each of the two lobes of the corpus cerebelli is divided into two lobules, both of which have suggestions of smaller divisions. The pattern is similar to that in the species above described, but the furrow which evidently corresponds to the primary transverse fissure is shallow. The length of this specimen is not stated and the length of my specimens, of which I had only the appparently mature heads, is unknown. Presumably Johnston's illustration was made from an older and larger animal. There can be no question that the smaller and the more primitive species retain the simple pattern of folding found in embryonic stages of Squalus, but the pattern becomes more complex in larger species.

The transverse folds and furrows, especially in the anterior lobe of the larger species, are suggestive of those in the vermis of small mammals. It is noteworthy, however, that the folds are unrelated to medullary rays, which are entirely lacking in elasmobranchs. In naming the principal transverse furrow the sulcus primus transversus Voorhoeve (1917) intended no implication of homology with the fissura prima of higher vertebrates (Ariens Kappers, Huber, and Crosby, 1936, p. 714). The fiber connections with the anterior and posterior lobe, described below, are similar in general to those of the anterior and posterior lobes of mammals. Taking these and the pattern of folding into consideration, the possibility must be recognized that the primary transverse fissure does correspond to the fissura prima of some reptiles and of birds and mammals, and that the anterior and posterior lobes of the large elasmobranch corpus cerebelli may be homologous to the anterior and posterior lobes of higher vertebrates. No experimental evidence of functional similarities, however, has been recorded.

The most pronounced folding of the cortex appears to occur in the largest rays. In addition, the folds are so displaced to one side or the other of the midline in the sting ray, Tryon (Sterzi), and the eagle rays, Myliobatis (Ariens Kappers), as to give the corpus cerebelli an asymmetrical form suggestive of the sigmoid vermis of some mammals.

An external sagittal fissure, the immediate floor of which is a molecular layer above the ependymal connection between the bilateral halves of the corpus cerebelli, has been mentioned in pup stages of development. This fissure begins just behind the anterior medullary velum and continues onto the posterior wall of the pars ventralis of the corpus cerebelli and, less deeply, onto the horizontal plate. The sharp caudal folding of this plate results in a deep anteriorly extending space which represents the external sagittal fissure of the posterior wall of the pars ventralis. It is continuous with the larger space between the corpus cerebelli and the pars medialis of the vestibulolateral lobe. These spaces, as well as the external sagittal fissure, are extensions of the cranial cavity between cerebellar structures. In adults of small species a median furrow is present on the dorsal surface of the corpus cerebelli, but in larger species the molecular layer has so thickened across the midline that the corpus cerebelli appears superficially to be unpaired.

A fold of the cortex and underlying fibrous layer of the horizontal plate is continued onto the ventrolateral surface of the posterior lobe on either side. This was called the lobulus posticus by Voorhoeve, the furrow delimiting it from the principal mass of the lobe being named the sulcus posticus. In Raja clavata the lobulus posticus extends obliquely medialward to the pars medialis of the vestibulolateral lobe, but in the sharks it blends into the

horizontal plate. Some species show a second cortical fold on the inferior part of the posterior wall of the corpus cerebelli and continuing onto the lateral surface. Sterzi (1909) called this fold the "lobo cerebellare inferiore." In Scyllium and Raja the margin of the caudal projection of the posterior lobe flares outward above the lobulus posticus. Ariens Kappers (1921) describes two constant paired lobules, the "lobi postici," as delimited by the "fissura postica."

Tilney (1923) demonstrated that after removal of the dorsal part of the corpus cerebelli ("cerebellum mediale" of Tilney) in Squalus acanthias the animal maintained its normal position in the water, swam, and rested belly down during the several days of postoperative life. If turned on its back the fish righted itself immediately and showed no tendency to lose its optimum physiological position while swimming, indicating no interference with vestibular reflexes. In propelling itself, however, the normal rhythmical series of intersegmental body movements seemed to be entirely absent, the paired fins were little used, and progression through the water was accomplished entirely by action of the tail, in strong contrast with the normal swimming movements of sharks. The dorsal part of the corpus cerebelli was regarded by Tilney as coordinating the intersegmental movements with those of the paired fins and tail.

The nucleus cerebelli. A large collection of cells in the eminentia ventralis cerebelli of Scyllium canicula was named the nucleus lateralis cerebelli by Edinger (1901), who, however, was uncertain of its connections. Ariens Kappers (1906, 1921) and van Hoevell (1916) designated the cell mass by Edinger's term in other species. It was considered as possibly homologous with the anterior octavomotor nucleus of petromyzonts by Ariens Kappers. Van Hoevell believed it also represented the primitive homologue of the cerebellar nuclei of higher vertebrates.

The recent studies of Rüdeberg (1961) on cell migrations from the columna dorsalis of early embryos and their relation to the formation of the cerebellar nuclei appear to have definitely set aside any relationship of these nuclei to the vestibular nuclei. In Squalus acanthias Rüdeberg describes cell "migration A_2" and a contribution from "migration B," both derived from the columna dorsalis, as forming nuclear rudiment A_2B. This becomes included in the eminentia ventralis cerebelli and develops into the nucleus cerebelli. It corresponds, according to Rüdeberg, to the nucleus lateralis cerebelli of Edinger and subsequent authors.

Sagittal sections of 165 mm and 170 mm pups of Squalus acanthias, stained by the Bodian method, show descending fibers from the corpus cerebelli that divide into small twigs. These terminate within the nucleus cerebelli in clusters of boutons, many of which make contact with the nuclear cells. Presumably the descending fibers are axons of Purkinje cells. Similar fibers and terminal twigs are shown in transverse sections of 160 mm and 170 mm specimens stained by the same method.

Fibers, some forming small fascicles, arise in the pars medialis and in the primitive eminentia granularis, especially beneath the superior or anteromedial fold of the auricle, and end in a similar manner in the nucleus cerebelli. No indication of subdivision of the nucleus was apparent, but the fibers from the vestibulolateral lobe appear to terminate in larger numbers in the posterior part of the nucleus.

The nucleus cerebelli of elasmobranchs, however, must be regarded as a common nuclear mass serving both the corpus cerebelli and the vestibulolateral lobe. Vestibular and lateral-line fibers to the nucleus were described by Ariens Kappers (1906, 1921) from Weigert preparations. In Bodian stained sections of pup stages such fibers can be followed into the rostral part of the eminentia granularis immediately behind the nucleus cerebelli, but not with any assurance into the nucleus.

THE CEREBELLAR CONNECTIONS

The fiber connections of the elasmobranch cerebellum have been described by Edinger (1901), Banchi (1903), Ariens Kappers (1906, 1927, 1947), Wallenberg (1907), Sterzi (1909) and Ariens Kappers, Huber, and Crosby (1936). My observations of these connections in Weigert preparations of Squalus, Scyllium, and Raja are in general accord with the summary of Ariens Kappers (1947). Pyridine-silver series of Mustelus and, especially, Bodian series of pup stages have added important details.

The afferent tracts. The ascending fascicles of the posterior and the ventral anterior lateral-line roots end by terminal branches with boutons among the scattered cells of the primitive eminentia granularis. Finer processes continue into the folds of the auricle, ending among the granule cells. Whether these represent continuations of root fibers or differ in origin could not be ascertained. There are indications that some of the fibers reaching the auricular folds arise from cells of the eminentia, thus representing secondary fibers. Also a diffuse fascicle accompanies the granular ridge which extends from the nucleus dorsalis to the posterolateral fold of the auricle. Numerous secondary fibers probably ascend, with the root fibers, from the nucleus medialis, but only fortunate Golgi preparations can resolve the questions of secondary fibers and of the sources of fibers ending in the folds of the auricle.

Two fascicles of VIII root fibers ascend into the primitive eminentia granularis medial of the lateral-line fascicles. These also distribute among the cells of the eminentia together with the presumptive secondary fibers to the auricular folds.

A compact fascicle, as it appears in transverse sections, gathers in the anterior part of the eminentia granularis and tapers toward the pars medialis. A little farther caudally it is joined by fibers that appear related with the auricle. In the pars medialis the fascicle becomes a sheet of somewhat loosely arranged fibers beneath the molecular layer. The component fibers of this fascicle and sheet are difficult to differentiate in fiber preparations. They appear to include a considerable proportion of ascending utricular fibers, many ascending lateral-line fibers and possibly a contingent of saccular fibers. The auricle-related fibers that join the fascicle probably include efferents from the auricular folds.

In Bodian preparations of pup stages of Squalus and Raja many of the fibers end in the interauricular granular band and in the medial granular ridge, and its expansion, of the pars medialis. Others end in the molecular layer. From the fibrous zone beneath the molecular layer fibers enter the deep cellular layer of the pars medialis and end among its more diffuse cells. The Bodian preparations, and also pyridine-silver preparations of Mustelus, clearly show fibers that decussate above the ependymal bridge which connects the bilateral halves of the pars medialis. These form a flattened commissure, more extensive in adult Mustelus than in the pup stages of the other species, which merges rostrally with the decussating fiber bundles of the horizontal plate of the corpus cerebelli. This commissure also is well shown in myelin preparations of adult specimens. A smaller commissure of unmyelinated fibers interconnects the expanded part of the medial granular ridge, as already noted.

Except as suggested by the components of the fascicle and fibrous sheet above described, the composition of the larger commissure is unknown in elasmobranchs. The much smaller and simpler vestibulolateral lobe of urodeles (p. 144) is entirely similar to that of elasmobranchs in its fundamental relations. The urodele cerebellum, studied from Golgi as well as Cajal and other fiber preparations and described below, has a vestibulolateral commissure comprising primary and perhaps secondary fibers, secondary lateral-line fibers from the eminentia granularis, and possibly lateral-line root fibers. It is not improbable that the principal constituents of the elasmobranch commissure correspond, and that it is primarily a vestibulolateral commissure.

Ascending branches of the bifurcated fibers of the dorsal root of the anterior lateral-line nerve extend rostralward beneath the granular ridge, which is continuous with the posterolateral fold of the auricle. Many of the fibers enter the cerebellar crest. Others appear to continue in a somewhat diffuse fascicle, already mentioned, beneath the auricular folds, and which follows their turns to the interauricular granular ridge. This fascicle appears also to include fibers of other origin, possibly secondary vestibular.

On the basis of Marchi degeneration in Scyllium, Wallenberg (1907) describes an interauricular commissure through the tegmentum (Haubenkommissur der Rautenohren). It decussates beneath and behind the decussation of the brachium conjunctivum, having a horseshoe-shaped course with the convexity directed forward. Wallenberg's illustrations of the position of the lesions and the course of degeneration indicate that the primitive eminentia granularis, as well as the auricle proper, was involved. In addition to degeneration of external arcuate fibers which constitute his commissure, so-called octavomotor fibers and fibers taking the path of the vestibulolateral commissure, above described (the latter not labeled), were involved. Wallenberg's Haubenkommissur is apparently a deep connection between the bilateral eminentiae granulares. Its fibers, more numerous and more concentrated, appear to correspond to those in the arcuate system of the medulla oblongata that interconnect the bilateral acousticolateral areas. Intereminential fibers in the pup stages of Squalus appear to represent Wallenberg's commissure. The lateral lobules of the vestibulolateral lobe, accordingly, are interconnected by a deep or tegmental commissure and also by a supraventricular acousticolateral commissure.

The afferent tracts to the corpus cerebelli arise in the spinal cord, medulla oblongata, midbrain, and, according to Ariens Kappers (1947), the inferior lobe of the hypothalamus. In addition, trigeminal root fibers are described by Edinger (1901) as clearly entering the cerebellum in front of the auricle, and Banchi (1903) includes cerebellar roots of the trigeminus with other sensory nerve roots described as reaching the cerebellum. In sagittal Weigert series of Scyllium I find a fascicle of ascending trigeminal root fibers extending to the base of the anterior lobe and appearing to enter it. Bodian series of pup stages of Squalus show this fascicle as ending, in part, in the sensory V nucleus, from which secondary fibers continue into the anterior base of the corpus cerebelli. It is not clear whether the secondary fibers are accompanied by root fibers, but probably they are.

A spino-cerebellar tract ascends to the anterior medullary velum and enters the anterior part of the corpus cerebelli. In its course through the medulla oblongata this fascicle corresponds to the spino-cerebellar tract of other Ichthyopsida and to the ventral spino-cerebellar tract of reptiles, birds, and mammals. Some of the fibers appear to decussate in the velum, but by far the most enter the fiber layer of the ipsilateral cortex, in which they distribute.

A second tract of spinal origin enters the posterior ventral part of the posterior lobe, distributing in the fibrous layer of the cortex, including the lobulus posticus. Before reaching the corpus cerebelli this tract passes through the medulla oblongata, near its dorsolateral surface, and arches dorsomedially beneath the primitive eminentia granularis. It probably is homologous with the dorsal spino-cerebellar tract of higher vertebrates (Ariens Kappers, Huber, and Crosby, 1936).

Olivo-cerebellar fibers, in large numbers, accompany the spino-cerebellar tracts. They have their origin in the contralateral inferior olive and, after decussating with the arcuate system, take a rostral course in the ventral superficial part of the medulla oblongata. Turning dorsalward between the levels of the roots of the V and VIII nerves they enter the posterior inferior part of the corpus cerebelli and are distributed to the entire cortex (Ariens Kappers, 1921). It is probable that reticulo-cerebellar fibers accompany those from the inferior olivary nucleus which is well developed in elasmobranchs.

According to Ariens Kappers, Huber, and Crosby (1936) a tractus mesencephalo-cerebellaris superior arises, in part, in the most rostral part of the mesencephalic tegmentum and enters the corpus cerebelli in front of the granular ridge of the ventral wall of the anterior lobe. Other fibers appear to have their origin in the rostral part of the optic tectum. Ariens Kappers (1947) labels the collection of fibers from the midbrain to the cerebellum the tecto-cerebellar tract. Whether this corresponds to the tecto-cerebellar tract of teleosts (p. 116), also called tractus mesencephalo-cerebellaris anterior, or to the superior mesencephalo-cerebellar tract, or both, is not clear. I am unable to add anything on the subject.

The lobo-cerebellar tract, according to Ariens Kappers (1921, 1947), passes from the caudal part of the inferior lobe of the hypothalamus to the ipsilateral anterior part of the corpus cerebelli. Sterzi (1909) describes both direct and crossed lobo-cerebellar tracts.

It is evident that the afferent connections of the vestibulolateral lobe and the corpus cerebelli are quite distinct from each other and indicate pronounced functional differences between these two divisions of the cerebellum. Ariens Kappers, Huber, and Crosby (1936, p. 722) call attention to this difference with reference to the "auricles and the body of the cerebellum."

The efferent fibers. Purkinje cell axons to the nucleus cerebelli from the vestibulolateral lobe and the corpus cerebelli already have been mentioned. Fibers from the nucleus cerebelli, accompanied by Purkinje cell axons that by-pass the nucleus, take a ventrorostral and medial course, decussating behind the roots of the III nerve and above the interpeduncular nucleus. This aggregation of fibers constitutes the brachium conjunctivum and its decussation. After giving off descending fibers to the reticular formation of the medulla oblongata, part of its fibers join the medial longitudinal fascicle and continue in it to reach the oculomotor nucleus, according to Ariens Kappers (1947). Most, however, pass into the basal part of the midbrain and of the thalamus, disappearing among large reticular cells.

The primitive eminentia granularis and the auricle give rise to fibers, probably Purkinje cell axons, which take a ventrorostral course behind those of the brachium conjunctivum and cross in the caudal part of its decussation. A posterior cerebello-tegmental tract is formed of fibers which pass along the wall of the fourth ventricle and end in the tegmentum of the medulla oblongata, both ipsilaterally and contralaterally. Most of these fibers, both crossed and uncrossed, run caudally in company with descending vestibular fibers, near or in the medial longitudinal fascicle. They end in relation to motor and reticular cells of the medulla oblongata and spinal cord.

THE HISTOLOGY

The acousticolateral area. The nucleus dorsalis, nucleus medialis, and vestibular area constitute the primarily cellular part of the acousticolateral area. The crista cerebelli is its molecular layer. The cells of the nuclei have been described from Golgi preparations by Houser (1901) and Sterzi (1909). The crista also includes cells, much more widely scattered than in the nuclei, among its fine fibers. These have been described from Golgi and cytological preparations by Houser.

The nucleus medialis (the tuberculum acusticum of these authors) has an irregular layer, immediately beneath the crista, of large cells that resemble Purkinje cells. Three or four dendrites, that may arise from one large process, extend into the cerebellar crest. Sterzi illustrates dendrites also extending into and branching in the nucleus medialis. The outward directed dendrites divide into slender perpendicularly directed processes on which small excrescences occur. The dendritic branches in the nucleus ramify irregularly. The axons descend into the arcuate fiber system of the medulla oblongata. These cells are similar to the primitive Purkinje cells of Johnston (1901) in the nucleus medialis of Acipenser (p. 79) and are regarded as such in elasmobranchs. Scattered among the primitive Purkinje cell bodies are small numbers of granule cells which have three or four short

dendritic processes, and a long slender axon extending into the cerebellar crest. The deeper part of the nucleus includes polymorphic cells of various sizes, some as large as Purkinje cells and others as small as granules. All have many dendritic processes that branch and end within the nucleus. The axons of the larger cells pass ventromedially into the arcuate fiber system.

The nucleus dorsalis (the lateral-line lobe of Sterzi) is similar in internal structure to the nucleus medialis, according to Sterzi.

The vestibular area or nucleus ventralis has relatively fewer small cells than the nucleus medialis and more numerous neurons of large size. The large multipolar cells of Deiters's nucleus and the smaller cells that probably correspond to the tangential nucleus already have been mentioned. The large cells dorsomedial of Deiters's nucleus that give rise to the median fascicle of Stieda apparently are migrated reticular elements from the motor tegmentum that replace, functionally, the transitory Mauthner's cell.

The crista cerebelli or molecular layer, as seen in Bodian stained sections of Squalus pups (figs. 32, 33), is formed of innumerable fine fibers among which the small cells, above mentioned, are scattered. These cells, called molecular neurons by Houser in Mustelus, differ from the granules in cytological preparations and, in Golgi sections, their radiating dendrites and their axons also differ (Houser). They are most numerous in the deep part of the crista. Small branches of lateral-line fibers spread through the outer part of the crista, their terminal ramifications ending among the dendritic tips of the Purkinje cells and sometimes near the cell bodies. Other minute fibers are said to end between the molecular neurons. The axons of the granule cells add another element of fine fibers that presumably pass through the dendritic spread of the primitive Purkinje cells as in the cerebellar cortex. It is not clear if root fibers of the VIII nerve or their branches enter the crista as in teleosts (p. 101). The evidence is ambiguous in younger stages of Squalus and in older stages the ventral anterior lateral-line root fibers are so intermingled with VIII root fibers that their distribution, except as the ascending and descending fascicles above described, is impossible to differentiate.

The cerebellar crest of the nucleus dorsalis is separated from that of the nucleus medialis, as already noted, by a deep external furrow. Rostrally, however, the two bands of crista merge. Each is a layer of neuropil which correlates the impulses received from its underlying nucleus, including contralateral impulses mediated by the fibers of commissural function among the internal arcuates. The fused anterior part of the crista probably is functionally more complex.

The vestibulolateral lobe. The cells of the primitive eminentia granularis, in Bodian stained preparations, are similar to those of the nucleus medialis. They are more closely arranged owing to a greater proportion of small cells, some of the more peripheral of which probably are granules. The folds of the auricles consist of granules and somewhat larger rounded elements that probably are Golgi cells. The numerous fibers from the auricles to the pars medialis and acousticolateral commissure suggest that many are Golgi type I cells, but favorable Golgi material, or study by experimental methods, is necessary to establish such cells and fibers. Purkinje cells line the crista cerebelli as it passes around the base of the auricle.

The pars medialis has a well-defined layer of Purkinje cells beneath its molecular layer. The deep part of the medialis is well delimited from the interauricular granular band in the pup stages, but in the adult migrated granule cells have invaded the zone of larger scattered elements so that a gradation has resulted. The median granular ridge and its enlargement consists predominantly of granules, among which are found larger elements that resemble Golgi cells of the ridges in the corpus cerebelli.

The corpus cerebelli. The cortex of the corpus cerebelli comprises an external molecular layer, a layer of Purkinje cells, and a fibrous layer throughout its extent. On either side of the internal sagittal fissure a granular layer is added in the form of the longitudinal granular folds (fig. 37). The Purkinje cells disappear near the midline and the fibrous layer is reduced in thickness as its fibers enter the lateral part of the bases of the granular ridges and spread out in the granular layer. The molecular layer is continuous from side to side, covering the ependymal bridge connecting the bilateral halves of the corpus cerebelli (fig. 37).

Purkinje cells were described in elasmobranchs by Viault (1876), Rohon (1878), and others but were first demonstrated in Golgi preparations by Sauerbeck (1896). More comprehensive descriptions were provided by Schaper (1898) and Houser (1901). The cell body is rounded, oval, or triangular, the size depending upon its position. The largest cells are found in the part of the cortical folds which curves sharply to their summits, the smaller cells in the walls of the folds. In other words, the size of the cell body varies with the thickness of the region of molecular layer into which its dendrites extend. The dendrites are attached to the peripheral pole of the

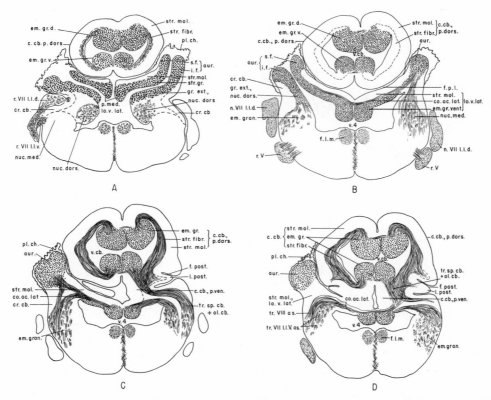

Figure 37. Transverse sections of cerebellum of Scyllium. A. Level of entrance of VIII nerve. B. Level of entrance of V nerve. C, D. Level of acousticolateral commissure. Right side more rostral than left. ×8.

cell body and extend only into the molecular layer. They are less branched than in teleosts and rarely branch beyond divisions of the third order. Their spread is in the sagittal plane but more compactly than in teleosts or mammals. Gemmules, ranging from mere points, slender spines, and knobs to mushroom-like excrescences occur on the branches (Houser, 1901). The axons enter the fibrous layer and turn sharply, collectively constituting an important element of this layer. They appear to have no collateral branches (fig. 38A).

The two medial ridges which represent the granular layer may be much thicker than the molecular layer at the summits of the cortical folds but decrease toward the depth of the folds. The cells, as seen in Golgi preparations, are of two distinct types: granule cells and Golgi type II neurons. The granules (fig. 38B), which are by far the most numerous, have rounded cell bodies, three to four short dendrites, most of which end as small claws or brush-like processes, and a very slender axon which arises from the cell body or one of the dendrites. The axons ascend through the granular layer into the molecular layer, changing to a horizontal direction at the boundary between the two layers. In the molecular layer the axon divides, in a characteristic T-form, into two

branches that continue parallel with the cerebellar surface, passing through the dendritic spread of the Purkinje cells. The Golgi cells are slightly larger than the granules and have a more rounded form. Several radiating dendrites increase slightly in size by swellings at intervals, but branch sparsely. The axon passes into the deep part of the granular layer, soon giving rise to collaterals and dividing into fine terminal twigs (fig. 37C).

The fibrous layer, in addition to axons of Purkinje cells, includes afferent fibers to the cortex from a variety of sources. Great numbers of these penetrate the Purkinje cell layer to enter the molecularis, in which they ramify and terminate. Ariens Kappers, Huber, and Crosby (1936) include primitive climbing fibers that twine loosely about the Purkinje cell dendrites. Other fibers lose their myelin sheaths in the granular ridges and disappear among the granules. These may represent primitive mossy fibers but the terminals characteristic of such fibers in higher vertebrates have not been demonstrated.

The molecular layer is formed of the terminals of afferent fibers already mentioned, parallel fibers derived from granule cell axons, branching dendrites of Purkinje cells, and many small stellate cells and their branches (fig. 38D–G). The dendrites of these cells spread, in gen-

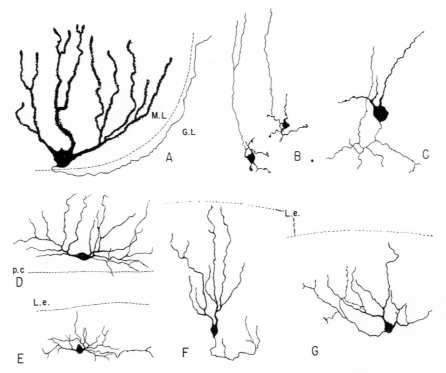

Figure 38. Nerve cells from the cerebellum of Mustelus vulgaris. A. Large Purkinje cell from a portion of cerebellar plate where the granular layer is lacking. B. Small granule cells. C. Large granule cell. D, E, F, G. Cells from the molecular layer. G.L., granular layer; M.L., molecular layer; p.c., layer of Purkinje cells. Golgi method. (Schaper, 1898.)

eral, in the sagittal plane. The axons are variously directed but disappear in the molecular layer. Basket cells have not been identified in elasmobranchs, but Sterzi (1909) describes fusiform cells which occur as a rule in the deep part of the molecularis. Their axons, after a short horizontal course, turn toward the Purkinje cells and terminate near their bodies. The molecular layer constitutes a greatly spreadout mass of neuropil which discharges through the axons of the Purkinje cells.

Supporting elements. Sauerbeck (1896) demonstrated ependymal cells in the cerebellum of Mustelus by the Golgi method. They are described as resting on the internal limiting membrane and having processes that reach the external limiting membrane. Several varieties were found in the same species by Schaper (1898). Near the midline of the cerebellar plate primitive ependymal cells occur which have rounded or triangular cell bodies and one or two smooth processes that end with a conical expansion against the limitans externa. A number of processes from different cells usually unite to form column-like structures. Short, branched processes frequently arise from the deep pole of the cell. Most of the other ependymal cells, according to Schaper, have lost their connection with the external limiting membrane, but a few in the thinner part of the cortex retain such a connection by a conical expansion. Sterzi (1909), from Golgi preparations of Squalus, also describes and illustrates some ependymal fibers ending as conical expansions against the external limiting membrane, whereas others end short of this membrane. None were found by Houser (1901) extending beyond the granular layer, but he makes no specific mention of the thin part of the cortex.

The ependymal cells form the lining of the ventricular cavity. They have an irregular pyramidal form, the ependymal fibers continuing as stout processes from their apices. The fibers may divide into large branches and shorter twigs, or they may give rise to numerous small twigs that give the fiber the appearance of an elongated round brush. The twigs of the closely adjacent fibers form an interlacing network which supports the nervous elements.

Schaper and Houser both describe fibers, arising from cells situated between the Purkinje cells, that extend in a nearly direct course to the external limiting membrane, ending against it by conical enlargements. These fibers are limited to the molecular layer and are regarded by the authors as homologous to Bergmann's fibers of higher vertebrates. The cell body has few processes but the fiber is covered by a dense outgrowth of fine processes that may become matted at intervals. Sterzi illustrates similar fibers arising from cells at the level of the Purkinje cell layer, calling the cells modified ependyma. The cells that give rise to Bergmann's fibers of Schaper and Houser were regarded by Houser as a variety of neuroglia. In addition Schaper describes cells of irregular outline and with many short unbranched processes radiating from the cell body. These were regarded as homologous to astrocytes. Sterzi also described neuroglia cells in Squalus.

The close proximity of the ependymal fibers and the interlacing network formed by their branches and twigs results in a complex supporting framework for the nervous elements and fibers of the deep part of the cortex, including the granular ridges. The outer part is supported largely by the neuroglial elements, including the apparent fibers of Bergmann or, according to Sterzi, by such elements and ependymal fibers.

Comparison of the elasmobranch cerebellum with that of petromyzonts makes it clear that the vestibulolateral lobe of the former corresponds to all of the externally visible cerebellum of lampreys. The relations of the acousticolateral area are identical but there are differences in the degree of differentiation and development. The diffuse cell mass of the lateral lobule in petromyzonts, which is continuous posteriorly with the nucleus medialis of the acousticolateral area, is the precursor of the primitive eminentia granularis and the deep cellular part of the pars medialis of elasmobranchs. No auricles or subtenial granular ridges are found in petromyzonts, unless the small string of granule-like cells extending rostromedially from the anterior end of the nucleus dorsalis is a precursor of these. In elasmobranchs, by contrast, the auricles proper and the granular ridges are the most prominent features of the lateral lobule and are relatively larger than in any other ichthyopsid type.

The large corpus cerebelli of sharks and rays, developed from the anterior part of the columna dorsalis, corresponds morphologically to the small and submerged corpus cerebelli of lampreys. In elasmobranchs, however, it not only has become the predominant feature of the cerebellum but has differentiated into distinct molecular, Purkinje cell, and granular layers, the last named being represented by the granular ridges.

The afferent root fiber connections of the externally visible cerebellum of petromyzonts and of the vestibulolateral lobe of elasmobranchs are identical except in the size of the nerve roots and the tracts to which these roots give rise. The spino-cerebellar, trigemino-cerebellar, and tecto-cerebellar tracts to the corpus cerebelli of elasmobranchs are represented by smaller similar tracts in petromyzonts.

DIPNOI

NEOCERATODUS FORSTERI

THE cerebellum of the principal groups of fishes above the Elasmobranchii in the phylogenetic scale differs so greatly from that of sharks and rays that homologies of its subdivisions with those of elasmobranchs are often difficult to recognize. The cerebellum of Dipnoi, as represented in Neoceratodus, described by Holmgren and van der Horst (1925) and van der Horst (1925), differs from that of elasmobranchs as well as of teleostomes but has certain characteristics of each of these groups. Lacking dipnoan material for firsthand study I shall attempt to interpret the descriptions and illustrations of Holmgren and van der Horst, and of van der Horst, in terms of the cerebellum of other fishes described in this volume.

The cerebellum of Neoceratodus is simple in form but well developed. The acousticolateral area resembles that of elasmobranchs and Acipenseriformes in the size and relations of its nuclei. The simple pattern of the cerebellum and of the relations of some of its subdivisions to the acousticolateral area elucidates the cerebellar subdivisions of teleostomes in which the variations of form, degree of development, and subdivisions of the organ are very great. It also helps to bridge the wide gap of differences between the cerebellar subdivisions of elasmobranchs and those of teleostomes.

In Neoceratodus the cerebellum forms a strongly caudalward tilted plate, each side of which arches ventralward and is continuous with the medulla oblongata (fig. 39). Transverse sections show the organ as an arch above the fourth ventricle, comprising an outer molecular layer and an inner granular layer (fig. 40). Part of the lateral surface lacks a molecular layer, the granular layer reaching the external surface of the organ. Anteriorly the median part of the plate forms a broad ridge above the rounded lateral part on either side, but the posterior part of the plate is flattened and has a convex caudal border.

This flattened part is connected on both sides with the dorsal margin of the medulla oblongata by a choroid membrane which forms the lateral wall of a recessus lateralis of the fourth ventricle (fig. 40). This membrane

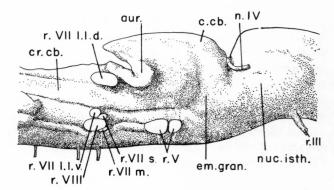

Figure 39. Lateral view of the cerebellum of Neoceratodus. (Modified from Holmgren and van der Horst, 1925.)

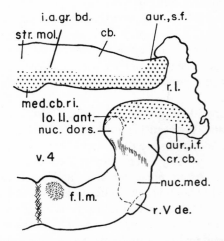

Figure 40. Transverse section of brain stem of Neoceratodus at the level of lateral recess of fourth ventricle. (Modified from van der Horst, 1919.)

62

corresponds to that which covers the folds of the auricle in elasmobranchs. Although not so described in Neoceratodus, it undoubtedly is continuous with the choroid roof of the fourth ventricle which attaches to the posterior margin of the cerebellum. Such attachment in Neoceratodus would be afforded by the thin convex posterior border. Farther rostrally the posterior part of the plate arches increasingly ventralward on each side until it becomes continuous with the medulla oblongata.

In the ventricular surface of the cerebellum two longitudinal fissures, one on each side of the midline, begin near the decussatio veli, become very deep about midway between the anterior and posterior borders of the organ, and gradually disappear posteriorly. Between these two fissures a prominent ridge projects into the ventricle, becoming reduced caudalward. It consists of a median layer of molecular substance, which is continuous with the external molecular layer, and a granular layer on either side and ventrally. Both the ridge projecting into the ventricle and the broader external ridge above it are unpaired, but a trace of bilateral origin of the cerebellum is shown by a shallow furrow in the midline of the anterior part of the organ (Holmgren and van der Horst, 1925).

The external and ventricular median ridges appear to represent the corpus cerebelli, *sensu strictiori*, to which we shall return. A granular mass on either side of the ventricle, in the anterior part of the cerebellum, is called the eminentia granularis by van der Horst (1925). As in elasmobranchs there is no valvula cerebelli. Where the posterior part of the plate becomes continuous with the medulla oblongata the granular layer projects laterally and folds around a continuation of the recessus lateralis toward the nucleus dorsalis of the acousticolateral area. This projection of the granular layer forms a well-defined auricle which is similar to the auricle proper of elasmobranchs but is relatively smaller (fig. 39).

THE LATERAL-LINE AND ACOUSTIC NERVES AND THE ACOUSTICOLATERAL AREA

The peripheral distribution of the lateral-line and acoustic nerves of Neoceratodus has not been described. According to Holmgren and van der Horst (1925) the anterior lateral-line nerve has a dorsal and a ventral root; the posterior lateral-line nerve enters the medulla oblongata by a single root. The dorsal root of the anterior nerve is larger than the ventral and enters the acousticolateral area above the cerebellar crest, while the ventral root enters ventral of the crista (fig. 39). The dorsal and ventral roots exchange many fibers before entering the medulla oblongata, according to van der Horst (1925). The VIII nerve has a single large root which enters the medulla oblongata beneath the ventral anterior lateral-line root and between the sensory and motor roots of the VII nerve (fig. 39).

The acousticolateral area comprises a nucleus dorsalis (van der Horst's lobus liniae lateralis dorsalis); a nucleus lobus ventralis of van der Horst which, however, includes the nucleus of the VIII nerve; and a crista cerebelli, situated on the lateral surface of the medulla oblongata between the two nuclei. Since the anterior part of the nucleus medialis of other fishes is merged with the area vestibularis, whereas the more caudal part of the same cell column has no such intimate relations to the vestibular nuclei in other fishes, it seems preferable to employ the term nucleus medialis in Neoceratodus also. The embryonic origin of the nucleus medialis of elasmobranchs from the columna dorsalis, and of the vestibular nuclei, according to Hugosson (1957), from the columna dorsolateralis, indicates that the nuclear masses differ though they become more or less fused anteriorly.

The nucleus dorsalis, situated dorsal of the cerebellar crest in Neoceratodus (fig. 40), forms a prominent elongated mass extending caudalward to the level of the anterior root of the X nerve. It is the nucleus of the dorsal anterior lateral-line root, which enters the nucleus above the cerebellar crest. The nucleus medialis is continuous with the eminentia granularis, rostrally, and extends to the caudal end of the medulla oblongata. It is the nucleus of the ventral anterior and posterior lateral-line roots, both entering ventral of the cerebellar crest. The ventral part of van der Horst's nucleus ventralis receives the root fibers of the VIII nerve. Holmgren and van der Horst (1925) found that coarse fibers collected in the dorsocaudal part of the root apparently come into synaptic relations with the lateral dendrite of Mauthner's cell. Granule cells are scattered throughout the nucleus dorsalis but in the nucleus medialis such cells are said to be few except near the ventricular surface. In an illustration of a transverse section passing through the anterior part of the nucleus dorsalis, the lateral part of the nucleus shows a large mass of closely arranged granules which is continuous with a compact granular mass that continues to the auricle (fig. 40).

Some of the fibers of the dorsal anterior lateral-line root are said to bifurcate in the nucleus dorsalis but it is not certain that all do so. The ventral root fibers divide in the nucleus medialis, descending branches of this root, and ascending and descending branches of the posterior lateral-line root distribute in the same region of the nucleus as in elasmobranchs. Ascending branches of both roots extend rostralward. The crista cerebelli extends posteriorly much farther than the nucleus dorsalis; anteriorly it arches dorsalward and is continuous with the molecular layer of the cerebellum.

THE AURICULA CEREBELLI

A lateral ridge-like mass of granules which is continuous with a granular zone in the anterior part of the nucleus dorsalis, as already noted, is delimited from the dorsal nucleus by a shallow furrow. This ridge merges rostrolaterally with the ventral fold of the auricle. Whether it should be regarded as part of this fold or as corresponding, in much abbreviated form, to the elongated granular ridge which passes from the posterolateral fold of the auricle to the nucleus dorsalis in Squalus is not clear. The ventral fold of the auricle expands in Neoceratodus and joins the dorsal fold around the end of the recessus lateralis (fig. 39). The dorsal fold is continuous, medially, with the granular layer in the posterior margin of the cerebellum (fig. 40). It is not evident from Holmgren and van der Horst's descriptions and photographs whether this marginal part of the granular layer forms an interauricular granular band, as in elasmobranchs and Acipenseriformes (p. 76), or is the marginal part of the general granular layer of the cerebellum. The granules appear to be more closely arranged, however, in the posterior border of the layer. The laterally projecting dorsal and ventral folds of the auricle correspond without question to the anteromedial and posterolateral folds, respectively, of elasmobranchs. The ventral fold, like the posterolateral fold in sharks and rays, is related, either directly or through a short granular ridge, to the nucleus dorsalis. Possibly the thin median part of the flattened posterior region of the cerebellum corresponds to the pars medialis of the vestibulolateral lobe of elasmobranchs and other species, but the description of the Neoceratodus cerebellum does not enable one to judge.

According to van der Horst the auricle is related almost entirely to the area of the lateral-line nerves. In elasmobranchs the lateral-line nerves that enter the nucleus dorsalis, from which fascicles continue to the granular ridge and the auricle, are the dorsal root of the anterior lateral-line nerve and a fascicle from the ventral root. The latter may be represented in Neoceratodus by ventral root fibers that pass to the dorsal root before entering the medulla oblongata. Presumably fibers are present in Neoceratodus that correspond to those, in elasmobranchs, that follow the granular ridge to the auricle.

THE EMINENTIA GRANULARIS

The granular layer thickens in the anterior part of the cerebellum and reaches the lateral surface, the molecular layer being represented only in the dorsal part of this region of the organ. The lateral granular mass is continuous caudally with the fused nucleus medialis and vestibular area; rostralward it extends along the side of the midbrain as far as the level of the III nerve, according to Holmgren and van der Horst (1925). The rostral part is regarded by van der Horst (1925) as the nucleus isthmi and the cerebellar part as the eminentia granularis. Seen in transverse section the eminentia arches lateralward, forming an expansion which can be compared with the anterior part of the lateral lobule of Acipenser and Polyodon (p. 73), although it projects less strongly and is less differentiated. Dorsomedially an external furrow, probably corresponding to the posterolateral fissure of many other Ichthyopsida, delimits the projection from the median part of the cerebellum. A ventricular sulcus lateralis, which is continuous with the sulcus lateralis of the medulla oblongata, delimits the eminentia ventrally. The sulcus lateralis of the medulla oblongata delimits the ventricular surface of the acousticolateral area from the remainder of the sensory area.

The afferent connections of the eminentia granularis, according to van der Horst, are from the lateral-line and VIII nerves. Presumably these include ascending ventral anterior and posterior lateral-line and VIII root fibers and secondary vestibular connections, as in elasmobranchs and other Ichthyopsida described below. The complex of fibers to the eminentia, accordingly, is more inclusive than that to the auricle. The eminentia apparently correlates ventral anterior and posterior lateral-line and vestibular impulses, whereas the auricle appears to be limited to impulses from the two roots of the anterior lateral-line nerve.

The differences in afferent connections and in morphological relations of the auricle and eminentia granularis indicate that they are distinct, although functionally somewhat related, subdivisions of the cerebellum. However there also are differences. Van der Horst (1925) presents the same view.

The lateral part of the cerebellum, including the eminentia granularis anteriorly, and the auricle posteriorly, together with the dorsomedially directed continuation of the crista cerebelli between them, are suggestive of the lateral lobule of Acipenser and Polyodon, described below. Commissural interconnections between the lateral lobules, such as are found in many other Ichthyopsida, have not been described in Neoceratodus. If they exist, as presumably they do, one could speak of a cerebellar division comparable with the vestibulolateral lobe of elasmobranchs and other Ichthyopsida.

THE CORPUS CEREBELLI

The median part of the cerebellum, according to van der Horst, receives chiefly secondary tracts from the spinal cord, medulla oblongata, and midbrain which conduct impulses originating in somatic sensory organs not related to those of the acousticolateral system. It corresponds in this and other respects to the corpus cerebelli, *sensu strictiori*, of elasmobranchs. Apparently it includes, as indicated in figure 39, the dorsal part of the cerebellum which is situated between the bilateral external furrows, mentioned above as probably representing the posterolateral fissure, and the median ridge which projects into the ventricle, as does the entire corpus cerebelli of chondrosteans. The inversion of the median part of the cerebellum in this group results in a deeper projection of the corpus. The unpaired ridge of Neoceratodus, with its median molecular layer, is similar to the unpaired corpus cerebelli of Acipenseriformes (p. 77), except that the granular layer is continuous from one side to the other instead of forming a large mass on either side of a molecular and cellular layer. The ventral part of the granular layer possibly corresponds to the granular ridges of elasmobranchs, fused across the midline instead of being separated by a median ventricular fissure, as in elasmobranchs.

It must be emphasized that while the interpretations offered appear plausible on the basis of the evidence available, they nevertheless are hypothetical. Other species of Dipnoi may have variations that would substantiate or refute them. Even more important, developmental stages if available would reveal the morphological relations more clearly.

The valvula cerebelli. The valvula, which is continuous with the corpus cerebelli and eminentia granularis in several other groups of fishes, is lacking in Neoceratodus, as already noted. The ganglion isthmi of van der Horst, which is continuous with the eminentia granularis and also has connections from the acousticolateral area, is suggested by the Dutch author as possibly homologous with the valvula; instead of projecting into the mesencephalic ventricle it has extended forward along the midbrain.

The nucleus cerebelli. A mass of cells in the most rostral part of the eminentia ventralis of the cerebellum projects into the ventricle lateral of the longitudinal furrow. Holmgren and van der Horst (1925) regard this mass as possibly corresponding to the nucleus lateralis cerebelli of Edinger in elasmobranchs, and to the nucleus cerebelli of the frog (Larsell, 1923).

POLYPTERIFORMES

THE chondrosteans, including the Polypteriformes and the Acipenseriformes, have in common a relatively large inverted cerebellum which includes a prominent valvula projecting into the mesencephalic ventricle. The relative size of the subdivisions of the cerebellum differs considerably in the two orders and there are other differences, described below. Also the acousticolateral system of nerves and sense organs and the acousticolateral area differ greatly.

Lacking material of the Polypteriformes, formerly included by ichthyologists with the Crossopterygii, I have taken the descriptions of these fishes from the literature, but attempted to interpret the various features in terms of my own studies of Acipenseriformes and other fishes.

THE LATERAL-LINE ORGANS AND NERVES

The cephalic lateral-line system of Polypterus, according to Allis (1900), comprises paired supraorbital, infraorbital, and preoperculo-mandibular canals, a transverse commissural canal, and six short lines of superficial sense organs on each side of the head. The superficial organs correspond to pit organs in certain other fishes. The lateral-line organs of the body are represented by a series of sensory patches occupying short linear spaces on the outer surface of some of the scales. They are arranged in a principal ventral line, a dorsal line, and an irregular line midway between the other two. Fragmentary descriptions of the lateral-line nerves of the head were given by Pollard (1892) and Allis (1900), but the innervation of the lines on the body appears not to have been described.

THE ACOUSTICOLATERAL AREA

The acousticolateral areas of Calamoichthys and Polypterus are briefly described by van der Horst (1925). The nucleus dorsalis of Calamoichthys is reduced and faces medially as the dorsal part of the lateral wall of the fourth ventricle. It receives fibers of a much-reduced dorsal root of the anterior lateral-line nerve. The dorsal and ventral roots combine, however, immediately outside the medulla oblongata and van der Horst regards it as quite certain that fibers corresponding to those entering the dorsal root in elasmobranchs and Acipenseriformes enter by the ventral root in Polypteriformes and reach the nucleus medialis. This nucleus is said to be much larger than the nucleus dorsalis and receives all the ventral root fibers.

The crista cerebelli, in transverse section, forms a semilunar area lateral of the nucleus dorsalis and dorsal of the nucleus medialis, facing laterally (fig. 43). The root of the acoustic or VIII nerve enters a zone beneath the nucleus medialis which apparently is closely related to this nucleus but the description is scanty.

The Cerebellum

The cerebellum of Polypterus and Calamoichthys is, according to van der Horst (1919), divided into bilaterally symmetrical halves by a "sulcus medianus longitudinalis" (fig. 41). The two inverted halves are connected by a layer of ependyma in the floor of this fissure, and nerve fibers form a thin layer which crosses from one side to the other in the ependyma, van der Horst (1925) states. Posterodorsally the bilateral halves are connected by a broad, apparently fibromolecular, zone. In elasmobranchs, as already noted, and in teleost embryos, as Schaper (1894a, 1894b) has shown, the ependymal connection between the two halves of the cerebellum forms the roof of a dorsal continuation of the ventricular cavity which becomes the cerebellar ventricle. The medial longitudinal fissure of Polypteriformes, by contrast, is an inward extension of the pericerebellar space which may be compared with the external sagittal fissure of the elasmobranch cerebellum.

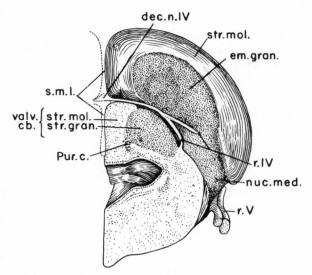

Figure 41. Polypterus bichir. Frontal view of wax model of cerebellum. (van der Horst, 1919.)

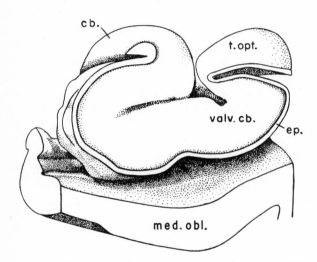

Figure 42. Polypterus bichir. Medial view of wax model of cerebellum. (van der Horst, 1919.)

Caudally the ventral cerebellar fold arches dorsorostrally so that a dorsal fold results. This, in turn, arches posteriorly and tapers toward the posterior cerebellar margin. The choroid tela of the fourth ventricle is attached to this margin. Anteriorly the ventral fold is continuous with the valvula (fig. 42).

THE LOBULUS LATERALIS

In the rostral part of this bilateral rounded division is situated an expanded granular mass, termed eminentia granularis by van der Horst (1925), which tapers ventrocaudally and is continuous with the nucleus medialis of the acousticolateral area. This granular expansion appears to correspond, in relatively enlarged form, to the

cell mass and intermingled fibers in the lateral lobule of petromyzonts, and to the eminentia granularis of elasmobranchs and Neoceratodus, above described, and of chondrosteans (p. 74).

The lateral posterior margin of the cerebellum is continuous, ventrolaterally, with the acousticolateral area (fig. 43). An aggregation of granules extends to the lateral surface, where the cerebellar margin arches caudally to merge with the acousticolateral area and is covered by a fold of choroid tela so that this surface is ventricular. This, in Polypterus, is called the auricle by van der Horst. From the auricle a band of granules continues medially in the cerebellar margin, corresponding to the superior fold of the auricle and the interauricular granular band of elasmobranchs, chondrosteans, and other Ichthyopsida. Ventromedially and caudally the auricle is continuous by a granular band with the nucleus dorsalis of the acousticolateral area (fig. 43). The cerebellar crest arches in front of the auricle to merge with the molecular layer of the cerebellum. As defined and described by van der Horst (1925) the auricle of Polypterus corresponds in morphological relations to the much larger auricle, *sensu strictiori*, of elasmobranchs and Neoceratodus and, as will appear, of chondrosteans. In Calamoichthys the auricle is reduced to a narrow band of granules, covered externally by molecular substance that represents the zone of merger of the cerebellar crest and the molecular layer of the cerebellum, as in Amia and most teleosts (pp. 87, 108).

The rounded rostrolateral division of the cerebellum, including the eminentia granularis rostrally and the auricle in its caudolateral margin, corresponds to the lateral

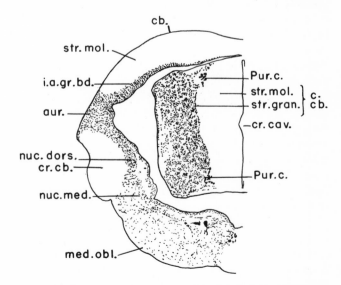

Figure 43. Polypterus bichir. Transverse section of cerebellum. (van der Horst, 1925.)

67

lobule of elasmobranchs as above defined, and also of chondrosteans (p. 73). The interconnection between the bilateral lobules (located by van der Horst between the bilateral parts of the "corpus cerebelli") he only mentions. Assuming that it includes decussating fibers as well as the interauricular granular band shown in figure 43, it appears to correspond to the pars medialis of the vestibulolateral lobe of elasmobranchs. Other considerations of a hypothetical nature discussed below add plausibility to this interpretation. The two lateral lobules and the pars medialis together correspond to the vestibulolateral lobe of elasmobranchs and to the entire externally visible cerebellum of petromyzonts.

THE CORPUS CEREBELLI

The corpus cerebelli, *sensu strictiori*, appears to be represented by part of the inverted median division of the cerebellum (figs. 42, 43). Its limits and the deep relations with the sensory column of the ventricular floor cannot be determined from van der Horst's descriptions. A comparison with the developing corpus cerebelli of elasmobranchs, however, can be made by considering the infolded part of the cerebellum of Polypterus as an inverted, instead of an exverted bursa, having a narrow opening to the exterior. If the everted bursa of the 120 mm Squalus embryo were inverted, its inferior posterior margin being displaced dorsalward as a result, the pattern would be quite similar to that of Polypterus except for the absence of a valvula in Squalus. The ependymal roof of the ventricular median anteroposterior sulcus of elasmobranchs would become the floor of the cleft between the massive bilateral halves of the cerebellum. This cleft, which is a narrow intrusion of the cranial cavity, extends rostrally between the two halves of the valvula of Polypterus, and caudodorsally between the posterior and dorsal bilateral halves of the remainder of the cerebellar mass (fig. 41). It appears to be bridged from one side to the other of the caudally turned margin to which the choroid tela attaches, but this is not clear from van der Horst's description or illustrations.

The paired inverted halves of the cerebellum of Polypterus correspond to the bilateral halves of the single median mass of chondrosteans which has resulted from bridging the infolded cleft of the cranial cavity seen in Polypterus. Only a layer of ependyma which crosses the midline of the ventral surface of the median mass in Acipenser appears to correspond to the ependymal floor of the cleft of Polypterus.

The granular mass facing the ventricle on either side in Polypterus, illustrated in figure 43, corresponds to similar granular masses in chondrosteans which represent the granular layer of the corpus cerebelli. The shallow groove in the medial wall of the molecular layer divides the ventral from the dorsal fold at the level illustrated. It is continuous rostrally with the broader cleft, in the horizontal plane, which separates the cerebellum from the optic tectum.

The valvula, as in chondrosteans, is continuous with the corpus cerebelli without identifiable boundary. Its gray layer emerges to the ventral anterior surface of the external fissure which separates the principal mass of the cerebellum from the optic tectum.

In the absence of embryonic material for checking the validity of the interpretations suggested, the cerebellum and its subdivisions of Polypterus appear to correspond to the general ichthyopsid pattern.

ACIPENSERIFORMES

THE cerebellum of Acipenser fulvescens and Polyodon spathula comprises a pair of lateral expansions and an unpaired medial division which dips into the fourth ventricle and extends forward into the ventricular cavity of the midbrain (figs. 44, 46). The paired expansions, called lateral lobes by Johnston (1901) and auricles by Palmgren (1921), van der Horst (1925), and Hocke Hoogenboom (1929), I shall call lateral lobules. The median mass comprises the "body of the cerebellum" (Johnston) or "corpus cerebelli" (Hocke Hoogenboom), posteriorly, and the valvula cerebelli anteriorly. These two subdivisions are delimited dorsally by the rhombomesencephalic fissure, but ventrally no boundary is apparent (fig. 46). The median cerebellar mass as a whole is similar to that of Polypterus except for the disappearance of the fissure with ependymal floor which separates the bilateral halves in Polypterus. The fusion of the molecular walls of the fissure, already mentioned, may be the result of thickening of these walls in Acipenser and Polyodon or, possibly, of thickening of a molecular layer above a fibrous layer corresponding to that which crosses beneath the external sagittal fissure of elasmobranchs. As such a layer increases in thickness, dorsalward, the fissure would disappear, as does the homologous external furrow in the larger species of elasmobranchs. The result of either process would be an unpaired median division with ependymal thickening along the midline of the ventral surface, as found in young Acipenser by Palmgren (1921) and also shown in adult specimens. As will appear from its fiber tract connections, this division of the cerebellum represents the corpus cerebelli, *sensu strictiori*. It extends caudalward and also has a dorsal tilt which is more prominent in Polyodon than in Acipenser.

The rostral part of the corpus is continuous on either side with the lateral lobule and anteriorly with the val-

vula (figs. 44, 45). Ventrally there is a ridge of white substance which is separated from the floor of the fourth ventricle by a narrow ventricular space (fig. 47). This ridge, the "keel" of Goronowitsch (1888), the "keel of the body of the cerebellum and valvula" of Johnston

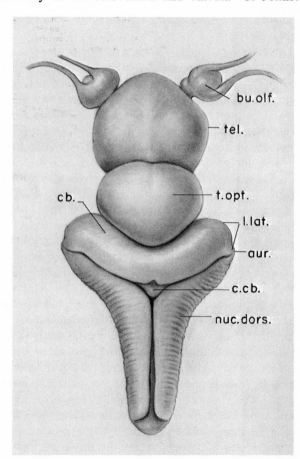

Figure 44. Dorsal view of brain of Polyodon folium lacep. (Hocke Hoogenboom, 1929.)

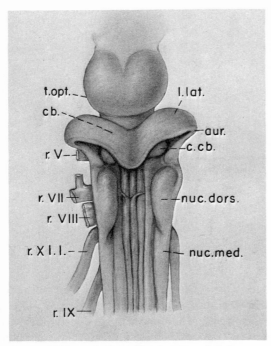

Figure 45. Dorsal view of brain stem of Acipenser.
(Johnston, 1901.)

(1901), and the "median molecular ridge" of Palmgren
(1921), continues into the valvula. The dorsal surface
of the corpus cerebelli of Acipenser forms the floor of a
caudally tapering triangular space between the dorsal
swellings of the lateral lobules. This space is filled with
connective tissue, but it disappears in large specimens of
Acipenser, as noted by van der Horst (1925). In Polyodon the dorsal surface of the corpus cerebelli lies at
about the same level, posteriorly, as the lateral lobules
or even a little higher, so that the posterior part of the entire cerebellum may have a flattened or slightly convex
surface. The lateral lobules of Polyodon, however, extend
forward on either side of the optic tectum (fig. 44). In
the less uptilted and smaller cerebellum of Acipenser the
lobules do not extend so far rostralward as in Polyodon.

A groove at the junction of the floor of the space with
the lateral lobule, on each side in Acipenser, extends rostrolaterally and continues beneath the expansion of the
lobule, delimiting this expansion from the medulla oblongata. These bilateral grooves correspond to the lateral
segments of the posterolateral fissure. Palmgren believed
them to be homologous with the para-auricular sulcus of
Voorhoeve in elasmobranchs which, as already noted, I
regard as the posterolateral fissure. In accord with Palmgren, I find no medial segment (sulcus postremus of
Voorhoeve and of Palmgren) of the posterolateral fissure in Acipenser.

The valvula arches dorsalward and posteriorly to become continuous with a short anterior medullary velum.
It forms the dorsorostral surface of the median segment
of the rhombomesencephalic fissure, of which the corpus
cerebelli forms the floor. The bottom of the fissure can be
considered the dorsal boundary between valvula and corpus cerebelli, but there is no recognizable boundary in
the ventricular surface of the median mass (figs. 46, 47).

The lateral lobule is formed around the recessus lateralis and an anterior diverticulum of this recess of the
fourth ventricle (fig. 45). Folds of choroid plexus cover
the recess laterally and, in part, dorsally in Acipenser.
The choroid tela is attached to the rhombic lip, the posterolateral and dorsal margins of the lateral lobule, and,
farther medially, to a projection above the posterior end
of the median part of the cerebellum (fig. 53).

A more detailed analysis of the subdivisions of the
cerebellum is dependent on an understanding of the relations between the lateral lobules and the central connections of the acousticolateral system of nerves and
sense organs. This system and the acousticolateral area
will first be described before we consider further the cerebellum itself and its finer structure.

THE LATERAL-LINE AND ACOUSTIC NERVES

The anterior lateral-line nerve of Polyodon has an ex-
traordinary development and distribution, associated with
an extensive occurrence of primitive sensory pores and
sacs which are believed to be related to the lateral-line
organs (Norris, 1925). An estimated total of 50,000 to
75,000 sacs were found by Nachtrieb (1910) on the bill,

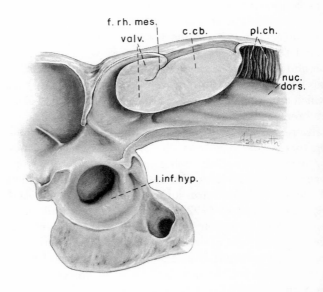

Figure 46. Midsagittal section of cerebellum and adjacent
parts of the brain of Acipenser. (Johnston, 1901.)

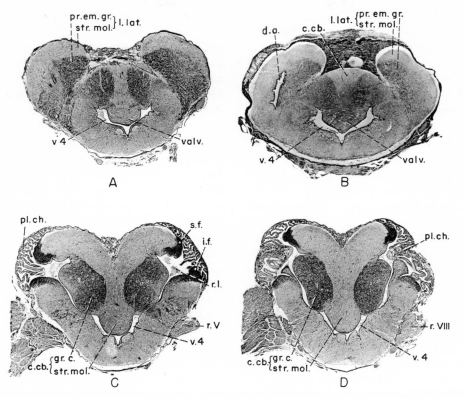

Figure 47. Transverse sections of the rhombencephalon of Acipenser. A. Section through rostral part of cerebellum. B. Section through anterior diverticulum of lateral recess (left side). C. Level of entrance of V root. D. Level of entrance of VIII root. (Johnston, 1901.)

head, and operculum of the paddlefish. The anterior lateral-line nerves and sensory organs of Acipenser are less extensively distributed but are well developed.

The anterior lateral-line nerve enters the medulla oblongata at approximately the level of the VII and VIII nerve roots, by a dorsal and a ventral root. The anterior part of the medulla oblongata of Acipenser and Polyodon is everted (fig. 45), as in some elasmobranchs, the nucleus dorsalis of the acousticolateral area lying dorsal of the crista cerebelli, and the nucleus medialis lies ventral (fig. 55). The dorsal root of the nerve enters the dorsal nucleus and the ventral root the medial nucleus, being separated by the crista as in Neoceratodus. The posterior lateral-line nerve enters the medulla oblongata by a root slightly dorsal and anterior of the sensory root of the IX nerve.

The acoustic or VIII nerve has anterior and posterior branches as in all fishes. These enter the medulla oblongata by a large bundle of root fibers in which anterior and posterior roots are not distinguishable (fig. 45), as Schepman (1918) noted in Acipenser and Hocke Hoogenboom (1929) in Polyodon. The anterior part of the root lies between the motor and sensory roots of the VII

nerve and the posterior part beneath the ventral root of the anterior lateral-line nerve.

THE ACOUSTICOLATERAL AREA

The acousticolateral area, as in elasmobranchs, comprises a large nucleus dorsalis, prominent nucleus medialis and crista cerebelli, and an area vestibularis or nucleus ventralis. The crista, as already noted, is situated between the dorsal and ventral nuclei instead of on their external surfaces and between them. Anteriorly the area is continuous with the lobulus lateralis (figs. 44, 45).

The nucleus dorsalis in Acipenser forms a rounded and elongated elevation in the upper lateral wall of the fourth ventricle, extending forward from the level of the root of the IX nerve to a blunt anterior end behind the lateral recess. A rounded ridge, continuous with the anterior part of the lateral surface of the nucleus but partly separated from the anterior end by a short deep furrow, extends forward to the lateral margin of the lobulus lateralis (fig. 45). This ridge represents a segment of the rhombic lip in which granule cells have accumulated in large numbers (fig. 47C). The nucleus dorsalis, as in elasmobranch embryos, no doubt is formed by a splitting of the columna dorsalis of Bergquist and Källén, and develops medial of the tenia of the rhombic lip. The ridge of granules is evidently derived from the tenial ependyma and intervenes between the rostral part of the nucleus and the tenial border. The posterior end of the ridge spreads over the laterodorsal surface of the anterior part of the nucleus as a broad, dense layer of granules. Similar cells beneath this layer are progressively more diffusely distributed in the interior of the anterior part of the nucleus. Throughout the remainder of the nucleus granule-like cells are rather evenly scattered among fibers and larger cells. The granular ridge is much shorter in Polyodon than in Acipenser. Hocke Hoogenboom (1929) considers it and its spread on the lateral surface of the nucleus dorsalis a part of the "auricle" (lateral lobe). In Acipenser the granular layer on the surface of the massive nucleus dorsalis appears to be part of this nucleus. The more elongated granular ridge, which is continuous with it beneath the fissure, is related to the nucleus dorsalis and also to the auricle, *sensu strictiori*.

In Polyodon the nucleus dorsalis is larger than in Acipenser and is also more elongated, concealing the floor of the ventricle (fig. 44). Anteriorly it turns lateralward, but the rostral part of the nucleus is hidden beneath the lobulus lateralis. Sections, however, clearly show that its relations to the recessus lateralis and, by the short ridge of granules, to the lateral margin of the lobulus lateralis, are very similar to those of Acipenser.

The dorsal nucleus is formed of large and small cells scattered among the fibers and their branches of the dorsal root of the anterior lateral-line nerve (fig. 52). The cap of granules, related to the granular ridge, which covers the lateral surface of the anterior part of the nucleus, should be considered as belonging to it. Primitive Purkinje cells of Johnston (1901), arranged along the cerebellar crest, send their dendrites into the crista (fig. 55). Most, if not all, of the dorsal root fibers bifurcate within the nucleus into ascending and descending branches. These remain within the nucleus, giving off collaterals that terminate among the cells. A fascicle of small fibers, however, ascends from the nucleus, beneath the lateral ridge of granules, to the inferior fold of the auricle proper. Whether this fascicle represents ascending branches of bifurcated root fibers, or is a distinct fascicle from the dorsal root, or, possibly, a continuation of a fascicle of ventral root fibers that enters the nucleus dorsalis but loses its identity among the other fibers, is not clear. Attempts to follow fibers of the ascending tract to possible cells of origin within the dorsal nucleus have been unsuccessful.

The nucleus medialis extends caudalward to the approximate level of the calamus scriptorius. Anteriorly it is continuous with the principal cell mass of the lateral lobule of the cerebellum (fig. 52). The nucleus includes primitive Purkinje cells, bordering on the cerebellar crest; irregularly scattered polymorphic cells, called transitional cells by Johnston; and granules. The last are especially numerous in front of the anterior lateral-line roots, where they occur as irregular masses. In addition, the nucleus includes the fascicles of lateral-line root fibers.

The fibers of the ventral root of the anterior lateral-line nerve enter the nucleus and bifurcate into ascending and descending branches. The ascending branches, as in elasmobranchs, form fascicles that distribute in the anterior part of the nucleus and continue into the lobulus lateralis. The descending branches distribute in the nucleus nearly to the level at which the posterior lateral-line roots enter the nucleus. From Golgi preparations Johnston (1901) described ventral anterior lateral-line root fibers to the nucleus dorsalis also. These, already mentioned, pass through the dorsal part of the nucleus medialis, arch around the medial surface of the cerebellar crest, and enter the ventrolateral angle of the nucleus dorsalis. In Polyodon, according to Hocke Hoogenboom (1929), some fascicles of the medial nucleus pass to the dorsal nucleus, and fibers also enter the cerebellar crest. I have observed ventral root fibers to the nucleus dorsalis in both species. The anterior part of the nucleus medialis is merged with the anterior region of the vestibular area, this region including ascending VIII root fibers in addition to the lateral-line fascicles.

Posterior lateral-line root fibers also enter the nucleus medialis. It is not clear if all bifurcate, and Hoogenboom is doubtful of the existence of descending fibers of this root in Polyodon. In reduced silver preparations I find descending fibers, and Johnston described them in Acipenser, as did Goronowitsch (1888). Most of the ascending posterior root fibers form a fascicle beneath the lateral surface of the medulla oblongata. Others form a small root fascicle which enters more ventrally and continues deeper into the nucleus medialis before its fibers bifurcate into ascending and descending branches. The latter distribute in the region of the nucleus situated between the posterior and ventral anterior roots, this region being a common terminus of fibers from both roots, as noted by Hoogenboom. The ascending posterior root fibers end, in part, in the nucleus medialis and, according to Hoogenboom, in the cerebellar crest; but most of them appear to reach the lobulus lateralis, as Johnston describes them. Lateral-line fibers, either anterior or posterior, to the cerebellar crest are not mentioned by Johnston and I have found none in Golgi material of Acipenser. Reduced silver material of Polyodon, however, shows fibers passing into the crista.

The crista cerebelli begins near the caudal end of the nucleus medialis. In transverse sections of Polyodon it forms a somewhat triangular area between the dorsal and ventral nuclei throughout much of its length, facing laterally. A layer of fibers is interposed between its medial surface and the ventricular cavity. Caudal of the shorter nucleus dorsalis of Acipenser the crista faces dorsolaterally.

The vestibular area or nucleus ventralis is merged with the nucleus medialis anteriorly, but is fairly distinct caudally. It includes relatively more numerous large cells than the other two nuclei. Hocke Hoogenboom describes very large cells near the ventricle at the level of the caudal part of the roots of the VIII nerve and posteriorly, which she regards as the precursor of Deiters's nucleus although the cells are more ventrally situated than in other fishes. Johnston describes a nucleus of elongated cells in Acipenser, which is reached by vestibular root fibers that also form a small fascicle in the medial part of the acousticolateral area. According to Hoogenboom part of the VIII nerve root fibers end in relation to the cells of Deiters's nucleus, but the greater number bifurcate into ascending and descending fascicles. The ascending fascicle is situated dorsolateral of the spinal tract of the V nerve, while the descending fascicle lies dorsal of this tract. The ascending fascicle, as seen in Golgi preparations of Acipenser and reduced silver series of Polyodon, ends chiefly in the principal nuclear mass of the lateral lobule (fig. 52), in accord with Johnston (1901). The descending fascicle, probably including fibers from the primitive nucleus of Deiters, was followed in part to the level of the calamus scriptorius by Hocke Hoogenboom. In silver preparations the fascicle appears to continue into the spinal cord, but the wealth of intermingled fibers makes this uncertain.

The axons of the larger cells of the nucleus dorsalis and nucleus medialis form arcuate fibers. Some from the nucleus dorsalis pass between the medial surface of the cerebellar crest and the ventricular surface, ascending in the ipsilateral fasciculus longitudinalis lateralis. Others continue medially beneath this fascicle, crossing the midline and ascending in the opposite lateral longitudinal fascicle. Still others do not enter this fascicle but appear to ascend or descend beneath it on either side. The nucleus medialis gives rise to ventral arcuate fibers at all levels; these accordingly are found farther caudalward than those from the nucleus dorsalis, as well as at rostral levels. Their distribution is similar to those from the dorsal nucleus.

The fasciculus longitudinalis lateralis, to which arcuate fibers from both nuclei contribute, terminates chiefly in the torus semicircularis of the midbrain. It is less certain that arcuate fibers from both the dorsal and the ventral nuclei enter the fasciculus longitudinalis medialis. Ascending fibers of this fascicle reach the midbrain and descending fibers reach the spinal cord.

The vestibular area gives rise to ventral internal arcuate fibers that enter the ipsilateral and contralateral medial longitudinal fasciculi. The large cells of the primitive nucleus of Deiters give rise to fibers that are intermingled with the descending fascicle of root fibers already mentioned so that they cannot be followed specifically. Presumably they enter the cord, ipsilaterally, as a vestibulospinal tract. Smaller cells of the vestibular area give rise to fibers that pass anteriorly, some probably reaching the principal cell mass of the lobulus lateralis, as in Amia (p. 89).

A pair of giant cells of Mauthner is situated at the caudal level of the roots of the VIII nerve in both species. Mauthner's cell was also described in Polyodon by Hocke Hoogenboom (1929). These cells are reticular elements whose axons become closely related with the contralateral medial longitudinal fascicle and continue into the cord. As in other Ichthyopsida the chief lateral dendrite has synaptic connections with root fibers of the VIII nerve.

THE VESTIBULOLATERAL LOBE

All afferent fibers to the lateral lobules are related to the acousticolateral system. The two lobules are interconnected by commissural fibers, described below, and an external molecular layer which is continuous, lateroventrally, with the cerebellar crest is common to both. In a complex pattern it also is continuous with the molecular layer of the corpus cerebelli. Together with their commissures the two lateral lobules form a unit which is comparable with the vestibulolateral lobe of elasmobranchs and with all of the externally visible cerebellum of petromyzonts. Differences of external form, relative size, and degree of development of the lobules and of compactness of the commissures obscure homologies, but an analysis of the lobule and its connections demonstrates that its subdivisions correspond to those of other Ichthyopsida.

The lobulus lateralis. The lateral lobule of Acipenseriformes represents a greatly expanded and dorsally turned modification of the acousticolateral area. It comprises a large cellular and fibrous mass which is continuous with the anteriorly merged nucleus medialis and vestibular area; a marginal band of granule cells, continuous with the granular ridge which begins on the lateral surface of the anterior part of the nucleus dorsalis; and an expanded molecular layer, already noted (fig. 54). The lobule forms massive walls around an anterior diverticulum of the recessus lateralis of the fourth ventricle (fig. 52). The medial and anterior walls are made up of a thick fibrous and cellular layer, which is continuous with the merged nucleus medialis and vestibular area (fig. 52); an external molecular layer covers part of the cellular layer. The dorsolateral wall, except anteriorly where the cellular layer extends into it, is formed of a thick molecular layer, an irregular zone of Purkinje cells, and a fibrous layer between this zone and the ependyma. This part of the lateral wall is less extensive, anteroposteriorly, in Polyodon than in Acipenser. Posteriorly the dorsolateral wall includes a thin layer of granules which follows the diverticular surface for a variable distance from the marginal granular band, with which it is continuous. A thin granular layer also extends from the marginal granular band for a variable distance on the external surface, beneath the pia mater. We shall return to the marginal band and these extensions. Part of the dorsal lateral wall presents the simple histological pattern seen in the cortex of the corpus cerebelli of elasmobranchs, in which only a layer of fibers, one of Purkinje cells, and a molecular layer are found external of the ependyma. In Acipenser and Polyodon, however, this pattern is limited to part of the lateral lobule (fig. 50).

The ventromedial wall is continuous with the median mass of the cerebellum and, caudally, with the cellular and fibrous mass beneath the floor of the recessus lateralis which faces the ventrolateral surface (ventral in Polyodon) of the lobule. Many of the ascending fascicles from the acousticolateral area form a fibrous layer immediately adjacent to the ependyma on either side and in front of the diverticulum; others continue into the principal cell mass of the lobule (fig. 50).

The principal mass of cells and fibers is homologous with the primitive eminentia granularis of elasmobranchs, and I shall call it by this name in Acipenser and Polyodon. The marginal granular band is homologous with the auricle, *sensu strictiori*, and its folds and granular ridges. The lateral lobule, accordingly, comprises two component cell masses, one related with the nucleus medialis and area vestibularis, and the other with the nucleus dorsalis. Part of the molecular layer separates them superficially, just as the cerebellar crest separates the nucleus medialis and the nucleus dorsalis.

The eminentia granularis. The merged nucleus medialis and anterior vestibular area increases in size rostralward, as in elasmobranchs, expanding still more in the lateral lobule as the primitive eminentia granularis (figs. 48–52). A zone of transition from one to the other, in which no boundaries are recognizable, shows the relations most clearly. As already noted, the number of granule cells increases anteriorly of the entrance of the ventral anterior lateral-line and the VIII roots. Farther rostrally a zone of granules appears at the ventrolateral

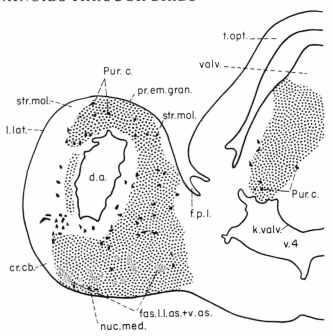

Figure 48. Transverse section of rhombencephalon of Polyodon. Neutral red stain. ×20.

surface (in Acipenser, ventral in Polyodon) of the medulla oblongata. This superficial zone is continuous with irregular groups of cells within the nucleus medialis by chains of similar cells, interspersed among the ascending fascicles, which are spread mediolaterally near the surface. Larger cells are also scattered among the fibers. The superficial zone of granules corresponds to a zone described by Hocke Hoogenboom (1929) as a nucleus of

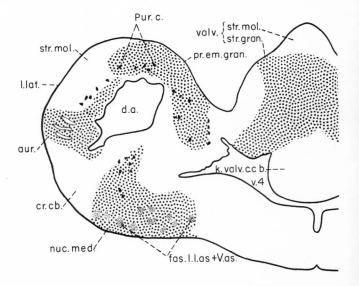

Figure 49. Transverse section of rhombencephalon of Polyodon. Neutral red stain. ×20.

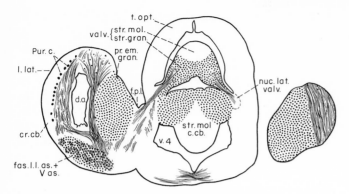

Figure 50. Transverse section of rhombencephalon of Polyodon. Silver stain. ×20.

migrated cells. Anterior of the entrance of the roots of the V nerve there is a greater increase of granules among the fascicles, resulting in a broad mass of cells and fibers. This then arches dorsomedially in the medial wall of the diverticulum and also continues into the anterior and, to some extent, the dorsolateral walls. In this expanded part of the cellular and fibrous mass the granules are rather evenly distributed among the fibers and larger cells. They are more numerous in Acipenser than in Polyodon. Irregularly arranged primitive Purkinje cells occur near the borders of the molecular layer (figs. 48, 49).

The proportionate number of granule cells increases toward the rostromedial part of the cell mass. In Acipenser the rostromedial portion, which reaches the external surface, is a large zone composed almost entirely of gran-

ule cells. This dense mass of granules resembles the eminentia granularis of Amia as identified by van der Horst (1925) and Pearson (1936a). The corresponding zone is smaller in Polyodon, and Hocke Hoogenboom (1929) regarded it as corresponding to only part of the eminentia granularis of Franz (1911a) in teleosts. The granular masses on the sides of the median cerebellar mass were believed by Hoogenboom to represent the homologues of the greater part of the granular eminences. These masses, however, face the fourth ventricle entirely and, as will appear, are part of the corpus cerebelli, *sensu strictiori.* They correspond to the granular layer of the corpus in the holosteans and teleosts (pp. 88, 113). Insofar as the eminentia granularis of these fishes faces the ventricular cavity it forms part of the wall of the recessus lateralis or its anterior diverticulum (figs. 50, 51).

The densely granular part of the eminentia granularis of Acipenser and Polyodon extends above the level of the median cerebellar mass and also rostrally beyond the zone of attachment of the lateral lobule to the median mass. It is separated from the median mass by the fascicles that ascend to, or descend from, the optic tectum. Behind these fascicles a thin zone free of cells, or with a few that are scattered between the denser cell masses, separates the eminentia from the granular mass of the corpus cerebelli (fig. 54). The posterior part of the primitive eminentia which forms the medial wall of the diver-

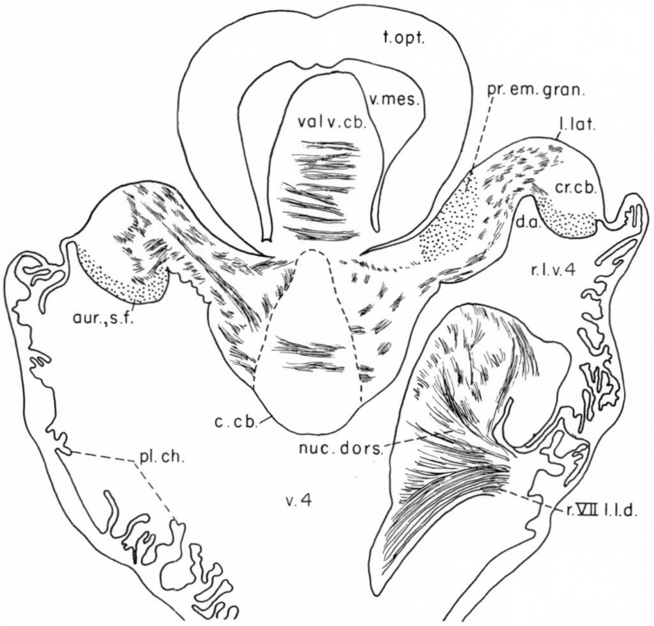

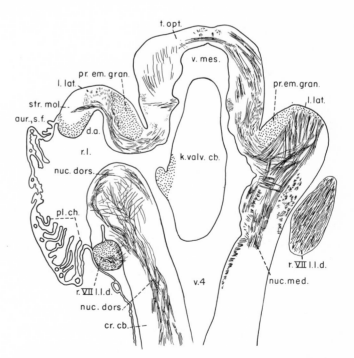

Figure 51. Horizontal section of brain stem of Polyodon. ×12.5.

Figure 52. Horizontal section of brain stem of Polyodon. Same series as fig. 51. ×12.5.

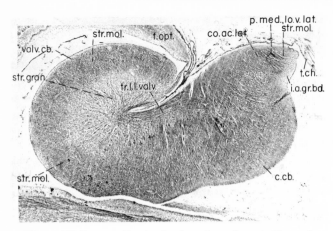

Figure 53. Paramedian sagittal section of cerebellum of Polyodon. Silver stain. ×18.

ticulum is connected by commissural fibers, already mentioned, with the contralateral cell mass.

The auricula cerebelli. The marginal band of granules begins at the lateral surface of the anterior part of the nucleus dorsalis. In Acipenser (fig. 47A, B) it continues forward as a ridge to the inferior part of the lateral lobule, following the margin of the lobule dorsolaterally and then caudomedially in the roof of the lateral recess. The most lateral part of the band, at which a sharp change of direction occurs, corresponds to the auricle of Holmgren and van der Horst (1925) in Neoceratodus, and to the auricle, *sensu strictiori*, of elasmobranchs. The caudomedial continuation corresponds to the "lateral string of granule cells" of Palmgren (1921), in young Acipenser, and to the dorsomedial fold of the auricle and interauricular granular band of elasmobranchs, as most clearly seen by comparison with Squalus embryos above described. On approaching the midline the granular band follows the margin of a caudal projection which is a continuation of the dorsolateral arms of the Y seen in more rostral transverse sections, and then dips beneath the border of this tongue onto the posterior surface of the ventral median cerebellar mass.

This medial part of the granular band corresponds to Palmgren's "string of granule cells" (1921), in young Acipenser, which turns posteriorly before fusing across the midline and then continues as paired "medial strings of granule cells" on the ventral surface of the keel. These are separated by paired ependymal thickenings. In the 43 cm, and larger, specimens of Acipenser that I have studied the pattern of the granular band varies in this median region. The smallest specimens show fusion of the granular strings across the midline, forming a fairly thick granular layer dorsally but only a thin layer on the posterior surface of the more ventral part of the median mass. This continues onto the ventral surface of the keel, where ependymal thickenings also occur. The significance of the thin granular layer on the keel and posterior surface of the corpus cerebelli is obscure. The thicker dorsal layer of granules which crosses the midline appears to correspond to the granular ridge of the pars medialis of the vestibulolateral lobe of elasmobranchs. Other features of the dorsocaudal part of the median cerebellar mass also correspond to the pars medialis of elasmobranchs, and Palmgren calls it the pars medialis of the auricular lobe in Acipenser. This lobe corresponds to the vestibulolateral lobe of elasmobranchs, and I shall use this term for it in Acipenser and Polyodon.

In the larger cerebellum of Polyodon (fig. 54) the initial segment of the granular ridge, extending from the nucleus dorsalis to the lateral lobule, is very short. Hocke Hoogenboom includes it, and also the granular layer medial of the furrow which separates the ridge from the anterior part of the nucleus medialis, with the "auricle," that is, the lateral lobule. The course of the marginal granular band corresponds, in general, to that of Acipenser and the band crosses the midline, as shown in figure 54. In some specimens it tapers toward the midline and descends onto the posterior surface of the median cere-

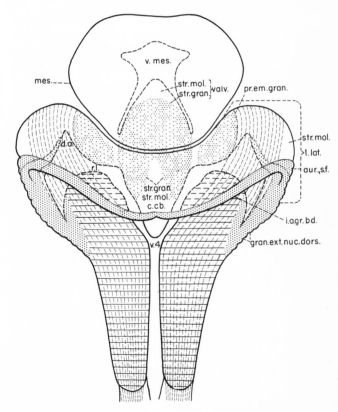

Figure 54. Polyodon. Diagram cerebellum.

bellar mass. A thin but widespread granular layer occurs on this surface. Its significance in Polyodon as well as in Acipenser requires further investigation of embryonic stages of the cerebellum.

A thin and somewhat tapering layer of granules, already mentioned, extends from the granular band between the ependymal layer and the zone of Purkinje cells in the dorsolateral wall of the diverticulum. It approaches the border of the eminentia granularis more closely in the larger specimens than in small ones. In an "older" specimen of Polyodon folium, illustrated by Hoogenboom, it appears to be continuous with the eminentia at some levels. Sections of Polyodon, stained with neutral red, show a zone of scattered cells between the more compact eminentia and the layer related to the marginal band. In Acipenser a similar but wider zone is found. A similar but thinner layer extends from the outer border of the marginal band beneath the external (pial) surface of the lobule. This also is more extensive in larger specimens. The significance of these granular extensions is obscure. Possibly the subpial extension represents an incipient external granular layer corresponding to the transitory stratum granularis externae of higher vertebrates. In chondrosteans, however, it is not transitory if one may judge by its presence in fully mature specimens.

THE CORPUS CEREBELLI

The corpus cerebelli, *sensu strictiori*, constitutes most of the median part of the cerebellum. It is continuous with the anterior part of the medulla oblongata on either side of the fourth ventricle, into which it is inverted to form an unpaired body (figs. 47, 50, 53). Behind this junction with the medulla oblongata the corpus is massively continuous, dorsolaterally on either side, with the lobulus lateralis (figs. 50, 51). Farther caudally the continuity with this lobule is with the thinner dorsolaterally arching part which consists largely of a molecular layer but whose caudal margin is the granular cell band above described. A ventricular furrow delimits the corpus cerebelli from this thinner part of the lateral lobule. This furrow continues around the upper posterior end of the median mass, delimiting the pars medialis of the vestibulo-lateral lobe from the more ventral rounded part, which is the posterior end of the corpus cerebelli.

The corpus cerebelli comprises a large granular mass, on either side, called the "Seitenwulst" by Goronowitsch (1888), and the "granular mass of the corpus cerebelli" by Palmgren (1921); and a median layer of fibers and cells that extends beneath the level of the granular masses. The ventrally extending part forms the "keel" of Goronowitsch and that of Johnston (1901) (fig. 52). The fibrous part of this median layer is continuous dorsolaterally with the fibromolecular layer of the lateral lobule, dividing into a Y in Acipenser or a T in Polyodon, as seen in the transverse sections. Fascicles of fibers pass through it transversely, interconnecting the bilateral granular masses. These fascicles are accompanied by masses of granules that are continuous with the large lateral masses and extend variable distances into the median layer, forming a continuous cellular bridge at some levels. In the transition zone to the valvula the cellular continuity between the bilateral granular masses is increased. Scattered large and small cells among the fibers of the "keel" form an irregular median zone of gray substance. The large elements are Purkinje cells with widespreading dendrites; the smaller are larger than granules and stain less deeply. Paired ependymal thickenings on each side of the midline of the ventral surface of the keel and a thin granular layer which is fused across the midline, already mentioned, are no doubt related to the corpus cerebelli proper. Their significance requires embryonic material for elucidation.

If the corpus cerebelli of Acipenser were everted as in elasmobranchs or, for better comparison, in Lepisosteus and Amia (p. 88), the median fibrous and molecular layer would be separated, along its presumptive zone of fusion across the midline, into bilateral halves. These would be displaced dorsolaterally in such a manner that the ependymal thickenings of the "keel" would become the ependymal roof of a median ventricular fissure, as in the species above named. The lateral granular masses would be shifted to face this fissure and would correspond to the paired granular layer of the corpus cerebelli of Amia and Lepisosteus. The fibromolecular median layer would cover the median ependymal bridge and would turn lateralward on either side as the superficial molecular layer of the corpus cerebelli. These theoretical considerations, based on patterns in adult specimens and Palmgren's (1921) descriptions and figures of young specimens of Acipenser and Lepisosteus, are only suggestive, and their validity must be checked on embryonic material. They are presented as a plausible explanation of the morphological peculiarities of the corpus cerebelli of Acipenser and Polyodon.

The valvula cerebelli. The valvula projects forward from the corpus cerebelli into the mesencephalic ventricle (fig. 53), turning dorsally and caudally to become continuous with the anterior medullary velum medially, and laterally with the base of the tectum and a zone beneath this base. In Polyodon the bilateral granular masses, which continue from the corpus cerebelli into the valvula, fuse across the midline so that the median fibrous layer disappears. It remains as the "keel" of the valvula and the continuation of the keel around the anterior end and onto the rostrodorsal surface of the valvula. In Acipenser there is a zone of fusion of the granular masses beneath the median molecular layer.

The cerebellar nuclei. A group of cells, many of which are multipolar, is situated in the ventricular wall of the zone of transition from medulla oblongata to corpus cerebelli, forming a projection into the lateral part of the ventricle. Since the position of this group corresponds to that of the nucleus cerebelli of elasmobranchs, it is probable that these cells represent the nucleus cerebelli in Acipenser. Hocke Hoogenboom (1929) describes a similarly situated cell group in Polyodon as the nucleus lateralis cerebelli, which I regard as entirely homologous with the nucleus cerebelli.

The nucleus lateralis valvulae of Herrick is represented by a group of rather scattered cells in the zone of junction of the valvula and the tectum (fig. 50). This nucleus was also described in Polyodon by Hoogenboom.

THE CEREBELLAR CONNECTIONS

The afferent tracts. Most of the ascending fibers from the acousticolateral area to the lateral lobule terminate in the eminentia granularis. Some continue to the valvula and a small fascicle follows the marginal granular band. Those ending in the eminentia comprise ventral anterior and posterior lateral-line and VIII root fibers, to which secondary vestibular fibers probably are added. The fascicles subdivide and become so intermingled that those from the individual sources are not identifiable within the cellular mass. According to Johnston (1901) Golgi preparations of Acipenser show the vestibular fibers ending among the cells. Intercellular terminal fibers are also shown in reduced silver preparations of Acipenser and Polyodon, but whether they represent vestibular or lateral-line fibers or both could not be determined.

The fibers to the valvula are assembled into a fairly compact fascicle in the ventromedial and rostral zone of transition from the eminentia to the granular layer of the valvula. The fascicle tapers medially and rostrally, its fibers then radiating in the valvula. Many of them cross to the opposite side as commissural bundles. The smaller fascicles that converge rostromedially to form the more compact valvular bundle probably include ventral anterior and posterior lateral-line root fibers, as in teleosts.

The fascicle which follows the marginal granular band is situated in the deeper part of the cerebellar crest and its continuation with the molecular layer of the lateral lobule. It is a small bundle of rather fine fibers, many of which appear to enter the granular band. The fascicle, however, is not impregnated in Golgi preparations. Caudoventrally it appears to be related to, or continuous with, the fascicle, above mentioned, which emerges from the anterolateral part of the nucleus dorsalis and follows the

granular ridge connecting the granular cap of this nucleus with the auricle proper. The fascicle is visible in modified Giemsa and reduced silver preparations but its relations to the nucleus dorsalis are uncertain.

Ventromedially arching fibers from the anterior part of the nucleus dorsalis, and also from the granular ridge lateral of it, form beneath the ventral surface of the medulla oblongata a superficial band-like layer which crosses the midline. Hocke Hoogenboom calls this fiber mass in Polyodon the interauricular commissure of Wallenberg. Aside from pointing out that it is not interauricular in any strict sense, I can add nothing regarding connections of its fibers.

The spino-cerebellar tract in Polyodon forms an ill-defined fascicle along the periphery of the medulla oblongata and parallel with the spino-tectal tract. It turns dorsomedially through the roots of the V nerve and enters the cerebellum, reaching the lateral part of the corpus cerebelli proper. Some of the fibers appear to cross, but the greater part of the fascicle ends ipsilaterally. A similar fascicle was described by Hocke Hoogenboom (1929) in Polyodon. Johnston (1901) did not recognize a spino-cerebellar tract in Acipenser, but I find a fascicle corresponding to that of Polyodon.

An ascending trigeminal tract was described by Johnston (1901) in Acipenser as running rostralward near the ventricular wall and entering the "nucleus of the median trigeminus" (Johnston, 1898) in the anterior part of the medulla oblongata. Most of the ascending V root fibers pass through the nucleus to the corpus cerebelli. I find a similar but smaller ascending V fascicle and a corresponding nucleus in Polyodon. The V root fibers that enter the corpus cerebelli appear to be augmented by fibers from the nucleus.

Bulbo-cerebellar fibers of undetermined origin accompany the spino-cerebellar tract. Johnston (1901) described an inferior olive in Acipenser and followed axons of its cells into the opposite side of the medulla oblongata. If these reach the cerebellum they do so through the bulbo-cerebellar complex. According to Kooy (1917) an olive is recognizable in Acipenser and Polyodon; I have found the small group of cells described by Johnston, but could follow the axons of the cells only a short distance in the opposite side of the medulla oblongata.

An anterior mesencephalo-cerebellar (tecto-cerebellar) tract was described by Johnston in Acipenser as consisting of two parts. Part I, formed of coarse fibers, is said to have its origin chiefly in the rostral part of the tectum and to pass around the lateral tectal border as a compact fascicle which distributes to the corpus cerebelli and valvula. Part II is described as a larger bundle of fine fibers, ventral of Part I, which assembles from the lateral part of the tectum and passes to the corpus cerebelli, the valvula, and the medial part of the lateral lobule. According to Hocke Hoogenboom (1929), Weigert-Pal preparations of Acipenser show only one fascicle in a position corresponding to Johnston's tract. In Polyodon Hoogenboom found a fascicle of thinly myelinated fibers from the lateral part of the tectum which corresponds to that she observed in Acipenser, but of much smaller size. My review of this fascicle in the two species does not enable me to reconcile the two descriptions except on the basis suggested by Hoogenboom, namely that one of Johnston's divisions represents spino-cerebellar fibers. Instead of originating in the tectum they are branches of ascending fibers that terminate among large, unimpregnated tectal cells. These branches thus correspond to collaterals of spino-tectal fibers in Ambystoma larvae that reach the cerebellum as described by Herrick (1914b).

The tegmento-cerebellar or posterior mesencephalo-cerebellar tract has its origin in the lateral nucleus of the valvula and from cells of the tegmentum of the midbrain, as described in Polyodon by Hoogenboom. The tract passes to the valvula where it decussates completely or nearly so. In Acipenser this tract, called bundle y by Johnston, has a similar origin and distribution.

A lobo-cerebellar tract is described in Polyodon by Hoogenboom as consisting of unmyelinated fibers that have their origin in the lateral region of the inferior lobes of the diencephalon. Its course is difficult to follow, but the tract appears to turn caudalward in the ventral thalamus or the base of the midbrain. In reduced silver series of Polyodon an ill-defined tract corresponding to the above description appears to reach the valvula and corpus cerebelli. According to Johnston direct and crossed lobo-cerebellar tracts, in Acipenser, in company with lobo-bulbar tracts, arise in the lateral part of the inferior lobe of the hypothalamus. The direct tract is unmyelinated and all its fine fibers may reach the bulb; the crossed tract, however, which is larger, consists of myelinated fibers of medium size that pass to the cerebellum. I have confirmed Johnston's description and find in addition that many of the fibers appear to end in the valvula.

The efferent fibers. The efferent fibers of the cerebellum of Polyodon are divided by Hocke Hoogenboom into anterior and posterior groups. Most of them are probably direct processes of Purkinje cells, although the axons of the latter are difficult to follow in Golgi material of Acipenser; but some fibers arise from the nucleus cerebelli. Purkinje cells in the ventral part of the lateral lobule give rise to axons that form arcuate fibers. Most of these pass ventrally and somewhat caudally along the ventricular wall. Many cross the midline and continue caudally in the medial longitudinal fascicle. A smaller number of the more rostral fibers pass, after decussating, with the medial longitudinal fascicle into the midbrain. Some of the fibers from the eminentia granularis appear to end in the nucleus cerebelli, which may also receive Purkinje cell axons from the corpus cerebelli. Others end in the medulla oblongata, forming a primitive but scattered cerebello-bulbar tract.

The nucleus cerebelli gives rise to a fascicle of fibers, augmented by direct processes of Purkinje cells in the lateral lobule and corpus cerebelli, which corresponds to the brachium conjunctivum. The fascicle passes ventrolaterally and then ventromedially, decussating beneath the fasciculus longitudinalis medialis, in the rostral part of the medulla oblongata and in the midbrain. The fibers continue beyond the decussation into the tegmentum of the midbrain and, apparently, into the diencephalon.

Fibers arising in the auricle and eminentia granularis arch ventrolaterally and rostrally beneath the surface of the medulla oblongata and decussate at a much more rostral level. Hoogenboom describes myelinated fibers from the medial part of the lateral lobule ("auricle" of this author), and unmyelinated fibers from the lateral part, apparently the auricle as above defined. The two contingents are said to form anterior and posterior parts, respectively, of a commissure regarded as corresponding to the interauricular commissure of Wallenberg in elasmobranchs and other vertebrates. In reduced silver preparations of Polyodon it is evident that these fibers decussate ventral of the decussation of the brachium conjunctivum, but I have been unable to follow the crossed fibers very far. It appears doubtful that fibers from the lateral lobule, after decussation, turn caudodorsally to end in the contralateral lobule.

THE HISTOLOGY

The cell types of the acousticolateral area and of the cerebellum in general are similar, but the larger elements in the cerebellum are more specialized. Johnston (1898, 1901) made a comprehensive study of the neurons in Golgi material of Acipenser, and Hocke Hoogenboom (1929) described them in cresyl violet preparations of Polyodon. I have reviewed Johnston's Golgi preparations rather intensively and have studied neutral red and reduced silver series of Polyodon, with results that confirm the descriptions of the authors cited but add nothing to their analysis of the neurons. The following descriptions are therefore based chiefly on Johnston's accounts.

The neurons of the acousticolateral area range from small granule cells to large elements comparable with the Purkinje cells of the cerebellum. These large neurons in the nucleus medialis have elongated cell bodies, situated beneath the crista cerebelli, and branching dendrites that spread in the crista. Some also send dendrites ventralward toward the vestibular area (fig. 55). They are primitive Purkinje cells. Other more deeply situated large neurons distribute their dendrites within the nucleus medialis and in the ventrally adjacent region, but none reach the cerebellar crest. These, together with neurons of many sizes and with every possible degree of variation, are included in a single general type called transitional cells by Johnston. A third principal type which is considered the typical or primitive cell of the nucleus comprises polymorphic neurons with two or more dendrites, their axons forming arcuate fibers that pass to the opposite side of

lecular layer. Some, however, as already noted, are found in the portion of the lateral wall of the anterior diverticulum which lacks a granular layer. All send richly branching and wide-spreading dendrites into the molecular layer only, and must be considered fully differentiated Purkinje cells (figs. 56–58). In reduced silver series of Polyodon the cell bodies appear as greatly elongated spindle-shaped structures that give rise to the dendrites at one end and the axon at the other. The main dendrites frequently are tortuous, richly branching trunks whose subdivisions form dense arbors in the molecular layer. Golgi material of Acipenser, possibly from smaller speci-

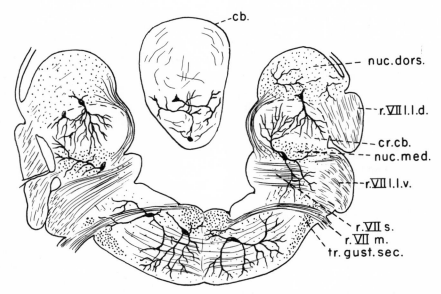

Figure 55. Transverse section of rhombencephalon of Acipenser at the level of VII and VIII roots. Golgi method. (Johnston, 1906.)

the medulla oblongata. Relatively small cells having fusiform bodies and single elongated dendrites that usually take a course parallel with the ventricular surface occur in the medial part of the nucleus. Some Golgi type II cells, whose dendrites branch profusely and whose axons are short, with many ramifications, are found chiefly in the anterior part of the nucleus. Granule cells also are most numerous anteriorly. The neuron types of the nucleus dorsalis are entirely similar to those of the medial nucleus (fig. 55).

The axons of most of the Purkinje type and transitional cells pass to the ventral part of the medulla oblongata as internal arcuate fibers. Some gather in the ipsilateral fasciculus longitudinalis lateralis and others cross the midline to enter the corresponding contralateral fascicle. Still others join the fasciculus longitudinalis medialis. In the lateral lobule of the cerebellum, Purkinje cells occur at or near the borders of the eminentia granularis and mo-

mens, showed less tortuosity of the dendrites. There appears to be no regularity of the dendritic spread with reference to the planes of the cerebellum, but individual Purkinje cells seem to spread their dendrites in one plane.

The axons of the Purkinje cells are difficult to follow. Johnston believed that they pass into the molecular layer. In Golgi series of Acipenser I was unable to trace them far enough to warrant any modification of Johnston's view, but in reduced silver sections of Polyodon my observations point to an irregular zone between the granular and molecular layers.

In addition to granule cells, the eminentia granularis includes two varieties of Golgi type II cells. One, having a club-like, thickened axon, occurs only near the zone of connection between eminentia and corpus cerebelli proper. The second variety is scattered more widely among the granule cells but occurs in largest numbers near the zone of connection. It is similar to Golgi type II

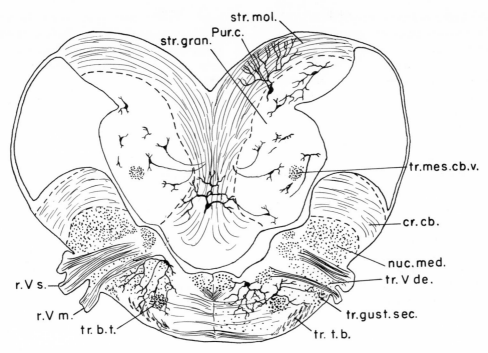

Figure 56. Transverse section of rhombencephalon of Acipenser at the level of the V root. Golgi method. (Johnston, 1906.)

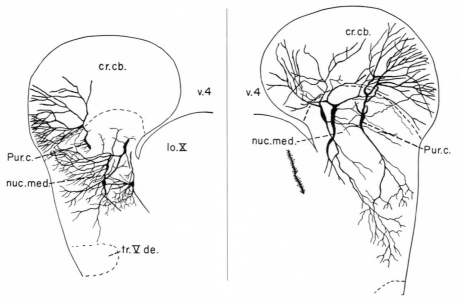

Figure 57. Transverse section of acousticolateral area of Acipenser to show cells of the medial nucleus and a Purkinje cell. Golgi method. (Johnston, 1906.) *Figure 58.* Transverse section of the acousticolateral area of Acipenser to show cell types intermediate between Purkinje cells and cells of the medial nucleus. Golgi method. (Johnston, 1906.)

cells, described below, in the corpus cerebelli. The marginal granular band and auricle proper appear to consist entirely of granule cells.

The molecular layer of the lateral lobule includes occasional small cells and a few that are somewhat larger. Some of the latter have pryamidal cell bodies and inwardly directed dendrites. Others are stellate cells whose dendrites and axons extend parallel with the surface.

The granular mass on each side of the corpus cerebelli consists of closely arranged granules and a smaller number of scattered larger neurons. The latter are most numerous in the vicinity of the tectocerebellar tract and in the ventral part of the corpus, near the nucleus of the ascending V tract.

The granules usually have two short dendrites that branch into a few terminal twigs having a slight resemblance to the claws of granule cell dendrites of higher vertebrates. The axon takes origin from one of the dendrites. In the caudal part of the corpus cerebelli the axons run dorsomedially into the posterior part of the molecular layer (fig. 56). Farther anteriorly they first pass ventromedially into the median molecular layer between the bilateral granular masses and then turn dorsolaterally into the molecular layer of the lateral lobule. Whether all remain ipsilateral or some cross is unknown. The fibers do not appear to bifurcate but frequently give off one or two collaterals within the granular mass, as noted also by Johnston.

The larger cells in the ventral part of the granular mass are irregular in form and have three or four long curved dendrites that branch profusely at their ends. The axon arises from one of the dendrites, at some distance from the cell body. Most of the axons remain in the granular layer, but some leave the cerebellum and appear to join arcuate fibers that issue from the primitive eminentia granularis. All these cells are so situated that their dendrites come into relation with the tecto-cerebellar tract and with the ascending fascicle of the V root and other tracts that enter the ventral part of the cerebellum.

Other neurons have ovoid to fusiform cell bodies and richly branched dendrites whose smaller rami show bead-like thickenings. The cells near the tecto-cerebellar tract have two dendrites, the larger one directed forward among the fibers of the tract, the smaller directed caudalward and ending abruptly, except for a few slender branches that continue from the blunt end. The axon arises at some distance from the cell body, but usually at the abrupt termination of the smaller dendrite.

The two sizes and varieties of Golgi type II cells vary most near the borders of the granular mass adjacent to the eminentia granularis and the tectum. The smaller ones have ovoid or stellate cell bodies situated in the molecular layer; their axons enter the granular layer and divide into several long branches. The second and larger variety, also ovoid or stellate in form, has several dendrites with concrescences; the axon is of medium size and presents enlargements at which it branches into smaller collaterals that have bead-like enlargements and often divide into rich terminal tufts or may present a vague basket-like appearance.

The Purkinje cells of the corpus cerebelli are situated in the cellular and fibrous layer which separates the granular masses. They vary in form, many being so elongated that the cell body is only an enlargement of a spindle which continues as the dendrites; the cell body of others is sharply defined. The principal dendrites are large and spread widely; their branches have characteristic spines. A few small dendrites arise from the sides of the cell body. The end of the neuron opposite the origin of the large dendrites gives rise to the axon. This often takes a course in the molecular layer which is parallel to that of the granule cell axons, but the Purkinje cell axons are soon lost.

The smaller cells, already mentioned in the median layer, that differ in size and appearance from granule cells, were not impregnated in Golgi preparations.

The granules of the valvula are similar to those of the corpus cerebelli. Their axons pass ventromedially or rostromedially toward the molecular keel and the median fibrous and molecular layer of the valvula which are continuous, respectively, with the keel and median layer of the corpus cerebelli, the dorsal part of the median layer also continuing caudolaterally with the molecular layer of the lateral lobule.

The Purkinje cells of the valvula are variable in form, many resembling the primitive Purkinje cells of the acousticolateral area. In the median part they correspond more closely to those of the corpus cerebelli. They tend to occur in groups, but rows are also found and scattered Purkinje cells are seen in the molecular layer. In the rostral and dorsal parts of the valvula appear numerous cells with long dendrites like those of Purkinje cells and also with dendrites that lack spines but have varicosities and bead-like swellings. Near the anterior medullary velum all the dendrites of the larger cells are of this type. The cells with varicosed dendrites are situated near the fibers from other parts of the brain.

Golgi type II cells of the two varieties described in the corpus cerebelli also occur in the valvula. The smaller ones lie in the molecular layer, while the larger neurons with club-like processes are most numerous near the border of the valvula and the lateral nucleus of the valvula and in the region where fibers enter the valvula from the eminentia granularis.

HOLOSTEI

THE cerebellum of the holostean fishes Amia calva and Lepisosteus osseus is everted and differs greatly in appearance from the inverted organ of chondrosteans. The corpus cerebelli is elevated (fig. 59) and the valvula projects less strongly into the mesencephalic ventricle (fig. 60). A lateral expansion on either side of the corpus cerebelli corresponds, in modified form, to the lateral lobule of Acipenseriformes. It includes an eminentia granularis and an auricle, *sensu strictiori*. A transverse plate between the bilateral auricles, representing the posterior margin of the embryonic cerebellum but modified in relative position and enlarged, corresponds to the pars medialis of the vestibulolateral lobe of elasmobranchs and other Ichthyopsida. In holosteans the anteroventral portion of this plate extends forward into the ventricular

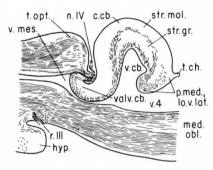

Figure 60. Sagittal section of brain stem of Amia calva. Pyridine-silver method. ×10. (Modified from Pearson, 1936b.)

cavity, partly dividing it into a dorsal space, the cerebellar ventricle, and a ventral subcerebellar part of the fourth ventricle (fig. 61C). The lateral lobules, pars medialis, and the commissural connections associated with them constitute a vestibulolateral lobe which differs in many respects from this lobe in elasmobranchs but, as will appear, has the same fundamental pattern.

The acousticolateral area differs considerably from that of Neoceratodus, elasmobranchs, and Acipenseriformes. Its subdivisions are modified so that their relations are more similar to those of teleosts.

THE LATERAL-LINE ORGANS AND NERVES

The distribution and arrangement of the lateral-line organs were described by Allis (1889, 1904) in Amia, and by Norris (1925) in Amia and Lepisosteus. Canal organs and pit organs occur in both species. According to Allis the lateral-line system of Amia is completely and typically teleostean (see p. 95). Norris says that this is true also of Lepisosteus, differences from teleosts in both species being minor.

The anterior lateral-line nerve in both species has but one root, this corresponding to the ventral lateral-line

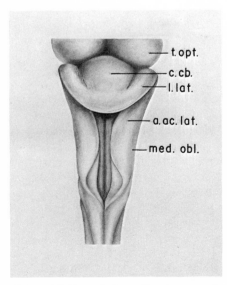

Figure 59. Dorsal view of brain stem of Amia. (Kingsbury, 1897.)

root of elasmobranchs (Norris, 1925). A single root is described in Amia by van der Horst (1925) and Pearson (1936a). According to van der Horst it includes both large fibers, characteristic of the dorsal root in petromyzonts and elasmobranchs, and smaller fibers such as characterize the ventral root in these two groups of Ichthyopsida.

Posterior lateral-line fibers are described in both the IX and X nerves of Amia by Kingsbury (1897), and confirmed in Amia and Lepisosteus by Norris (1925). Each nerve has a supratemporal branch and a branch of the IX nerve extends to the gular pit organs. The principal nerve is the lateral-line trunk of the X nerve to the body. Immediately behind the lateral-line X ganglion, this trunk gives off a dorsal branch to the pit organs in the dorsal part of the body. The main nerve trunk supplies the lateral-line canal.

THE ACOUSTICOLATERAL AREA

The acousticolateral area of Amia (fig. 61), as described by van der Horst (1925) and Pearson (1936a), comprises a dorsal cap of cerebellar crest; a nuclear mass, immediately beneath the crista, called the ventral lateral-line lobe by van der Horst and the nucleus medialis by Pearson; and a nucleus ventralis, recognized by Kingsbury (1897) and others. The nucleus dorsalis is entirely lacking, according to van der Horst (1925)

and Pearson (1936a). This is true so far as the presence of a nuclear mass dorsal of the crista cerebelli is concerned in adult Amia. Certain features of the development of the anterior region of the acousticolateral area suggest, however, that the nucleus medialis of Pearson may include the homologue of the nucleus dorsalis.

The anterior part of the acousticolateral area is everted, in early growth stages of Amia, and the developing cerebellar crest faces the external surface of the area. Transverse sections of a 25 mm total length specimen show a layer of cells covering the crista dorsally and dorsomedially, as does the nucleus dorsalis of Acipenser. A cell column beneath the crista corresponds to the nucleus medialis of Acipenseriformes. The cap of cells in Amia is short and is continuous, rostrally, with the auricle described below. If this cap be regarded as a greatly reduced nucleus dorsalis and the granular ridge leading to the auricle, the pattern is presented, more simply and on a greatly reduced scale, of the nucleus dorsalis and its relations to the cerebellar crest and also to the auricle in Acipenser.

Lacking subsequent growth stages of Amia I have been unable to follow the steps in the transformation of the acousticolateral area into its adult form. It appears probable, however, that the area is gradually folded medialward and also compressed dorsoventrally, the process of inversion carrying the cell cap ventromedial-

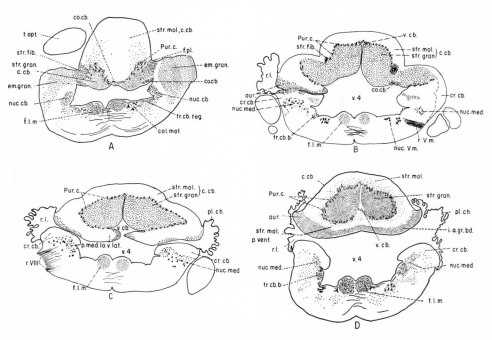

Figure 61. Transverse sections of rhombencephalon of Amia calva. ×12.5. A. Section through cephalic portion of cerebellum. B. Level of V motor nucleus and root. C. Level of lateral recess of fourth ventricle. D. Section through caudal portion of cerebellum. (Redrawn from Pearson, 1936b.)

ly. As the crista expands it covers the cell mass which the inversion has brought to a medial, instead of a dorsomedial and dorsal, position.

Pearson (1936a) distinguishes between a pars dorsalis and a pars ventralis of the nucleus medialis in adult Amia. The pars dorsalis, consisting of small cells, can be differentiated from the pars ventralis, which has larger, irregular cells for a short distance only. Followed caudalward, it soon becomes scattered, whereas the pars ventralis is continuous with the remainder of the nucleus medialis. The evidence is incomplete, but so far as presently available it suggests that part of the nucleus medialis, perhaps Pearson's pars dorsalis, possibly corresponds to the nucleus dorsalis of Acipenseriformes and some other fishes.

The nucleus medialis is continuous rostrally with the eminentia granularis and, caudally, to a level slightly anterior of the calamus scriptorius. No definite boundary delimits it, however, from the posterior funicular nuclei of the spinal cord.

The crista cerebelli forms a dorsal and dorsomedial molecular layer above the entire length of the medial nucleus and is continuous with the pars medialis and the molecular layer of the eminentia granularis. Most of its surface is ventricular, only a part of the lateral surface facing externally in the adult (fig. 61).

The nucleus ventralis or area vestibularis is closely related to the nucleus medialis, no boundary between the two being apparent. A group of scattered large multipolar cells is situated medially in the path of the entering VIII root. These cells probably correspond to Deiters's nucleus in higher vertebrates.

Contributions to an understanding of the distribution of the lateral-line and VIII root fibers in Amia were made by Kingsbury (1897) and by Ariens Kappers (1907) in Amia and Lepisosteus. Pearson (1936a) has added to our knowledge from study of pyridine-silver preparations of Amia, and I have reviewed the tracts in modified protargol preparations of Amia and Lepisosteus.

The root of the anterior lateral-line nerve divides into ascending and descending fascicles, the fibers of which probably represent bifurcated branches of the root fibers. The ascending fibers distribute in the nucleus medialis and eminentia granularis, many also entering the pars medialis of the vestibulolateral lobe. The descending fibers distribute in the nucleus medialis. The posterior lateral-line root fibers probably bifurcate in part. Many form a large ascending fascicle which reaches the eminentia granularis and the pars medialis. Other ascending fibers distribute in the nucleus medialis, as in elasmobranchs and Acipenseriformes. Descending fibers distribute in the posterior part of this nucleus.

Some of the fibers of the VIII root are believed to bifurcate, but many pass directly medialward to the nucleus of Deiters in Amia. Other fibers, many gathered into small fascicles, take a rostral or a caudal course. The anteriorly directed fibers distribute, in part, in a zone of fusion of small elements, related to the area vestibularis, with the nucleus medialis. Other fascicles continue forward into the eminentia granularis. In a protargol stained sagittal series of Lepisosteus a large fascicle continues rostrodorsally from the ventral root of the VIII nerve to the eminentia granularis, in which it spreads. Before reaching the eminentia this fascicle gives off a number of smaller fascicles that enter the pars medialis. Other VIII root fibers in Lepisosteus terminate in the vestibular area both anterior and posterior to the entering roots. A prominent descending fascicle from the ventral root appears to reach the spinal cord, but whether ipsilaterally entirely, or in part contralaterally, is not clear. It is intermingled with more scattered descending fibers from Deiters's nucleus, which constitute a direct vestibulospinal tract, to such an extent that the two tracts could not be differentiated from each other in the caudal part of the medulla oblongata.

The efferent fibers of the acousticolateral area. Efferent fibers from the nucleus medialis of the acousticolateral area cross the midline ventral of the fasciculus longitudinalis medialis and accumulate as the fasciculus longitudinalis lateralis of Ariens Kappers (1907, 1921). This is the lemniscus lateralis of Ariens Kappers (1947) and the acousticolateral lemniscus of Herrick (1914b) and others. According to Pearson (1936a), the fibers in Amia collect in close relation to the general bulbar lemniscus, but the tract is distinct for part of its course. It passes lateral of the nucleus lateralis valvulae, into which it appears to send fibers, and ends in the torus semicircularis of the midbrain.

In addition to the relay pathway represented by the acousticolateral lemniscus, the nuclei of the acousticolateral area give rise to a scattered system of efferent fibers designated the acousticolatero-motorius system by Pearson (1936a). These fibers pass along the ventrolateral wall of the fourth ventricle toward the fasciculus longitudinalis medialis, entering it and also the region of the motor cell column. Some of the fibers cross the midline to corresponding parts of the opposite side.

The Development of the Cerebellum

The cerebellum of young specimens of Amia, 12–18 mm in length, is represented by a transverse arch which is cellular on either side of a median sagittal zone of ependyma. Commissural fibers, spinal and probably trigeminal, anteriorly, and acousticolateral, posteriorly, cross the midline above the ependyma. The bilateral cell masses spread rapidly and the cerebellar plate elongates anteroposteriorly. The decussating fibers become segregated into anterior and posterior commissures that are increasingly separated as the plate elongates, and, on each side of the midline, also thickens. Presently the plate begins to arch dorsalward, but the median part of its posterior margin, through which decussating VIII root and other fibers pass, remains as a transverse arch which forms the most dorsal part of the cerebellum at the 25 mm stage of growth. Ventrolaterally the posterior cerebellar margin is continuous with the rhombic lip of the medulla oblongata.

The lateral walls of the cerebellar part of the fourth ventricle at the 25 mm stage have become a thick mass of cells covered superficially by a molecular layer. A narrow oblique zone of loosely arranged cells divides each half of the lateral wall into a large dorsolateral and dorsal division and a smaller ventral and ventromedial division. The narrow boundary zone is indicated by a furrow in the lateral wall of the fourth ventricle and one in the medial wall of the recessus lateralis and its anterior diverticulum.

The dorsolateral cell mass is continuous ventrolaterally with the nucleus medialis of the acousticolateral area; dorsomedially it reaches the sagittal ependymal zone but does not fuse with the contralateral cell mass. The dorsolateral cell mass represents the rudiment of the eminentia granularis. In silver series of adult Amia the bilateral eminentiae are interconnected by commissural fibers that pass through the pars medialis of the vestibulolateral lobe. In the 25 mm Amia the pars medialis is represented by the dorsally arched median part of the posterior cerebellar margin which, in subsequent development of the cerebellum, assumes a ventral position, as described below. A smaller mass of closely packed cells, already mentioned as the auricle proper, is found immediately behind the region of transition of eminentia granularis to nucleus medialis. The auricle is continuous with a small band of similar cells which follows the posterior tenial margin. The eminentiae granulares, pars medialis, and auricles together correspond to the vestibulolateral lobe of Acipenser and Polyodon.

The ventromedial division of the cerebellum of early growth stages of Amia forms the ventral part of the lateral wall of the fourth ventricle and the ventral medial wall of the lateral recess and anterior diverticulum. Ventrocaudally it is continuous with the general somatic area of the medulla oblongata. It extends rostrodorsally and medially beneath the eminentia granularis, reaching the

ependymal zone in front of the pars medialis, but the bilateral masses do not fuse across the midline. This division is the rudiment of the corpus cerebelli. In further growth it expands into a dome-like projection between the bilateral granular eminences and in front of the pars medialis. As the dorsal projection of the corpus increases the posterior cerebellar margin, represented by the pars medialis, is gradually displaced ventralward from its earlier dorsocaudal position. Eventually it becomes a transverse plate, projecting ventrorostrally into the ventricular space and dividing it into a cerebellar part of the fourth ventricle. In contrast with the inverted corpus cerebelli of chondrosteans, the corpus of Amia is everted.

The Adult Cerebellum

The fully developed cerebellum of Amia presents a pair of lateral projections and a median dome-like elevation which is delimited by a furrow, on either side, from the projections (fig. 59). The lateral projections are continuous, around the rostrolateral angle of the recessus lateralis, with the acousticolateral area. They include the eminentia granularis and the auricle and correspond, on a smaller scale, to the lateral lobules of Acipenseriformes. The posteroventral marginal part of the cerebellum of Amia constitutes a thickened pars medialis which arches above the fourth ventricle as a transverse plate (fig. 61C). The pars medialis is also continuous with the acousticolateral area. Commissural and other connections tie the lateral lobules and pars medialis together as a unit corre-

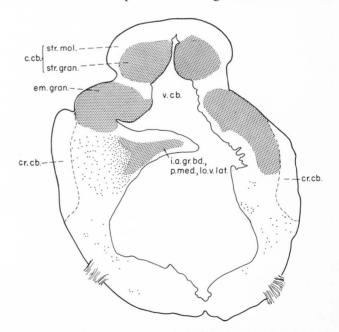

Figure 62. Transverse section of rhombencephalon of Lepisosteus at cerebellar level.

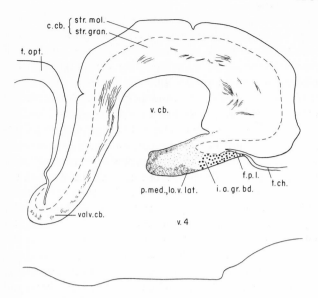

Figure 63. Sagittal section of cerebellum
of Lepisosteus.

sponding to the vestibulolateral lobe of other Ichthyopsida.

The median dome, which is tilted slightly forward in Amia, is the corpus cerebelli. The dorsal arching of the corpus has resulted in a ventricular space between the anterior and posterior folds, as seen in sagittal section, and between the lateral walls of the dome, constituting a cerebellar ventricle. The corpus cerebelli of Lepisosteus projects farther above the remainder of the cerebellum than in Amia (fig. 62). It also is tilted caudalward, instead of rostrally, to such an extent that the transverse plate of the pars medialis lies beneath it (fig. 63). The cerebellar ventricle has a rounded outline in sagittal section and is considerably larger than in Amia. The pattern of the two cerebella, however, is very similar.

THE VESTIBULOLATERAL LOBE

The lateral lobules and pars medialis of holosteans are closely related with the acousticolateral area on either side. The continuation of the nucleus medialis with the eminentia granularis in Lepisosteus swings upward in a wide arc. In the more compact cerebellum of Amia it passes more directly dorsalward to the eminentia. The auricle is closely related to the pars medialis, but is situated in the lateral part of the lateral lobule, as in Acipenseriformes. Commissural connections, described below, tie the bilateral lobules and the pars medialis together into a unit which corresponds to the vestibulolateral lobe of elasmobranchs and Acipenseriformes.

The eminentia granularis. The granular eminence (fig. 61A) spreads caudalward and rostralward. Poste-

riorly the bilateral masses approach each other but do not merge across the ventricular cleft. The two masses are interconnected, however, by commissural fibers that pass through the pars medialis. The posterior part of the eminentia is so intimately fused with the granular layer of the corpus cerebelli that no boundary between the two is visible. Rostralward the eminentia diverges laterally and, in Lepisosteus, a distinct zone devoid of granules and containing but few other cells separates the two granular masses. In Amia only the rostral part of the eminentia is distinctly separated from the granular layer of the corpus cerebelli, a layer of fibers interconnecting the midbrain with the medulla oblongata and cord passing between the granular eminence and the corpus cerebelli (fig. 61A).

The granular eminence reaches the cerebellar surface throughout much of its length in Lepisosteus, only the posterior part being covered by a molecular layer. In Amia only the anterior part of the granular mass is exposed superficially. In Lepisosteus it bows outward around a shallow lateral extension of the ventricle, forming the greater part of a laterally rounded structure which corresponds to but is smaller than the lateral lobule of Acipenseriformes. The eminentia of Amia is a more compact granular mass which has a small, tapering ventricular space caudally; rostrally it surrounds a small but rounded extension of the ventricular cavity.

The auricula cerebelli. The auricle is represented in adult Amia and in Lepisosteus by a granular mass at the lateral angle of the recessus lateralis and immediately behind the dorsal deflection of the cerebellar crest into the molecular layer of the cerebellum (fig. 61B). This cell mass extends to the lower lateral surface of the lobulus lateralis, where it faces an external space which is covered by a fold of choroid plexus. The granular mass continues ventralward in front of the recessus lateralis, which has become reduced to a nearly horizontal cleft in adult Amia (fig. 61C). In some brains it continues beneath this cleft, forming a thin layer of granules on the dorsal surface of the cerebellar crest which appears to correspond to the layer already noted in the 25 mm stage of young Amia. Also there are suggestions of continuity between the dorsal layer, around the medial border of the crista, with the "nucleus medialis pars dorsalis" of Pearson (1936a), already mentioned as possibly corresponding to the nucleus dorsalis of elasmobranchs and Acipenseriformes, but the evidence is too tenuous and incomplete to warrant conclusions.

In some fully developed cerebella a band of granules, which correspond to the superior fold of the auricle and the interauricular cellular band of young Amia, follows the dorsal margin of the pars medialis (fig. 61C). Granules are also scattered in the pars medialis, except in the strictly molecular layer. Other cerebella, possibly from older specimens, show no well-defined granular band, but granules are diffused throughout the pars medialis and among its fascicles. Frequently the cells have a linear arrangement among the fascicles. The appearance of the pars medialis in such instances suggests migration of cells from the more compact cellular bands.

The auricle of Lepisosteus is represented by a relatively large mass of granules in the roof of the anterior extremity of the recessus lateralis. No cells were found, however, in the immediate floor of the recess, i.e., covering the cerebellar crest. A sheet-like layer of granules arches dorsomedially from the auricle into the pars medialis, there forming a thin granular layer which faces the ventricular surface and is continuous across the midline with the corresponding contralateral layer. No distinct interauricular granular band is seen in Lepisosteus, the cells of the entire granular layer being closely arranged except anteroventrally.

The pars medialis. The pars medialis of Amia (fig. 61C) comprises the interauricular granular band, more diffuse granules, above described, and a fibrous and molecular layer. In Lepisosteus the fibromolecular layer is more sharply delimited from the compact granular layer (fig. 62), but small fascicles of fibers pass from the fibrous layer into the granular mass. The more strictly fibrous part of the fibromolecular layer occupies, chiefly, the anteroventral zone of the pars medialis. It includes ascending lateral-line and VIII root fibers, these decussating in large part and corresponding to the acousticolateral commissure of other Ichthyopsida. The molecular part of the pars medialis is continuous with the cerebellar crest.

THE CORPUS CEREBELLI

Defined as the division of the cerebellum whose afferent connections are unrelated to the acousticolateral systems, primarily, the corpus cerebelli of holosteans is represented by the median dorsally everted arch already mentioned. It comprises a granular layer on each side of the sagittal cleft of the cerebellar ventricle, and a molecular layer which is continuous across the midline (figs. 61, 62).

If the corpus cerebelli of Amia and Lepisosteus were inverted downward into the fourth ventricle, the pattern represented in chondrosteans would result. The ependymal and molecular roof of the cerebellar ventricle would become the floor of an external sagittal fissure corresponding to that of Polypterus. If the molecular walls of this fissure were to merge, an unpaired median fibromolecular layer, corresponding to that of Acipenser and Polyodon, would be formed. The granular masses that form the walls of the ventricular sagittal fissure of holosteans would be displaced to the lateral positions occupied by the granular masses of the corpus cerebelli of chondrosteans. Without carrying the comparison further it need only be mentioned that the relations of the eminentiae granulares would undergo but little change except in position with reference to the corpus cerebelli.

The valvula cerebelli. The valvula of Amia projects ventralward into the fourth ventricle and continues forward into the mesencephalic ventricle, turning dorsalward and then posteriorly to become continuous with the anterior medullary velum (fig. 60). It comprises a dorsal and median molecular layer and paired granular layers which are connected by commissures. The molecular layer is continuous with the molecular layer of the corpus cerebelli, and the granular layer with the corresponding layer of the corpus and also, laterally, with the eminentia granularis. There is no boundary between the valvula and the corpus cerebelli but the granular projection, on either side of the midline, into the fourth ventricle appears to represent the posterior part of the valvula. These granular masses are continuous rostrally with the bilateral granular layer of the anterior part, and fascicles of fibers enter them from the eminentiae granulares, some forming commissural bundles beneath the molecular layer. Other bundles between the bilateral masses probably consist of fibers arising in the valvula.

The strongly dorsally arched cerebellum of Lepisosteus has only a small anterior projection into the mesencephalic ventricle (fig. 63). Differences between the dome of the cerebellum and the ventral part of the anterior arch indicate that the latter represents most of the valvula. The molecular layer of this part forms a median zone which is continuous dorsally with the wider molecularis of the corpus cerebelli; ventrally it turns forward into the anterior projection. An external sagittal furrow partly divides it into bilateral halves, but there is continuity from one to the other in the floor of this furrow. The upper part of the median molecular zone is flanked on both sides by fascicles of fibers that represent the connections between the midbrain and medulla oblongata and cord. The granular layer is represented by bilateral strips beneath the molecularis. These are continuous with the granular layer of the corpus cerebelli, dorsally, and, ventral of the fiber tracts above mentioned, with the eminentiae granulares, laterally. Ventrally they project into the ventricle and turn forward into the anteriorly projecting part of the valvula. The granular masses of the valvula are bilateral throughout their length. They face in succession the fourth ventricle, the short aqueduct, and the mesencephalic ventricle (fig. 63).

The nucleus cerebelli. A mass of gray substance in the

lateral wall of the ventricle and beneath the rostral part of the cerebellum of Amia (fig. 61A) represents the nucleus cerebelli, according to Pearson (1936a). It is separated from the granular eminence by fascicles of fibers. At the level of transition from corpus cerebelli to valvula the nucleus lies dorsal of the ventricle. The cells are multipolar and also differ in other respects from those of the granular layer. Pearson regards this cell mass as corresponding to the nucleus lateralis cerebelli of Polyodon, as described by Hocke Hoogenboom (1929) and to the nucleus cerebelli of Ceratodus (Holmgren and van der Horst, 1925). Near the ventral border of the nucleus cerebelli a cell mass which is homologous with the secondary gustatory nucleus of Herrick extends toward the lateral nucleus of the valvula.

The nucleus lateralis valvulae. The nucleus lateralis valvulae is an aggregation of small neurons situated lateral of the gray layer of the valvula and ventral of the torus semicircularis of the midbrain. In Amia it extends from the level of the nucleus of the III nerve to a level slightly rostral of the anterior end of the corpus cerebelli. Fascicles of fibers separate the nucleus from the valvula and it is also bordered laterally by fibers.

THE CEREBELLAR CONNECTIONS

The afferent tracts. Contributions to an understanding of cerebellar connections in Amia and Lepisosteus were made by Ariens Kappers (1907). Pearson (1936a) described the fiber tracts more fully in pyridine-silver preparations of Amia, and I have reviewed these connections in brains of both species stained by a modified protargol technique, and in Golgi material of young Amia 18 mm to 25 mm in length.

Ascending fascicles of anterior and posterior lateral-line root fibers to the eminentia granularis already have been mentioned. Some of the fibers of both roots traverse the eminentia and reach the valvula. Ascending VIII root fibers also distribute in the granular eminences. Golgi series of young Amia show a large fascicle of VIII root fibers ending by short branches in the eminentia, predominantly ipsilaterally (fig. 64). Some fibers cross the midline in the commissure of the still dorsoposteriorly tilted cerebellar margin and terminate contralaterally. The median part of the cerebellar margin, through which these and other fibers cross, becomes the pars medialis of the vestibulolateral lobe, as already noted.

Fibers that take origin from small elongated cells in the nucleus medialis, the anterior part of the vestibular area, and in the transition zone to the eminentia granularis are directed rostrodorsally and dorsomedially. Many end in the ipsilateral eminentia, but others cross to the opposite side with the VIII root fibers. These secondary

fibers are scattered and probably correspond to the diffuse secondary acousticolateral fibers included by Pearson in a bulbo-cerebellar system.

Sagittal sections of adult Lepisosteus, stained with protargol, show a prominent tract from the VIII root to the eminentia granularis which gives off fascicles that enter the pars medialis. Lateral-line fascicles, situated beneath the cerebellar crest, turn dorsomedially with the continuation of the crista into the molecular layer of the pars medialis and continue into the fibrous zone of the pars medialis. Many of these fibers cross the midline. Together with the decussating VIII root and other crossing fibers,

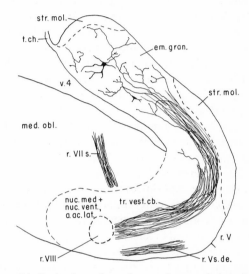

Figure 64. Sagittal section of rostral part of rhombencephalon of young Amia calva. Golgi method.

including commissural fibers between the bilateral granular eminences, they constitute an acousticolateral commissure. The lateral-line component of this commissure includes posterior and, probably, anterior lateral-line root fibers. Uncrossed fibers of both roots distribute in the ipsilateral eminentia granularis, some possibly reaching the valvula.

Sagittal sections of Lepisosteus show a small fascicle, similar to one illustrated by Pearson in Amia, which extends from the pars medialis into the caudal part of the corpus cerebelli. This fascicle probably corresponds to the vestibular fibers that reach the lobulus posticus of elasmobranchs. A furrow in the caudal part of the molecular layer of Lepisosteus, not found in Amia, suggests the sulcus posticus of Voorhoeve in the sharks and rays.

A small fascicle of lateral-line fibers reaches the auricle. These are ipsilateral and, apparently, are derived from the anterior lateral-line root. Fine fibers that continue from the cerebellar crest into the molecular part of the fibromolecular layer of the pars medialis are augmented in Lepisosteus by innumerable small fascicles that appear to arise, at least in part, from the granular sheet which continues dorsomedially from the auricle to the granular layer of the pars medialis. Numerous granules form chains between these fascicles.

The afferent connections of the corpus cerebelli are represented by spino-cerebellar, bulbo-cerebellar, trigemino-cerebellar, tecto-cerebellar and lobo-cerebellar tracts. A posterior mesencephalo-cerebellar tract terminates in both corpus cerebelli and valvula.

The spino-cerebellar tract in Amia forms a large fascicle which passes forward, ventral of the descending tract of the V root, as far as the entering roots of the V nerve. It then turns dorsomedially into the anterior base of the corpus cerebelli. The more medial fibers cross the midline, forming a cerebellar commissure, while the remaining fibers turn medially and dorsally into the ipsilateral part of the corpus, ending in the granular layer. According to Pearson (1936a), some of the lateral fibers end in the eminentia granularis and the ascending part of the tract includes fibers that connect the spinal cord with the acousticolateral area. If such connections with the acousticolateral area and granular eminence are confirmed in Golgi or experimental material they would indicate a less complete differentiation of the general somatic sensory from the acousticolateral system in Amia than appears to prevail in teleosts.

An ascending trigeminal fascicle which reaches the base of the anterior part of the corpus cerebelli and decussates, in part, through the cerebellar commissure is shown in Golgi series of young Amia. Pearson describes secondary trigeminal fibers from the descending V nucleus as part of a complex which he calls the bulbo-cerebellar system. In this system he includes fibers originating in the acousticolateral area. Some end in the eminentia granularis and some in the corpus cerebelli, those to the corpus, especially, being said to decussate in the cerebellar commissure. It is probable that Pearson's bulbo-cerebellar system represents two distinct but more or less intermingled groups of fibers, one corresponding to the secondary fibers from the acousticolateral nuclei to the eminentia granularis of young Amia, above described, and the other representing secondary trigeminal connections with the corpus cerebelli. The latter were not identified, however, in Golgi preparations.

Other bulbo-cerebellar fibers, of uncertain specific origin, accompany the spino-cerebellar and trigemino-cerebellar tracts. In Lepisosteus they collect into a well-defined fascicle which probably represents an olivo-cerebellar tract. According to Kooy (1917), inferior olivary cells are identifiable in Amia and Lepisosteus.

The tecto-cerebellar system of Amia, according to Pearson, comprises a lateral and a medial tecto-cerebellar tract, the latter being the larger. The fibers of the lateral tract arise in the caudal part of the efferent layer of the tectum and pass caudally and ventrally and then, lateral of the valvula, dorsally into the corpus cerebelli. Pearson's medial tecto-cerebellar tract is said to arise in the caudal part of the efferent layer of the tectum, then turn medially and enter the anterior medullary velum, in which it decussates more or less completely. The fascicle then passes rostrally and laterally, joining the posterior mesencephalo-cerebellar tract, with which it enters the cerebellum. It distributes to the corpus cerebelli and, according to Pearson, to the valvula. I can confirm this tract in Golgi series of young Amia but do not find fibers to the valvula.

The posterior mesencephalo-cerebellar tract, Pearson reports, takes origin in the nucleus lateralis valvulae and in the torus semicircularis. It forms a layer of fibers between the lateral nucleus of the valvula, on the one hand, and the ventricular wall and granular layer of the valvula on the other. Continuing caudalward, it enters the cerebellum ventral of the tecto-cerebellar system. The fibers distribute in the valvula and corpus cerebelli.

The lobo-cerebellar tract has its origin from cells in the inferior lobe of the hypothalamus. The fibers take a caudal and dorsal course to the cerebellum. In Golgi series of young Amia some of the fibers enter the valvula and others distribute in the corpus cerebelli (fig. 66). The lobo-cerebellar tract is one component of a larger fascicle of rather loosely arranged fibers. These may represent cerebello-hypothalamic fibers, but no certainty could be established regarding their terminations.

The efferent fibers. A cerebello-motorius fiber system was described by Ariens Kappers (1907) as arising from the Purkinje cells. It comprises small bundles of fibers that take a ventral course from the cerebellum and spread rostralward and caudalward to the midbrain and medulla oblongata. Many individual fibers take a similar course. Some cross the midline, after passing through the medial longitudinal fascicle or dorsal of it, but most of them pass ventral of this bundle and many enter it. The others turn rostrally or caudally and appear as scattered fibers lateral of the medial longitudinal fascicle.

The cerebello-tegmental tract or brachium conjunctivum is a more compact fiber mass which rises in part from Purkinje cells and in part from the nucleus cerebelli. The fibers pass rostrally and ventralward from the base of the corpus cerebelli, collecting into a fascicle which curves toward the midline and decussates between the medial longitudinal fascicle and the interpeduncular nucleus, behind the oculomotor nucleus. Some of the fibers turn ventralward more sharply and cross at a more caudal level; others appear to extend forward into the tegmentum of the same side. The crossed cerebello-tegmental fibers terminate in part in the tegmental gray of the midbrain. In part the crossed fibers terminate in the ventral region of the diencephalon.

A tractus cerebello-bulbaris, named cerebello-spinalis by Pearson, arises, in part, in the nucleus cerebelli and passes caudalward close to the ventricular wall. At the level of the entering root of the facial nerve it assumes a more lateral position and continues through the medulla oblongata, joined by fibers from the vestibular nucleus to the spinal cord.

A tractus cerebello-tectalis passes rostrally, lateral of the valvula, and turns dorsally and laterally behind the torus semicircularis to end in the tectum. Its fibers are intermingled with those of the lateral parts of the tecto-cerebellar and the spino-tectal tracts.

THE HISTOLOGY

The main features of the internal structure of the cerebellum of Acipenseriformes are evident from the figures 61, 62, and 63. Golgi preparations (figs. 64–69) disclose details characterizing the various types of neurons.

The cellular masses of the eminentia granularis, corpus cerebelli, and valvula constitute the granular layer of the respective subdivisions. The eminentia is partly covered by a molecular layer, the corpus cerebelli is completely covered, and the valvula has a median molecular layer, as already noted. The granular layer of the corpus cerebelli is continuous with the eminentia caudally, but the two are increasingly separated rostralward. In Lepisosteus the separation begins farther caudally than in Amia. Both the eminentia and the granular layer of each half of the corpus are continuous with the bilateral granular layer of the valvula. The granular layer of the pars medialis and its continuation with the auricle on either side is distinct from the other granular masses and is the only granular mass the bilateral halves of which merge across the midline.

Taking into consideration the inversion of the corpus cerebelli of Acipenseriformes and the modifications of position of the granular masses of the corpus associated with this inversion, the pattern of the granular masses of holosteans and Acipenseriformes is very similar. The molecular layer of the corpus cerebelli of Amia and Lepisosteus, however, is entirely superficial and crosses the midline above the cerebellar ventricle (figs. 61, 62), instead of dipping into the corpus cerebelli and fusing to form a median molecular layer of the corpus. The molecular layer of the pars medialis is situated beneath the posterior part of the corpus cerebelli instead of above

it as in Acipenseriformes, and the molecular layer of the eminentia granularis covers the posterior and postero-lateral part of the gray mass (fig. 61A).

A layer of large cells occurs in the outer border of the granular layer of the corpus cerebelli and in the borders of the eminentia that are covered by a molecular layer, especially the ventral border which faces the pars medialis. This is the layer of Purkinje cells (fig. 61). In many places it is two or three cells deep, the deeper cells lying among the granules. In preparations stained by modifications of the Nissl method the cells frequently have triangular bodies and several elongated and large dendritic processes that usually extend into the molecular layer. In Lepisosteus these spread widely in a more or less horizontal plane before turning into the molecularis. Some of the large processes, especially at the ventral border of the posterior part of the eminentia, extend inward among the granules.

In Nissl or protargol stained brains of adult animals these cells have little resemblance to Purkinje cells except in position. Their wide-spreading dendrites, arising from different parts of the cell body, give them the appearance of multipolar cells. Golgi material of young Amia shows a more typically Purkinje cell form (fig. 65). In the posterior part of the eminentia granularis several dendrites, studded with small gemmules, extend into the molecular layer, while one or more dendrites lacking gemmules branch among the granules (fig. 69). Some of the branches are slender, elongated processes that may represent axons. Cells similar in other respects give rise to the axon from the cell body. In the corpus cerebelli the Purkinje cells send dendrites into the molecular layer only. The neurons described in the posterior part of the eminentia granularis appear to be transitional cells whose dendrites into the molecular layer have become the characteristic dendritic process of fully differentiated Purkinje cells.

An intricate plexus of nerve fibers interweaves among the cells of the eminentia granularis and fascicles of fibers traverse it. Many of the fibers of the plexus branch into short terminal twigs ending as bouton-like expansions that tend to cluster (fig. 69). Occasionally an elongated terminal enlargement is encountered, but none with any close resemblance to the mossy fibers of higher vertebrates appear to be present. Some bouton-like terminals end on the deep dendrites of Purkinje cells. Thin fibers extend into the molecular layer, passing among the dendrites of Purkinje cells toward the surface. No conclusions regarding the relations of these fibers to deeper fibers or elements could be reached.

Granule cells of the eminentia have two or three short,

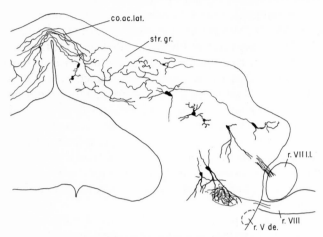

Figure 65. Transverse section of cerebellum of young Amia calva. Golgi method.

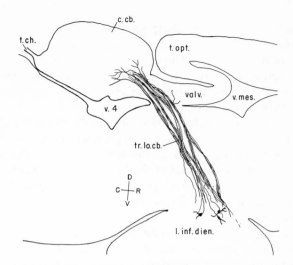

Figure 66. Sagittal section of brain of Amia calva (three sections combined). Golgi method. ×70.

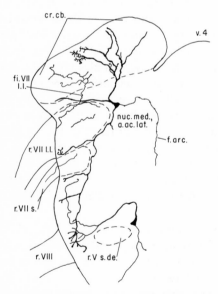

Figure 67. Transverse section of acousticolateral area of young Amia calva. Golgi method. ×150.

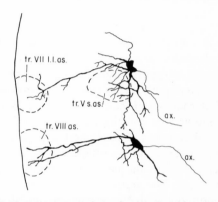

Figure 68. Transverse section of medulla oblongata of young Amia calva rostral to entrance of V root. Golgi method. ×150.

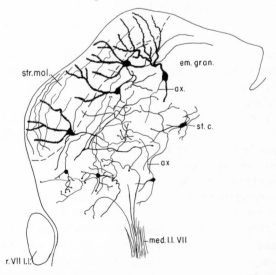

Figure 69. Transverse section of eminentia granularis of young Amia calva. Golgi method. ×150.

branching dendritic processes that end as small knobs (fig. 69). Slender axons of the granules pass into the molecular layer, but whether they branch in typical fashion into parallel fibers was not ascertained. In addition to granules the eminentia includes stellate cells. The granules of the corpus cerebelli are similar. Occasional neurons of Golgi's type II also occur in the corpus, but no neurons suggestive of basket cells were found. Cells of stellate type, interspersed among the granules, have dendrites that spread in the granular layer but their axons could be followed only a short distance from the cell body.

The granular layer of the corpus cerebelli is similar, in general, to the eminentia granularis with reference to minute structure. The fibrous plexus, however, is less intricate and has a more longitudinal arrangement. Short terminal twigs with boutons occur as in the eminentia. Fibers extend into the molecular layer from tracts that ascend in the border between the granular and molecular layers (fig. 66).

TELEOSTEI

THE cerebellum of the bony fishes varies greatly in size and form in different species. According to van der Horst (1925), this variation is closely related to the phylogenic position and the habits of individual species. The cerebellum of inactive fishes is small, but in strong swimmers it is large. The relative development of the cerebellar subdivisions is correlated with the importance in different species of the afferent systems from which fiber tracts enter the respective subdivisions.

Various features of the teleostean cerebellum were described by the earliest students of fish brains (Stieda, 1861; Fritsch, 1878; Mayser, 1881; Fusari, 1887; S. Ramon y Cajal, 1890; Malme, 1892; and others). Schaper (1893, 1894a,b) described the finer anatomy of the organ and its development. Catois (1901) contributed to an analysis of its histological elements and the fiber tracts. Banchi (1903), Goldstein (1905), Ariens Kappers (1906), Wallenberg (1907), Tello (1909), Franz (1911a, 1911b), Addison (1923), Burr (1928), Charlton (1933), Shanklin (1934), Tuge (1934b, 1935), and Pearson (1936a) described the fiber tracts in a variety of species. With reference to morphology Franz (1911a) divided the principal mass of the cerebellum into corpus cerebelli, in a general sense, and a valvula. A laterally projecting mass of granules which is continuous with the principal granular core of the cerebellum Franz called the eminentia granularis, but recognized that in many species continuity is incomplete. In siluroids the granular eminence lies somewhat posterior instead of lateral to the chief granular mass of the corpus cerebelli.

Further differentiation of the morphological features, in comparison with the cerebellum of other Ichthyopsida, was made by Palmgren (1921), Herrick (1924), van der Horst (1925), and Pearson (1936a). The inferior posterior part of the cerebellum of young salmon was called the pars auricularis by Palmgren; the median segment of this division is separated from the overhanging posterior part of the corpus cerebelli by a fissure, the sulcus posticus of Palmgren, and was called the pars medialis auriculi. A "string of granular cells" is illustrated as extending from one side of the pars auriculi to the other. Herrick (1924) regards the eminentiae granulares of teleosts as corresponding in position and functional connections to the auricle of elasmobranchs. The two eminences are described as connected by a mass of granules, the "pars postrema," which occupies the posteroventral margin of the cerebellum. The eminentiae and pars postrema together are regarded by Herrick as the primary vestibulolateral division of the cerebellum. An auricle, *sensu strictiori*, was identified in teleosts, however, by van der Horst (1925) who emphasized that it must be differentiated from the eminentia granularis on the grounds of morphology and fiber tract connections. The pars medialis auriculi of Palmgren is called the ventral molecular mass and is described as forming the entire ventricular surface of the cerebellum beneath the corpus cerebelli. Van der Horst differentiates the eminentia granularis from the granular layer of the corpus cerebelli and mentions a band of granules in the roof of the fourth ventricle which connects the two granular eminences.

The term corpus cerebelli is used by various authors in a general sense to designate the principal mass of the cerebellum. Van der Horst (1925), however, recognized that "the middle part of the cerebellum," or corpus cerebelli, is chiefly the terminus of secondary tracts from the midbrain, medulla oblongata, and spinal cord that carry somatic sensory impulses. The valvula cerebelli was described by Franz (1911a) and many subsequent authors in its numerous variations. Van der Horst (1925) emphasized the relation of the valvula to the acousticolateral area on the grounds of the continuity, in many species, of its granular layer with the eminentiae granulares, and of lateral-line fiber connections. The comparative studies of Pearson (1936a) on the acousticolateral area and cerebellum of petromyzonts, Amia, and a number of teleosts have demonstrated the fundamental pattern common to all these Ichthyopsida and have provided many descriptive details.

All of the principal subdivisions of the ichthyopsid cerebellum, as they occur in modified form in teleosts, have thus been described more or less completely. The picture of their pattern and of their relations to each other and to the subdivisions of the cerebellum of elasmobranchs, chondrosteans, and some other Ichthyopsida which emerges is vague and uncertain in many respects. In an attempt to clarify the morphology and homologies of the subdivisions of the teleostean cerebellum, the lateral-line and vestibular systems, which are functionally related to part of the cerebellum, will first be described.

THE LATERAL-LINE ORGANS AND NERVES

The lateral-line organs of teleosts occur in pits and canals and, in general, are so similar in distribution and structure to those of elasmobranchs that a detailed description is unnecessary. There are great variations, however, in the relative development of the lateral-line system and its nerves in different species of teleosts.

Herrick described the lateral-line components of the cranial nerves and their distribution in Menidia (1899) and subsequently in North American siluroid fishes (1901). The latter contribution also includes a detailed description of the lateral-line sensory organs, which present a considerable range of size in the species described. More recently Dijkgraaf (1952) has briefly described the structure of the lateral-line system and canal organs in fishes generally.

In Menidia, according to Herrick, lateral-line fibers are distributed with the superficial ophthalmic branch of the V nerve to the supraorbital lateral-line canal, as is most common also in other species. Lateral-line fibers to the infraorbital canal at first accompany the maxillary trunk but separate from it distally, forming a ramus buccalis of the VII nerve; in most teleosts this ramus is independent over the greater part of its course. A lateral-line component of the ramus hyomandibularis of the VII nerve distributes to the hyomandibular lateral-line canal. The root and ganglion of the posterior lateral-line nerve are closely related to the X nerve, but in many fishes posterior lateral-line fibers also are included in the root of the IX nerve.

The dorsal and ventral roots of the anterior lateral-line nerve arise together in Ictalurus, as described by Herrick (1901). As seen in Cajal preparations of young specimens of Ictalurus melas, and described by Pearson (1936a), the anterior lateral-line nerve comprises coarse and medium-sized fibers and enters the medulla oblongata by a dorsal and a ventral root. The dorsal root is said to include fibers of the superficial ophthalmic and buccal branches. The ventral root fibers are distributed by the hyomandibular branch of the VII nerve; they separate from the motor VII fibers before entering the medulla oblongata in close proximity to the dorsal root.

Functional differences between the dorsal and ventral roots of the anterior lateral-line nerve have not been demonstrated, but the larger fibers characteristic of the dorsal root probably have a faster conduction rate than the smaller ones of the ventral root. This suggests differences in the end organs with which the respective fibers are connected. Although a dorsal root is lacking in most teleosts, van der Horst (1925) regards the presence of both coarse and fine fibers in the ventral root as indicating that the dorsal root is combined with the ventral as the fibers enter the medulla oblongata.

The posterior lateral-line nerve of Ictalurus, according to Pearson (1936b), arises from two small roots of the IX nerve and a larger root of the X nerve. These roots enter the acousticolateral area near its caudal end.

In Carassius the anterior lateral-line nerve has dorsal and ventral roots, as in Ictalurus, the two uniting into a compact fascicle on entering the medulla oblongata. The posterior lateral-line nerve enters the medulla oblongata with the root of the X nerve. In addition to fibers from the lateral-line organs of the body, the root includes several small twigs from lateral-line organs of the head.

The lateral-line system of Silurus glanis, described by Berkelbach van der Sprenkel (1915), is much more strongly developed than in Menidia, Ictalurus or Carassius. The anterior lateral-line nerve enters the medulla oblongata with the V and sensory VII roots. It comprises a small number of very coarse fibers, ventrally situated, and a large number of fine fibers. The most rostral fascicles of the entering root include fine fibers exclusively; these were regarded by van der Sprenkel as a small dorsal root of the nerve. The posterior lateral-line nerve in Silurus is very large; its root enters the medulla oblongata at the level of the root of the IX nerve. The lateral-line organs and nerves of Mormyrus caschive, especially the posterior system, are greatly hypertrophied and their central connections attain great size.

An example of great reduction of the lateral-line nerves and their central connections is presented by the open-sea sunfish, Orthagoriscus mola, described by Burr (1928). This species is a large, lethargic, and slow-moving fish, the trunk of which is greatly reduced and the tail almost lacking. For sensory intake the animal is dependent to a large extent on the visual apparatus. The lateral-line nerves are reduced to two small bundles, an anterior and a posterior, which enter the medulla oblongata separately.

THE MEMBRANOUS LABYRINTH AND THE ACOUSTIC NERVE

The acoustic or VIII nerve and the membranous labyrinth of teleosts have been described most precisely by Retzius (1881), de Burlet (1929, 1934), and Pearson (1936b). The nerve has two principal branches, the anterior and the posterior; these distribute, respectively, to the pars superior and the pars inferior of the membranous labyrinth. The nerve enters the medulla oblongata by an anterior and a posterior root, each corresponding to the similarly named peripheral branch. Both roots include large, medium, and small fibers.

The pars superior of the labyrinth comprises three semicircular canals and their ampullae and ampullary cristae, the utricle and its macula, and the macula neglecta. The pars inferior of the labyrinth is formed of the sacculus and lagena and their respective maculae. The two divisions of the labyrinth communicate by a narrow passage in most species, but in some this connection is completely interrupted, the labyrinth consisting of two separate parts (Dijkgraaf, 1952). The organs of the labyrinth have many similarities to those of the lateral-line organs in structure, but they also have important differences and transitional patterns between the extremes, Dijkgraaf states.

The anterior division of the VIII nerve, in most teleosts, sends branches to the cristae of the anterior and lateral semicircular canals and to the crista of the posterior ampulla, macula neglecta, macula sacculi, and papilla lagenae. In Ictalurus and Carassius, according to Pearson (1936b), the ramus to the sacculus includes a fascicle of very coarse fibers which reaches the anterior part of the macula; the posterior two thirds is served by less coarse and small fibers.

The anterior part of the macula sacculi of siluroids, according to de Burlet (1929), is covered by a special otolith and is situated above a perilymphatic space which may receive vibration waves from the swim bladder through mediation of the Weberian ossicles. The central connections of the coarse fibers from this part of the macula differ from those of the fibers from the remainder of the receptor, Pearson (1936b) points out.

The cells of the very coarse fibers have a rostral position in the VIII ganglion. In some teleosts that have an otic capsule well differentiated from the cranial wall, Weston (1939a) found the ganglion cells of fibers to the crista of the posterior ampulla situated nearer the sensory epithelium than other cells of the ganglion. In siluroids ganglion cells were similarly found nearer the anterior part of the macula sacculi than elsewhere. These differences in relative position of the ganglion cells are regarded by Ariens Kappers (1947) as related to differences in the stimuli received by the respective sensory patches.

With reference to the functions of the subdivisions of the labyrinth of fishes, it is generally accepted that the ampullary cristae are stimulated by active and passive angular accelerations of movement and serve dynamic reflexes. The macula utriculi serves static vestibular reflexes concerned with spatial orientation. The anterior and medial parts of the macula utriculi of clupeids, according to Tracy (1920), are stimulated by changes in hydrostatic pressure, transmitted through the adjacent part of the perilymphatic space. Resulting reflexes may regulate the air in the swim bladder.

An auditory sense in fishes was demonstrated by Piper (1906), Mangold (1913), Westerfield (1922), Manning (1924), von Frisch (1936, 1938), and others. Parker (1918) and Manning (1924), among others, regarded the macula sacculi as the receptor of acoustic stimuli in siluroids. The more recent studies of Dijkgraaf (1950, 1952, 1960) and Poggendorf (1952) have expanded our knowledge of hearing in fishes. Dijkgraaf (1960) says there are two groups of bony fishes with reference to auditory sensibility, the "specialists" in auditory perception and the "normal" fishes. The "specialists" are fresh-water species for the most part and possess sound-reinforcing mechanisms. Dijkgraaf places the Weberian apparatus and gas chambers connected with the labyrinth in this category. The upper limit of sound perception, in the "specialists," is found at several thousand cycles per second. At frequencies below 1,000 c.p.s. these fishes are more sensitive than man, but above 2,000 c.p.s. they are less sensitive, according to observations of Poggendorf (1952). The "normal" fishes are marine species as a rule, with an upper auditory range between 400 c.p.s. and 1,000 c.p.s.

Tones of about 25 c.p.s. and up to the upper limit of hearing are perceived by the pars inferior of the labyrinth in some sound "specialists," both the sacculus and the lagena participating. According to Dijkgraaf the macula sacculi is stimulated by movements of the wall of the swim bladder. Destruction of the Weberian apparatus elevates the auditory threshold 20 to 30 decibels. Below 500–600 c.p.s. skin receptors for touch or vibration are said to have a part in sound perception. In "normal" fishes equilibrium is not disturbed by removal of the pars inferior of the labyrinth, but hearing is affected. Removal of the utriculus, in addition, results in further loss of hearing. The utriculus, according to Dijkgraaf (1960), serves in general as a gravity receptor, while the sacculus and lagena are sound receptors. Each of these organs, however, appears capable of fulfilling both functions in exceptional cases.

Parker and van Heusen (1917a, 1917b) and others have considered the lateral-line organs capable of low-frequency sound reception. According to Dijkgraaf (1960), however, no behavioral response to sound has been shown to be mediated by the lateral-line organs.

Many fishes are known to produce special sounds, Dijkgraaf (1947b, 1960) points out, some of intensities of more than 100 decibels. Frequencies range from 20 c.p.s. to 500 c.p.s., but fall below 400–500 c.p.s. in most species. The sound-producing mechanism is better developed or may be exclusive in the male. The sounds are produced only during mating or breeding activities in some species, in others they have a threat function (Dijkgraaf, 1947b). Guarding the nest, defending territory, and possibly locating by means of echoes have also been suggested as the uses of the sounds produced (Griffin, 1958).

According to Dudok van Heel (1956), the minnow (Phoxinus laevis) perceives tones in a range of approximately 20–2,000 c.p.s., the sacculus and lagena serving as the receptor organs. Two tones of different frequency also can be distinguished. The upper limit of pitch discrimination rises with a rise in temperature, but general activation of the animals by higher temperatures was not the primary cause of this rise in the upper limit.

THE ACOUSTICOLATERAL AREA

The acousticolateral area varies greatly in extent and form in different species of teleosts. In Ictalurus and Carassius it is roughly wedge-shaped and crowded into the dorsolateral region of the medulla oblongata by the visceral sensory lobes of the VII and X nerves (Pearson, 1936a, 1936b), which are hypertrophied in these species. Tapering caudally into a small triangular zone, lateral of the X lobe, it rapidly disappears in Ictalurus; in Carassius it ends bluntly behind the level of junction of the VII and X lobes. In both species the nuclei of the area are completely separated from the dorsal gray substance of the spinal cord. Hypertrophy of the VII and X lobes results in a forward position of the area also in the carp. The gray substance is more scattered and the nuclei are less distinct in the sunfish, Eupomotis, Pearson (1936a) states. In the trout the gray substance is continuous with the dorsal gray of the cord, as in petromyzonts, chondrosteans, and holosteans. The acousticolateral area of Megalops cyprinoides, as described by van der Horst (1926), is greatly developed and extends to the spinal cord. In Silurus glanis, according to Berkelbach van der Sprenkel (1915), the gray substance is divided into two elongated masses that extend from the cerebellum to the caudal part of the medulla oblongata, each having a cerebellar crest.

The bilateral acousticolateral areas of some species, for example cod and guppy, are connected above the fourth ventricle by the commissura acustica of Ariens Kappers (1906). In Megalops, Silurus, and other species the two areas are fused in greater or less degree above the ventricle.

The gray substance of the acousticolateral area is situated immediately beneath the cerebellar crest. This has been designated by various names. Tello (1909), regarded it in the carp as part of the dorsal nucleus of Ramon y Cajal (1908b), which corresponds to the fused anterior parts of the nucleus medialis and vestibular area of lower fishes already described. In the trout and catfish Pearson (1936a, 1936b) calls it the nucleus medialis, but in young Ictalurus melas two distinct cell groups are visible anteriorly which this author calls the nucleus medialis pars dorsalis and nucleus medialis pars medialis. The pars dorsalis is continuous anteriorly with the eminentia granularis and extends, posteriorly, to the level of entrance of the posterior lateral-line nerve. The pars medialis and the crista above it are described as continuous with the caudomedial part of the cerebellum; posteriorly it merges with the pars dorsalis beneath the lobe of the visceral sensory root of the VII nerve. My observations of these cell masses in young and adult Ictalurus are in good accord with Pearson's. The pars dorsalis and pars medialis of the nucleus medialis are also recognizable in Carassius, according to Pearson (1936b), but the nuclear groups are less distinct. Both Ictalurus and Carassius have dorsal as well as ventral roots of the anterior lateral-line nerve. In late larval Salmo gairdneri and in young Oncorhynchus there are suggestions of similar cell groups, but in mature specimens of both species the two groups have merged.

Although the nucleus dorsalis of Neoceratodus, Acipenser, and Polyodon lies dorsal of the cerebellar crest, and the nucleus medialis beneath the crista, in elasmobranchs the nucleus dorsalis is situated dorsomedial or even medial of the nucleus medialis, and the cerebellar crest forms a dorsal to dorsolateral cap. The shift in relative position is owing to inversion of the rostral part of the acousticolateral area.

This inversion is more complete in Ictalurus than in elasmobranchs and the cerebellar crest is a thick, undivided dorsal cap covering the nuclei. The nucleus medialis pars dorsalis of Pearson corresponds in relative position and in its fiber tract connections, described below, to the nucleus medialis of elasmobranchs. This homology also is indicated by its continuity with the eminentia granularis and, caudally, with the unmistakable homologue of the nucleus medialis of other Ichthyopsida. The nucleus medialis pars medialis of Pearson is confined to the anterior part of the acousticolateral area. Its position and fiber connections correspond to those of the nucleus dorsalis of elasmobranchs. Although it lies beneath the cerebellar crest, as in the sharks and rays, it also corresponds to the nucleus dorsalis of Neoceratodus, Acipenser, and Polyodon, which is situated dorsal of the crista.

The dorsal root of the anterior lateral-line nerve enters the medulla oblongata beneath the lateral margin of the greatly enlarged crista of Ictalurus, instead of above the crista as in Neoceratodus and Acipenser, or between the partly separated cristae of the nucleus dorsalis and nucleus medialis, as in elasmobranchs. The two roots merge as they enter the medulla oblongata, in many other teleosts, and continue into a nuclear mass which may be called the nucleus medialis et dorsalis, situated immediately beneath and behind the cerebellum. The lateral part of this nucleus is continuous rostrally with the eminentia granularis and caudally with the "lobe of the lateral-line nerves" of Ariens Kappers (1947). This lobe is the part of the cell column in which the ascending posterior lateral-line fibers terminate, with the exception of a fascicle which reaches the pars medialis and the eminentia granularis, and in which descending fibers of the ventral anterior lateral-line root also end. The rostral continuation of the gray column was called the dorsal nucleus of the static (acousticolateral) area by Ariens Kappers. In addition to ascending anterior lateral-line root fibers, it receives fibers of the VIII root whose peripheral connections are with the sacculus and lagena.

Differences in the afferent connections of the anterior and the posterior parts of the gray column of the acousticolateral area, indicate functional differences that probably are more specific than in the more generalized fishes. Confusion in understanding the relations of the acousticolateral area to the eminentia granularis and the auricle, described below, in comparison with similar relations in other Ichthyopsida will be avoided, however, if the entire longitudinal cell column, from the eminentia granularis to the caudal end of the acousticolateral area, but excepting part of the nucleus medialis et dorsalis, is recognized as homologous with the nucleus medialis of lower Ichthyopsida.

The dorsal and ventral roots of the anterior lateral-line nerve of Ictalurus merge on entering the medulla oblongata, as already noted, forming a compact fascicle. According to Pearson (1936b) this takes a caudal course for a short distance and then divides into medial and de-

scending fascicles, some of the fibers of both representing bifurcated branches of root fibers. The medial fascicle is said to distribute to the pars medialis nucleus medialis (that is, the nucleus dorsalis as above defined), to the auricle, the rostral end of the nucleus medialis proper, and the eminentia granularis.

Since this fascicle includes both dorsal and ventral root fibers, these possibly distribute differentially. In a Cajal series of young Ictalurus I have observed a small fascicle from the dorsal part of the entering root passing directly to the nucleus dorsalis. Further differential distribution, if it exists, can only be established in selective Golgi preparations. The fibers to the eminentia granularis form compact fascicles and are accompanied by fibers that apparently originate in the nucleus medialis and by ascending fibers of the posterior lateral-line root. The descending fibers distribute to all of the dorsolateral region of the nucleus medialis, Pearson (1936b) states. He further says that the dorsal and ventral anterior lateral-line roots of Carassius also merge and that the distribution of fibers is very similar to that in Ictalurus.

The posterior lateral-line root of Ictalurus passes rostralward through the dorsolateral part of the acousticolateral area near the ventral border of the nucleus medialis proper, into which its fibers are chiefly distributed. According to Pearson collaterals reach the nucleus dorsalis. The fascicle becomes reduced and less compact as it approaches the cerebellum, but it reaches the eminentia granularis.

In Weigert series of Gadus, Arius, and Pleuronectes, Addison (1923) followed anterior lateral-line fibers into the eminentia granularis, where most of them end. Such fibers were also followed to the valvula in Gadus, but in the other two species the intermingling of fibers in the granular eminence prevented tracing lateralis fibers to the valvula. Pyridine-silver preparations of Salmonidae and carp, Pearson (1936a) reports, show root fibers of the anterior lateral-line nerve distributed throughout the nucleus medialis and to the eminentia granularis and valvula. In Cajal preparations of larval carp, Tello (1909) found lateral-line fibers ending in the crista cerebelli, nucleus medialis, dorsal nucleus of Cajal, and cerebellum. He also describes fibers as crossing in the "velo," which appears to correspond to the pars medialis of the vestibulolateral lobe.

Posterior lateral-line root fibers, says Pearson, are distributed throughout the extent of the nucleus medialis, to the eminentia granularis of both sides, and to both sides of the valvula in the Salmonidae and carp. He believes that some ascending spinal fibers also make synaptic connections with the nuclei of the acousticolateral area.

My own observations on reduced silver preparations

of Oncorhynchus, Lebistes, and Minytrema confirm the descriptions of Addison and Pearson except with respect to the spinal fibers to the acousticolateral area described by Pearson. In addition I find innumerable terminal lateral-line fibers in the cerebellar crest, as did Tello (1909), and fascicles of lateral-line fibers to the pars medialis of the vestibulolateral lobe.

Silurus glanis and Mormyrus caschive have greatly hypertrophied acousticolateral areas and very large lateral-line nerves which have been described by Berkelbach van der Sprenkel (1915). In Silurus the most rostral fascicles of the anterior lateral-line nerve, which are small and which van der Sprenkel believes represent the dorsal root, pass toward the cerebellum and disappear. In Golgi preparations of Catostomus I have observed similar root fibers that enter the auricle without bifurcating and continue into the granular layer of the pars medialis.

The remaining root fibers of the anterior lateral-line nerve of Silurus, according to van der Sprenkel, enter a mass of cells and fibers which he calls the anterior lateral-line or medial lobe. The posterior lateral-line root fibers terminate in the posterior lateral-line or lateral lobe of van der Sprenkel. He employs the terms anterior and posterior to refer to the root fibers ending in the respective lobes, whereas medial and lateral as he uses them refer to the position of the lobes with respect to each other. The anterior lateral-line lobe continues forward beneath the caudal part of the cerebellum, there fusing with its contralateral representative. It also merges with the cerebellum by continuity of its cerebellar crest with the cerebellar molecular layer and of its enlarged granular mass with a granular swelling, on each side of the cerebellum. The swelling appears to correspond to the eminentia granularis of Ictalurus. Caudalward the "anterior lateral-line lobe" extends farther than the "posterior lateral-line lobe." Van der Sprenkel refers to a "so-called dorsal nucleus of the acusticum," formed of a large number of medium-sized cells beneath the crista and its accompanying fiber layer. The cell mass receives a descending tract of fine anterior lateral-line root fibers, but this author includes it in his anterior lateral-line lobe. It probably corresponds to the nucleus dorsalis of Ictalurus.

The posterior lateral-line lobe of van der Sprenkel is much larger, rostrally, than the anterior lobe. It fuses with the corresponding contralateral lobe, forming a large arch dorsal of the fused anterior lateral-line lobes. The separate cerebellar crest of this arch is continuous with the molecular layer of the cerebellum. The posterior lateral-line root fascicle, Berkelbach van der Sprenkel says, gradually shifts medialward in its rostral course and is soon covered by cerebellar crest. It passes through the posterior lateral-line lobe, forming a flattened layer of myelinated fibers in the dorsolateral border of the lobe. The ventral part of this layer also includes descending anterior lateral-line root fibers, so that the posterior lobe of van der Sprenkel, in this respect, is similar to the nucleus medialis of other teleosts above described. The posterior lateral-line fascicle is said to end rostrally in the "gray substance lateral to the cerebellum," that substance evidently corresponding to the eminentia granularis.

The hypertrophy of the lateral-line nerves in Silurus is thus accompanied by individual enlargement of the central connections of the two nerves. The continuous nucleus, which in most teleosts receives the root fibers of both nerves, is divided into two longitudinal cell columns, one for each nerve, and these have, in Silurus, individual cerebellar crests.

The relations of the subdivisions of the acousticolateral area in Mormyrus are similar to those in Silurus, Berkelbach van der Sprenkel states. The posterior lateral-line lobe is very much larger than the anterior lobe, in keeping with the greatly hypertrophied posterior lateral-line nerve of Mormyrus. Both hypertrophied lobes are fused across the midline throughout their length, giving the appearance of one unpaired lobe. Ascending posterior lateral-line fibers reach the gigantic valvula in large numbers.

The great reduction of the lateral-line nerves of Orthagoriscus is correlated with a corresponding reduction of the acousticolateral area of this species. The root of the anterior lateral-line nerve comprises a single slender fascicle which sweeps forward into the cerebellum, and a ventral division which ends in a region of small cells caudal of the vestibular nucleus, as pointed out by Burr (1928). This zone of cells, which represents a greatly reduced nucleus medialis, also receives posterior lateral-line root fibers.

In addition to the afferent connections from the lateral-line nerve, Pearson (1936a) describes spinal fibers ending in the acousticolateral area. He also describes a tecto-acousticolateral tract in the trout and carp, saying that the fibers have their origin in the efferent layer of the tectum and pass caudalward to the rostral part of the acousticolateral lemniscus. They follow the lemniscus into the medulla oblongata and, after crossing the midline, distribute to the contralateral acousticolateral area.

The crista cerebelli. The cerebellar crest of Ictalurus is a thick molecular layer which, as seen in transverse sections, forms a continuous dorsal plate from the lateral to the medial border of the acousticolateral area. Rostrally it is tilted dorsomedially and covers both the nucleus medialis and the nucleus dorsalis. A partially detached medial part of the anterior crista, which includes small cells as well as a fascicle of entering fibers, may be more closely related to the nucleus dorsalis, but I have been unable to analyze it satisfactorily. Caudally the crista continues approximately to the level of the entrance of the posterior lateral-line root. Anteriorly it is continuous with the molecular layer of the pars medialis of the vestibulolateral lobe.

In the salmons and guppy the crista continues forward beneath the transverse plate. Caudally it gradually disappears at approximately the level of entrance of the posterior lateral-line root. The double crista of Silurus, already mentioned, differs from the anteriorly more or less divided crista of elasmobranchs. In Silurus the lateral band of crista is the molecular layer of the nucleus of the posterior lateral-line nerve, whereas the medial band, which also extends farther caudalward, is the molecular layer of the anterior lateral-line nerve. In elasmobranchs the dorsal part of the crista, anteriorly, is the molecular layer of the nucleus dorsalis, and the ventral part and its caudal continuation are the molecular layer of the entire nucleus medialis.

The anterior part of the cerebellar crest, dorsal of the entering roots of the anterior lateral-line and VIII nerves, receives innumerable terminal fibers from these roots. Tello (1909) describes both lateral-line and VIII root fibers to the crista in young carp. In reduced silver and Golgi preparations of Oncorhynchus, Lebistes, Catostomus, and other species the lateral-line fibers can be followed with ease, but VIII root fibers are less certain. The root fibers divide, immediately beneath or within the crista, into several prong-like branches that extend toward the surface (fig. 89). In the most favorable reduced silver and Golgi preparations many of these branches can be seen to ramify, within the crista, into very fine fibers that spread and terminate in minute boutons. Some of the fibers may wind loosely about dendritic branches of cells beneath the cerebellar crest, as Tello describes, but these cells differ considerably from the Purkinje cells of the vestibulolateral lobe, in the same sections, both in appearance and in staining qualities in reduced silver preparations. In Golgi preparations of Ictalurus and Catostomus I have failed to find neurons with dendrites of Purkinje cell type in the cerebellar crest, but well-impregnated neurons of medium size, situated in the underlying nucleus medialis, send long slender dendrites into the crista (fig. 89). These dendrites divide into small terminal branches that interlace with fine terminal twigs of ascending and descending lateral-line fibers which, in turn, wind loosely about the dendrites. The cells giving rise to these dendrites appear to be Golgi cells. The axons of some ramify in the underlying nucleus (fig. 89).

Golgi preparations of Ictalurus nebulosus and other teleosts show relatively coarse lateral-line root fibers en-

tering the nucleus medialis and ramifying within it. Some branches continue into the cerebellar crest and divide into the small twigs that end as boutons. Individual fine fibers and small fascicles of such fibers, apparently originating in the underlying nucleus, also enter the crista. These divide into branches that may be followed for varying distances before they ramify into twigs that terminate as small boutons. The rostral part of the cerebellar crest includes numerous fibers that resemble the parallel fibers of the molecular layer of the cerebellum. All of these fine fibers apparently arise from granule cells of the rostral part of the underlying nucleus, where such cells are numerous. In the region of transition from the cerebellar crest to the fibromolecular layer of the pars medialis, fine ascending fibers from the crista to this layer and similar descending fibers from this layer that end in the crista are numerous. Besides individual fibers, small fascicles of fine fibers also appear to pass in both directions. These are relatively few in the guppy and are found chiefly in the deep part of the crista. In adult Ictalurus and Oncorhynchus they are very numerous, filling the greater part of the transition zone.

The descending fine fibers appear to be axons of granule cells in the pars medialis; the ascending fibers appear to be axons of granules in the acousticolateral area. Possibly, in part, they represent elongated terminal branches of lateral-line root fibers. In small fishes and species with reduced lateral-line systems granule cells appear to be restricted to the anterior region of the nucleus medialis et dorsalis. Larger species with well-developed lateral-line systems show such cells farther caudally, while in Silurus and Mormyrus, according to Berkelbach van der Sprenkel (1915), granules are numerous throughout the length of the lateral-line nuclei.

The various sources from which the crista receives fibers that come into synaptic relations with dendrites from neurons of the underlying nuclei emphasize its role as a zone of neuropil. The caudal region, which receives some posterior lateral-line root fibers and possibly some fibers related to the ascending spinal tract by connections in the nucleus medialis, is the least complex. Such connections, however, to the ascending spinal tract have not been demonstrated. The zone between the posterior and the anterior lateral-line roots, receiving more numerous fibers from both these roots and the underlying nucleus, is more complex. The anterior part, which receives VIII root fibers in addition, is the most complex.

The acoustic nuclei. The vestibular area of the trout embryo was differentiated by Ramon y Cajal (1908b) into nucleus of Deiters, tangential nucleus, dorsal nucleus, and descending nucleus. These usually are called the vestibular nuclei but the evidence above cited that some of them serve auditory function makes the less specific term acoustic nuclei more appropriate.

The nucleus of Deiters (the nucleus ventralis of Pearson) lies in the path of the anterior root of the VIII nerve. It comprises large ovoid or fusiform elements that form a distinct group. Followed caudalward, the cells become smaller and the nucleus disappears. In embryos the cells have short dendritic processes, but in adult fish the processes are elongated and branched. A large axon arises from the internal face of each cell.

The tangential nucleus is a robust and compact group of medium-sized and small cells situated near the surface of the medulla oblongata among the more caudal fibers of the anterior root of the VIII nerve (fig. 88). Tello (1909) and Beccari (1931) divide this nucleus into dorsal or superior and ventral or inferior parts.

The dorsal nucleus of Ramon y Cajal is a zone of small cells dorsal of Deiters's nucleus and beneath the cerebellar crest. According to Ramon y Cajal (1908b), it continues as a descending cell mass which follows Deiters's nucleus. Since it is a terminus of lateral-line as well as VIII root fibers, it corresponds to the zone in which vestibular area and nucleus medialis merge in many other Ichthyopsida.

The descending nucleus is a slender column of small cells which continues posteriorly from the dorsal nucleus and the nucleus of Deiters. Caudally it merges with the ventral border of the nucleus medialis of the acousticolateral area.

All the large fibers of the two roots of the VIII nerve end on cells of the tangential nucleus by large spoon-like synaptic terminals. Some large fibers from the papilla neglecta also enter this nucleus (Ariens Kappers, 1947). Tello (1909) states that the large fibers from the anterior and lateral ampullae end in the inferior division and the basal part of the superior division of the tangential nucleus; those from the posterior ampulla and papilla neglecta end in the more dorsal part of the superior division. Beccari (1931) describes the superior division as receiving the large fibers from the anterior and posterior cristae and the papilla neglecta.

The ventral or inferior division of the tangential nucleus receives large fibers from the crista of the lateral ampulla and from the macula utriculi (Beccari). All the large ampullary fibers have spoon-like terminals as described by Ramon y Cajal, Tello, Beccari, Pearson and others. No fibers from the cristae appear to reach the cerebellum. The ventral tangential nucleus gives rise to a crossed descending tract (tractus vestibularis cruciatus descendens) which ends in the nucleus of the VI nerve and in the spinal cord as pointed out by Wallenberg (1907).

All the utricular fibers, Tello states, but only those of medium size according to Beccari, end in Deiters's nucleus. Fine utricular fibers also reach the superior tangential nucleus.

Descending branches of anterior VIII root fibers, not specifically identified as to origin, distribute to the nucleus descendens and the caudal part of the nucleus medialis (Pearson, 1936b).

Fine fibers from the sacculus bypass the tangential nuclei, as found by Tello (1909), Beccari (1931), and Pearson (1936b) but send collaterals to Deiters's nucleus, continuing to the dorsal nucleus of Cajal. Some terminate in the crista cerebelli of both sides (Ariens Kappers, 1947). Some of the fine saccular fibers and also utricular fibers reach the eminentia granularis of the cerebellum. Small fibers from the lagena probably end in the dorsal nucleus.

The efferent fibers of the acousticolateral area. The efferent fibers of the lateral-line part of the acousticolateral area are grouped by Ariens Kappers (1947) into reflex motor pathways and projection tracts to higher centers of correlation. The motor paths arise from large cells of the nucleus medialis bordering the cerebellar crest. Most of these fibers cross the midline and are said to descend in the contralateral fasciculus longitudinalis medialis, forming the spinal reflex pathway.

More deeply situated cells send their axons into the fasciculus longitudinalis lateralis, also called acousticolateral lemniscus or lateral lemniscus. This is a crossed ascending system which terminates in the torus semicircularis, the nucleus isthmi, and, in part, in the optic tectum. The tract is situated lateral of the medial longitudinal fascicle and is augmented by additional fibers in its rostral course, forming a well-defined fascicle as it enters the midbrain. It becomes reduced in the midbrain, as the fibers distribute, and disappears rostral of the level of the III nucleus as the fibers spread into the torus semicircularis (Pearson, 1936a). This tract has been described in various species by Ariens Kappers (1906, 1921, 1947), Wallenberg (1907), Berkelbach van der Sprenkel (1915), Addison (1923), van der Horst (1926), and Pearson (1936a). In Silurus and Mormyrus separate systems of fibers arise from hypertrophied nuclei of the anterior and posterior lateral-line nerves and cross the midline of the medulla oblongata in great numbers. The two systems merge to form a very large fasciculus longitudinalis lateralis, Berkelbach van der Sprenkel (1915) states.

The efferent paths of the acoustic nuclei have been described by Ramon y Cajal (1908b), Tello (1909), Beccari (1930, 1931), Pearson (1936a), and Ariens Kappers (1947). According to Beccari the dorsal tangential nucleus, which receives large fibers from the anterior and posterior ampullary cristae and from the pars neglecta, gives rise to a crossed tract most of whose fibers ascend in the fasciculus longitudinalis medialis and terminate by spoon-like endings in the III and IV nuclei and also among large cells considered a possible primitive nucleus ruber. The axons of the ventral tangential nucleus, which receives large fibers from the lateral ampullary crista and the utriculus, form a crossed descending tract to the VI nucleus and the spinal cord (Wallenberg, 1907).

All the utricular fibers according to Tello, but only those of medium size according to Beccari, end in the nucleus of Deiters. This nucleus gives rise to a large ipsilateral vestibulo-spinal tract.

The descending vestibular nucleus gives rise to fibers that pass toward the midline, which many cross to enter the medial longitudinal fascicle. They may contribute to the ipsilateral vestibulo-spinal tract, but this is uncertain, Pearson (1936a) says.

The Development of the Cerebellum

The morphological development of the cerebellum of the trout, Salmo trutta, was described by Schaper (1894a,b). The formation of the cell layers by migrations from the columna dorsalis of Bergquist and Källén has recently been described by Rüdeberg (1961) in Esox lucius and Salmo salar. Schaper's classic contribution was made before many now-recognized features of the teleostean cerebellum had been analyzed. Modifications of some of his interpretations are therefore necessary and his descriptions need amplification. The numerous illustrations of models in Schaper's publications, however, show the principal morphological features that I have found in late larval stages of Salmo gairdneri and young Oncorhynchus. The following description of morphogenetic phases of the cerebellum is therefore based on Schaper's illustrations and text, with modifications of interpretation and terminology based on my study of the salmons and Ictalurus, young and adult, and adults of other species.

In the trout embryo, 36 days after fertilization, a prominent infolding of the neural tube has appeared at the boundary between the mesencephalic and rhombencephalic brain vesicles, an infolding accompanied by a thickening of the folds of the tube. The infolding of the neural tube begins laterally and extends medialward and gradually dorsalward toward the midline, but the dorsally directed part of the groove is shallow. The entire groove constitutes the mesencephalo-cerebellar fissure. The bilaterally symmetrical posterior walls of this fissure form the paired rudiment of the cerebellum. In the 46 day embryo (fig. 70) the rudiment is represented by laterally

and rostrodorsally expanded bilateral thickenings that are tilted dorsalward at nearly right angles to the floor of the rhomboidal fossa and connected across the midline only by a narrow ependymal bridge at the dorsal margin. The two plate-like rudiments form the walls of a narrow, laterally expanded cleft which is the posterior opening of the future cerebral aqueduct. Behind the cerebellar rudiments the rhomboidal fossa expands laterally on each side, forming the broad anterior part of the rhomboidal fossa. The rhombic lip, representing the rudiment of the acousticolateral area of the medulla oblongata, is continuous with the ventrolateral margin of the cerebellum and, through it, with the remainder of the cerebellar margin (fig. 70).

The cerebellar rudiment expands rapidly and thickens on either side. The narrow connecting bridge between the bilateral halves also becomes thicker and expands ventrodorsally, the median part of the mesencephalo-cerebellar fissure forming a deep cleft, in the 57 day embryo, between the cerebellum and the midbrain. At this stage of development the cerebellum has begun to tilt caudalward and a suggestion of a recessus lateralis of the rhomboidal fossa, which may now be called the fourth ventricle, has appeared. The ventrolateral part of the cerebellar rudiment has expanded into a prominent swelling, on either side, which is continuous posteriorly with the developing acousticolateral area. This swelling is the rudiment of the eminentia granularis (fig. 71), recognizable also in the 46 day embryo. The median part of the cerebellar rudiment also projects forward slightly into the mesencephalic ventricle in the 57 day embryo. This median projection represents the rudiment of the valvula cerebelli (fig. 71B).

In the 79 day embryo the cerebellum, including the valvula, has begun to elongate anteroposteriorly and its posterodorsal part has begun to arch downward (fig. 72). The downward growth is so marked in the 91 day embryo that it forms the posterior wall of a dorsal recess of the fourth ventricle above which the cerebellum has a vault-like shape (fig. 73). The posterior wall is thicker at the 100 day stage and turns forward ventrally, the choroid tela turning sharply in a dorsocaudal direction from its ventral margin. This forward deflection of the posterior wall constricts the dorsal recess of the fourth ventricle into a cerebellar ventricle, the lateral walls of which are ovoid swellings projecting into it (fig. 74).

Externally a groove has appeared on either side of the midline, delimiting the cerebellar margin from the vault-like part of the cerebellum. Medially the groove merges with the tenial sulcus, but in late larval Salmo gairdneri and young Oncorhynchus the corresponding groove forms a deep furrow which crosses the midline as the pos-

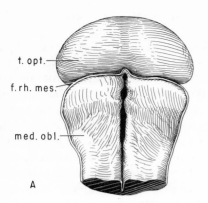

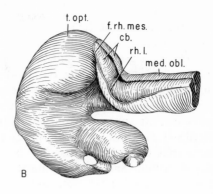

Figure 70. Brain of 46-day-old trout embryo. A. Posterior view. B. Lateral view.
×50. (Redrawn from Schaper, 1894.)

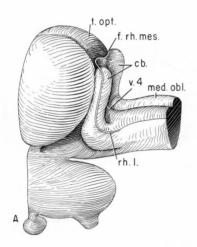

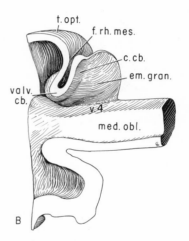

Figure 71. Caudal half of brain of 57-day-old trout embryo.
A. Lateral view. B. Median section. (Redrawn from Schaper, 1894a.)

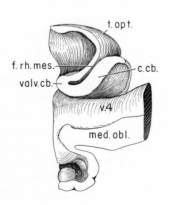

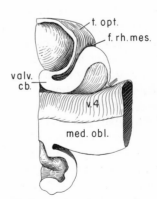

Figure 72. Caudal half of brain of 79-day-old trout embryo, median section. (Redrawn from Schaper, 1894a.) Figure 73. Caudal half of brain of 91-day-old trout embryo, median section. (Redrawn from Schaper, 1894a.)

103

terior or median segment of the posterolateral fissure. In the 91 day trout embryo a shallow groove appears between the eminentia granularis and the vaulted part of the cerebellum. A corresponding but more prominent groove in Oncorhynchus and in the adult stage of many other species represents the lateral segment of the posterolateral fissure. It appears justified to consider these grooves in the 91 day trout as the external boundaries between the corpus cerebelli, represented by the vaulted part of the cerebellum, and the vestibulolateral lobe, represented by the posterior margin and the eminentiae granulares. The posterior margin is much thickened in the 6-month-old trout, forming the pars medialis of the vestibulolateral lobe (fig. 75). Laterally the pars medialis

ventricle. The valvula has enlarged and begun to fold in the mesencephalic ventricle (fig. 75).

The differentiation of the cell layers of the cerebellum has been described by Rüdeberg (1961) in the pike, Esox lucius, on the basis of cell migrations from the columna dorsalis of Bergquist and Källén. After an early phase of closely crowded cell nuclei in the cerebellar region, a distinct migration layer, the columna dorsalis, appears. The neuro-epithelium remains as a thin layer. The columna dorsalis which, as already noted, is a continuation of the dorsal column of the medulla oblongata and ends at the isthmic fold, then expands rapidly and spreads so far ventrally that it overlaps the columna dorsolateralis. The ventral part thickens and splits into a lateral

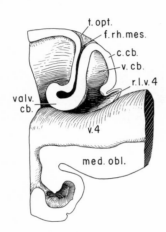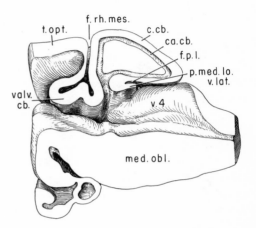

Figure 74. Caudal half of brain of 100-day-old trout embryo, median section. (Redrawn from Schaper, 1894a.) *Figure 75.* Caudal half of brain of 6-month-old trout, median section. (Redrawn from Schaper, 1894a.)

is continuous, by a sharp caudal deflection, with the acousticolateral area. This sharp turn forms a lateral recess of the fourth ventricle. Late larval Salmo gairdneri and young Oncorhynchus show a layer of granules in the lateral part of the dorsal wall of this recess which represents part of the auricle, to which we shall return. Earlier stages of the auricle are probably to be found in younger larvae of the salmon and the trout but this division of the vestibulolateral lobe is not mentioned by Schaper.

The corpus cerebelli, which is a dorsally directed vault in the 100 day embryo (fig. 74), gradually loses its cerebellar ventricle by a thickening of its lateral walls, the bilateral ovoid medially swelling masses, which represent the developing granular layer, gradually fusing across the midline. In the 6-month-old trout the cerebellar ventricle has disappeared except for a cerebellar canal around the periphery of the fused granular mass (fig. 75). The corpus cerebelli elongates and, in the 6-month-old trout, tilts caudalward above the pars medialis and the fourth

sheet called "migration A" and a medial "migration B." The splitting possibly includes the dorsal part also, but the dorsal portion of "migration A" is described as very thin and possibly corresponds to the superficial granular layer; Rüdeberg, however, regards it as "migration A."

The ventral part of "migration A" is a large cell mass which gives off a "migration A_2," the principal remaining part being designated A_1. This principal cell mass develops into the eminentia granularis, whereas "migration A_2" is joined by cells from "migration B," forming cell mass A_2B, which develops into a lateral extension of the granular layer dorsomedial of the eminentia granularis.

The granular layer (of the corpus cerebelli) and also the layer of Purkinje cells are, according to Rüdeberg, derived from "migration B." Elasmobranchs are different in that in them the layer of Purkinje cells may be related to the dorsal part of "migration A" (Rüdeberg, 1961, p. 43). Rüdeberg does not mention the granular auricles or the granular layer of the pars medialis, described below.

Assuming that the nucleus medialis and the reduced or vestigial nucleus dorsalis of the acousticolateral area of teleosts are formed by the splitting of the bulbar part of the columna dorsalis, as in elasmobranchs, it appears to follow that the continuity of the nucleus medialis with the eminentia granularis and of the nucleus dorsalis (in Ictalurus) with the auricle and granular layer of the pars medialis, is an expression, within the cerebellum, and further differentiation of the division seen in the acousticolateral area in simpler form.

The transitory superficial granular layer, Schaper states, arises at the transition of the cerebellum to the choroid tela, in the region of the recessus lateralis and in the roof plate of the median sagittal fissure. From these points it spreads, by migration of its elements, over the entire external surface of the cerebellum.

The Adult Cerebellum
THE VESTIBULOLATERAL LOBE

The vestibulolateral lobe of teleostean fishes comprises an eminentia granularis and a relatively large transverse plate which is derived from the cerebellar part of the rhombic lip. The posterodorsal part of the transverse plate is delimited from the corpus cerebelli by the posterior segment of the posterolateral fissure; a shallower lateral segment of this fissure is recognizable in most species between the lateral surface of the corpus cerebelli and the eminentia granularis (fig. 76). The transverse plate of Ictalurus forms a keystone-like structure above the fourth ventricle and between the anterior ends of the bi-

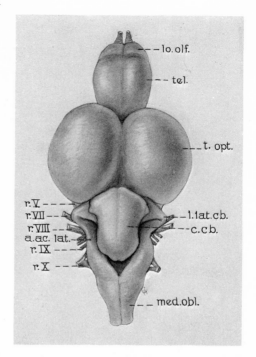

Figure 77. Dorsal view of brain of young salmon, Onchorhynchus tscharvytscha.

lateral acousticolateral areas which, in the catfish, are more dorsally situated than in most other species. The cerebellar crest and the fiber tracts beneath it turn medially into the plate, forming a fibromolecular layer of transversely directed fibers. At each end of the plate a compact dorsolaterally directed mass of granules represents the auricle. The fibromolecular layer between the auricles and granules related to it constitute the pars medialis of the vestibulolateral lobe. In the salmons the transverse plate has a much more caudal tilt and is elongated anteroposteriorly (fig. 77). It tapers rostroventrally between continuations of the bilateral cerebellar crests toward its base, which is situated behind the base of the corpus cerebelli. The posterolateral fissure is much deep-

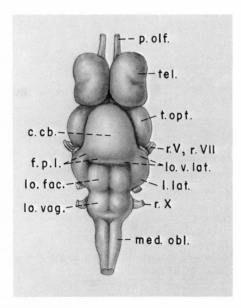

Figure 76. Dorsal view of brain of Ameiurus catus, 7½ cm long. (Redrawn from Herrick, 1891.)

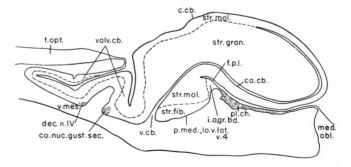

Figure 78. Paramedian sagittal section of cerebellum of young salmon.

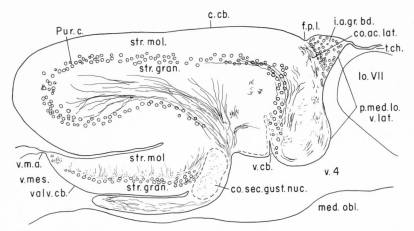

Figure 79. Midsagittal section of cerebellum of Ameiurus melas, 43.5 mm long.

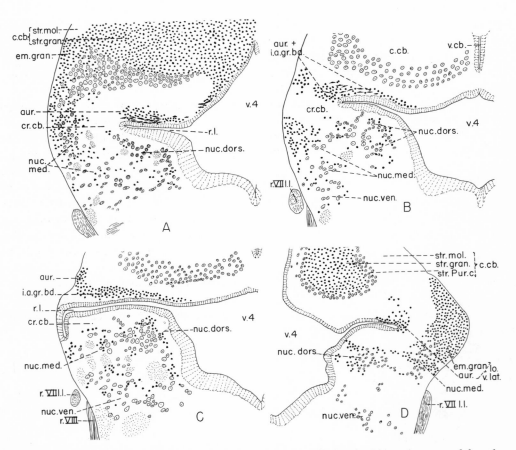

Figure 80. Transverse sections of rhombencephalon at the level of lateral recess of fourth ventricle. A–C. Rainbow trout, 17 mm long. D. Salmon, 43 mm long.

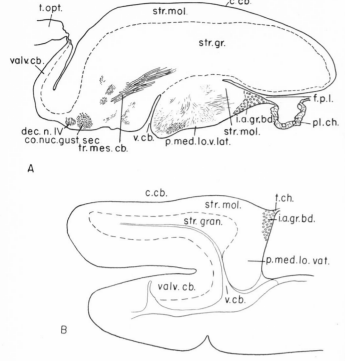

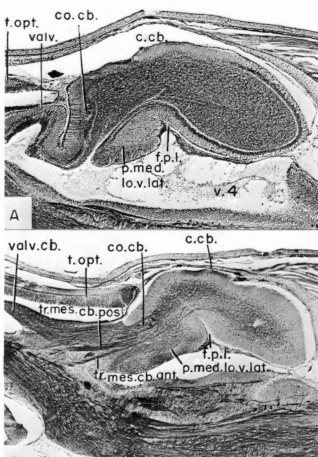

Figure 81. Sagittal sections of cerebellum of
guppy (A) and Ictalurus (B).

er in the salmons and guppy than in Ameiurus and Ictalurus owing to the caudal tilt of the corpus cerebelli above the plate, as appears in figures 78–82.

The eminentia granularis. The granular eminence varies in size and in position with reference to the corpus cerebelli in different species, but in all it is a prominent feature of the cerebellum (figs. 83–87). As defined by Franz (1911a), who introduced the term, the eminentia granularis appears to include the auricle, as noted by Ariens Kappers, Huber, and Crosby (1936). The auricle was recognized, however, as a distinct structure by van der Horst (1925, 1926) and Pearson (1936b). The granular eminence is separated from the auricle by the dorsal and dorsomedial continuation of the cerebellar crest into the pars medialis. It is a modified and enlarged rostral continuation of the cell column represented in the acousticolateral area by the nucleus medialis in the restricted sense. In this respect and in its fiber tract connections it corresponds to the eminentia granularis of other Ichthyopsida, but in teleosts it is a relatively larger and more compact mass of granules. Most of its external surface is covered by pia mater, only a small part having an outer molecular layer in most species.

In Ictalurus the cell column of the nucleus medialis enlarges rapidly rostralward and expands into an eminence

Figure 82. Sagittal sections through cerebellum of salmon, 43
mm long. A. Near median plane. B. Lateral plane.
Cajal method.

situated lateral and posterior of the principal mass of the cerebellum but merging with it medially. A faint lateral segment of the posterolateral fissure delimits the granular mass from the molecular layer of the corpus cerebelli, but in sections the eminentia merges anteromedially with the granular layer of the corpus (fig. 86). A medially continuing band of larger cells crosses the midline behind a dorsally directed recess of the fourth ventricle, interconnecting the bilateral granular eminence.

Late larval Salmo gairdneri and young stages of Oncorhynchus show a laterally situated zone of small cells, representing the caudal part of the granular eminence, which is separated from the transverse plate by a dorsal continuation of the cerebellar crest. Farther rostrally, in Oncorhynchus, the eminentia forms a somewhat conical projection from the ventrolateral part of the cerebellum.

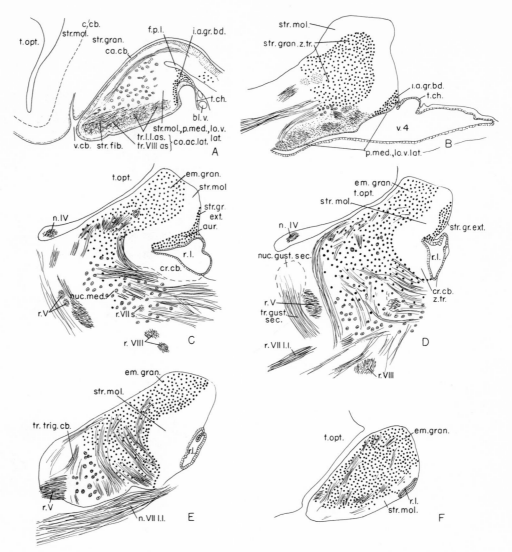

Figure 83. Series of sagittal sections, from a median (A) to a lateral plane (F), through vestibulolateral lobe of cerebellum of salmon, 43 mm long. Cajal method. ×56.

Its posterior surface is covered by a molecular layer which is continuous with the fibromolecular layer of the transverse plate. The steelhead salmon (seagoing adult *Salmo gairdneri*) shows a large rounded granular mass.

The form of the granular mass and its position with reference to the corpus cerebelli varies in other species. In the guppy most of the eminentia faces the rostrolateral external surface of the inferior part of the cerebellum. Megalops cyprinoides, according to van der Horst (1926), has a very large eminentia which is confined to the rostral part of the cerebellum. In Anguilla (van der Horst, 1925) the granular eminence extends anteroposteriorly throughout the entire length of the flattened cerebellum. It reaches a little farther laterally than the granu-

lar layer of the corpus cerebelli, which also is exposed on the lateral surface, but the posterolateral fissure separates the two granular masses. In a species of sucker (Minytrema?) the corpus cerebelli spreads laterally above the eminentia granularis as well as projecting dorsalward. A thin horizontal septum, which begins at the furrow, separates the two granular layers for a considerable distance rostralward before they merge. Other variations in a large number of species have been described by Franz (1911a) and by van der Horst (1925).

The auricula cerebelli. An auricle, *sensu strictiori*, has been identified in a number of teleosts by van der Horst (1925) and by Pearson (1936b). In the primitive species, Megalops cyprinoides, van der Horst (1926) states,

108

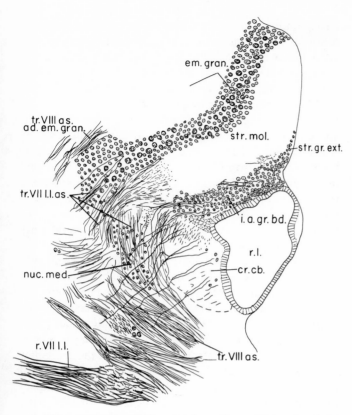

Figure 84. Salmon. Same series as figure 83, at a level three sections medial of D.

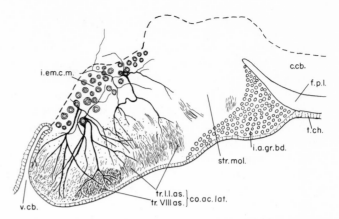

Figure 86. Paramedian sagittal section of medial part of vestibulolateral lobe of cerebellum of guppy. Cajal method.

the auricle forms a distinct lateral projection, above a small recessus lateralis, which is covered externally by a fold of choroid plexus. The projection is delimited from the remainder of the external surface of the cerebellum by a relatively deep furrow which van der Horst regards as corresponding to the para-auricular sulcus of Voorhoeve in elasmobranchs, that is, the lateral segment of the posterolateral fissure, as above defined. Pearson (1936b) describes the auricle (fig. 87) in the trout as a rostral continuation of the "stratum granulosum pars ventralis"; this is the granular layer of the pars medialis of the vestibulolateral lobe, described below.

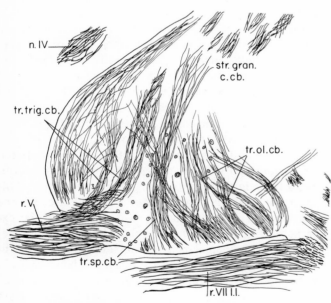

Figure 85. Salmon. Same series as figure 83, at a level between C and D.

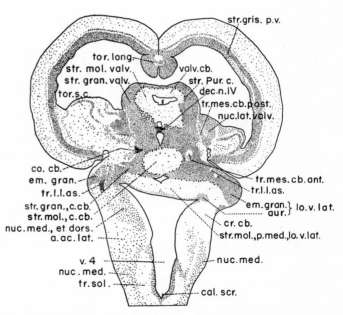

Figure 87. Horizontal section of brain stem of brook trout (Salvelinus fontinalis), passing through valvula cerebelli and calamus scriptorius. Toluidine blue. ×15. (Slightly modified from Pearson, 1936b.)

The auricle is closely related by chains of granules, or by a more diffuse continuity, with the granular layer of the pars medialis, but differs in its afferent connections, as will appear. With reference to position it is closely related to the recessus lateralis of the fourth ventricle (figs. 80, 83C, 87). This recess is so variously modified in different species that it must first be described before the teleostean auricle can profitably be compared with the auricle of other Ichthyopsida.

In Ictalurus a narrow lateral recess of the ventricle separates the lateral part of the transverse plate from the large lobe of the VII nerve of this species. The recess continues dorsorostrally between the rounded posterolateral border of the pars medialis and the cerebellar crest, forming a trough whose walls consist of an immediate granular layer and, external to this, the cerebellar crest and its deflection into the pars medialis, which forms the medial wall. Dorsolaterally the recess is covered by choroid membrane which continues caudally above the nucleus of the VII nerve. Young stages of Ictalurus show the dorsorostral part of the recess as a narrow, rostrally directed cleft which opens dorsolaterally into a space covered by choroid membrane.

The cerebellar crest of the salmons extends much farther rostralward with reference to the broad posterior surface of their strongly tilted wedge-like transverse plate. A short distance anterior of the widest part of the plate the dorsolateral border of the crista turns dorsally and medially around a lateral ventricular cleft which separates the transverse plate from the floor of the ventricle. The cleft continues anteroventrally and medially, gradually becoming narrower and finally disappearing in the subcerebellar part of the ventricle. The cleft, which may be called the pars anterior of the recessus lateralis, is confluent posteriorly with a larger ventricular space beneath the posterolateral part of the transverse plate. This space is enclosed laterally by choroid membrane and corresponds to the recessus lateralis of most other vertebrates (figs. 80, 83). The pars anterior differs in having thick walls and in its considerable rostral continuation beneath the cerebellum, but it corresponds to the groove in Ictalurus, which may be regarded as beginning between the dorsolateral margin of the transverse plate and the cerebellar crest and continuing ventromedially to the fourth ventricle. If the VII lobe were removed in the catfish and the corpus cerebelli and transverse plate were rotated caudoventrally from the base of the plate, the relative positions of the parts of the lateral recess and of the plate and corpus cerebelli would become very similar to those in the salmons. The relations in the guppy are similar to those in the salmons except that the transverse plate is broad at its anteroventral base and the entire plate is so

strongly tilted caudalward that the thick-walled pars anterior of the recessus lateralis is relatively longer.

In Perca flavescens the transverse plate is tilted but slightly caudalward and tapers laterally to a truncated lateral border, to the dorsal margin of which is attached the choroid tela. The cerebellar crest lies ventral of the lateral part of the plate, a dorsoventrally wide ventricular space between the two corresponding in position to the recessus lateralis. This space is continuous with an extrabulbar space, covered by a continuation of the choroid membrane which forms the roof of the fourth ventricle; the extrabulbar space extends forward as a small sac behind the eminentia granularis. Various modifications of these patterns and relations of the recessus lateralis occur in other species.

Returning to the auricle, the layer of granules already mentioned in the anterior and dorsomedial walls of the recessus lateralis of Ictalurus is represented in young catfish by a layer of small cells between the recess and the zone in which the cerebellar crest and related fiber tracts turn medially into the transverse plate. This layer is continuous, around the ventromedial border of the cerebellar crest, with the nucleus dorsalis of the acousticolateral area. This nucleus, already described, is less compact than the nucleus medialis and its cells are smaller in the young stages of Ictalurus. A fascicle of fibers from the dorsal root of the anterior lateral-line nerve distributes among the cells, some fibers possibly continuing into the cell mass in the wall of the recess. The cerebellar crest forms a dorsomedial cap above the nucleus medialis and the nucleus dorsalis. A small median part of this cap, which includes some very small cells, is partially detached at some levels. Possibly this medial part is more closely related to the nucleus dorsalis, but I have been unable to analyze it satisfactorily.

A transverse series of an 11.8 mm Ictalurus shows a chain of cells from the nucleus dorsalis, around the medial border of the principal part of the crista and between its dorsomedial surface and the recessus lateralis, forming a layer in the ventrolateral wall of the recess. This layer continues into the anterior wall and also into the dorsomedial wall, expanding as it approaches the external surface of the transverse plate. It is continuous medially with a subtenial band of similar cells in the posterodorsal margin of the transverse plate; this band joins the corresponding contralateral band across the midline. Later stages show a layer of cells extending from beneath the medial part of the crista, along its medial and dorsomedial surfaces, and into the anterior wall of the recess. This layer is accompanied by a diffuse fascicle of fibers which, in part, appears to be a continuation of the dorsal root fibers seen in the younger stage; intermingled are fibers of a second fascicle which emerge from the partially detached portion of the cerebellar crest. Some fibers continue medially, parallel with the posterodorsal marginal band of cells, but whether from one or from both fascicles could not be determined.

The relations of the auricle to the nucleus dorsalis as found in sharks and rays and also in chondrosteans and Neoceratodus are recognizable in young Ictalurus, if one regards the chain of cells which continues from the nucleus dorsalis into the ventrolateral wall of the recessus lateralis as corresponding, in much reduced and shortened form, to the granular ridge and posterolateral fold of the auricle in elasmobranchs; and further considers the continuation in the anterior and dorsomedial walls of the recess as corresponding to the remainder of the elasmobranch auricle. There is no indication of cellular continuity between the granular layer in the walls of the recess, and a zone of diffuse cells beneath the medial part of the crista in adult Ictalurus, but the two fascicles above mentioned have the relations and distribution found in the young specimens.

The granular layer in the anterior and dorsomedial walls of the lateral recess is relatively much thicker in the adult, but in the ventromedial wall no definite layer occurs, although granules are diffused among the fibers of the adjacent part of the cerebellar crest. The increased thickness of the granular layer has reduced the recess to a shallow groove instead of the distinct cleft seen in young specimens.

The granular layer in the walls of the recessus lateralis of Ictalurus bears little resemblance to the large auricle of elasmobranchs, and the lateral recess appears to have but little in common with the recessus lateralis and the narrow continuation from it which separates the folds of the elasmobranch auricle. Differences in relative size and position of the crista cerebelli, eminentia granularis, and pars medialis, and the distortions produced by the large VII lobe of Ictalurus, add to the difficulties of comparing the lateral recess and auricle of the catfish with these features in the sharks and rays.

The relatively small eminentia granularis of elasmobranchs forms the floor of the medial part of the lateral recess. The continuation of the cerebellar crest around the peduncle of the auricle to the molecular layer of the pars medialis separates the granular eminence superficially from the auricle. In Ictalurus the cerebellar crest is much larger and extends medially between the floor of the ventricle and the eminentia, which is displaced to a lateral position. The crista also completely separates the granular eminence from the auricle. Instead of extending beyond the medial deflection of the crista, as in elasmobranchs, the reduced auricle occupies only the groove

formed by the sharp dorsomedial deflection of the large mass of fibers and molecular substance. The laterally displaced eminentia granularis expands in a rostral direction, at first beneath the crista and then on the inferior lateral surface of the cerebellum.

The folds of the large auricle of Squalus merge beneath the distal part of the narrow rostrolateral continuation of the lateral recess and around its end. A similar pattern is presented in the 11.8 mm Ictalurus, above described, except that the continuity of the two folds is entirely anterior of the recessus lateralis, with none around its end. In adult Ictalurus the granular layer extends from the ventricular to the external ends of the lateral recess, that is, from the ventral base of the transverse plate to its dorsolateral margin. Here it expands and is also continuous medially with the posterodorsal subtenial granular band, which corresponds to the interauricular granular band of elasmobranchs. The morphological relations of the granular layer in the wall of the recessus lateralis correspond so closely in most respects to those of the elasmobranch auricle that it appears justified to regard this layer as the auricle in Ictalurus.

In adult Salmo gairdneri a band of granules begins at the rostroventral end of the roof of the pars anterior of the recessus lateralis, occupying a position in the lateral part of the roof of the recess. It is covered laterally and dorsally by the dorsomedially deflected crista cerebelli, which also forms the floor of the recess. The band continues posterodorsally to the laterally expanded membrane-covered part of the recess, here enlarging into an irregular granular mass in the broadest part of the transverse plate. Since this plate tapers rostroventrally from this broad exposed part, the granular band takes a caudolateral as well as caudodorsal course. In late larval stages of Salmo and young Oncorhynchus the transverse plate is relatively short and the granular band takes a much more lateral direction and also extends into the anterolateral and lateral walls of the pars anterior of the recess.

The anterior end of the band in adult Salmo is continuous with a periventricular layer of small cells, beneath the rostral end of the crista, behind which larger cells are irregularly distributed. In a reduced silver sagittal series of a 37 mm Oncorhynchus a small fascicle of scattered fibers extends into the corresponding region from the acousticolateral area, but the specific origin of the fibers is uncertain. Possibly they represent anterior lateral-line fibers of dorsal root type that are mingled with ventral root fibers in the single anterior lateral-line root of this species and continue forward into a vestigial nucleus dorsalis. Anterior lateral-line root fibers and secondary fibers from the acousticolateral area enter the rostroventral part of the transverse plate, some of the root fibers forming a fascicle which accompanies the granular band. This band and its caudolateral expansion correspond to the auricle in Ictalurus. A subtenial granular band extends from the expanded part of the auricle to the midline, following the posterodorsal margin of the transverse plate.

The truncated lateral extremity of the slightly tilted transverse plate of Perca flavescens lies behind the eminentia granularis but is separated from it by a fibromolecular layer which is continuous with the cerebellar crest and its related fiber tracts. The truncated part of the plate, forming the anterior wall of the vaulted recessus lateralis, is a layer of granules which also faces the external sac above mentioned. This granular mass constitutes the auricle. It covers the upward-arching continuation of the cerebellar crest from the ventral beginning of the arch. Beyond the level where the dorsolateral tenial margin of the transverse plate turns laterally as the attachment of the choroid tela of the external choroidal sac, behind the eminentia granularis, a reduced granular band continues from the auricle to the granular layer of the pars medialis.

Except for the absence of the ventrocaudal continuation, dorsal of the horizontal part of the cerebellar crest, which would correspond to the ventral fold of the auricle, and the granular ridge to the nucleus dorsalis of Acipenser, the relations of the auricle of Perca are more similar to those in the sturgeon than to those of the catfish and salmons.

The pars medialis. The pars medialis of the transverse plate (figs. 82, 83) comprises a fibromolecular layer, a granular layer, the closely related dorsolateral and posterodorsal subtenial granular band, and a deep layer of larger cells which, in some species, continues across the midline from the eminentia granularis of one side to the other. In other species this layer extends only toward the midline, commissural fibers affording the only connections between the granular eminences. All of the pars medialis except its dorsal surface faces the fourth ventricle. The dorsal surface forms the floor of the posterolateral fissure (fig. 82) or, in Ictalurus (fig. 81B), the dorsal surface of the cerebellum behind the shallow corresponding furrow. The posterior part of the pars medialis is so thick in the salmons and the guppy that it forms a more or less rounded projection into the ventricle (figs. 78, 81A).

Among the species I have investigated in the adult stage the granular layer of the pars medialis is most simply represented in the guppy. In this species this layer is a compact mass of cells, triangular in sagittal section near the midline, the greater part of which faces the fourth ventricle (fig. 81A). The base of the triangle lies beneath

the tenial border and the floor of the posterolateral fissure. Farther laterally the gray layer becomes a band which is continuous with the posterolateral granular band and faces only the ventricle. A few short chains of granules extend from the lateral part of this band into the molecular part of the fibromolecular layer. There are variations in individual specimens that may be related to relative maturity since they suggest, in less extreme form, differences between young and adult cerebella of Ictalurus, Salmo gairdneri, and Oncorhynchus.

The posterodorsal subtenial band of cells in early postlarval stages of Ictalurus is compact, but in later stages the cells have lost their close arrangement and small fascicles of fine fibers are interspersed among them. Chains of similar cells also extend medially from the auricle. All these cells are larger than the granules of the adult catfish, but evidently give rise to the granule cells. In the adult the subtenial band has become a zone of compactly arranged granules; great numbers of chains, irregular masses, and diffuse granules are also found between and among numerous small fascicles of fine fibers from one side to the other of the pars medialis. The granules, however, are less abundant near the midline than laterally and, in sagittal sections, a triangular zone is shown, one side of which faces the nonventricular surface of the pars medialis as in the guppy (fig. 81B). Both the late larval and the adult stages of Salmo gairdneri have prominent chains and masses of granules laterally and posteriorly in the pars medialis, among somewhat larger fascicles of fibers than in Ictalurus. In adult Oncorhynchus few granules remain in the subtenial granular band, but great numbers are diffused among very numerous fascicles of fine fibers. Apparently the diffused cells represent migrant elements from the subtenial band and from chains that pass medially from the auricle.

The fibromolecular layer of the pars medialis (fig. 86) includes medially deflected fascicles of the ascending lateral-line and VIII root tracts, secondary fibers from the acousticolateral nuclei, an intereminential commissure, and the medially deflected part of the cerebellar crest. The intereminential commissure and acousticolateral tracts occupy the ventral and posteroventral parts of the layer. The vestibular and lateral-line fibers, with the possible exception of those of the anterior lateral-line root, decussate as the acousticolateral commissure. Above and anterior of the zone of commissural fibers a larger area, in sagittal sections, consists of fine fibers similar to those of the cerebellar crest. In the ventral part of this zone the fine fibers are aggregated into numerous small fascicles between chains or masses of granule cells, already mentioned. The dorsal part of the area, in front of the granular layer, consists of fine fibers not arranged in fascicles. In Ictalurus and adult Oncorhynchus, however, this area is so encroached upon by the small fascicles that it is relatively small as compared with the guppy, in which fascicles of fine fibers are confined to the region immediately dorsal and anterior of the commissural bundles. Many of the small fascicles can be followed into the anterior bulbar part of the crista, but numerous others appear to arise from the auricles, the marginal granular bands, and the chains of granules that extend from them into the pars medialis.

The relations of the fine fibers are obscured by the fascicles in Ictalurus and the adult salmons, but are more clearly shown in horizontal reduced silver sections of the guppy, in which the posterodorsal part of the pars medialis is relatively narrow. In this region small fascicles and also individual fibers cross from the posterolateral granular band of one side to the other. Short terminal branches of individual fibers end among the granule cells, fibers apparently having their origin in granules of the contralateral band. Other fine fibers of uncertain origin end in the fibromolecular layer. The submerged part of the transverse plate of the guppy broadens causing the auricles to diverge so far in their rostral course that individual fibers cannot be followed from one auricle to the other. In the sucker, however, the submerged continuation of the auricle forms the entire roof of the pars anterior of the lateral recess. This roof slopes dorsomedially from either side to a peak, above which the granular masses meet and are interconnected by fine fibers. At some levels only the fibrous interconnections appear. Horizontal sections of young Oncorhynchus show numerous small fascicles of fine fibers entering the fibromolecular layer from the eminentia granularis; presumably these are axons of granule cells. The small fascicles between the fibromolecular layer and the cerebellar crest presumably include both ascending and descending fibers.

In summary: the fibromolecular layer, in addition to the commissural fibers between the bilateral acousticolateral areas and eminentiae granulares, includes smaller fibers that interconnect the auricles and their related chains of granules, and also an extensive layer of neuropil formed by fibers from the cerebellar crest, numerous fascicles of fine fibers from the eminentiae granulares, the auricles, and the chains of cells in the pars medialis.

THE CORPUS CEREBELLI

The corpus cerebelli of some teleosts such as Lophius and Crystallogobius forms only a small and simple hump directed dorsally and slightly caudalward. In Perca the corpus is somewhat elongated in a dorsocaudal direction and expands into an ovoid mass, as seen in sagittal section, the posterior part of which projects above the transverse plate. The salmons, guppy, and many other species have an elongated corpus cerebelli which is tilted caudalward so strongly that its dorsal surface is more or less horizontal, the posterior part in some species dipping ventralward (figs. 78, 81A, 82). Ictalurus and other siluroids have a strongly rostralward tilted corpus cerebelli, much of which overlies the optic tectum (fig. 81B). In the large catfish of Europe, Silurus glanis, however, Addison (1923) found that the corpus is divided into anteriorly and posteriorly directed parts. Other large teleosts (Scomber, Caranx, Thynnus, Pelamys), described by Franz (1911a), also have anterior and posterior divisions above a broad peduncle-like base which corresponds, in general, to the pars ventralis of the corpus cerebelli of elasmobranchs. The similarity is obscured, however, by the position and large size of the eminentia granularis which in most teleosts merges with the ventrolateral part of the corpus cerebelli. In Megalops, according to van der Horst (1926), the corpus cerebelli is displaced dorsalward by a large fold of the valvula, and the dorsal part of the corpus tilts rostralward.

The corpus cerebelli of most species comprises a nearly solid core of granules, covered by a zone of Purkinje cells and an outer molecular layer (figs. 79, 82). In the Salmonidae and many other species a cerebellar canal remains of the embryonic cerebellar ventricle (figs. 78, 82A). A narrow dorsal recess of the ventricle leads to the canal in Ictalurus. According to van der Horst the cerebellar ventricle of Megalops is represented by a fissure-like cleft owing to incomplete fusion of the bilateral granular masses. This characteristic is shared by other primitive teleosts, states van der Horst.

As seen in sections of the cerebellum, the fusion of the granular layer of the corpus with the eminentia granularis is so intimate in many species that no internal boundary between the two granular masses can be established (fig. 87). In the sucker (Minytrema?), as already noted, a thin septum separates them for a considerable distance inward from the surface before they fuse. In Anguilla the granular layer of the corpus reaches the lateral surface of the cerebellum but is delimited from the eminentia granularis by a furrow, van der Horst (1925) points out. This furrow is undoubtedly a continuation of the posterolateral fissure.

As in other Ichthyopsida the corpus cerebelli of teleosts receives only fiber tracts not related to the acousticolateral systems. It therefore constitutes a distinct functional as well as morphological division of the cerebellum.

The valvula cerebelli. The valvula of teleosts varies in

size and form much more widely than the corpus cerebelli. It is small and simple in the guppy, whereas in Mormyrus, Franz (1911b) states, it is a complex structure with large and highly specialized lateral lobules. The ratio of size of the valvula, in this fish, to that of the remainder of the brain is probably greater, Franz says, than the ratio of the cerebral hemispheres to the brain stem in man.

The bilateral rudiments of the embryonic valvula merge across the midline, forming a rostral projection from the base of the cerebellum (figs. 78–82). This projection differentiates into a median and two lateral lobules that vary in size in different species, both as compared with the corpus cerebelli and in comparison of the lateral with the median lobule. In Ictalurus the median part of the valvula extends forward as a tapering projection beneath the rostrally tilted corpus cerebelli, its anterior tip continuing with a short anterior medullary velum (fig. 81B). A thin cleft of the cranial cavity separates this part of the valvula from the corpus cerebelli. Laterally the valvula expands as a simple lateral lobule, on each side, which projects into the ventricle beneath it. Although simple in pattern the valvula of Ictalurus is relatively large. The much smaller valvula of the guppy comprises small lateral lobules connected across the midline by a thin median plate. It projects slightly into the mesencephalic ventricle and tapers dorsally to the anterior medullary velum (fig. 81A). In the salmons and many other species the valvula is strongly folded into the mesencephalic ventricle, the recess of the cranial cavity extending ventralward into a sac whose walls and floor are formed by the folds (fig. 78). Other species have a simple sac-like valvula with little or no folding. The granular layer in this type of valvula, according to Franz (1911a), is laterally situated and extends from the dorsal to the ventral part of the sac. In Megalops, van der Horst (1926) states, the valvula is unusually large but lacks lateral lobules. The median part is greatly elongated and has six folds under the roof of the midbrain, in addition to an elongated fold, already mentioned, in the fourth ventricle beneath the corpus cerebelli.

The lateral lobules of the valvula are the most variable subdivisions of the teleostean cerebellum. They attain their largest size in cyprinoids, siluroids and mormyrids, becoming enormous in Mormyrus, as described by Franz (1911b), Stendell (1914), Berkelbach van der Sprenkel (1915), and Suzuki (1932). In this species they dilate the mesencephalic ventricle and then burgeon outward in such fashion as to cover the remainder of the brain.

According to Ariens Kappers (1947) the lateral lobules are added to the median part of the valvula in fishes, such as siluroids and cyprinoids, that have a well-developed gustatory system. Berkelbach van der Sprenkel (1915), however, emphasizes the hypertrophy of the lateral-line system, especially the posterior lateral-line nerve and its central connections in Mormyrus, in which the gustatory system is relatively small, as the predominant factor related to hypertrophy of the lateral lobule.

The nucleus cerebelli. Ramon y Cajal (1894) described a "ganglio subcerebelloso" in the trout which he subsequently (1908b) believed to correspond to the nucleus lateralis cerebelli of Edinger in elasmobranchs. Goldstein (1905) and Ariens Kappers (1906) regarded the "Rindenknoten" or secondary vagus nucleus of earlier authors as the nucleus lateralis cerebelli of teleosts. The "Rindenknoten," however, bears only a topographical relation to the cerebellum, as Franz (1911a) emphasized. It is the secondary gustatory nucleus of Herrick (1905) or secondary visceral-gustatory nucleus of other authors, and, in Salmonidae, it is relatively small. Franz found no clearly differentiated cerebellar nucleus in teleosts, but suggests that clusters of cells in the Purkinje cell layer are incipient nuclear masses.

A definitive nucleus cerebelli was described in two species of trout and in the carp by Pearson (1936b), who suggests that it corresponds to the nucleus cerebelli of the frog described by Larsell (1923, 1925), and of Neoceratodus (Holmgren and van der Horst, 1925). According to Pearson the nucleus lies lateral of the fourth ventricle and between the eminentia granularis and the cerebellar commissure. It comprises a characteristic group of neurons that stain differently from the Purkinje cells. The relations of the nucleus are modified in the carp by the large secondary visceral-gustatory nucleus of this species, from which the nucleus cerebelli is separated by a layer of fibers.

Rüdeberg (1961) was unable to identify the nucleus cerebelli of Pearson with certainty in the pike or Salmo salar in his analysis of cell migrations from the columna dorsalis. "Migration A_2B," which in elasmobranchs gives rise to the nucleus cerebelli, merges with "migration A_1" in these species, Rüdeberg states, forming one continuous cell mass called A_1A_2B. The dorsomedial part of this mass differs in structure from the remainder and forms a separate bulge on the cerebellar surface. The A_2B portion of the entire cell mass he regards as probably forming the part of the stratum granulosum which extends lateralward above the eminentia granularis, the A_1 portion becoming the granular eminence, as already noted. Cell mass A_2B, with probable accretions from the superficial granular layer, he believes to be probably homologous with the cerebellar nuclei of other vertebrates.

In late larval Salmo gairdneri and young Oncorhynchus there is no grouping of cells corresponding to Pearson's nucleus cerebelli in the brook trout and landlocked salmon, and none could be identified with assurance in adult Oncorhynchus, Ictalurus, Perca, and Minytrema, or in other species less thoroughly studied. In the steelhead salmon, however, I find a cell group which corresponds to Pearson's description of the nucleus cerebelli in Salmonidae.

The nucleus lateralis valvulae. The lateral nucleus of the valvula of Herrick (1905) is related to afferent systems of the cerebellum, especially those of the valvula, and is present in all species. It is situated lateral and, in part, lateroventral of the valvula and medial of the torus semicircularis (fig. 87), projecting into the mesencephalic ventricle as an elevation between these structures in the salmons. In the catfish it lies ventral of the lateral part of the valvula from which, in all species, it is more or less completely separated by fiber tracts. The caudal part of the nucleus is entered by fiber tracts so that in some planes of section it is divided into two masses for a short distance.

THE CEREBELLAR CONNECTIONS

The afferent tracts. The afferents of the vestibulolateral lobe have been described in the consideration of the acousticolateral systems and need only be summarized here. Ascending fascicles of anterior lateral-line root fibers terminate in the auricle, pars medialis, eminentia granularis, and valvula (figs. 83, 84). In Ictalurus dorsal anterior lateral-line root fibers appear to reach the auricle but not the granular eminence. Ascending posterior lateral-line root fibers terminate in the eminentia granularis and the valvula of both sides, the crossed fibers decussating in the acousticolateral commissure. Possibly the crossed fibers are accompanied by decussated anterior lateral-line root fibers, but this is uncertain. An ascending fascicle of utricular fibers continues from the anterior root of the VIII nerve to the eminentia granularis and, according to Ariens Kappers (1947), saccular fibers enter the "basal part," evidently the transverse plate, of the cerebellum, but none from the ampullary cristae reaches any of the cerebellar subdivisions.

Secondary acousticolateral fibers pass to the eminentia granularis, as described by Pearson (1936b). Some enter the acousticolateral commissure and small fascicles of fine fibers that appear to arise in the anterior part of the nucleus medialis enter the fibromolecular layer of the pars medialis. The larger secondary fibers also appear to derive from the nucleus medialis and, possibly, from some of the vestibular nuclei, but their origin can be established only in fortunate Golgi preparations. As already noted, ascending fibers of the acousticolateral systems, neither primary nor secondary, terminate in the

corpus cerebelli except for a small fascicle from the pars medialis to the inferior posterior part of the corpus. This fascicle probably consists of vestibular fibers that turn dorsalward from the acousticolateral commissure.

The spino-cerebellar tract was demonstrated in Cyprinus and Tinca by Wallenberg (1907) in Marchi preparations. He describes it as decussating dorsal of the decussatio veli and the commissure of the secondary visceral-gustatory nucleus, terminating in the ventrolateral parts of the cerebellum. Herrick (1907) describes a dorsal spino-cerebellar tract as especially well developed in Prionotus and other fishes that have specialized feelers among their fin rays. The corresponding part of the spino-cerebellar system is larger than the ventral part in the flatfish, Pleuronectes, according to Addison (1923). Franz (1911a), Ariens Kappers (1921), and Pearson (1936b) describe the spino-cerebellar system in various species, the last named regarding a division into dorsal and ventral tracts as arbitrary.

In reduced silver series of young Chinook salmon the spino-cerebellar tract is shown as a superficially situated fascicle immediately ventral of the descending tract of the V root. At the level of entrance of the V roots the tract turns dorsalward, fascicles of its fibers passing between the root bundles and uniting as a common fascicle which reaches the cerebellum and decussates. The distribution of the fibers is limited to the corpus cerebelli (fig. 85).

An olivo-cerebellar tract is closely associated with the spino-cerebellar fascicle. The fibers decussate in the medulla oblongata so that the system appears to be entirely crossed. Turning dorsalward with the spino-cerebellar tract the fibers accompany the tract into the corpus cerebelli (fig. 85).

Trigemino-cerebellar fibers clearly pass into the base of the corpus cerebelli in the reduced silver series of the salmon (fig. 85). Apparently they do not decussate. No secondary trigemino-cerebellar fibers could be recognized with any certainty.

The tractus mesencephalo-cerebellaris anterior (the tractus tecto-cerebellaris of Ariens Kappers, 1947, the tractus pretecto-cerebellaris of Burr, 1928) is shown in the catfish and in silver series of the salmon as having its origin in the region where the tegmentum and the torus longitudinalis come together at the anterior border of the optic tectum. The tract was similarly described by Addison (1923) in Gadus, Arius, and Pleuronectes. The torus longitudinalis of teleosts is a projection of the deep, small-celled layer of the dorsomedial wall of the tectum into the mesencephalic ventricle, following the curve of the optic tectum caudodorsally. According to Kudo (1923, 1924) the torus receives fibers from the intertectal commissure and cerebellum, sending correlated impulses through a toro-tectal tract. It also sends fibers to the entopeduncular nucleus. Charlton (1933) gives the origin of the anterior mesencephalo-cerebellar tract in the blindfishes, Troglichthys and Typhlichthys, more specifically as the optic tectum, the pretectal nucleus, the lateral geniculate body, and, possibly, the nucleus anterior thalami. Franz (1911b) found degeneration of the tract when the roof of the midbrain was destroyed, thus establishing its cerebellipetal nature. The tract takes a caudal course in the tegmentum beneath the floor of the mesencephalic ventricle, gradually turning dorsomedially beneath the nucleus lateralis valvulae to enter the corpus cerebelli (fig. 81A). Within the cerebellum it forms a prominent fascicle on either side of the midline and frays out posteriorly. According to Franz (1911a) its fibers terminate in the molecular layer. In my well-differentiated reduced silver series of the salmon, however, the fibers divide into more slender branches and small twigs that clearly end among the granule cells. Terminal twigs in the molecular layer are present in great numbers, in the reduced silver series, as branches of fibers intermingled with those that terminate among the granules. In Golgi series of Ictalurus, branching fibers, ending among the granules, do not extend into the molecular layer but other more slender fibers traverse the granular layer and divide into terminal twigs in the molecularis. The anterior mesencephalo-cerebellar tract is one of the afferent fascicles which distributes among the granule cells, but the origin of the fibers ending in the molecular layer is uncertain. Wallenberg (1907) describes the anterior mesencephalo-cerebellar tract as ending posterior of the valvula only, but according to Pearson (1936b) it distributes in the valvula as well as the corpus cerebelli.

Franz (1911b) and Addison (1923) considered the anterior mesencephalo-cerebellar, or tecto-cerebellar, tract as related to the optic system in fishes because variations in its size appear to be correlated with variations in the degree of development of the visual apparatus in different species. The pretecto-cerebellar tract of Burr (1928) probably is the corresponding pathway in the open-sea sunfish, Orthagoriscus. In this species the large eyes provide the principal sensory intake, the lateral-line and other sensory systems being much reduced, as already mentioned; the pretecto-cerebellar tract is the largest that reaches the cerebellum. Charlton (1933), however, maintains that the anterior mesencephalo-cerebellar tract, although in development it may parallel the secondary visual centers from which it has origin, does not vary in size in proportion to the visual function of individual species. He found it as large in totally blind cave fishes as in some of the catfishes that possess all the elements necessary for vision, although perhaps on a reduced scale. Obviously the tract is not merely a relay path for optic impulses but must also serve other sensory systems that have connections with the region of its origin. Ariens Kappers, Huber, and Crosby (1936) hold that it does not correspond to the tecto-cerebellar tract of reptiles, birds, and mammals, to which I would add petromyzonts and amphibians. In all these groups the tecto-cerebellar tract has its origin in the caudal part of the tectum, has no relation to the tegmentum, and enters the cerebellum by way of the anterior medullary velum.

The tractus mesencephalo-cerebellaris posterior, or tegmento-cerebellar tract of Ariens Kappers, passes from the nucleus lateralis valvulae to the valvula and corpus cerebelli. In Megalops, according to van der Horst (1926), most of the fibers reach the valvula. The fibers to the corpus cerebelli leave the nucleus as fascicles which converge and decussate, then taking a caudodorsal course above the anterior mesencephalo-cerebellar tract but merging with it more or less. The tegmento-cerebellar tract is large in siluroids and cyprinoids that have a well-developed secondary gustatory nucleus and a large valvula. In the Mormyridae, which have a greatly hypertrophied lateral-line system and an enormous valvula, it is very large (Ariens Kappers, 1947). Some of the afferent connections of the nucleus lateralis valvulae have been described above, but others are imperfectly known. Evidently impulses from the torus semicircularis, nucleus isthmi, secondary gustatory nucleus, and possibly other sources are correlated in this nucleus.

The tractus lobo-cerebellaris has its origin in the inferior lobe of the hypothalamus and takes a caudodorsal course to the cerebellum, passing beneath and behind the nucleus lateralis valvulae. Many of its fibers enter the valvula but the majority, in the Chinook salmon, appear to accompany the posterior mesencephalo-cerebellar tract into the corpus cerebelli. Connections between the hypothalamus and the cerebellum were described by Mayser (1881), Haller (1898), Ariens Kappers (1906, 1921, 1947), Burr (1928), and others. Franz (1911b) designated the fascicle the tractus diencephalo-cerebellaris, and Wallenberg (1907) showed by the Marchi method that it is cerebellipetal in Cyprinus and Tinca. In sagittal Golgi sections of Ictalurus I have observed cells in the inferior lobe of the hypothalamus from which axons enter the lobo-cerebellar tract as in Amia. The lobi inferiores have gustatory (Herrick, 1905) and olfactory (Sheldon, 1912) connections and, according to Ariens Kappers (1920–21), represent part of the correlation area involved in feeding. Addison (1923) found this tract to be relatively larger in Arius than in Gadus or Pleuronectes, suggesting a correlation with the gustatory system, which is well developed in siluroids.

The inferior lobes are also connected, however, with a receptor organ in the saccus vasculosus which is probably stimulated by changes in fluid pressure. Ariens Kappers, Huber, and Crosby (1936) suggest that stimuli from this receptor may be relayed through the lobo-cerebellar tract. In Golgi sections of Ictalurus and other species, and in reduced silver sections of the salmon, fibers of other origin and distribution are closely associated with the lobo-cerebellar tract in much of its course, but I have been unable to analyze them. These fibers may correspond to the cerebello-lobar and cerebello-hypothalamic tracts of Ariens Kappers described below.

The efferent fibers. The cerebellar efferent fibers, according to Pearson (1936b), comprise a cerebello-motor system and a cerebello-tegmental tract or brachium conjunctivum. The cerebello-motor system distributes to the motor nuclei of the midbrain, medulla oblongata, and spinal cord; the brachium conjunctivum distributes to the tegmentum of the midbrain and to the diencephalon. A clear distinction between the two systems, however, cannot be drawn.

According to Addison (1923) the cerebello-motor fibers of Gadus, Arius, and Pleuronectes collect from the cerebellar cortex, probably from the Purkinje cells, into fascicles that pass medial of the mesencephalo-cerebellar tracts and then ventrally and laterally around the sub-cerebellar part of the fourth ventricle. They then turn medially and cross the midline, the decussation extending as far forward as the ansulate commissure. In Gadus nearly all the fibers emerge from the cerebellum behind the commissure of the secondary visceral-gustatory nuclei, the most rostral fibers arching forward beneath the commissure and continuing as the "brachium conjunctivum anterius." The brachium is especially large in Arius and arises in great part from the well-developed valvula of this species. A contingent of fibers emerging from the cerebellum forms an anterior division in front of the secondary visceral-gustatory commissure and another contingent emerges behind this commissure. The posterior fibers turn caudalward, forming the tractus cerebellomotorius proper of Addison. In Pleuronectes the anterior part of the tract emerges in front of the commissure, but most of the fibers, Addison (1923) states, have their origin in the corpus cerebelli. The most anterior fibers of the brachium conjunctivum anterius are described as ending in the vicinity of the torus semicircularis. In Salvelinus, according to Pearson (1936b), the efferent fibers begin to separate into the two systems beneath the cerebellar commissure.

The cerebello-motor system, according to Pearson, divides into a pars bulbaris and a pars mesencephalica. The pars bulbaris, Pearson says, forms a loose decussation at about the level of the cerebellar commissure. From this decussation crossed and uncrossed fibers pass into the fasciculus longitudinalis medialis, and others turn caudalward and distribute to the motor nuclei of the medulla oblongata. The pars mesencephalica passes rostralward close to the ventricular wall, distributing in part to the medial longitudinal fascicle, largely ipsilaterally, and to the nucleus of the IV nerve.

The brachium conjunctivum passes forward with the cerebello-motor system but takes a more ventrolateral position. At the level of the IV nucleus and mostly beneath the medial longitudinal fascicles it begins to form a conspicuous decussation from which scattered fascicles continue forward as crossed and uncrossed fibers to the tegmentum of the midbrain. Some accompanying fibers that pass to the nucleus of the III nerve Pearson believes represent a cerebello-motor component of the brachium conjunctivum.

According to him, efferent fibers from the Purkinje cell layer of the corpus cerebelli and the valvula pass dorsally and in front of the commissura cerebelli and then ventrorostrally, curving toward the midline, many of them decussating. These fibers are said to form cerebello-tegmental and cerebello-motor tracts, the cerebello-motor tract distributing to the nuclei of the III and IV nerves while the cerebellotegmental tract passes to the mesencephalic tegmentum and the diencephalon. An uncrossed component of the cerebello-motor system in the carp is described as passing caudalward near the ventricular wall, distributing to the motor column along its course. At the level of the VIII roots other fibers of the tract turn lateralward into the nucleus of Deiters.

According to Tuge (1935), who studied the distribution of cerebellifugal fibers in the goldfish by the Marchi method, the rostrally directed fibers begin to decussate a little in front of the roots of the III nerve and terminate in the nucleus of the fasciculus longitudinalis medialis, the nucleus of the III nerve, and the nucleus reticularis mesencephali of Ariens Kappers. These ascending fibers Tuge regarded as the brachium conjunctivum.

He found no degenerated fibers of the anterior group beyond the midbrain. According to Brickner (1929), however, some of the fibers reach the region of the posterior commissure and also the ventral thalamus. The cerebello-hypothalamic tract, above mentioned, is described by Ariens Kappers (1947) as originating, apparently, in all parts of the cerebellum, and the cerebello-lobar fascicle as arising in the region of the nucleus lateralis valvulae. Tuge (1934b) found experimental evidence of a cerebello-tectal tract which he states may have a connection with the torus semicircularis. Charlton (1933) described as a cerebello-mesencephalic tract, in blindfishes, fibers that terminate chiefly in the torus semi-circularis, though some continue into the optic tectum. Presumably this tract corresponds to Tuge's cerebello-tectal tract, with a variation in distribution related to the functional difference of the optic tectum in blind fishes and the goldfish. Fritsch (1878), Mayser (1881), Haller (1898), and Pearson (1936b) describe cerebello-tectal fibers under various names.

The descending cerebellar fibers, according to Tuge (1935), are crossed and uncrossed. They provide connections with the IV, VI, motor VII, and possibly motor V nuclei and also with the motor tegmentum and the nucleus of the raphe, the last two connections being described as the most important. He believes that no fibers reach the spinal cord, though Ariens Kappers (1947) includes connections with the reflex centers of the cord among the cerebellifugal fibers.

The efferent cerebellar fibers predominantly appear to be axons of Purkinje cells. According to Tuge (1935) the cerebello-tectal tract, however, originates at a deeper level of the corpus cerebelli than the Purkinje cell layer. The cerebello-tegmental tract or brachium conjunctivum of Salmo salar and Salvelinus, according to Pearson (1936b), arises from Purkinje cells and from the nucleus cerebelli, as do fibers of the cerebello-motorius system. In Oncorhynchus I have been unable to identify a distinct nucleus cerebelli, but efferent fibers appear to derive from cells in the deep part of the corpus cerebelli as well as from Purkinje cells of this division and of the valvula.

The commissures. The spino-cerebellar and perhaps the trigeminal fibers that cross in the anteroventral part of the corpus cerebelli constitute a commissura cerebelli corresponding to that of most other Ichthyopsida, but it is not certain that the trigeminal component includes secondary fibers.

The posterior and perhaps the anterior lateral-line root fibers that, together with fibers of the VIII root, cross in the ventral portion of the pars medialis to the contralateral eminentia granularis make up an acoustico-lateral commissure (fig. 86). Added to this are secondary fibers from one granular eminence to the other, forming an intereminential commissure. A fascicle which follows the posterior margin of the vestibulolateral lobe appears to constitute an anterior lateral-line commissure. In Ictalurus this is related to the dorsal root of the anterior lateral-line nerve. In species having a single root of this nerve the commissure may be related to the dorsal root type fibers. Whether the fine fibers that pass through the pars medialis from the lateral part of the subtenial granular band of one side, to end in the contralateral band, are small terminal branches of the larger commissural fibers and may be therefore regarded as commissural is not clear. As above noted, many of them, at least, end among the granules of the contralateral band, but the origin of the fibers is uncertain.

The so-called interauricular commissure of Wallenberg (1907) is prominent in Ictalurus, as also described in the siluroid Arius glanis by Ariens Kappers, Huber, and Crosby (1936). According to these authors the commissure is but slightly developed in Gadus. I have been unable to identify it in the salmons and guppy. Van der Horst (1926) regards a commissural interconnection between the granular eminences of Megalops that lies above the fourth ventricle instead of taking a ventral course immediately beneath the surface of the medulla oblongata, as in Siluroids, as homologous with Wallenberg's commissure. It appears more probable that the commissure in Megalops corresponds to the intereminential commissure above described in other species, including Ictalurus.

The commissure of Wallenberg in Ictalurus is formed of fibers issuing from the auricle proper and from the eminentia granularis, the latter contributing the majority. These fibers converge into compact fascicles that soon unite to form one which arches ventromedially beneath the lateroventral and ventral surfaces of the medulla oblongata. On approaching the midline the fascicle subdivides into several smaller bundles, but all appear to cross and reassemble into a larger compact tract. Most of the fibers spread in the lateral part of the eminentia granularis especially, some appearing to end among its cells; others presumably take their origin from some of the cells, but no specific cells could be related to the efferent fibers. A smaller fascicle, which splits off and passes to the auricle, spreads and disappears among the granules.

Ariens Kappers, Huber, and Crosby (1936) associate the large size of the intergranular commissure in Arius with the marked development of the lateral-line system in this species. The dorsally situated intereminential commissure of Megalops, in which the lateral-line system is also well developed, and the corresponding commissure in other species, comprises fibers that probably serve both vestibular and lateral-line systems. Possibly Wallenberg's commissure is more closely related to the lateral-line system since it interconnects the auricles as well as the granular eminences, and the auricular part of the commissure is predominant in elasmobranchs. Conclusive evidence in support of this suggestion, however, is lacking.

THE HISTOLOGY

The corpus cerebelli comprises three layers: molecular, Purkinje cell, and granular (figs. 79, 82, 87), which, Schaper (1893) and Franz (1911a) pointed out, are

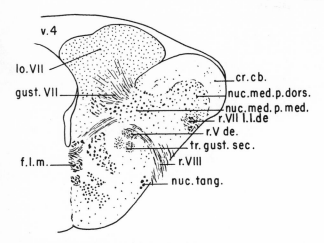

Figure 88. Transverse section of medulla oblongata of Ameiurus melas at the level of the VIII nerve root. Toluidine blue. ×22. (Slightly modified from Pearson, 1936a.)

homologous with those of higher vertebrates. The molecular layer completely surrounds the granular layer except where the latter is continuous with the eminentiae granulares and the valvula. Rostrally the molecular layer is continuous with the molecularis of the valvula and, caudoventrally, through a usually thinner zone, with that of the pars medialis of the vestibulolateral lobe (fig. 87). Laterally the molecular layer borders on the granular surface of the eminentia granularis. The Purkinje cells are arranged in a more definite layer between the molecularis and the granularis than in holosteans. At various points the Purkinje cell layer is two or more cells thick. The granular layer forms an almost solid core in species in which only a cerebellar canal remains of the cerebellar ventricle. Megalops, however, retains the narrow ventricular space which separates the right and left granular masses of the corpus cerebelli.

The valvula (fig. 87) has distinct molecular and granular layers, but the Purkinje cells are more irregular than in the corpus cerebelli. The molecularis forms the dorsal layer in the simpler types of valvula, the granular layer, which is continuous with that of the corpus cerebelli and the eminentia granularis, facing the ventricle (fig. 87). When the valvula is recurved, as in the guppy, the granular layer becomes anteriorly to dorsally situated in the upward folded portion, facing the posterior end and, in part, facing a posterior recess of the mesencephalic ventricle (fig. 81A). In species with a much folded valvula the same fundamental relations prevail.

The vestibulolateral lobe differs considerably from the remainder of the cerebellum in the arrangement of its molecular and granular layers. Most of the external surface of the eminentia granularis is formed of granules. In

the young salmon, however, a molecular layer covers the lower posterior surface (fig. 83). As already noted, the pars medialis comprises a ventral or ventrocaudal fibrous and molecular layer superficial to the intereminential cell mass and the interauricular granular band which partly separates the molecular layer from the ventricular surface.

Cells and fibers. Following earlier studies by Fusari (1887) the cell types of the teleostean cerebellum were described from Golgi preparations of the salmon by Schaper (1893) and by Franz (1911a) in the trout and goldfish. Catois (1901) and P. Ramon y Cajal (1894) added details about cell processes. I have reviewed serial sections of the brains of a number of species of teleosts prepared by the Golgi method. These preparations reveal details with regard to the shape of the neurons and the branching and distribution of the dendrites, as appears from figures 89–97. In addition I have studied Cajal ser-

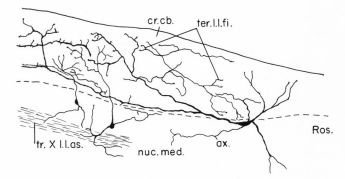

Figure 89. Cells and fibers in acousticolateral area of Catostomus caudal to the VIII nerve root. Golgi method.

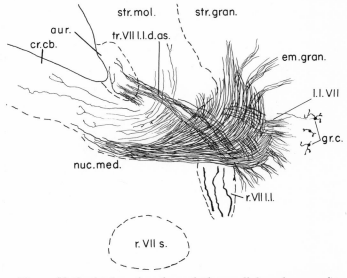

Figure 90. Sagittal section through the medial nucleus, auricle and eminentia granularis of Catostomus. Golgi method.

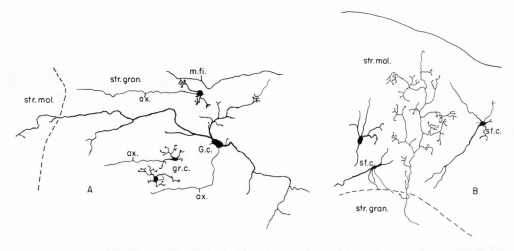

Figure 91. Cerebellum of Catostomus. A. Granular layer of corpus cerebelli with granule cells and a Golgi type II cell. B. Molecular layer of corpus cerebelli with tufted terminal fibers and stellate cells. Golgi method.

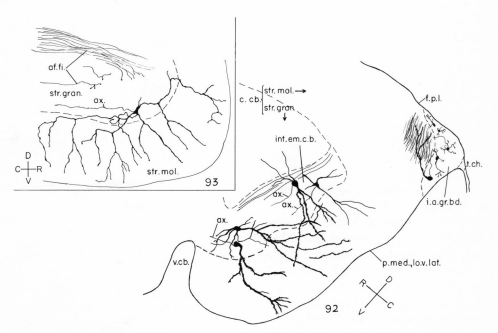

Figure 92. Sagittal section of medial part of vestibulolateral lobe of cerebellum of Ameiurus, showing primitive Purkinje cells. The fibers adjacent to the interauricular granular band are traceable from the acousticolateral area. Golgi method. *Figure 93*. Sagittal section through rostral end of corpus cerebelli showing a large Golgi type II cell and afferent fibers. Adult Ameiurus. Golgi method.

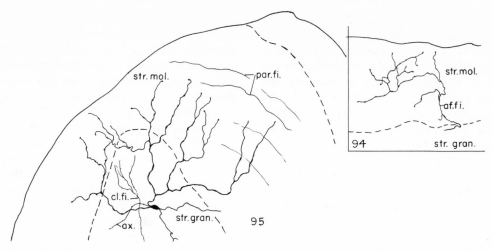

Figure 94. Climbing fiber in cerebellum of Ameiurus. Fibers of similar type have been seen in loose winding about dendrites of Purkinje cells. Golgi method. *Figure 95*. Large Golgi type II cell in a sagittal section through lateral part of corpus cerebelli of adult Ameiurus. Golgi method.

ies of young and adult catfish and salmon and adult guppies. My observations of cell types in the corpus cerebelli confirm, in general, those of Schaper and Franz, but the finer structure of the vestibulolateral lobe, as was not recognized by these and other earlier authors, differs in some respects from that of the corpus cerebelli.

The molecular layer of all parts of the corpus cerebelli is formed of innumerable transversely arranged parallel fibers, dendrites of Purkinje and Golgi cells and stellate or fusiform neurons and their processes, situated entirely within the molecularis (figs. 93, 95). Terminal fibers of some of the tracts that distribute in the corpus cerebelli end in the molecular layer as fine forked twigs, similar to those of the VIII and lateral-line root fibers in the cerebellar crest (fig. 91B). Some of the fusiform cells, as described by Schaper, have long dendritic processes that extend so far rostrally and posteriorly in the sagittal plane that they may encompass a third of the upper surface of the cerebellum of the young salmon. These dendrites give rise to numerous shorter branches which, with their ramifications, extend close to the external cerebellar surface. The axons of these cells pass between the Purkinje cells and turn at right angles, becoming lost in the tangle of fibers that surround the Purkinje cell bodies. Catois (1901) described rudimentary baskets around Purkinje cells in teleosts, but connections between these and collaterals of the axons of the fusiform cells have not been established. The fusiform cells of the molecular layer appear to be precursors of the basket cells of higher vertebrates. Smaller cells of stellate form send their dendrites into the surrounding molecularis (fig. 91). The axons of these cells are difficult to identify.

The Purkinje cells of the corpus cerebelli have pyriform cell bodies that give rise to a single dendritic stem. This divides into two or three primary branches that spread widely in the sagittal plane, taking a nearly horizontal course. These give rise to secondary branches that extend toward the cerebellar surface and ramify into numerous tertiary branches directed perpendicularly, many ending just beneath the cerebellar surface. The secondary and tertiary branches are studded with small spines. The Purkinje cell dendrites vary in relative length and spread in different species of teleosts. As illustrated in the salmon by Schaper (1893), they are long and spread

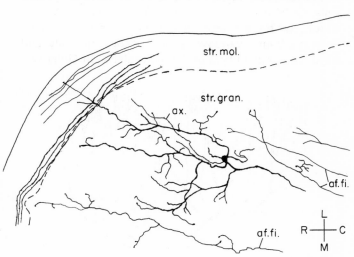

Figure 96. Large Golgi type II cell and afferent fibers immediately beneath molecular layer of dorsal surface. Horizontal section of corpus cerebelli of adult Ameiurus. Golgi method.

121

widely. I find a similar pattern in many other species, but in Ictalurus the dendrites are relatively short and spread less widely. Franz (1911a) mentions stunted Purkinje cells in the dorsocaudal part of the corpus cerebelli of the trout. The axons of the Purkinje cells do not enter the granular layer, but are directed obliquely or horizontally among neighboring Purkinje cells and traverse the zone where the granular layer impinges on the molecular substance of the cerebellum. They form a layer of myelinated fibers at the periphery of the granular layer or in the superficial part of the white layer. According to Ramon y Cajal (1911) collaterals of these axons are limited to one or may be entirely absent. Bielschowsky and Wolff (1904) and Franz (1911a) are inclined to regard collaterals as nonexistent. I have found none.

In the vestibulolateral lobe the Purkinje cells are less typical. Golgi sections of Ameiurus, cut in the sagittal plane, show large neurons, situated in the intereminential cellular mass, that send elongated dendrites into the fibrous and molecular layer of the pars medialis (fig. 92). Some of the cells also give off dendritic branches into the surrounding cellular substance, these processes being smooth while those to the fibrous layer are studded with spiny excrescences and also have terminal tufts of small dendritic branches. In addition, smaller neurons send unstudded branches into the fibrous layer as well as among the cells of the gray substance. The larger cells appear to correspond to the transitional and primitive Purkinje cells of the acousticolateral area of Acipenser. Similar neurons, but lacking spines, were found in Cajal preparations of the guppy.

The granular layer includes, in addition to granule cells, Golgi cells (figs. 95, 96). The granule cells (fig. 91A) have three or four small dendritic branches ending in protoplasmic varicosities; their axons bifurcate and form the parallel fibers of the molecularis. In Golgi sec-

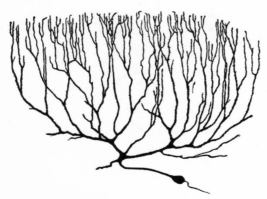

Figure 97. Purkinje cell from 10.5 cm long perch. ×140. (Ariens Kappers, Huber, and Crosby, 1936, after Schaper, 1893.)

tions of Ameiurus and other teleosts I have found well-impregnated typical granules in the corpus cerebelli, the eminentia granularis, and the rostral part of the nucleus medialis et dorsalis of the acousticolateral area. Large cells, found immediately beneath the molecular layer or close to it, send their dendrites chiefly or entirely into the molecularis. Others lie deeper in the granular layer, their dendritic spread extending chiefly in the granularis; but some dendrites reach the molecular layer. Both these types correspond to the association cells of Schaper and Franz. Histologically they are Golgi cells. The cell bodies of the submolecular cells tend to an elongated or spindle form and their slender axons frequently can be followed into the molecular layer. The deeper cells are irregular in form and their axons are frequently difficult to identify or soon disappear in the granular layer. Sometimes, however, the axons extend toward the molecular layer and probably enter it.

Simple mossy fibers were described by Catois (1901) in the granular layer of the teleost cerebellum. Such fibers occur both in the granular layer of the corpus cerebelli and in the eminentia granularis, according to my observations (fig. 96). Ariens Kappers (1947) regards the mossy fibers as terminals of spino-cerebellar and olivo-cerebellar fibers. The presence of mossy fibers in the eminentia granularis, which does not receive spino-cerebellar contributions but is the principal terminus of secondary vestibular and lateral-line fibers, suggests that these fibers end as the simple mossy formations in the eminentia. The mossy fibers of the corpus cerebelli are probably related to the spino-cerebellar tract.

The molecular layer of the corpus cerebelli has two types of terminal fiber. One type is climbing fibers (fig. 94) that wind about the bodies and principal dendrites of the Purkinje cells. Such fibers have not been specifically described in the restricted molecular layer of the eminentia granularis, but should not be ruled out. The second type ends as freely branching terminal brushes in the middle and upper parts of the molecular layer. In Golgi preparations of Catostomus such terminals were encountered in great numbers in the anterior part of the corpus cerebelli (fig. 91B), and less densely elsewhere in the corpus. Whether the large numbers in the anterior part of the corpus represented an actual concentration of such terminals in this region or a greater response to the Golgi technique is not clear. Smaller and simpler terminals of the same kind were generally distributed in the anterior basal part of the corpus cerebelli of Ictalurus.

The sources of these two types of fiber have not been established in teleosts. In mammals Dow (1942a) reasoned that climbing fibers have their origin in cells of the inferior olive. Szentágothai and Rajkovits (1959) demonstrated experimentally that the inferior olive is at least the principal source of climbing fibers in the cat. Since teleosts investigated by Kooy (1917) have a well-defined inferior olive, the climbing fibers of these fishes presumably originate in its cells. If olivo-cerebellar fibers reach the eminentia granularis and other parts of the vestibulolateral lobe, as Brodal (1940b) demonstrated is true of the partly homologous flocculonodular lobe of mammals, one might expect to find climbing fibers on Purkinje cells related to the vestibulolateral lobe of teleosts.

The terminals of vestibular and lateral-line root fibers in the crista cerebelli, which Tello (1909) believed to be simple climbing fibers in the carp, are unrelated to the climbing fibers of the cerebellum. These terminals are forked branches of root fibers that may wind loosely about the dendrites of large cells situated immediately beneath the crista. In favorable Golgi preparations of Ictalurus and in reduced silver preparations of young salmon the terminal branches of the forked fibers spread as fine threads in the crista, ending in boutons in the neuropil, without specific relations to the large dendrites.

The second type of terminal fiber in the molecular layer of teleosts has not been described in other classes of vertebrates, unless it is represented in urodeles. Possibly it represents the terminal of the lobo-cerebellar tract fiber.

URODELA I

THE cerebellum of urodeles varies from a reduced and, in some respects, rudimentary organ in the more primitive species such as Proteus anguineus and Necturus maculatus to a small but relatively massive structure in the higher members of the class. Other species present gradations between the extreme types (fig. 98).

Hirsch-Tabor (1908) and Bindewald (1911) regarded the cerebellum of Proteus as comprising only a fascicle of myelinated fibers, which Bindewald called the intertrigeminal commissure, which arches above the fourth ventricle through a small fold of tela attached to the posterior border of the midbrain. In Cryptobranchus (Megalobatrachus) Bindewald recognized other fibers in addition to those interconnecting the sensory V nuclei of the medulla oblongata. It remained for Herrick (1914a) to lay the foundation for an understanding of the morphology and connections of the urodele cerebellum by demonstrating, in Necturus and other species, that a rostrolateral projection on either side of the anterior end of the medulla oblongata, though continuous posteriorly with the acousticolateral area, is part of the cerebellum. The two projections, which he called "auricular lobes" of the cerebellum, are connected by the "commissura lateralis cerebelli," which passes through a small plate bridging the fourth ventricle immediately behind the optic tectum. The median part of the cerebellum, which also is paired, Herrick called the "corpus cerebelli." The bilateral halves are connected by a second commissure, the "commissura cerebelli" of Herrick, which also passes through the roof of the fourth ventricle. Herrick's definitions of the auricular lobes and corpus cerebelli are modified in the following pages, but the fundamental pattern of the urodele cerebellum and its commissures was firmly established by him. As will appear, the auricular lobe and part of the corpus cerebelli of Herrick correspond to the lateral lobule of the cerebellum of fishes; the greater part of the remainder of Herrick's corpus cerebelli corresponds in its afferent connections to the corpus cerebelli, *sensu strictiori*, of other Ichthyopsida.

The urodeles include species ranging from an aquatic to an entirely terrestrial habitat in the adult stage. Pro-

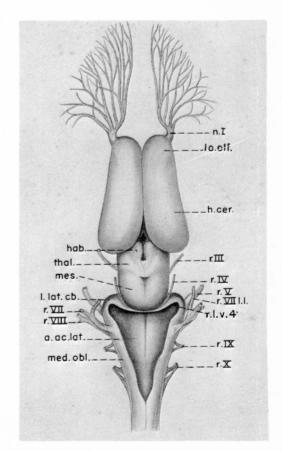

Figure 98. Dorsal view of brain of Triturus torosus.

124

teus anguineus and Necturus maculatus are permanently larval species possessing gills throughout life, but also having lungs. Proteus is blind and lives in completely dark caves. Siren lacertina retains gills in the adult stage; this species, which attains a length of two and a half to three feet, sometimes leaves the water to crawl about on moist ground by means of small functional forelimbs, but hindlimbs are lacking.

Necturus, which grows to a length of 12 to 16 inches, has small eyes and small, weak legs that enable it to make short journeys on land. Cryptobranchus alleghaniensis, attaining a length of 18 to 24 inches, and Cryptobranchus (Megalobatrachus) japonicus, 5 to 6 feet long, are semilarval aquatic species with gill clefts (only one in M. japonicus) but no gills in the adult stage. Both species have lungs, small eyes, and short, stout limbs. The American species is capable of living out of the water for some time. The newts, represented by Triturus torosus, are hatched in the water and have gills in the larval stage. After a few months the gills disappear and a land habitat is assumed which lasts for two or three years, after which the mature animal returns to the water permanently. Triturus torosus lacks both gills and gill clefts in the adult stage; it attains a length of about 7 inches. Ambystoma punctatum (6 to 7 inches long) and Ambystoma tigrinum (7 to 8 inches long) also undergo complete metamorphosis; the adults are terrestrial and may wander some distance from the water. Salamandra maculosa (5 to 6 inches long) is said to be the most terrestrial of the salamanders, the adults living in moist holes or crevices in hilly terrain. The newts and salamanders have sturdy limbs that stand out from the trunk and support the weight of the body.

The diversity among urodeles between an entirely aquatic and a partially or wholly terrestrial habitat in the adult stage is reflected in the lateral-line system and the division of the cerebellum with which it is related, and in the development of the corpus cerebelli, *sensu strictiori*, of various species.

The Acousticolateral System

THE LATERAL-LINE ORGANS AND NERVES

The lateral-line system of most urodeles, as of fishes, comprises an anterior or lateral-line VII and a posterior or lateral-line X division of nerves and sense organs. The latter are rows of pit organs rather than canals. The peripheral nerves of the anterior division typically comprise supraorbital, infraorbital, and mandibular branches to the head region. Variations have been described in different species by Kingsbury (1895b), Coghill (1902, 1906), Beccari (1908), Norris (1911, 1913), and Her-

rick (1930). The posterior or lateral-line X division comprises dorsal, medial, and ventral rows of neuromasts on each side of the trunk, supplied by corresponding branches of the posterior lateral-line nerve.

The diversity of gradations among urodeles between an entirely aquatic and a wholly terrestrial habitat is reflected in the lateral-line system of the various species. According to Noble (1931) lateral-line organs are present in all thoroughly aquatic species and their larvae, in some mountain brook species, and in the larvae of all the Ambystomidae. The adult stage of the last presents various degrees of degeneration of the lateral-line organs in different species.

The larval stage of the newt, Triturus viridescens, has a full complement of lateral-line organs, but during the terrestrial stage these organs undergo partial atrophy and become covered with epidermis. When aquatic life is resumed by the adult the organs reappear on the surface (Noble, 1931). In the Oregon newt Triturus torosus, the skin, rough and thick during the terrestrial period, becomes smooth and slimy and the tail becomes finned in the adult water stage. According to Kreht (1930), Salamandra maculosa has no posterior lateral-line nerve. The anterior lateral-line nerve root fibers, which are present in the larva as three well-defined bundles, become fewer in the adult; their entering roots are indistinct and they continue as a small ascending fascicle which ends in the medial wall of the lateral recess of the fourth ventricle. The descending fascicle of these roots is so small that its terminal relations could not be clearly determined.

Proteus anguineus finds its prey and snaps it up when the prey moves in the water (Gadow, 1901). Presumably the lateral-line organs, especially of the head, are the receptors involved, possibly aided by smell. Scharrer (1933) found that larvae of Ambystoma punctatum reacted with a snapping reflex to minute streams of water directed toward the side of the head. After the rudiments of the lateral-line organs were removed from one side of the head and the eye was extirpated the larvae reacted only when the stimulus was applied to the unoperated side. The experiment suggested that the lateral-line organs of the head play a part in obtaining food. After extirpation of the eye and olfactory organ of Ambystoma larvae, Detwiler (1945) found that the lateral-line organs were able to detect food in motion. The newts are said to prey on the larvae of insects, tadpoles, and worms, and on other small objects that attract attention by their movement in the water.

The peripheral lateral-line nerves enter the medulla oblongata by three or four roots of the anterior nerve and two roots of the posterior nerve. The anterior lateral-line roots were described as four by Coghill (1902) in larval

Ambystoma, but Herrick (1914b, 1930, 1948) recognized only three in larval and adult Ambystoma and in Necturus. The supraorbital and infraorbital fibers of Necturus form an anterior nerve trunk before separating into the distributing branches (Kingsbury, 1895b; Herrick, 1930). Kreht (1930, 1931) found three roots in larval Salamandra and four in adult Proteus. In Molge (Triturus) cristata, Schepman (1918) describes three roots, the most dorsal including two divisions. Triturus torosus shows four fascicles of root fibers which I designated dorsal, dorsomedial, medial, and ventral (1931). The two divisions of the dorsal root of Schepman, the dorsal and dorsomedial roots of my earlier description, and the single dorsal root of Herrick in Necturus and Ambystoma appear to correspond to the dorsal lateral-line VII root of Johnston (1901, 1902) in Acipenser and Petromyzon. The medial and ventral roots of urodeles apparently are the equivalent of the ventral lateral-line VII root of Johnston. In Necturus, Kingsbury (1895b) and Herrick (1930) found fibers from the anterior trunk and the mandibular branch in the dorsal root, and believed that the medial and ventral roots receive fibers from both sources. Herrick states that in Ambystoma the dorsal root receives fibers from all three lateral-line branches to the head and that the medial and ventral roots probably also do so. The two posterior lateral-line roots are formed by division of the posterior nerve into two bundles just before entering the medulla oblongata. All the lateral-line root fibers dichotomize and form ascending and descending fascicles, in the fibrous layer of the acousticolateral area, that correspond respectively to the individual nerve roots.

THE MEMBRANOUS LABYRINTH AND THE ACOUSTIC NERVE

The acoustic or VIII nerve of urodeles is similar, in general, to that of fishes, but shows some modifications in peripheral distribution that are related to further differentiation of the membranous labyrinth. Retzius (1881) states that the anterior branch of the VIII nerve supplies the anterior and lateral ampullae and the macula utriculi. The posterior branch serves the posterior ampulla, the macula sacculi (as in elasmobranchs, but with variations in some species), the papilla lagenae, papilla amphibiorum, and papilla basilaris. The papilla neglecta is lacking in all amphibians except Gymnophiona, de Burlet (1929) states. The papilla basilaris, which is the primordium of the cochlea, is absent in some species (Proteus, Necturus, Amphiuma, and Menobranchus) and is small in all others. The papilla amphibiorum is structurally related to the auditory receptor apparatus (de Burlet, 1928, 1934).

The VIII nerve enters the medulla oblongata by two incompletely separate roots, a ventral or anterior and a dorsal or posterior. Both include small fibers and some very large. According to Schepman (1918) the most dorsocaudal fibers of the dorsal root in Molge (Triturus), which are fine filaments, pass peripherally to the lagena and papilla basilaris. Collectively they were called the cochlear nerve by Schepman. In Necturus, which lacks the papilla basilaris, Herrick (1930) did not find a primordium of the cochlear nerve of Schepman.

SENSORY INNERVATION OF SKIN AND SKELETAL MUSCLE

Urodeles, in common with all vertebrates and many invertebrates, have dermal nerve plexuses supplying cutaneous innervation. These plexuses serve pain and tactile sensibility except the more refined types. Sensory receptors also are found in the skeletal muscles.

Giacomini (1898a, 1898b) found only "terminazione nervosa a paniere" in the trunk muscles of five species of urodeles. In the limb muscles of Triturus torosus, however, Mather and Hines (1934) demonstrated not only the basket terminals of Giacomini, related to the ends of muscle fibers at their insertion into tendons and on the tendons themselves, but also primitive neuromuscular spindles on the bellies of the muscle fibers. These consist of muscle fibers arranged singly or in groups of three or four small intrafusal fibers, upon which terminate slender outgrowths of sensory fibers from the dorsal roots of the spinal nerves. No suggestion of a connective tissue capsule was found about the muscle fibers where these terminals occur. The limb muscles, accordingly, have two types of sensory endings, one corresponding to the "terminazione a paniere" of fishes and the second representing primitive neuromuscular spindles.

The impulses of deep proprioception in the jaw muscles probably are conducted by the mesencephalic V root fibers, Herrick (1948) says. Piatt (1946) found that these fibers, whose cells are situated in the mesencephalic V nucleus, distribute chiefly to the jaw muscles, but some of the more posterior cells of the nucleus probably have other connections. The mesencephalic V tract passes close to the corpus cerebelli, and cells of mesencephalic V type are occasionally found in the cerebellum, but no connections with cerebellar structures have been demonstrated. Descending mesencephalic V fibers to the reticular formation of the medulla oblongata appear to act directly on motor nuclei and on the neuromotor coordinating apparatus of the bulb. These connections Herrick regards as facilitating the feeding reactions. The proprioceptive aspects of cutaneous sensibility in the head Herrick believes to be served by the superior V nu-

126

cleus and the related intertrigeminal commissure. Both V root fibers and secondary fibers from the superior V nucleus contribute to this commissure, some ending in the ipsilateral, and some in the contralateral corpus cerebelli. The greater part of the commissure, however, ends in the neuropil of the contralateral superior V nucleus.

The Histological Pattern of the Urodele Brain

Before considering the acousticolateral area and other subdivisions of the medulla oblongata that are related to the cerebellum or from which it receives afferent fibers, it is important to emphasize that the histological pattern of the adult urodele brain is primitive and generalized, retaining some embryonic features, as Herrick (1948) has pointed out. This pattern has been described in great detail in numerous contributions on the brains of Necturus and Ambystoma by the late Professor Herrick, and in his 1948 monograph, *The Brain of the Tiger Salamander.* For the sake of correlating the urodele pattern with that of other Ichthyopsida and of higher vertebrates the principal features of organization, as described by Herrick, will be briefly reviewed.

The cell bodies of nearly all neurons lie in a deep layer of gray substance, immediately adjacent to the ventricular cavity (fig. 99A). A superficial layer of fibers and neuropil, into which the dendrites of the neurons project and branch, constitutes the white substance. The axons

of the cells most frequently arise from the dendrites, but they may arise from the cell bodies. Some axons are short and have many branches; others are long, some with collateral branches, some without. Both myelinated and unmyelinated fibers occur. Terminals of the long fibers intertwine with branches of the short ones and with dendritic twigs to form a neuropil which permeates the entire brain as a synaptic field but varies in different regions. Some of the long fibers, both myelinated and unmyelinated, are gathered into fascicles that connect cells of certain regions with areas of neuropil in more or less distant parts of the brain. Many of these fascicles can be homologized with specific fiber tracts of other vertebrates (fig. 99A).

The fiber connections of some fields of neuropil conform with those of specific nuclei of higher brains, but such fields contain no cell bodies in urodeles. In anurans and reptiles, however, corresponding fields show all stages in the differentiation of true nuclei by migration of cells from the central gray layer into the white layer, Herrick (1927, 1948) points out. Well-defined nuclei are few in the gray layer of urodeles, but precursors of many nuclei of higher vertebrates are represented by locally specialized elements or by connections of fiber fascicles recognizable as corresponding to specific fiber tracts in other vertebrates.

Herrick's comprehensive histological and physiologi-

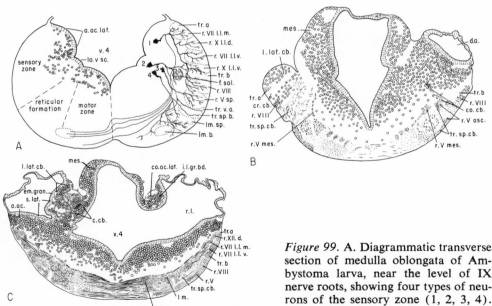

Figure 99. A. Diagrammatic transverse section of medulla oblongata of Ambystoma larva, near the level of IX nerve roots, showing four types of neurons of the sensory zone (1, 2, 3, 4). ×100. (Modified from Herrick, 1948.)

B. Transverse section of brain stem of 29 mm long Ambystoma tigrinum at level of the lateral lobule. Cajal method. ×95. (Redrawn from Larsell, 1932a.) C. Transverse section of brain stem of 28 mm long Ambystoma tigrinum at the level of lateral recess of fourth ventricle. Cajal method.

cal analysis led him to recognize three bilateral longitudinal zones of the brain: a dorsal sensory, a ventral motor, and an intermediate correlative and integrative or reticular zone. All these include both gray and white substance. The boundaries between the intermediate zone and the other two are arbitrary (fig. 99A).

The primitive histological pattern is very evident in the medulla oblongata. The gray layer is continuous, posteroanteriorly, from the spinal cord to the isthmus and, transversely, from the tenia of one side of the fourth ventricle to the other. The fibrous layer is also uninterrupted, but in the intermediate zone it appears as a lighter field, in myelin-stained sections, owing to the presence of fewer and smaller myelinated fibers than in the motor and sensory zones.

The axons of cells of the sensory and intermediate zones usually arise from the elongated main dendrite immediately before it begins to branch. They remain ipsilateral or cross to the opposite side, those from the subdivisions of the sensory zone, especially, collecting into fascicles.

Herrick (1948) divides the gray layer of the anterior part of the medulla oblongata into the isthmic and the trigeminal tegmentum. The isthmic tegmentum is bounded anteriorly by the isthmic sulcus and the fovea isthmi, but caudally it merges with the trigeminal tegmentum without distinct boundary. The trigeminal field of tegmentum forms a low elevation, the eminentia trigemini of Herrick, in the floor of the fourth ventricle medial of the entrance of the V roots. The gray layer beneath this eminence includes small-celled and large-celled parts. The small-celled part is continuous anterodorsally with the isthmic tegmentum and, caudally, extends beneath the ependyma of the paramedian sulcus of the ventricular floor. The large-celled part is continuous with the large-celled component of the isthmic tegmentum, the motor V nucleus being included among these large tegmental cells. The reader is referred to the monograph of Herrick (1948) for details regarding the tegmental subdivisions and the motor and intermediate zones. The sensory zone of the medulla oblongata, however, requires further description because of its intimate relation to the cerebellum.

THE SENSORY ZONE OF THE MEDULLA OBLONGATA

The sensory zone of the medulla oblongata extends from the spinal cord to the isthmus. It is similar, in general, in the various species of urodeles, some modifications in certain species being noted below. Anterior of the calamus scriptorius the sensory zone forms the dorsolateral wall of the fourth ventricle and most of the floor of the recessus lateralis (figs. 100–105).

The dorsal part of the ventricular wall is formed by an elongated ridge of gray substance which projects into the ventricular cavity. It is bounded dorsolaterally by the tenial margin of the medulla oblongata and ventromedially by a ventricular furrow, the sulcus lateralis already mentioned (figs. 105, 106). This ventricular ridge is the cell layer of the acousticolateral area. In Necturus the ridge becomes reduced at the level of the first roots of the X nerve and shrinks rapidly posterior of this level, disappearing entirely below the last vagal root (Herrick, 1930). The fourth ventricle of Necturus is so elongated that the calamus scriptorius is situated well behind this last root. Rostrally, in all species, the gray of the acousticolateral area is continuous, by a reduced column beneath the lateral recess, with the cell layer of the lobulus lateralis cerebelli (fig. 106).

The small cells of the eminentia trigemini, already mentioned, are situated in the lateral part of the eminence in Necturus, Herrick (1930) states. Their dendrites extend toward the sensory V roots and into a zone of neuropil which represents the superior V nucleus. Larger cells beneath the medial part of the eminence form the motor V nucleus. In Ambystoma and Triturus the small-celled part of the trigeminal eminence is dorsally situated and the large-celled part lies ventral of it, closely related to the isthmic tegmentum.

The small neurons are the cell elements of the superior V nucleus and were so described by Woodburne (1936) as well as by Herrick. A chain of similar cells extends medially and caudally along the medial border of the descending V root and among its fibers. These are poorly differentiated from the general mass of the gray layer which continues from the trigeminal eminence to the spinal cord. The sensory part of the trigeminal eminence and its related zone of neuropil, together with the submerged and attenuated descending cell chain, constitute the general somatic sensory part of the sensory area.

A ridge of gray substance, the visceral-gustatory lobe, begins a short distance behind the lateral recess. It is delimited from the acousticolateral gray area by the sulcus lateralis. This lobe is narrow rostrally but enlarges caudalward. It includes the nucleus of the fasciculus solitarius.

The fibrous layer of the sensory zone consists chiefly of sensory root fibers of the V, VII, VIII, IX, and X nerves. To these are added tracts *a* and *b* of Kingsbury (1895a), who regarded them as correlation fascicles (fig. 99). The root fibers, after entering the medulla oblongata, bifurcate into ascending and descending branches that are gathered into fascicles corresponding to the individual root bundles. Secondary tracts and arcuate fibers form the more ventral part of the fibrous layer of the sensory zone.

The secondary sensory fibers include ascending fibers in tracts *a* and *b*, bulbo-cerebellar connections, crossed and uncrossed bulbo-spinal connections, reflex connections with the motor zone of both sides of the medulla oblongata by direct arcuate fibers or after synapse in the intermediate zone, and the lemniscus systems that connect the sensory zone of the medulla oblongata with higher levels of the same zone (Herrick, 1948). Most of the lemniscus systems decussate in the ventral commissure of the medulla oblongata.

The acousticolateral area. The acousticolateral area is strongly inverted as far forward as the entrance of the anterior lateral-line and vestibular roots in Necturus, somewhat less so in Cryptobranchus and Triturus, whereas in Ambystoma it forms the dorsolateral margin of the medulla oblongata. Rostralward of the level of the roots named it slopes gradually outward in most species described, but in Cryptobranchus the acousticolateral area constitutes the dorsal portion of a slightly inward inclined to nearly vertical lateral wall of the fourth ventricle, only the rostralmost part having a lateral inclination before turning dorsomedially into the cerebellum. These differences have a relation to the form of the lateral lobule of the cerebellum in the various species.

The extent and boundaries of the ventricular ridge which represents the gray layer of the acousticolateral area have already been noted. Externally the "sulcus areae acousticolateralis externus" of Röthig (1927a) marks the ventral boundary of the fibrous layer of the area in front of the roots of the VIII nerve. This furrow is less evident in Triturus (fig. 98) than in the much larger Megalobatrachus japonicus, but it continues forward beneath the lateral lobule, delimiting this lobule from the rostrolateral surface of the medulla oblongata. Turning dorsomedially, it reaches the dorsal surface of the cerebellum in Triturus and Cryptobranchus alleghaniensis, forming the boundary between the medial part of the lateral lobule and the corpus cerebelli. A corresponding but unlabeled furrow is shown in several of Röthig's figures of Megalobatrachus japonicus. I have not found a similar groove in other urodeles, possibly owing to smaller size of the cerebellum and to varying methods of fixation. There can be little doubt that this furrow is the posterolateral fissure, or that the external acousticolateral sulcus of Röthig represents its continuation onto the upper lateral surface of the medulla oblongata, as in embryos of higher vertebrates.

The *structural pattern* of the acousticolateral area of urodeles is relatively simple. The root fibers of the lateral-line and VIII nerves bifurcate, on entering the medulla oblongata, into ascending and descending branches that are collected into fascicles corresponding to the divisions of the respective roots. These fascicles, instead of entering the gray substance of the area, as in other Ichthyopsida, remain external to it and form the greater part of the fibrous layer (fig. 99). As already mentioned with reference to the sensory zone in general, neurons of the periventricular gray send dendrites into this overlying fibrous layer, as Herrick (1914a, 1914b, 1930, 1948) has shown in great detail. At the levels of entrance of the posterior and anterior lateral-line roots the gray layer is thickened. Groups of small cells also extend from it toward the entering sensory root fibers, among which their dendritic processes branch, as is evident in Cajal series of Triturus. These cell aggregations are more prominent in Cryptobranchus, but in Triturus as well as Cryptobranchus the posterior aggregation is larger than the anterior. The thickened zones correspond, on a reduced scale, to the posterior and anterior lateral-line regions, respectively, of the nucleus medialis of the acousticolateral area of fishes. Scattered cells of uncertain nature also occur among the lateral-line fascicles.

The ventral part of the gray layer, opposite the entrance of the VIII roots, includes large and small cells that increase the thickness of this region. In Triturus and Cryptobranchus, and also in Necturus (Herrick, 1930), the small cells send short dendritic processes among the entering VIII root fibers. The larger cells direct their dendrites medialward. They form a group of cells which Herrick (1930) called the VIII nucleus. It is more prominent in Cryptobranchus than in Triturus. A single Mauthner's cell situated in the intermediate zone of Herrick is found on either side, as in teleosts and other fishes.

In addition to the fascicles of root fibers, the fibrous layer includes tracts *a* and *b* of Kingsbury (1895a), who, as already mentioned, regarded them as correlation fascicles. The root fibers give off innumerable collaterals in their course. These interweave with dendritic terminals of neurons in the gray layer, forming a longitudinal pool of neuropil among the fascicles. This serves the function of the cerebellar crest of other Ichthyopsida, a crista being lacking in urodeles except as described below in a few species.

The ascending and descending fibers of the dorsal anterior lateral-line root are shorter than those of the other roots. They end in a dorsal zone of neuropil which Kingsbury (1895a), in Necturus, called the "dorsal island of alba." In Triturus, as already noted, the dorsal root of the anterior lateral-line nerve comprises dorsal and dorsomedial divisions. Some of the fibers of the latter divisions enter a fiber mass, ventrolateral of the "dorsal island," which is formed chiefly of medial and ventral anterior root fascicles. Apparently all the root fibers that enter the "dorsal island" bifurcate, in all species, into relatively short ascending and descending branches, as Herrick (1914b) described in midlarval Ambystoma. These branches give rise to slender collaterals that end in the neuropil (fig. 117). A number of relatively fine fibers collect rostrally, however, into a small fascicle which continues forward toward the lateral lobule of the cerebellum. This appears to correspond to the small fascicle similarly situated in petromyzonts and, probably, to that above noted in Catostomus and some other teleosts in which no descending branches of the presumptive division of the dorsal root fibers that give rise to it were found. Possibly the small ascending fascicle in Triturus represents a continuation of one of the two divisions of the dorsal anterior lateral-line root.

The relations of the dorsal anterior lateral-line roots to the "dorsal island" are entirely similar to those of the single corresponding root of petromyzonts, elasmobranchs, and Acipenseriformes to the nucleus dorsalis of the acousticolateral area of these Ichthyopsida. Furthermore, dendrites of cells whose bodies are situated in a layer of gray substance which encloses the "dorsal island" medially, dorsally, and, in part, laterally give rise to dendrites that arborize in the neuropil of the island. These neurons appear to correspond to those of small and medium size situated at the periphery of the nucleus dorsalis of petromyzonts, whose dendrites enter the nucleus and branch among its fibers. The neurons, branching fibers of the dorsal anterior lateral-line root, and neuropil of urodeles all add to the similarity of the "dorsal island" to the nucleus dorsalis of other Ichthyopsida, only granule cells being absent. There seems to be little question that the "dorsal island" corresponds to the nucleus dorsalis of some groups of fishes, but it must be differentiated from the "anterior lateral-line lobe" (the anterior part of the nucleus medialis), with which Norris (1908, 1913) compared the "dorsal island" of Siren and Amphiuma.

The fascicles of the medial and ventral anterior lateral-line roots extend throughout the length of the acousticolateral area, the ascending fascicles reaching the lobulus lateralis of the cerebellum (fig. 112). Both ascending fascicles contribute small fascicles to the "dorsal island" of adult Ambystoma, according to Herrick (1948); in larval Ambystoma only dorsal root fibers were found to the "dorsal island." In Triturus I have been able to identify only medial root fibers to this zone of neuropil, in addition to those of the dorsal root. The fibers of the ascending fascicles of the medial and ventral roots spread and terminate in the neuropil beneath the lateral part of the cell layer of the lateral lobule and, according to Herrick

(1948), in the posterior isthmic neuropil. The descending fascicles extend to the posterior end of the acousticolateral area, but none appears to enter the spinal cord.

The two roots of the posterior lateral-line nerve also enter the fiber layer of the acousticolateral area, the bifurcated fibers collecting into dorsal and ventral ascending and descending fascicles. The ascending fascicles reach the anterior part of the lateral lobule and the descending fascicles extend to the posterior end of the acousticolateral area. Kingsbury (1895a) found no descending branches of these roots in Weigert preparations of Necturus, but Herrick (1930) observed them in von Roth preparations. The root fibers lose their myelin sheaths soon after entering the brain in this species, but descending branches are visible as axis cylinders. In adult Ambystoma and Triturus the posterior as well as the medial and ventral lateral-line fascicles are myelinated throughout the greater part of their length.

Myelin-stained series of Triturus show a clear zone, ventral of the rostral part of the "dorsal island" but continuous with it, and bounded ventrally by the ascending medial and ventral anterior lateral-line fascicles. Laterally it reaches the surface of the acousticolateral area. Continuing forward beneath the rostrolateral projection of the cell layer of the lateral lobule, it merges with a similar zone in front of this cell mass and between the most rostrolateral part of its projection and the ascending VIII root fascicle. This zone, in turn, is continuous with the molecular layer of the cerebellar arch. Cajal preparations of brains fixed in solutions including chloral hydrate show great numbers of very fine fibers in the acousticolateral area portion of this zone and in its continuation in the lateral lobule. Larger fibers of the medial and ventral anterior lateral-line roots also distribute in it.

This short zone in the anterior part of the acousticolateral area has the relations with the layer of neuropil and fibers of the lateral lobule and the remainder of the cerebellum that are typical of the crista cerebelli in other Ichthyopsida, and I regard it as representing a true cerebellar crest in Triturus. A zone similar in its relations also occurs in Cryptobranchus, but it has not been studied in silver preparations in this species. Schepman (1918) described a crista cerebelli in Molge (Triturus) cristata. In Triturus torosus the continuation in the lateral lobule corresponds to the lateral part of the posterior isthmic neuropil of Ambystoma which, according to Herrick (1948), receives terminals of the lateral-line fascicles. In Triturus torosus such terminals appear to represent chiefly medial and ventral anterior lateral-line fibers, but posterior root fibers are probably included.

Both roots of the VIII nerve include many fine myelinated fibers with coarser ones intermingled. The fibers bifurcate and form dorsal and ventral ascending and descending fascicles, the ventral root fascicles being longer than those of the dorsal root. The ascending branches of the coarse fibers are small, whereas the descending branches remain large. The two ascending fascicles merge at the level of the entering V root. In Ambystoma, according to Herrick (1948), many of the ascending fibers end in the lateral lobule while others continue into the cerebellar arch, decussating in the acousticolateral commissure and terminating in the vestibular and lateral-line neuropil of the contralateral lobulus lateralis. In Triturus there is a rostral separation of the merged fascicle, so that two bundles again are seen: one distributes in the neuropil of the lateral lobule and the other continues into the acousticolateral commissure. In the most favorable Cajal preparations many of the fibers of this commissure are seen to terminate as fine branches in the molecular layer of the cerebellar arch, both ipsilaterally and contralaterally.

The two descending fascicles remain separate as far as the second root of the X nerve. The ventral fascicle continues beyond this level to the end of the acousticolateral area, some fibers entering the spinal cord. According to Herrick the latter continue for an undetermined distance in the cord, intermingled with the more ventral fibers of the dorsal funiculus. Terminal fibers and collaterals of the VIII root fascicles contribute to the common pool of the acousticolateral neuropil, according to Herrick.

Tract *a* extends from the lateral lobule to the spinal cord, closely following the tenia of the fourth ventricle for most of its course. Fibers from cells of the lateral part of the lobulus lateralis collect into the tract, but fibers also spread from the fascicle into the neuropil of the rostrolateral part of the lobule. The fascicle passes caudalward beneath the lateral part of the floor of the recessus lateralis, through and beneath the "dorsal island" and then, above the fascicles of the lateral-line roots, continuing into the medial fascicle of the dorsal funiculus of the spinal cord. From the region of the posterior lateral-line root forward it is augmented by fibers from the ipsilateral gray substance of the lateral-line field and by arcuate fibers arising contralaterally. These fibers, for the most part, are myelinated. Posterior of the calamus scriptorius, toward which the bilateral tracts converge, they are relatively small and the fibers are unmyelinated. Some secondary fibers from the lateral-line area may end in the nucleus funiculi before the tract continues into the cord (Herrick, 1944). The caudal part of the tract receives ascending fibers from the medial fascicle of the dorsal funiculus of the cord and also from the nucleus funiculi, in which most of the ascending fibers of the medial fascicle terminate. The ascending fibers from the cord and the nucleus funiculi continue rostralward in the tract for an undetermined distance (Herrick, 1948).

Tract *a* Herrick regards as a mixed collection of correlating fibers related primarily with the roots of the lateral-line nerves, a view supported by the disappearance of the fascicle in Salamandra. Arcuate fibers connect the tract with the ipsilateral and contralateral intermediate or reticular zones of the medulla oblongata. Some of the arcuates may be commissural fibers connecting the bilateral acousticolateral areas. Different ipsilateral levels of the area apparently are interconnected by ascending and descending fibers of the tract and such fibers also appear to interconnect the acousticolateral area with the lateral lobule and the nucleus funiculi (Herrick, 1944).

In Triturus ascending fibers end in the neuropil adjacent to the auricle proper as well as in the neuropil beneath and anterior to the eminentia granularis. Descending fibers arise from some of the cells of the lateral part of the eminentia. It is unlikely that any fibers having origin in the lateral lobule cross before entering tract *a*, but some of the descending fibers may constitute a cerebello-tegmental tract, part of which may cross with arcuate fibers of the medulla oblongata. The descending fibers to the cord should perhaps be regarded as efferent from the acousticolateral area and the lateral lobule. It appears justified to regard the ascending fibers of tract *a* that terminate in the lateral lobule as secondary lateral-line fibers similar to the secondary vestibular fibers of tract *b* described below. In land vertebrates, which have no remnant of the lateral-line system, there are no fibers that can be compared with tract *a*.

Tract *b* is situated in the ventral part of the fibrous layer of the acousticolateral area immediately dorsal of the ascending and descending VIII root fascicles and parallel with them in most of its course (fig. 99). Herrick (1944, 1948) regards it as primarily related with the roots of the VIII nerve. The tract includes ascending and descending fibers, crossed and uncrossed, that connect the vestibular areas of both sides with the cerebellum, the spinal cord, the tegmentum of the bulb, and with each other (Herrick, 1948). A probable connection with the fasciculus longitudinalis medialis was described in Proteus by Kreht (1931).

Ascending fibers are derived from the vestibular area and probably from the nucleus funiculi, Herrick (1948) says. Some of these reach the lateral lobule. Descending fibers from the lateral lobule and the vestibular area distribute in the medulla oblongata and, after merging with the descending VIII root fascicle at the bulbo-spinal junction, continue in the lateral fascicles of the dorsal funiculus of the spinal cord. Fibers of tract *b* pass to the motor field of the medulla oblongata as crossed and uncrossed arcuates, many of which divide into ascending and descending branches in the ventral funiculus. These may be secondary vestibular fibers that enter the fasciculus longitudinalis medialis, but Herrick (1948) was unable to follow details of their courses in Golgi preparations. Many of the ascending fibers that terminate in the lateral lobule spread and branch in the neuropil of the lobule, intermingling with those of tract a. Others end among the cells of the gray substance of the lobule. Whether those that end in the neuropil have the same source as those to the gray substance is unknown. Those arising in the vestibular part of the acousticolateral area are secondary vestibular fibers, compared by Herrick (1948) with the secondary vestibulo-cerebellar tract of mammals. They also appear to correspond to secondary fibers, probably vestibular, that end in the eminentia granularis of young Amia, already described. In Amia, however, the fibers do not form a compact fascicle. The secondary vestibular fibers of all vertebrates above the urodeles apparently end among the cells of the homologue of the eminentia granularis, namely the flocculus.

The descending fibers of tract b that reach the cord probably include ipsilateral fibers homologous with the vestibulo-spinal tract of other Ichthyopsida and of higher vertebrates. Others probably correspond to the crossed descending fibers of the medial longitudinal fascicle. Neither of these probabilities, however, has been specifically demonstrated.

Tracts a and b represent fibers from neurons of the acousticolateral area or the gray layer of the lateral lobule that found their way into the embryonic marginal layer and collected into fascicles. From these fascicles fibers are distributed to the various regions that are connected by more or less individual tracts in the more highly differentiated brains of fishes. Tract a appears to be represented in elasmobranchs, in part, by the dorsal fascicle of the anterior lobe, as it was called by Sterzi (1909). In teleosts the small tracts to the auricle proper may correspond in part to the ascending fibers of tract a of urodeles, but this is not certain. Tract b probably is represented in fishes by the secondary ascending and descending tracts and arcuate fibers whose distribution is similar to those of this tract in urodeles.

THE TRIGEMINAL NERVE AND ROOTS

The sensory division of the V nerve forms the dorsal part of a common root which, on entering the medulla oblongata, immediately divides into sensory, mesencephalic, and motor roots. Most peripheral branches of the sensory root distribute to the skin of the head, but some to deeper tissues. The cutaneous fibers, together with fewer cutaneous fibers that enter the medulla oblongata

through the roots of the VII, X, and, probably, the IX nerves, make up the general cutaneous component of the cranial nerves. The cutaneous distribution of the VII nerve has not been described, but Coghill (1902) found a widespread distribution of such fibers of the X nerve in Ambystoma. Herrick (1930) found some evidence of cutaneous fibers of the IX nerve in Necturus, but these fibers appear to be lacking in most urodeles. The mesencephalic V fibers, which are heavily myelinated, distribute peripherally with branches of the V nerve, the majority, according to Piatt (1946), going to the jaw muscles. The mesencephalic V root is believed to carry proprioceptive impulses.

Most of the fibers of the sensory root, but apparently not all in Necturus, according to Herrick (1930), after entering the medulla oblongata bifurcate into coarse myelinated descending branches and small unmyelinated or thinly myelinated ascending fibers. In Ambystoma Herrick (1948) describes large and small fibers of the sensory V root, saying that the larger ones take a deeper position before bifurcating. The ascending branches are smaller and unmyelinated in the adult animal. The finer root fibers are also said by Herrick to bifurcate into ascending and descending branches. According to Woodburne (1936), who studied Necturus, Proteus, and Ambystoma, a few caudally entering fascicles of large V root fibers pass dorsally, giving off fibers into the acousticolateral area and ending in the superior V nucleus. Some fibers continue into the cerebellum.

The descending branches of the sensory V root fibers form the spinal root or tract of the V nerve. It is situated immediately ventral of the fibrous layer of the acousticolateral area and continues into the spinal cord. The cutaneous fibers of the VII and X roots, mentioned above, enter the descending V tract. The smaller ascending V fascicle terminates chiefly in a zone of neuropil called the superior V nucleus by Herrick (1948), but some of the ascending fibers reach the cerebellum. The descending root fibers have short collaterals that form a longitudinal pool of neuropil which is contiguous with that of the acousticolateral area (Herrick, 1948).

The mesencephalic V root ascends to the posterior part of the optic tectum, in which its large cells form the mesencephalic V nucleus, some cells occasionally being found in the corpus cerebelli and nucleus cerebelli, as pointed out by Herrick (1948). These are generally regarded as cells derived from the embryonic neural crest but remaining within the neural tube. Like the sensory ganglion cells of the cranial and spinal nerves, they are unipolar, the single processes dividing into peripherally and centrally directed branches. The latter branches descend in the intermediate layer of the medulla oblongata as far as the level of the roots of the IX nerve, coming into direct relation with the motor nuclei and the mechanism of motor coordination (Herrick, 1948). The fibers that pass into the tectum are said to activate the deep neuropil and to come into relation here with terminals of the optic and lemniscus systems. The connections of the mesencephalic V fibers are regarded by Herrick as well adapted to coordinating the movements involved in the feeding reactions.

My own observations on the distribution of the roots of the V nerve in larval Ambystoma and adult Triturus are in accord with Herrick's descriptions, but I have not attempted to follow cutaneous fibers of the other cranial nerves.

THE VISCERAL SENSORY LOBE AND ITS CONNECTIONS

The visceral sensory lobes of the VII and X nerves are large and functionally important in many fishes, but no specific viscero-cerebellar connections have been described. In Ambystoma, however, Herrick (1914b, 1948) found connections between the secondary gustatory-visceral nucleus and the cerebellum, and experimental studies on mammals, to which we shall return, indicate visceral effects in the cerebellum of higher forms. The visceral sensory lobe of urodeles, therefore, merits description along with the other subdivisions of the sensory area.

This lobe in urodeles receives the roots of the branches of the VII, IX, and X nerves that serve the organs of taste or of visceral sensibility. According to Herrick (1944), the VII root fibers are chiefly gustatory, but those of the IX and X roots are general visceral sensory in function. Most of the fibers of the VII and IX roots bifurcate into ascending and descending branches; the majority of visceral X root fibers, however, descend without bifurcating. These ascending and descending branches constitute the fasciculus communis of Osborn or fasciculus solitarius. Terminal processes of gustatory and visceral sensory root fibers form a pool of neuropil in this fascicle which is similar to those of the acousticolateral area and the trigeminal root. It is separated from these pools, however, forming a second major zone of neuropil of the sensory area (Herrick, 1948). The cells of the visceral sensory lobe send their dendrites primarily into the fasciculus solitarius, with branches extending also into adjacent areas. The axons of these cells pass forward to an area of neuropil in the isthmic region which corresponds to the secondary gustatory-visceral nucleus of Herrick in fishes.

At the calamus scriptorius the gray of the visceral lobe is replaced by a compact group of small cells which surround the commissura infima of Haller. These cells constitute the commissural nucleus of Cajal. Above the calamus scriptorius it merges insensibly with the nucleus of the calamus scriptorius. The commissura infima is defined by Herrick (1944) as formed of descending visceral-gustatory root fibers and, probably, secondary fibers from the commissural nucleus. Sensory root fibers of the X nerve, apparently unrelated to those reaching the fasciculus solitarius, were found in Necturus by Herrick (1930). They terminate in a zone regarded as a precursor of the nucleus intercalatus of Staderini in mammals.

THE POSTERIOR ISTHMIC NEUROPIL

The ascending fiber tracts of the sensory area continue forward and medially into an extensive field of fibers and neuropil in the anterior part of the medulla oblongata. This field continues into the lateral lobule and forward into the isthmus. Dorsomedially it is continuous, in part, with the fibrous and molecular layer of the cerebellum. In larval Ambystoma and adult Triturus part of this field separates the gray layer of the projecting portion of the lateral lobule from the large lemniscus and other fiber systems of the isthmic region and from the isthmic tegmentum. This part of the field is limited caudally by the cell mass which connects the gray of the lateral lobule with that of the median part of the cerebellum and of the sensory area. In adult Ambystoma tigrinum the lateral lobule is relatively smaller and also is situated farther dorsally than in larval stages and in adult Triturus. Moreover, it projects laterally instead of rostrolaterally, its gray layer as a result being more directly continuous with that of the median part of the cerebellum. The layer of fibers and neuropil in front of the gray layer forms a broad zone extending from the isthmus to the lateral tip of the lobulus lateralis in Ambystoma, instead of the thick caudally directed zone which has thinner continuations in the lateral lobule and the isthmic region in Triturus and larval Ambystoma.

The neuropil of this wide area of white substance in adult Ambystoma was called the posterior isthmic neuropil by Herrick (1948). Dendrites from the adjacent gray substance, including the trigeminal tegmentum, extend into it. In this broad zone of neuropil Herrick identified the superior sensory V nucleus, the superior vestibular nucleus, the secondary gustatory-visceral nucleus, ascending fibers of tracts *a* and *b*, collaterals and terminals of the spinal lemniscus, and the precursor of the dorsal nucleus of the lateral lemniscus.

In silver series of Triturus the neuropil of the superior V nucleus is recognizable in the ventromedial part of the zone of white substance that separates the gray of the lateral lobule and the median gray. Ascending V root fibers branch and terminate in this neuropil and dendrites from cells of the medially situated trigeminal tegmentum extend into it. The ascending VIII fascicle enters the lateral part of the zone of fibers and neuropil, continuing dorsomedially beneath the gray layer of the lateral lobule. Many of the fibers end in the neuropil beneath and anterior to this gray layer, while a compact fascicle of others continues into the cerebellar arch. Golgi and Cajal preparations of Ambystoma larvae show the neuropil of the superior V nucleus in a medial position and the ascending VIII root and related neuropil, forming the superior VIII nucleus, laterally situated in the white zone.

THE EFFERENT FIBERS OF THE SENSORY ZONE

The elongated dendrites from the gray layer of the sensory zone that make synaptic connections in the pools of neuropil are processes of neurons of the second order. In midlarval Ambystoma Herrick (1914b) found some of these dendrites spread through the entire extent of the white substance of the sensory zone, bringing them into synaptic relations with terminals of all the fascicles (fig. 99A). Some of the secondary neurons, accordingly, may relay impulses from several types of receptors. Branches of dendrites directed to the sensory zone also extend into the intermediate or reticular zone. Other neurons have dendritic connections with only one or a few of the root fascicles. In adult Ambystoma a larger proportion of the neurons have synaptic connections with only one or a few adjacent fascicles of root fibers, but not many appear to be activated by impulses of a single sensory type (Herrick, 1948, p. 155). There is, however, a progressive specialization in the peripheral and central connections of the secondary sensory neurons and in the analytic mechanism which they represent.

Arcuate fibers arise from cells of the acousticolateral area throughout its extent in Triturus, as also described by Herrick (1930, 1948) in Necturus and Ambystoma. They pass to the motor and intermediate zones, both ipsilateral and contralateral; such fibers to the motor zone from tract *b* already have been noted. Many of the arcuate fibers bifurcate into ascending and descending branches, some extending long distances in the ventral funiculus of the fibrous layer. According to Herrick (1948) some of these appear to correspond to secondary vestibular fibers of the fasciculus longitudinalis medialis. Röthig (1927a) describes a tractus octavomotorius cruciatus to the ventral commissure of the medulla oblongata and the fasciculus longitudinalis medialis of Cryptobranchus (Megalobatrachus), and Kreht (1930, 1931) describes both crossed and uncrossed octavomotor tracts in Salamandra and Proteus. Since fibers from the vestibular region of the gray layer enter tract *b* both

ipsilaterally and contralaterally, Kreht suggests that this tract may be conceived as a crossed and uncrossed octavomotor fascicle. If limited to the efferent fibers of tract *b* that arise in the vestibular region of the acousticolateral area such an interpretation would be in general accord with our observations in silver material of urodeles. These efferent fibers of tract *b* would also correspond to fibers, in fishes, that have their origin in the vestibular nuclear complex and reach the spinal cord or become part of the fasciculus longitudinalis medialis.

In addition to the secondary ascending fibers of tracts *a* and *b*, already mentioned, a general bulbar lemniscus is formed of secondary fibers from all parts of the bulbar sensory zone. Apparently it relays impulses from all kinds of sensory fibers that enter the sensory zone. The bulbar lemniscus decussates in the ventral commissure of the medulla oblongata, according to Herrick (1948). In Triturus, as in Ambystoma, it ascends through the isthmus, turning dorsally, and distributes widely in the tectum of the midbrain, some fibers reaching the dorsal thalamus.

A more specific ascending secondary path, Herrick (1948) points out, has its origin chiefly from the vestibular part of the sensory zone. It ascends through the isthmus, closely associated with, but lateral of the bulbar lemniscus, and ends in the nucleus posterior tecti and the adjacent isthmic neuropil. This nucleus is regarded by Herrick as the primordium of the inferior colliculus. The fascicle, called the tractus bulbo-tectalis lateralis, is considered the precursor of the lemniscus lateralis proper, which is first recognizable in anurans as a definitive tract. My observations of the bulbar and lateral lemnisci in Triturus are much less detailed than those of Herrick in his extensive Golgi and other material of Ambystoma and Necturus; so far as they go they are in accord.

A secondary visceral-gustatory tract is described by Herrick (1944, 1948) as arising from neurons of the visceral sensory lobe and the commissural nucleus of Cajal. The tract also includes gustatory root fibers of the VII nerve and general visceral sensory root fibers of the X nerve. It ascends as an uncrossed fascicle ventral of the spinal V root and ends, in part, in the superior visceral-gustatory nucleus, in the isthmus, but also continues to the midbrain and hypothalamus. Some fibers from the nucleus fasciculus solitarius are described as crossing in the ventral commissure of the medulla oblongata but becoming lost in the general bulbar lemniscus. Barnard (1936) describes the secondary tract of the nucleus of the solitary fascicle in Necturus as beginning in the caudal region of the medulla oblongata and ending in the "auricular area."

The Development of the Acousticolateral Area and the Cerebellum

The development of the cerebellar region of Hynobius nebulosus was briefly described by Sumi (1926); Baker and Graves (1932) include the cerebellum in a contribution on the morphological differentiation of the brain of Ambystoma jeffersonianum. The development of the cerebellum and acousticolateral area, including fiber tracts and types of cells, was described by myself (1932a) from an extensive series of larvae of Ambystoma punctatum prepared by neurohistological methods. These earlier observations are here summarized and to some extent reinterpreted in the light of subsequent studies on the development and adult relations of the hindbrain in petromyzonts and fishes and on the relations of the acousticolateral area and cerebellum in adult urodeles. Although fiber tracts and other histological features, as they make their appearance, are of importance in analyzing the larval hindbrain, reference to them is minimized since they are described below in adult urodeles.

The earliest cerebellar cells, as identified by their subsequent history, are recognizable in Ambystoma punctatum embryos at the nonmotile stage of Coghill (Harrison's stage 30). In the early stages of formation of the

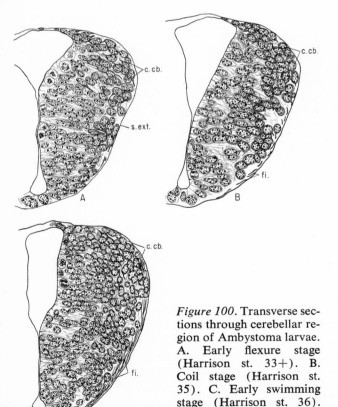

Figure 100. Transverse sections through cerebellar region of Ambystoma larvae. A. Early flexure stage (Harrison st. 33+). B. Coil stage (Harrison st. 35). C. Early swimming stage (Harrison st. 36). ×142. (Larsell, 1932a.)

cerebellar rudiment numerous mitotic figures in the matrix layer, or neural epithelium, indicate the source of its cells (fig. 100). Hugosson (1957) found no distinct migration layer in urodeles. The cells of the rudiment are approximately of the same size but some small ones occur, especially in the dorsal part of the rudiment bordering on the ependymal roof of the rhomboidal fossa. A small aggregation of cells has appeared in the dorsal part of the neural tube, however, which corresponds in position to the columna dorsalis of early Petromyzon embryos described by Rüdeberg (1961). Some cells at the level of the root of the V nerve are clearly neuroblasts. A few more elongated but otherwise similar cells opposite the ganglia of the lateral-line and VIII nerves indicate the incipient acousticolateral area. The cerebellar region of the nonmotile stage embryo is very similar to that of the 7 mm Lampetra tridentatus embryo except that the latter has a more prominent marginal zone.

At the early flexure stage (Harrison's stage 33+) of Ambystoma punctatum the dorsolateral region between the levels of the V root and the cephalic flexure shows a group of relatively large, rounded neuroblasts (fig. 100A). Many of them have short ventrolaterally directed processes, but in the dorsal region some of the processes take a dorsomedial direction. This group of cells represents the primordium of the cerebellum. The neuroblasts are predominantly oval in outline, but a few rounded cells of smaller size occupy the dorsomedial part of the primordium. The neural tube shows a slight lateral projection which is delimited ventrally by a shallow external groove. This projection, due in part to the group of neuroblasts above mentioned and in part to widening of the dorsal portion of the rhomboidal fossa, is the first external evidence of the cerebellar primordium. Proliferation of cells, indicated by numerous mitotic figures, is very rapid in this region of the rhombencephalon at this stage, as Coghill (1929) pointed out. Crowding of the cells soon obliterates an early suggestion of a boundary between the matrix layer, on the one hand, and the rudiment of the cerebellum and acousticolateral area, on the other hand.

At the S-reaction stage of Coghill (Harrison's stage 35–36) the cerebellar primordium has increased in volume and caudal extent by continued proliferation of cells (fig. 100B, C). The rhomboidal fossa is narrow immediately caudal of the cephalic flexure, but caudal of the cerebellar primordium it widens. The anterior lateral-line roots and the root of the VIII nerve enter the rhombencephalon, their fibers continuing rostralward a short distance as small fascicles. Ventrolateral migration of cells in the cerebellar primordium results in a marked lateral swelling by Harrison's stage 36 (fig. 100C).

At Harrison's stage 39, two days after the early swimming stage of Coghill, the bilateral cerebellar primordia form a broad anterior wall of the fourth ventricle, except medially. Behind the primordia the ventricle widens into an incipient recessus lateralis on either side (fig. 101). Between the primordia it continues, as a much narrower cavity, to the mesencephalic ventricle. The cerebellar primordia incline dorsomedially from either side, immediately behind the isthmus, and are connected above the ventricle by a narrow zone of ependyma. They thus form the lateral and dorsolateral parts of a cerebellar arch which bridges the ventricle (fig. 101C–E). In the earlier stages the median part of the arch is a thin ependymal layer, continuous with the midbrain, above which a fascicle of commissural fibers crosses from one side to the other. Behind the cerebellar primordium a faint sulcus limitans in the floor of the fourth ventricle marks the medial boundary of a slightly raised longitudinal zone which is the sensory area of the medulla oblongata (fig. 101F). This area is continuous rostrally with the cerebellar primordium. The lateral part of the area, extending to the lateral surface of the medulla oblongata, represents the future acousticolateral area.

The tenial margin of the lateral recess is continued dorsomedially as the thin posterior border of the cerebellar arch and reaches the ependymal plate between the bilateral halves of the cerebellar primordium. The commissural fibers above mentioned cross the midline, by Harrison's stage 37, near the posterior border of the ependymal plate. In sagittal sections of stage 39+ these fibers are seen to form a small fascicle which is the first indication of the acousticolateral commissure. The enlargement and dorsomedial extension of the anterior end of the sensory area on either side, together with the dorsomedial deflection of the tenial margin and its continuity with the corresponding margin of the opposite side, produce a total effect as if the anterior end of the lateral part of the rhombencephalon were turned dorsomedially from either side and connected across the midline by the ependymal zone and the commissural fascicle above it.

At Harrison's stage 39+ the lateral part of the anterior wall of the recessus lateralis begins a period of rapid growth, as indicated by numerous mitotic figures. This results in lateral and rostral enlargement of the ventrolateral part of the cerebellar primordium and widening of the lateral recess (fig. 102). By Harrison's stage 40 (fig. 103) a rostrolateral projection has appeared which is continuous, behind fiber tracts that represent the lemniscus systems from medulla oblongata to midbrain, with the remainder of the cerebellar rudiment. The tip of the recessus lateralis has turned forward (fig. 103C), forming a small anterior diverticulum, the floor of which is

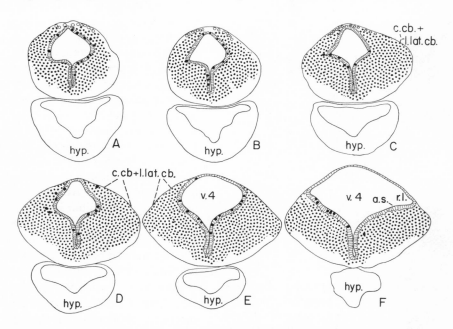

Figure 101. Transverse sections of brain stem of Ambystoma larva at two days after swimming stage (Harrison st. 39). A. Section through caudal part of midbrain. B. Section at border between midbrain and cerebellar region, the right side being slightly farther caudal. C–E. Sections through common anlage of lateral lobule and corpus cerebelli. F. Section through sensory area of medulla oblongata. Alum-cochineal and Lyons blue. ×50. (Larsell, 1932a.)

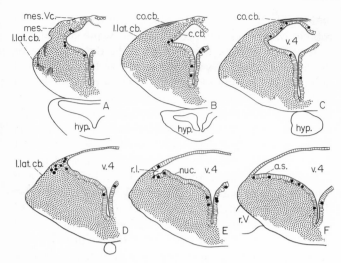

Figure 102. Successive transverse sections through cerebellar region of Ambystoma larva at three days after early swimming stage (Harrison st. 39+). Alum-cochineal and Lyons blue. ×55. (Larsell, 1932a.)

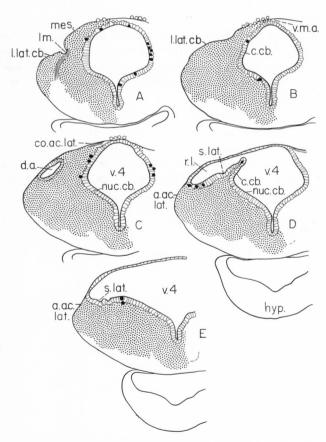

Figure 103. Successive transverse sections through the cerebellar region of Ambystoma larva at four days after early swimming stage (Harrison st. 40). Alum-cochineal and Lyons blue. ×66⅔. (Larsell, 1932a.)

continuous with the acousticolateral area. This area is delimited from the remainder of the sensory area of the medulla oblongata at this stage by a shallow furrow representing the sulcus lateralis of Herrick (fig. 103D, E). The anterior part of the projection lies ventrolateral of the caudal part of the midbrain and is separated from it by a prominent external furrow. It represents the projecting part of the rudiment of the lateral lobule of the cerebellum (fig. 103A). The cell mass behind the level of the lemniscus systems and between the anterior diverticulum and the fourth ventricle, with which it is continuous, is undifferentiated except caudally where a ridge arises from the floor of the ventricle forming the anterior wall of the medial part of the recess and the medial wall of the continuation of the recess as the anterior diverticulum. It merges with the medial part of the undifferentiated cell mass but subsequent development shows that it represents the base of the corpus cerebelli proper (fig. 103D).

Before describing later larval stages, the lobulus lateralis and corpus cerebelli, *sensu strictiori*, of urodeles should be defined. The terms auricular lobe and auricle have long been used more or less interchangeably and without precise definition in the literature of comparative neurology. As employed by Herrick (1914a, 1914b, 1924, 1930, 1944, 1948) and myself (1920, 1931, 1932a), in urodeles, they have designated the rostrolateral projection above mentioned. The "auricular lobe" of Necturus, as described by Herrick (1914a), comprises the walls and roof of an anterior diverticulum of the lateral recess of the fourth ventricle. These walls and roof are thin, but are formed of nervous tissue related to that of the acousticolateral area. The "auricular lobe" has the morphological features, on a greatly reduced scale, of the lateral lobule of Acipenser and Polyodon. Using the term "auricle" Herrick (1948) defines it in Ambystoma as an enlargement of the anterior end of the sensory zone of the medulla oblongata, with which he also associates a post-isthmial enlargement of the intermediate zone. Because this anterior part of the sensory zone receives terminals of ascending lateral-line, VIII root, and V root fibers, the related neuropil of which is intimately associated with that of the gustatory-visceral and lemniscus systems, Herrick does not segregate them anatomically. He regards the "auricle" as a common primordium of the superior V nucleus, the lateral-line and vestibular part of the cerebellum, and other structures which are differentiated in higher vertebrates.

My use of the term "auricle" and "auricular lobe," as Herrick points out, has included only the portion of his auricle whose connections are limited to the ascending lateral-line and VIII root fascicles and related tracts. This portion comprises the expanded cell mass which projects

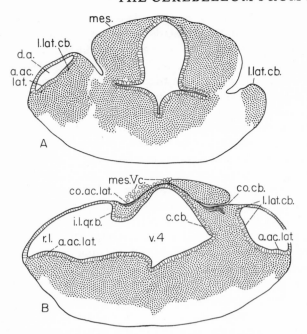

Figure 104. Transverse sections through cerebellar region of Ambystoma larva at two days after early feeding stage (Harrison st. 45), right side of sections being considerably rostral to the left side. Alum-cochineal and Lyons blue. ×66⅔. (Larsell, 1932a.)

and VIII root and related fascicles, together with the neuropil in which these end, constitute the white substance.

A review of my earlier work on the development of the cerebellum in larval Ambystoma and Triturus, and more recent restudy of midlarval stages of Ambystoma and of adult Triturus and other species in comparison with the cerebellum of fishes, especially Acipenser and Polyodon, make it clear that the auricular lobe or auricle of my earlier usage corresponds to the lateral lobule of fishes. The two lateral lobules are interconnected by the commissura lateralis cerebelli of Herrick. In Triturus and Ambystoma, at least, a fascicle of VIII root fibers also decussates in the arch of the cerebellum. Herrick (1948) describes this fascicle in adult Ambystoma but was not certain of it in Necturus (Herrick, 1930). This VIII root decussation and the lateral commissure together form an acousticolateral commissure which is accompanied by a cell layer extending caudomedially from the cell mass of the lateral lobule. The two lobules, acousticolateral commissure and the accompanying cells form a vestibulolateral lobe comparable with that of elasmobranchs and other fishes.

The corpus cerebelli as loosely defined hitherto has included the medial wall of the anterior diverticulum, anterior wall of the lateral recess, and all of the cerebellar arch. It may now be more specifically defined as the deeply situated median part of the cerebellum and related neuropil fields and molecular layer, the bilateral halves of which are connected by the commissura cerebelli, and which receives spinal, trigeminal, and other bulbar fibers not related to the acousticolateral system. In addition it has afferents from the midbrain and probably from the

rostrolaterally in Ambystoma larvae and, as will appear, in most adult urodeles. It is continuous caudally with the nucleus medialis of the acousticolateral area and, medially and ventromedially, with the cell mass of the median part of the cerebellum and the trigeminal and isthmic tegmentum. The terminals of ascending lateral-line

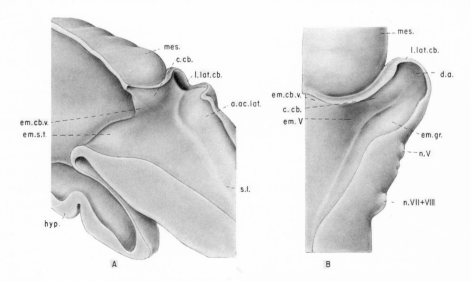

Figure 105. Model of brain stem of Ambystoma punctatum larva at walking stage. A. Caudomedial view. B. Dorsal view. (Larsell, 1932a.)

hypothalamus. The base of the corpus forms the anterior wall of the recessus lateralis and the lower medial wall of the posterior part of the anterior diverticulum. In species having the more massive cerebella the cell mass tapers rostromedially beneath the interlobular cell band but does not reach the midline, the bilateral cell masses being connected only by fibers included in the commissura cerebelli. In the lower urodeles the rostromedial continuation of the cell mass is limited. The base of the corpus cerebelli is continuous, caudally and medially, with the trigeminal tegmentum and rostromedially with the isthmic tegmentum.

To return to cerebellar development in larval stages: the lateral lobule at Harrison's stage 44+ extends considerably forward of the cerebellar and acousticolateral commissures. At stage 45 the rostrolateral part of the

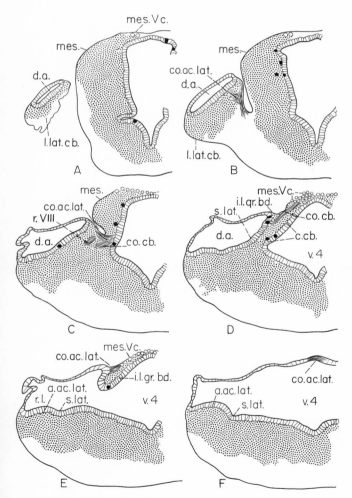

Figure 106. Successive transverse sections through cerebellar region of Ambystoma larva at walking stage, no leg reflex (past Harrison stages). Alum-cochineal and Lyons blue. ×66⅔. (Larsell, 1932a.)

lobule forms a prominent projection beyond the level of the now more extensive lemniscus zone. The anterior diverticulum, covered laterally by an incipient choroid membrane, extends rostrally into the projection (fig. 104A); the caudal part of its floor shows a forward continuation of the sulcus lateralis. The appearance of the cerebellar region and of the acousticolateral area immediately behind it is illustrated at four obliquely transverse levels, reading from the right to left sides successively of A and B of figure 104. The anterior part of the cell mass of the lateral lobule is delimited medially by a wide layer of white substance. The gray layer, however, is continuous caudomedially with the massive medial wall of the diverticulum. This is partially divided into lateral and medial parts by fascicles of fibers that contribute to the commissura cerebelli. The dorsomedial part of the cell mass extends toward the cerebellar arch as a medially tapering cell band which accompanies the acousticolateral commissure but ends considerably short of the midline (fig. 104B).

At the walking stage of the larva (beyond Harrison's stages) the projecting part of the lateral lobule turns dorsalward so that its tip lies lateral of the midbrain (figs. 105, 106). Dorsomedially and rostrally directed fascicles incompletely separate the cell mass between the ventromedial surface of the anterior diverticulum and the fourth ventricle into a lateral plate and a medial cell mass (fig. 106C). The lateral plate is directly continuous, anteriorly, with the cell layer of the rostrolateral projection. The medial cell mass represents the corpus cerebelli proper (fig. 106D). Collectively these fascicles, except the most lateral one and the large-fibered mesencephalic V root, represent components of the commissura cerebelli. The most laterally situated fascicle, as shown in silver preparations of midlarval stages, is formed of ascending VIII root and, possibly, secondary fibers that join the lateral commissure to form the commissura acousticolateralis (fig. 107).

At the arm-trunk reflex stage of the larva some of the larger cells of the lateral lobule send long dendrites medially and ventromedially that branch in the VIII root fascicle and its vicinity (fig. 111). In Golgi sections of midlarval stages, similar cells and relations to the VIII fascicle are found, and ascending lateral-line fascicles enter the caudolateral part of the lobule (figs. 111A, 112, 113). The more medial fascicles, ascending between the cell plate of the medial wall of the diverticulum and the gray mass forming the wall of the fourth ventricle, include the ascending V fascicle, which ends in part in this region; the mesencephalic V tract; and the spino-cerebellar tract. These, except the mesencephalic V tract whose connections with the cerebellum are obscure, are related

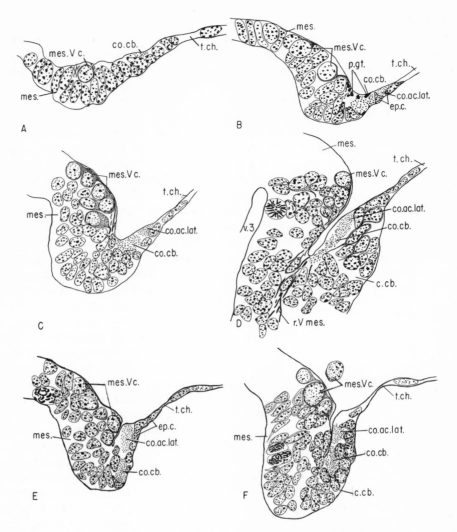

Figure 107. A. Midsagittal section through cerebellar region of Ambystoma larva at three days after early swimming stage (Harrison st. 39+). B. Midsagittal section through larva at early feeding stage (Harrison st. 44+). C. Same series, nine sections from median plane. D. Same series, sixteen sections from median plane. E. Midsagittal section through cerebellar region of Ambystoma larva at arm-trunk reflex stage. F. Lateral section from same series. Alum-cochineal and Lyons blue. ×360. (Larsell, 1932a.)

to the rudiment of the corpus cerebelli proper, as silver series of midlarval stages show. It is probable, however, that dendritic twigs of cells in both lateral lobule and corpus cerebelli overlap among the fascicles so that a sharp functional differentiation does not exist in larval stages. Dendritic connections are more diffuse, in general, in larval stages than in adult Ambystoma, according to Herrick (1948).

At the walking stage of the larva the sulcus lateralis delimits the zone of continuity between acousticolateral area and lateral lobule from the base of the corpus cerebelli. A faint groove, extending medially and dorsome-

dially in the floor and medial wall of the diverticulum, appears to be a continuation of the sulcus lateralis, delimiting the expanded cell mass of the anterior floor and medial wall of the diverticulum from the medial wall of the posterior part of the diverticulum. This part of the wall is formed by the corpus cerebelli (figs. 106D, 108). The groove continues medially between the corpus cerebelli and the medially tapering cell band continuous with the posterior upper wall of the diverticulum.

In midlarval stages the sulcus lateralis turns dorsomedially as a shallow groove in front of the base of the corpus cerebelli and then dorsomedially and caudomedially

140

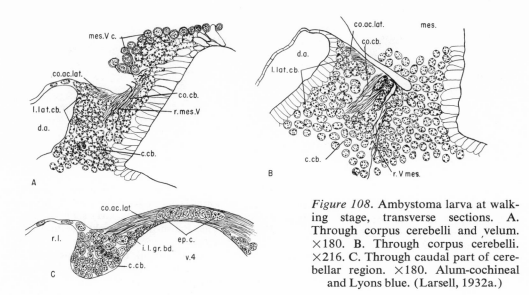

Figure 108. Ambystoma larva at walking stage, transverse sections. A. Through corpus cerebelli and velum. ×180. B. Through corpus cerebelli. ×216. C. Through caudal part of cerebellar region. ×180. Alum-cochineal and Lyons blue. (Larsell, 1932a.)

on the upper medial surface of the posterior part of the diverticulum. Sections of midlarval stages of A. tigrinum show a space between the cell mass of the corpus cerebelli and the posterior part of the dorsomedial wall. We shall return to a corresponding groove in adult Triturus.

The thick plate of cells rostral and rostrolateral of the medial deflection of the sulcus lateralis forms the anterior part of the ventromedial wall and anterior part of the floor of the diverticulum, turning dorsalward as the lower part of the anterior wall; laterocaudally it is continuous with the acousticolateral area (fig. 105).

Deferring comparison with other Ichthyopsida until the cerebellum of adult Triturus is described (p. 148), I shall state here that I regard this cell plate as the homologue of the eminentia granularis of fishes. A groove in the medial wall of the anterior diverticulum of 25 mm length Amia, which delimits the much larger corpus cerebelli from the eminentia granularis, has already been mentioned. The band of cells that tapers medialward along the acousticolateral commissure, reaching the midline in adult Ambystoma and Triturus, appears to be homologous with the cell layer of the pars medialis of the vestibulolateral lobe of elasmobranchs.

This continuity of the eminentia granularis as an interlobular band is hidden by the choroid tela in the view of the model of the cerebellum of the walking stage of Ambystoma illustrated in figure 105, but it is evident in sections of this and other stages. The band of cells and the fascicle of accompanying fibers represent a continuation, in the posteromedial margin of the cerebellum, of the vestibulolateral lobe (fig. 106D, E). The cell band was labeled corpus cerebelli in some of Herrick's (1914b) figures of midlarval Ambystoma and in some of my fig-

ures (1931, 1932a) of Triturus and Ambystoma. The term corpus cerebelli in these contributions was incorrectly used to include all of the median part of the cerebellum.

The corpus cerebelli, *sensu strictiori*, becomes increasingly differentiated from the lateral lobule with growth of the cerebellum. As it enlarges it pushes posteriorly into the recessus lateralis and laterally into the caudal part of the anterior diverticulum. The commissura cerebelli, which includes interconnections between the bilateral halves of the corpus cerebelli and other fibers described below, increases in size. The corpus cerebelli extends dorsomedially and rostrally beneath the commissure much as the interlobular cell band extends caudomedially along the acousticolateral commissure (figs. 106, 107, 108). The tapering cell mass of the corpus cerebelli and its accompanying commissure pass beneath the interlobular cell band on either side, assuming a ventrorostral position in the cerebellar arch, but the cell mass does not reach the midline. The cerebellar commissure alone represents the corpus cerebelli in the median sagittal plane.

Presumably the early development of the cerebellar region of A. tigrinum is similar to that of A. punctatum. There are differences, however, in the midlarval and subsequent stages examined. Whether they resulted from varying methods of fixation or represent species variations is not known. In a larva of A. punctatum 32 mm long the lateral lobule extends forward along the lateral wall of the midbrain, from which it is separated by a deep fissure. The anterior diverticulum is prominent, its dorsomedially sloping and massive medial wall, as already noted, representing the homologue of the eminentia granularis except caudomedially where the corpus cerebelli

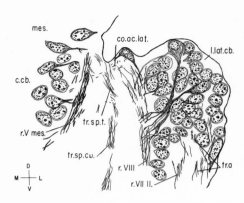

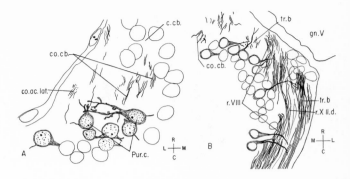

Figure 109. Transverse section through lateral lobule and corpus cerebelli of Ambystoma larva at arm-trunk reflex stage. Alum-cochineal and Lyons blue. ×300. (Larsell, 1932a.)

Figure 110. A. Horizontal section through corpus cerebelli in Ambystoma larva at four days after early feeding stage (Harrison st. 46+), showing early stage in differentiation of Purkinje cells. Paton-Bielschowsky method, oil immersion. ×587. B. Horizontal section through ventral cerebellar region in larva at arm-trunk total reaction stage (Harrison st. 44), showing transition cells and their relation to tracts ascending into lateral cerebellar lobe. Paton-Bielschowsky method. ×300. (Larsell, 1932a.)

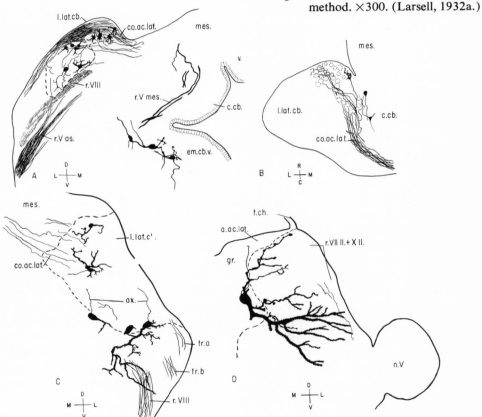

Figure 111. Ambystoma, late larval stage. A. Transverse section through lateral lobule and corpus cerebelli, showing lateral lobule cells and fibers. ×52. B. Horizontal section through lateral lobule, showing acousticolateral commissure and its terminals among cells of lateral lobule. ×85. C. Transverse section of part of lateral lobule and neighboring acousticolateral area. ×65. D. Transverse section through acousticolateral area at level of V nerve, same series. ×122. Golgi method. (Larsell, 1932a.)

142

is involved. The rostral part of the lateral lobule arches dorsalward but slightly. In A. tigrinum the lateral lobules turn much more sharply upward, as is shown in figure 99, and in Herrick's (1914b) figures of a model of the medulla oblongata and cerebellum of a 38 mm larva. The rostral extent of the lobule is greatly reduced and the anterior diverticulum nearly disappears. The lateral part of the anterior wall of the recessus lateralis of A. tigrinum appears to correspond to the rostral part of the medial wall and part of the floor of the anterior diverticulum of A. punctatum. In adult A. tigrinum the lateral recess turns forward somewhat so that the resemblance to the relations prevailing in A. punctatum is increased. Except for the absence of the massive lateral wall of the diverticulum which characterizes the lateral lobule of Polyodon and, to a lesser degree, that of Acipenser, the lateral lobule of both species of Ambystoma at midlarval and subsequent stages is morphologically similar to that of Acipenseriformes.

At Harrison's stage 45 two types of cell can be distinguished, in alum-cochineal and Paton-Bielschowsky preparations, by the size of the nucleus and the granules. Small nuclei have small granules that are scattered uniformly; the larger nuclei have more irregularly scattered larger granules and some small ones. In later stages there are some cells of still larger size that represent developing Purkinje cells (figs. 109, 110). One can therefore speak of small, intermediate, and large cells. The histogenetic relations of each type need further investigation, but the intermediate and large cells apparently are differentiated from cells derived from the matrix layer. The small cells are most numerous beneath the tenial margins of the lateral lobule and in the lateral part of the cerebellar arch, which is continuous with the margin of the lobule.

In Cajal series of midlarval stages of both Ambystoma punctatum and A. tigrinum a collection of small, dark-staining cells is found at the rostrodorsal tip of the lateral lobule. A chain of similar cells continues from this collection into the margin of the lateral part of the cerebellar arch, and another chain extends laterocaudally toward the acousticolateral area. The rostrodorsal collection is covered by a membranous fold which is attached to the rostral, medial, and lateral tenial margins of the lobule. The cells differ from the majority of those in the floor of the diverticulum both in size and in staining quality. The rostrodorsal collection appears to represent the auricle, *sensu strictiori*, and the chains of small cells continuous with it to correspond to the anteromedial and posterolateral folds of the auricle in elasmobranch embryos. As in embryos of Squalus, the ridge of small cells partly encircles the eminentia granularis. The lobulus lateralis of Ambystoma larvae, called auricular lobe or auricle by Herrick and myself in earlier contributions, accordingly includes two subdivisions, an eminentia granularis and an auricle, *sensu strictiori*, as in elasmobranchs and other fishes.

The bilateral halves of the corpus cerebelli and the component of the commissura cerebelli which interconnects them correspond, on a larger scale, to the submerged corpus cerebelli of petromyzonts. Homology with the corpus cerebelli proper of elasmobranchs and other fishes is obscured by the disparity in size and the differences in topographical relations of the large corpus cerebelli of fishes. The afferent fiber connections, described below in Triturus and adult Ambystoma, however, correspond to those of the corpus cerebelli of other Ichthyopsida, except for the presence in some groups of fishes of additional connections not found in urodeles.

A ventricular swelling beneath the cerebellum, called the "eminentia cerebellaris ventralis" by Herrick in earlier contributions, was named the "nucleus cerebelli" by him (1948) in adult Ambystoma. It is recognizable in the walking stage of larval A. punctatum as an eminence in the anterior wall of the recessus lateralis (fig. 105A). Behind the nucleus cerebelli a low elevation appears in the floor of the lateral recess as this increases in extent (fig. 105B). This elevation is the eminentia trigemini of Herrick, beneath which are situated the cells of the motor and superior sensory V nuclei. Axons of the latter form the intertrigeminal component of the commissura cerebelli.

The Golgi preparations of Ambystoma larvae reproduced in figures 111 to 118 reveal details of the finer structure of the rhombencephalon.

URODELA II

The Adult Cerebellum

THE urodele "auricle," as defined by Herrick (1948), is described as including the primordia of two quite distinct structures of higher vertebrates. One primordium is the end station of lateral-line and vestibular root fibers; the other is trigeminal and is regarded by Herrick as concerned chiefly with proprioceptive functions of the skin and deep tissues of the head. In midlarval Ambystoma and adult Triturus the lateral-line and vestibular tracts are laterally situated (fig. 112). Except for a fascicle of vestibular root and, apparently, secondary fibers that continue into the cerebellar arch the tracts terminate in the lateral lobule. The trigeminal fascicle is medially situated and terminates in a zone of neuropil immediately lateral of the tegmentum, some fibers continuing into the com-

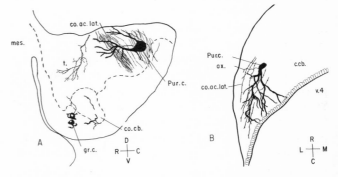

Figure 113. Ambystoma, late larval stage. A. Sagittal section through corpus cerebelli. t., terminal branches of afferent fiber. ×67. B. Horizontal section through corpus cerebelli. ×83. Golgi method. (Larsell, 1932a.)

missura cerebelli. The spino-cerebellar tract becomes closely associated with the ascending V fascicle (fig. 112); according to Herrick it connects only with the "non-vestibular body of the cerebellum." The neuropil of the vestibular and lateral-line zones is continuous with that of the trigeminal zone, as is the trigeminal and acousticolateral neuropil of the sensory area of the medulla oblongata.

Most of the differences, already mentioned, between Herrick's and my definitions of the urodele "auricle" or lateral lobule are accounted for by differences in form and position, as well as the relative degrees of development, of this part of the cerebellum. It is relatively larger and forms a more distinct rostrolateral projection in larval than in adult Ambystoma. In the adult water stage of Triturus it is considerably larger and projects rostrolaterally much more than in adult Ambystoma. The projection is separated from the isthmic and trigeminal tegmentum by a thick layer of fibers and neuropil (fig. 120). In adult Ambystoma tigrinum the lateral lobule projects dorso-

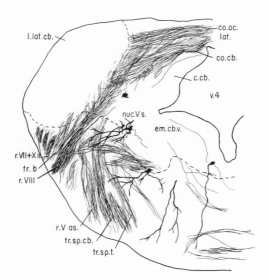

Figure 112. Ambystoma, late larval stage. Transverse section through cerebellar region. Golgi method. ×31. (Larsell, 1932a.)

144

laterally instead of rostrolaterally, and the layer of fibers and neuropil is spread on the anterior surface of the lobule, the thick layer of Triturus being represented only by a zone of increased thickness between the rostral surface of the nuclear gray and that of the projecting lobule.

As most clearly seen in the adult water stage of Tri-

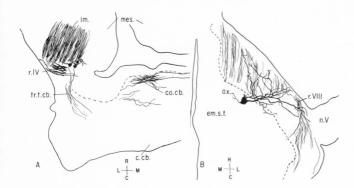

Figure 114. Ambystoma, late larval stage. A. Horizontal section through part of midbrain and corpus cerebelli, showing tecto-cerebellar tract. ×40. B. Horizontal section through subcerebellar region. ×50. Golgi method. (Larsell, 1932a.)

turus (fig. 98) and in Cryptobranchus (fig. 126) the rostrolateral projection of the hindbrain has the characteristics, in modified and much reduced form, of the lateral lobule of the cerebellum of Acipenser and Polyodon. The resemblance to the homologous part of the elasmobranch and teleostean cerebellum is less evident because of greater modifications of one or another feature in these fishes but it can be established. The term lobulus lateralis, already introduced in larval Ambystoma, therefore, is more appropriate than auricular lobe or auricle. The term "auricle" is reserved for a collection of small cells in the anterior and marginal portion of this lobule, already noted in midlarval Ambystoma (fig. 115A), which I now regard as corresponding, on a greatly reduced scale, to the Rautenohr of Burckhardt (1897), as above defined, in elasmobranchs; the auricle proper of Acipenseriformes; the auricle of Holmgren and van der Horst (1925) in Neoceratodus; and the reduced and usually concealed auricle of teleosts, as defined by van der Horst (1925), by Pearson (1936a), and in the preceding section of this book.

The principal cell mass of the lateral lobule, already

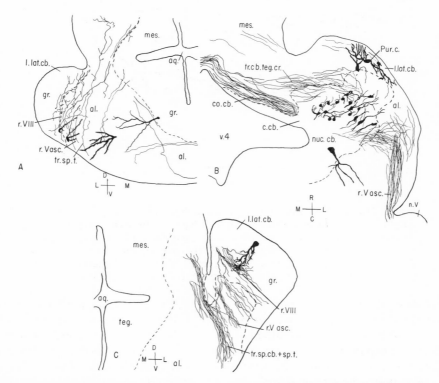

Figure 115. Ambystoma. A. Transverse section through rostral part of lateral lobule in late midlarval stage. ×67. B. Horizontal section through corpus cerebelli and lateral lobule of late larval stage. ×31. C. Transverse section through rostral part of lateral lobule of late larval stage. ×67.
Golgi method. (Larsell, 1932a.)

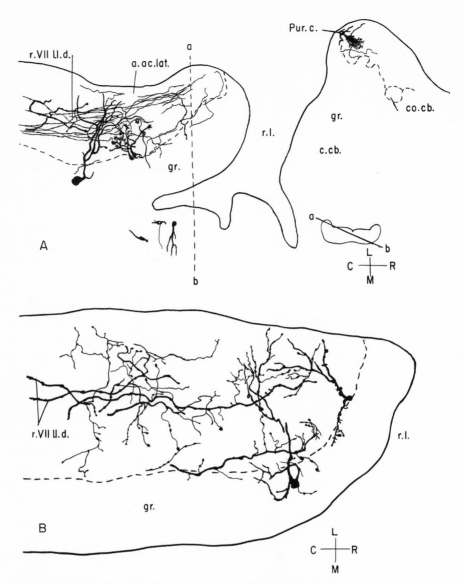

Figure 116. Ambystoma, late larval stage. Section between horizontal and sagittal planes (as indicated at lower right in figure), through rostral part of acousticolateral area and corpus cerebelli. Golgi method. ×78. (Larsell, 1932a.) *Figure 117.* Ambystoma, late larval stage. Horizontal section through rostral part of acousticolateral area, showing terminals of dorsal lateral-line VII root fibers. Golgi method. ×160. (Larsell, 1932a.)

mentioned in larval Ambystoma as the homologue of the eminentia granularis, differs from the gray layer of the acousticolateral area, with which it is continuous, by reason of its much greater expansion and in modifications of its cells, described below. It is also interconnected with the contralateral cell mass by the lateral commissure of Herrick. Other features, described in individual species in the following pages, add to its similarity to the granular eminence of other Ichthyopsida. The white layer of the lateral lobule consists of terminal fibers and neuropil

of the lateral-line and VIII root fascicles, closely related to the eminentia granularis (fig. 122).

The terms auricle and auricular lobe, both in the broad sense used by Herrick and in the more restricted but still too inclusive sense of my earlier usage, are discontinued with reference to the urodeles. Rather, the terms are restricted to the auricle, *sensu strictiori*, already noted in larval Ambystoma and described below in Triturus. The terms also have been employed to designate the more or less ear-like lateral appendages of the cerebellum of land vertebrates. Since the lateral-line system and its connections with the brain disappear, beginning with metamorphosed anurans, only the vestibular connection of the lateral-line and VIII root complex with the cerebellum remains. The part of the cerebellum involved corresponds to the mammalian flocculus. For the sake of more accurate indication of homologies, the term flocculus will be used in metamorphosed anurans, reptiles, and birds to designate this vestibular part of the cerebellum. The so-called auricle of birds includes both flocculus and a primitive paraflocculus, as Ingvar (1918) found, and as I described in greater detail (1948), calling the parafloccular part the "avian paraflocculus." The term "avian auricle," applied to this ear-like topographical projection in my earlier studies on birds, is retained (p. 234), but without reference to its floccular component. We shall return to the auricle proper and its fate in anurans and higher vertebrates.

The term corpus cerebelli has been employed in various senses in adult urodeles. Herrick (1914a, 1914b, 1930, 1948) so designated all of the median part of the cerebellum, including a portion of the lateral lobule, as above defined, on either side. This usage was followed by myself (1920, 1931, 1932a). Employing the term in a general sense, Röthig (1927a), in Cryptobranchus (Megalobatrachus) japonicus, included the bilateral parts that correspond to the lateral lobules of C. alleghaniensis (p. 154) with the median mass. The median mass and a lateral cell mass on either side which corresponds to the eminentia granularis of larval Ambystoma and, as will

appear, of adult urodeles, were all included in the corpus cerebelli of Salamandra maculosa, as the term was used by Kreht (1930). The more specifically defined corpus cerebelli already described in larval Ambystoma is also recognizable in adult urodeles.

The nucleus cerebelli is represented superficially by Herrick's eminentia cerebellaris ventralis. This is the posterior part of the subcerebellar eminence of the ventricular surface. In Necturus, Herrick points out (1914a), the ventral cerebellar eminence is directly continuous, in front of the recessus lateralis, with the "body of the cerebellum." Herrick (1914b) states furthermore that neurons in this eminence in Necturus and midlarval Ambystoma form part of the cerebellar efferent system. More specifically, in Necturus axons pass into the brachium conjunctivum which Herrick (1914a) found feebly developed in this species. The dendrites of these cells engage terminals of sensory roots of some of the cranial nerves and of the spino-cerebellar and other ascending tracts. According to Herrick (1930) many of the long dendrites in Necturus extend far beyond cerebellar territory, but the ventral cerebellar eminence has strong cerebellar connections. The eminence he regarded as a specialized part of the general reticular formation.

In adult Ambystoma I (1920) incorrectly applied the term nucleus dentatus to cells in the medial wall of the anterior diverticulum from which axons pass ventrorostrally into the brachium conjunctivum. Subsequent studies have shown that these neurons are primitive Purkinje cells that correspond to neurons in the medial wall

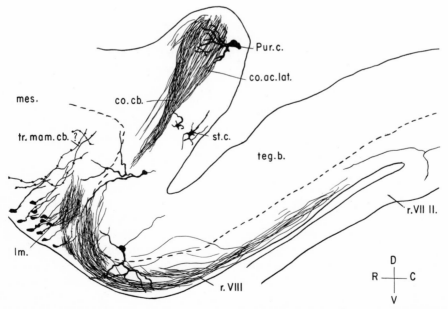

Figure 118. Ambystoma, late larval stage. Horizontal section through cerebellar region. Golgi method. ×100.

of the anterior diverticulum of Necturus whose axons are described by Herrick (1914a) as directed, in part, into the brachium conjunctivum. These and Purkinje cells in the corpus cerebelli of Ambystoma send their axons directly into the brachium conjunctivum.

The eminentia cerebellaris ventralis was called the nucleus cerebelli by Herrick (1948) in adult Ambystoma. He described it as a poorly defined region dorsal of the junction of the trigeminal with the isthmic tegmentum, occupying the position of the intermediate zone (reticular formation). It is intimately related with both the lateral lobule and the corpus cerebelli, as these divisions are above defined. A small proportion of the fibers of the brachium conjunctivum arise from its cells, as I can confirm in late larval Ambystoma.

The embryonic origin of the nucleus cerebelli of urodeles is not discussed by Rüdeberg (1961), and one can only guess at the sources of its cells. If they represent migrated elements from the cell mass which differentiates into corpus cerebelli and eminentia granularis, their origin, in principle, would be similar to that of the nucleus cerebelli of elasmobranchs and anurans, as described by Rüdeberg. Such an origin would in no wise conflict with the position of the nucleus in the intermediate zone of Herrick, the boundaries of which are quite arbitrary. The various connections of its neurons indicate that the function of the nucleus cerebelli is correlation, as is that of the intermediate zone in general.

The lateral lobule of adult Triturus is more clearly delimited from the corpus cerebelli proper than it is in most other species of urodeles, and both the lobule and the corpus are relatively large. In midlarval Ambystoma the lobule is more distinct than in the adult. The fiber connections of the two species are very similar. The cerebellum of Triturus torosus, therefore, will first be described in greater detail and in comparison with its development in larval Ambystoma; consideration of other species in which homologies are more difficult to recognize because of differences in relative size and position of the subdivisions will follow. Homologies with the subdivisions of the more generalized types of fish cerebellum also can be established with greater certainty by this sequence of description.

Triturus Torosus

The cerebellum of the mature water stage of Triturus is larger and more massive than in the land stage. The lateral lobule is more prominent and more elongated rostrolaterally, the anterior diverticulum of the lateral recess extending forward with the lobule (fig. 119). The base of the corpus cerebelli forms the anterior wall of the fourth ventricle, between the subcerebellar continuation

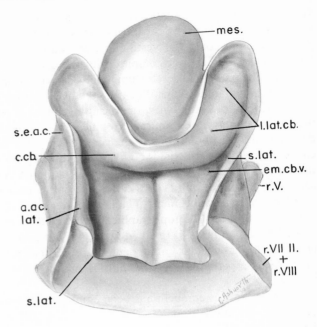

Figure 119. Model of cerebellum of Triturus torosus. ×50.

of this cavity and the posterior part of the diverticulum; the corpus cerebelli continues rostromedially from the base as the deep cellular part of the cerebellar arch.

The following description of morphological features and of fiber connections, as shown in myelin-stained preparations, are based on adult water stage specimens. The finer structure is described chiefly from silver preparations of large land stage specimens of Triturus and midlarval or later stages of Ambystoma. Since the fiber tracts of adult Ambystoma, described by myself (1920) and more fully by Herrick (1948), are nearly identical with those of Triturus, they are included in order to avoid repetition.

THE LOBULUS LATERALIS

The lateral lobule is separated from the ventrolateral wall of the midbrain by a continuation of the rhombomesencephalic fissure (figs. 98, 119, 120). On a reduced scale it has the form and relations that would be presented by the lobulus lateralis of Acipenser if it were rotated forward from its base. The anterior and medial walls of the Acipenser lobule would then correspond to the rostrally elongated floor and ventromedial wall of the anterior diverticulum of Triturus. The roof and lateral wall of the diverticulum in Triturus, however, are membranous instead of massive as in Acipenser.

The most prominent feature of the lateral lobule of Triturus, as seen in transverse section, is a thick dorsomedially tilted plate of cells (fig. 120). The rostral part

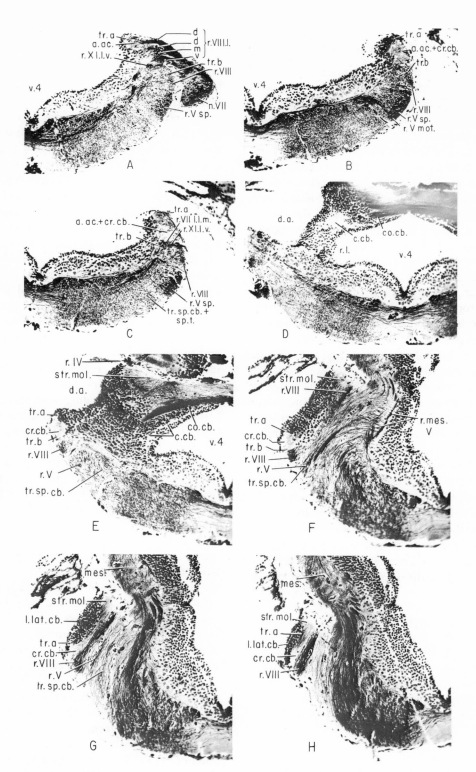

Figure 120. Transverse sections of the brain stem of Triturus torosus. A. Level of entrance of lateral-line VII roots. B. Level about midway between entrance of V and lateral-line roots. C. Level just caudal of entrance of V root. D. Section through acousticolateral area and portion of corpus cerebelli. E. Section through caudal level of corpus cerebelli and through acousticolateral area. F. Section through caudal level of lateral lobule and through corpus cerebelli. G. Section through middle level of lateral lobule. H. Section through rostral level of lateral lobule. Weigert method. ×50.

149

of this plate is separated from the lemniscus zone of the isthmic region and, farther caudally, from the isthmic tegmentum, by a thick layer of fibers and neuropil, as in larval Ambystoma (fig. 120). The caudomedial and caudolateral relations also are similar to those in mid-larval Ambystoma. The layer of fibers and neuropil forming the medial boundary of the rostral part of the plate is the forward continuation of the sensory zone of the medulla oblongata. Passing beneath the zone of continuity between the eminentia and corpus cerebelli the layer of fibers and neuropil expands behind the isthmus and, laterally, beneath the anterior part of the gray of the lateral lobule. The expansion is due to enlarged fields of neuropil among the fascicles of fibers, many of which terminate in this region. These pools correspond to the posterior isthmic neuropil of Herrick (1948) in adult Ambystoma. Instead of being spread laterally as a broad zone, however, part of this neuropil, in Triturus, lies between the isthmus and the rostrolateral projection of the lobulus lateralis as already mentioned.

The ventricular sulcus lateralis (fig. 121), which delimits the acousticolateral area from the more medial part of the bulbar sensory zone turns medialward in the floor of the anterior diverticulum, as in midlarval Ambystoma. In a model of the cerebellar region of a large adult water stage specimen, in which the lateral lobule was elongated more than usual, the medial deflection of the sulcus is well shown in the posterior part of the floor. The furrow is lost across the ventromedial part of the floor but reappears on the medial wall of the diverticulum and continues caudomedially to a flattened area beneath the posterolateral part of the cerebellar arch. The floor and ventromedial wall of the diverticulum anterior of this me-

dial and dorsal continuation of the sulcus lateralis are formed of the plate of cells already identified as the eminentia granularis. The lower medial wall of the diverticulum and its continuation medialward as the anterior wall of the fourth ventricle represent the base of the corpus cerebelli. Similar relations of the eminentia and the corpus cerebelli to the rostral part of the sulcus lateralis have already been noted in larval Ambystoma.

The medial wall of the diverticulum dorsal of the sulcus lateralis tapers caudomedially toward the midline of the cerebellar arch, forming the interlobular or intereminential cell band along the acousticolateral commissure. This cell band tapers toward the midline of the cerebellar arch, a few cells above the ependyma representing a tenuous continuity between the bilateral halves.

The principal cell mass of the lateral lobule corresponds morphologically and in its fiber tract connections, as will appear, to the eminentia granularis of Acipenser and Polyodon. The interlobular or intereminential granular band is more readily comparable with the pars medialis of the vestibulolateral lobe of elasmobranchs, although a corresponding intereminential connection formed of cells and fibers occurs also in Acipenseriformes, as already noted. The eminentia granularis of Acipenser and Polyodon has already been compared with that of other fishes. The homology of the eminentia of Triturus with the primitive granular eminence of elasmobranchs is obscured by the large auricle, *sensu strictiori*, of the sharks and rays and the reduction of this structure in urodeles.

The cells of the rostral tip of the lobule are smaller than most of those in the eminentia. They also stain darker, in iron-hematoxylin and toluidine-blue preparations, than the majority of cells of the eminentia (fig. 121). These cells are primitive granules and the rostral collection represents a small auricle, *sensu strictiori*, as in midlarval Ambystoma. It extends onto the anterior surface of the lobule but is covered by a fold of choroid membrane which is attached to a tenia on this surface and continues in the lateral and medial margins of the lobule. The auricle, accordingly, faces the ventricular space represented by the diverticulum (fig. 121). A subtenial chain of similar cells continues from the anterior collection caudomedially into the posterior margin of the cerebellar arch and another extends from the lateral part of the auricle toward the acousticolateral area, ending at the "dorsal island." These chains correspond, on a reduced scale, to the dorsomedial and ventrolateral folds of the auricle of elasmobranchs. The dorsomedial chain, in Triturus, follows the tenial border of the cerebellar arch but soon merges more or less completely with the intereminential cell band, as does the more prominent interauricular granular band of

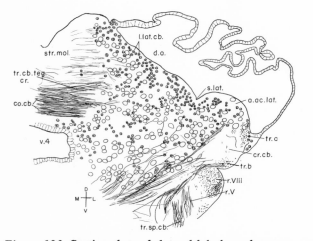

Figure 121. Section through lateral lobule and corpus cerebelli of adult water stage of Triturus. Iron-hematoxylin. Camera lucida. ×65. (Larsell, 1931.)

elasmobranchs with the pars medialis of the vestibulo-lateral lobe. The much larger auricle and its folds in elasmobranchs and also in Acipenseriformes, it will be recalled, are similarly covered by choroid membrane.

The cells of the auricle proper and its more rudimentary folds, in larval Ambystoma, appear to derive from the tenial ependyma as, apparently, do those of the auricles, *sensu strictiori*, of elasmobranch embryos and, judging from their relations to the tenial margin, those of Acipenseriformes. They correspond to the smaller cells of the two types already noted in the lateral lobule of larval Ambystoma. In these larvae, as in adult Triturus, the small cells are most numerous in the subtenial margins of the lateral lobule.

The eminentia granularis includes small, medium-sized, and large cells, those of medium size being most numerous, but there are gradations of size that make well-defined categories difficult to establish. The larger cells in larval Ambystoma and in Triturus send long dendrites into the neuropil related to the ascending lateral-line and VIII root fascicles (fig. 116). The medium-sized cells have short dendrites that radiate within the eminentia. The axons of some enter the commissura lateralis, while those of other similar cells appear to become part of tract *b*. Cells in the ventral and lateral parts of the eminentia and in the auricle contribute axons to tract *a*. Very fine fibers, in Cajal preparations, that enter the molecular layer of the cerebellar arch, are perhaps derived from the granule cells of the auricle and its related subtenial cell chains. Very few small cells were impregnated in Golgi preparations, however, and the origin of these fibers cannot be assigned with certainty to the granule cells.

Although the rostral mass of granules and its subtenial continuations are small in comparison with the auricles proper of elasmobranchs and Acipenseriformes, it appears justified to regard them as homologous structures both because of their granular nature and because of their position with reference to the tenial margins of the lateral lobule. In teleosts and holosteans the auricles proper are small and situated behind and more or less beneath the greatly enlarged eminentia granularis, but the fundamental relation to the recessus lateralis of the fourth ventricle, in the variations of this recess, is the same as in Triturus.

The lobulus lateralis of Triturus, accordingly, includes not only an eminentia granularis but also an auricle proper. These and their related fiber tracts and neuropil

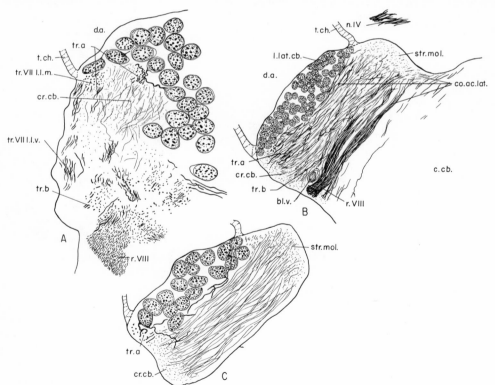

Figure 122. Triturus torosus. Transverse sections. A. Through acousticolateral area at level of V root. B. Through rostral part of lateral lobule. C. Through tip of lateral lobule. Cajal method. ×380. (Larsell, 1931.)

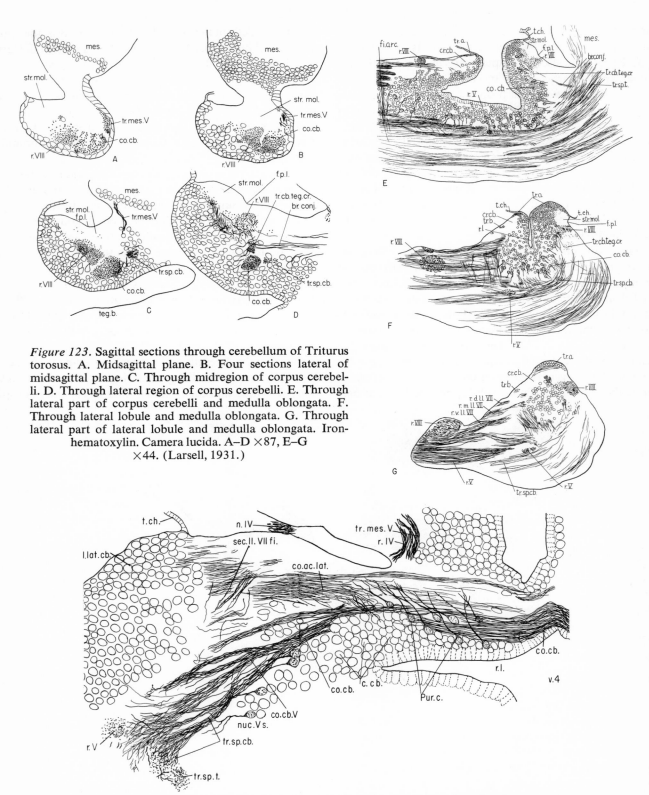

Figure 123. Sagittal sections through cerebellum of Triturus torosus. A. Midsagittal plane. B. Four sections lateral of midsagittal plane. C. Through midregion of corpus cerebelli. D. Through lateral region of corpus cerebelli. E. Through lateral part of corpus cerebelli and medulla oblongata. F. Through lateral lobule and medulla oblongata. G. Through lateral part of lateral lobule and medulla oblongata. Iron-hematoxylin. Camera lucida. A–D ×87, E–G ×44. (Larsell, 1931.)

Figure 124. Transverse section through cerebellum of Triturus torosus, showing acousti-colateral and cerebellar commissures, with trigeminal component of the latter. Cajal method. Camera lucida. ×130. (Larsell, 1931.)

correspond to the subdivisions of the lateral lobule of other Ichthyopsida. The two lobules and the commissura acousticolateralis form a vestibulolateral lobe as in the fishes, but on a reduced scale (fig. 122).

THE CORPUS CEREBELLI

The base of the corpus cerebelli, as already noted, forms the lower medial wall of the posterior part of the anterior diverticulum and also the anterior wall of the medial part of the lateral recess. The rostromedially tapering part forms the lateral wall and roof of the subcerebellar portion of the fourth ventricle. Most of it lies beneath the commissura cerebelli, whose course it follows nearly to the midline, but the bilateral halves are connected only by the commissure (figs. 120, 124). As shown in sagittal sections, the medial part of the tapering mass is fairly distinct from the intereminential cell band (fig. 123). An external molecular and fibrous layer of the cerebellar arch is related to both the corpus cerebelli and the intereminential cell band. This layer is broader, anteroposteriorly, in Triturus than in Ambystoma. A shallow furrow in the surface, which does not reach the midline, probably represents an incipient posterolateral fissure (fig. 123C,D).

The commissura cerebelli includes myelinated ascending V root fibers, secondary fibers from the superior V nucleus, fibers from cells in the corpus cerebelli, and spino-cerebellar fibers. Myelinated fibers of the ascending V root constitute a small fascicle, most of which ends in a field of neuropil between the corpus cerebelli and the lateral lobule. In myelin-stained as well as Cajal series it is clear, however, that some of the fibers pass into the cerebellar commissure (Larsell, 1931). Golgi and Cajal series of Ambystoma larvae also show such fibers, and I described them from Golgi preparations of adult Ambystoma (1920).

The secondary trigeminal fibers arise from cells whose dendrites extend into the neuropil of the superior V nucleus. The axons cross in the commissure and branch in the neuropil of the contralateral V nucleus (fig. 124), some fibers terminating in the corpus cerebelli. Herrick (1948) describes V root fibers accompanied by secondary fibers from the V nucleus, in adult Ambystoma, as joined by spino-cerebellar fibers and passing into the body of the cerebellum, some of the fibers decussating. The secondary trigeminal fibers justify the term intertrigeminal commissure of Bindewald (1911) in Proteus, and of Röthig (1927a) in Siren, and, less evidently, in Cryptobranchus (Megalobatrachus). Both these authors, however, probably included other fibers also.

Cells situated in the ventral and lateral parts of the corpus cerebelli send dendrites ventrolaterally into the cere-

bellar commissure as it begins to spread into the superior V nucleus. The axons of these cells pass medially into the commissure and apparently cross to the opposite side. The spino-cerebellar tract is joined by fibers from the sensory zone of the medulla oblongata and from the nucleus of the dorsal funiculus, as described by Herrick (1948). It terminates, in part, in the ipsilateral corpus cerebelli, but many fibers intermingle with the ascending V fibers and cross in the commissure. Terminals of crossed fibers may be seen among the cells of the corpus cerebelli in Cajal preparations, but which of the commissural components they represent could not be ascertained.

In addition to spinal and bulbar afferents the corpus cerebelli also receives a tecto-cerebellar and a hypothalamo- or lobo-cerebellar tract.

The *nucleus cerebelli* has already been described in general, chiefly from the descriptions of Herrick (1948) in Ambystoma. It appears to be entirely similar in Triturus.

Ambystoma Tigrinum
THE LOBULUS LATERALIS

Compared with that of lower urodeles, the cerebellum of Ambystoma is massive. It forms a well-defined external ridge which projects upward and laterally but only slightly rostrally from the dorsolateral margin of the anterior end of the medulla oblongata, turning caudomedially as the cerebellar arch. The anterior surface of the lateral projection dips rather sharply ventromedially to the isthmus, emphasizing the lateral projection which was called the auricle by Herrick (1948). As already noted, Herrick's "auricle" includes more than the lobulus lateralis, as above defined.

The cell layer of the cerebellum is similar, in general, to that of Triturus, but the eminentia granularis turns forward much less sharply and is more directly continuous with the median cell mass. The rostral continuation of the white layer of the bulbar sensory area, which in Triturus forms a prominent partition between most of the eminentia granularis and the median cell mass, produces a relatively slight indentation into the anteroventral surface of the gray layer in Ambystoma. The projection of the gray substance rostral of this thickened zone of the white layer is relatively slight. This gray, however, is continuous caudomedially with a large plate of cells forming most of the ventromedial floor of a ventricular space which is covered, dorsally and laterally, by choroid plexus. This space corresponds to the anterior diverticulum of the lateral recess in Triturus. The plate of cells in its floor is the eminentia granularis, as comparison with larval Ambystoma and adult Triturus clearly shows. Behind the thickened zone of the white layer it is continuous, medially with the corpus cerebelli and, caudolaterally, with the gray of the acousticolateral area.

At the dorsorostral tip of the projection a thin layer of small cells appears to represent an atrophied auricle, *sensu strictiori*. It forms the anterior part of the floor of the diverticulum and is enclosed by choroid membrane. Indistinct subtenial chains of cells continuing from the dorsomedial and ventrolateral margins of this layer probably correspond, in more rudimentary form, to the simple auricular folds of Triturus. The fiber tract connections of the eminentia are entirely similar to those of Triturus, but the pools of neuropil in which the lateral-line and VIII roots and related fibers terminate lie anterior to and medial of the eminentia, instead of ventral and medial.

Although modified in position and more compact than the lateral lobule of the adult water stage of Triturus, the eminentia and auricle together correspond to the lobulus lateralis in all other respects.

THE CORPUS CEREBELLI

The corpus cerebelli of adult Ambystoma is difficult to delimit from the eminentia granularis. The sulcus lateralis continues into the floor of the posterior part of the rostro-lateral region of the recessus lateralis; possibly a continuation into the cerebellum is represented by a slight furrow in the posterior cerebellar surface, but this is uncertain. The corpus cerebelli extends rostromedially beneath the commissura cerebelli, diminishing in volume as it approaches the midline. The commissure separates it more or less from the interminential cell band, but there is a scattering of cells between the two. Allowing for this greater fusion between the two medial extensions of cells, the pattern represented in Triturus can be indistinctly recognized.

The eminentia cerebellaris ventralis or *nucleus cerebelli* of Herrick is well shown in the ventricular wall of Ambystoma. Its relations have already been described.

Cryptobranchus Alleghaniensis

The cerebellum of Cryptobranchus is strongly arched caudalward as a relatively thick plate above the fourth ventricle and lateral recesses, owing to the posterior extent of the midbrain in this species (fig. 125). The caudal tip of the optic tectum covers the median part of the arch. In Cryptobranchus (Megalobatrachus) japonicus, as illustrated by Röthig (1927a), the midbrain does not extend so far posteriorly and most of the cerebellar surface is exposed. In both species the anterior end of the medulla oblongata arches strongly dorsalward on either side, a thick white layer which includes the lemniscus systems continuing with the white layer of the midbrain.

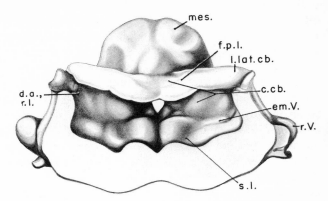

Figure 125. Model of cerebellum of Cryptobranchus seen from behind.

THE LOBULUS LATERALIS

The lateral recess of the fourth ventricle is turned laterodorsally by the upward arching of the medulla oblongata (fig. 126). Its dorsomedial, anterior, and ventrolateral walls are formed by a thick layer of cells which is covered by a relatively thick white layer. The dorsomedial and anterior walls correspond to the ventromedial wall and anterior part of the floor of the anterior diverticulum of Triturus and to the ventromedial wall and less pronounced anterior wall of Ambystoma tigrinum. The anterior wall is continuous laterally with the gray layer of the acousticolateral area. This expanded cell mass and its related layer of white substance correspond to the lateral lobule of Triturus and Ambystoma. The lobule is tilted dorsalward, as in Ambystoma but more strongly, instead of extending rostrolaterally as the ventromedial wall and floor of an anterior diverticulum, as in Triturus. The ventrolateral and dorsomedial walls of the lateral recess approach each other at the dorsolateral tip of the recess, but before they merge a sac-like fold of choroid plexus attaches to their tenial margins (fig. 126B).

The thick cell layer of the dorsomedial and anterior walls of the recess (fig. 126A) corresponds to the eminentia granularis of Triturus and Ambystoma; possibly part of the ventrolateral wall should be included. A thinner layer, continuous with that of the dorsomedial wall, extends into the cerebellar arch. This corresponds to the interminential cell band.

Smaller cells are closely crowded around the dorsolateral tip of the recessus lateralis, similar cells forming subtenial chains that extend into the cerebellar arch and the anterior part of the acousticolateral area. The dorsolateral collection (fig. 126) appears to correspond to the auricle proper of Triturus; the chains of cells continuous with it represent the dorsomedial and ventrolateral folds of the auricle. The dorsomedial chain follows the margin of the cerebellar arch; laterally it is distinct from the intereminential cell band, but medially the two blend so that its medial extent is difficult to determine. The ventrolateral chain can be followed to the "dorsal island," but disappears behind this level.

Small fibers from the lateral lobule pass into the fibromolecular layer of the cerebellar arch. These fibers appear to correspond to the lateral commissure of Herrick. The fiber tracts of Cryptobranchus, according to Herrick (1914a), conform in general to those of Necturus. These in turn are similar to those of Triturus and Ambystoma, except that vestibular root fibers in the cerebellar arch may be absent in Necturus. In Cryptobranchus a large commissural fascicle comprises two quite distinct bundles of fibers, one of which may be vestibular.

The lateral lobule of Cryptobranchus differs from that of Triturus in its uptilted position and relatively more massive structure. It comprises an eminentia granularis and an auricle proper having the same morphological re-

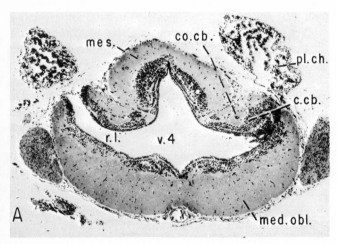

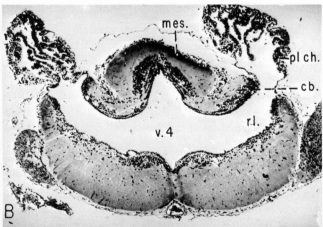

Figure 126. Cryptobranchus. Transverse sections of cerebellar region.

lations as in Triturus although differing topographically (fig. 126).

THE CORPUS CEREBELLI

The corpus cerebelli and the eminence of the nucleus cerebelli swell rather abruptly from the floor of the fourth ventricle (fig. 125). The base of the corpus cerebelli is relatively large; a small dorsomedially and rostrally tapering continuation passes beneath the commissural fascicle already mentioned. Laterally the commissure forms the general boundary between the cellular part of the cerebellar arch which is related to the corpus cerebelli and that which is continuous with the eminentia granularis. One of the two fascicles already noted of the commissure probably includes decussating spino-cerebellar fibers and an intertrigeminal commissure, as in Triturus and Ambystoma; but I have been unable to follow either of the two fascicles with any certainty to bulbar nuclei or tracts.

A groove in the dorsal surface of the cerebellar arch, which, however, does not reach the midline, delimits the anteromedial from the lateral part of the fibromolecular layer. It corresponds in position and relations to a similar groove in Triturus which I interpret as the incipient posterolateral fissure (fig. 125).

Nothing specific can be added from the available material of Cryptobranchus regarding the nucleus cerebelli. It probably is similar to this nucleus in Ambystoma.

Necturus Maculosus

My observations can add nothing to Herrick's (1914a, 1930) descriptions of the cerebellum of Necturus, but on the basis of comparison with other urodeles, here considered, and with other Ichthyopsida I venture some reinterpretations. As Herrick notes, this species is believed by many comparative anatomists to be an arrested larval stage of some extinct ancestral form which underwent metamorphosis. The reduced cerebellum, although approaching the primitive pattern found in petromyzonts, has a rostrolaterally projecting lobulus lateralis, and the corpus cerebelli is relatively much larger and further differentiated than in petromyzonts.

THE LOBULUS LATERALIS

The lateral lobule continues rostralward from the acousticolateral area, forming a blind sac, the cavity of which is an anterior diverticulum of the lateral recess of the fourth ventricle. The floor of the diverticulum is directly continuous with the gray layer of the acousticolateral area. The ventromedial wall is thick caudally and continuous medially with the corpus cerebelli and the tegmentum. Farther anteriorly the medial wall is separated from the tegmentum by a zone of fibers and neuropil, as in Triturus. The medial and lateral walls and the roof of the anterior part of the lobule are thin but comprise a white layer, a layer of cells, and a layer of ependyma. Caudally the dorsolateral wall becomes a choroid plexus. The walls of the diverticulum correspond to the much thicker walls of the dorsolateral part of the recessus lateralis of Cryptobranchus and to the very thick walls of the upward extending part of the recess in Acipenser. The gray layer corresponds to the eminentia granularis of these species. That of the ventromedial wall corresponds to the eminentia granularis of Triturus and Ambystoma. In Golgi preparations of Necturus, Herrick (1914a) found Purkinje cells in the lateral as well as in the thicker ventromedial wall, their dendrites spreading in the white layer. Purkinje cells occur in corresponding positions in Acipenser and Polyodon.

A subtenial chain of small scattered cells can be followed from the rostral end of the "dorsal island" of neuropil into the caudal part of the lateral wall of the diverticulum. In some of Herrick's (1914a) figures a ridge, which includes small cells, is delimited from the principal cell column of the acousticolateral area by a ventricular sulcus. It is suggestive of the posterolateral fold of the auricle, *sensu strictiori*, but the remainder of the auricle, unless represented by scattered cells along the lateral and dorsal tenial margins of the recessus lateralis, is not recognizable in Necturus.

The commissura lateralis cerebelli begins as a thin sheet in the lateral and anterior walls of the diverticulum and arches through the roof and into the arch of the cerebellum.

In the lateral part of the arch the commissure is accompanied by a thin layer of somewhat scattered cells, apparently representing a rudimentary interlobular cell band, but the medial part of the arch is entirely fibrous except for ependymal cells.

THE CORPUS CEREBELLI

The corpus cerebelli comprises bilateral swellings that form the anterior wall of the recessus lateralis and the caudal part of the medial wall of the diverticulum on either side. These swellings are connected through the cerebellar arch by the commissura cerebelli, which includes intertrigeminal and spino-cerebellar fibers (Herrick, 1930). Some cells are scattered along the commissure, forming a rudimentary cell layer which ends far short of the midline.

Siren Lacertina

The following account of the cerebellum of Siren is based on a transverse series of a small specimen, stained with iron-hematoxylin, in comparison with the illustrations of models and Weigert sections of this species in Röthig's (1927a) contribution.

The midbrain extends caudalward above the anterior part of the medulla oblongata, its posterior tip reaching a level behind the entrance of the roots of the anterior lateral-line and VIII nerves. The recessus lateralis of the fourth ventricle is directed rostrolaterally, the distal part turning forward more sharply and ending blindly in a rostrolateral projection ventrolateral of the midbrain on either side. This distal part of the recess corresponds to the anterior diverticulum of other urodeles; the thick-walled projection corresponds to the lateral lobule. The lateral wall of the diverticulum is continuous posteriorly with the acousticolateral area, this forming the posterolateral wall of the recessus lateralis. A wide furrow in the external surface marks the zone of transition from the acousticolateral area to the lateral lobule.

The gray layer enlarges in the lateral lobule, forming the walls and floor of the anterior diverticulum, the ventrolateral and medial walls being connected anteriorly by a layer of cells in the anterior wall and by continuity in the floor.

Anteriorly the medial wall is separated from the isthmic tegmentum by a broad zone of lemniscus fascicles. Behind this zone it is continuous with a large cell mass, beneath the caudally extending midbrain, which includes the isthmic and trigeminal tegmentum and the corpus cerebelli.

The anterior part of the medial and ventromedial walls of the diverticulum flare apart, their tenial borders affording attachment for a choroid membrane which forms the dorsolateral roof of the diverticulum and continues caudomedially as the roof of the lateral recess. The continuous cell mass of the walls and floor of the diverticulum correspond in their morphological relations to the eminentia granularis of other urodeles.

Beneath the tenial margins of both medial and ventrolateral walls of the anterior part of the diverticulum chains of small cells correspond to the small auricles proper and their rudimentary folds of Triturus, Ambystoma larvae, and Cryptobranchus. There is little indication, however, of an interlobular cell band, only a few cells accompanying a fascicle of myelinated fibers called the commissura cerebellaris by Röthig (1927a). This he describes as connecting the medial walls of the two lateral recesses and also including an intertrigeminal commissure which arises in the area of the roots of the V nerve. The fibers interconnecting the medial walls of the recesses, although myelinated, probably correspond to the lateral commissure of Herrick. This commissure is unmyelinated in Necturus but includes lightly myelinated fibers in Ambystoma and some other species.

The corpus cerebelli proper of Siren is small and submerged, but is larger than in petromyzonts. It is represented by a cell mass in the anterior wall of the part of the fourth ventricle from which the lateral recess begins to extend rostrolaterally. The rostral and lateral limits of the corpus are difficult to define. Presumably the bilateral masses are interconnected by commissural fibers, as in petromyzonts and other urodeles, but such fibers are uncertain in iron-hematoxylin preparations.

Other Urodeles

The cerebellum of Proteus anguineus, already mentioned, was restudied by Kreht (1931) in Weigert and Bielschowsky preparations. The recessus lateralis of the fourth ventricle is described as extending rostralward as far as the level of emergence of the roots of the III nerve. Only the anteromedial wall of the recess consists of compact nervous tissue, the posterolateral wall being formed chiefly of choroid plexus. The anteromedial wall, in Kreht's figures, corresponds to the eminentia granularis of Triturus and other urodeles. The "corpora cerebelli" are said to be represented only by a narrow commissural plate which also forms the caudal limit of the midbrain. In this plate are included the fibers of a "commissura cerebellaris." These include heavily myelinated fibers of various systems, fibers that gather beneath the gray layer (eminentia granularis) of the anteromedial wall of the lateral recess, and perhaps a trigeminal connection, after synapses, forms commissural fibers. The term intertrigeminal commissure, applied by earlier authors to the entire commissural bundle, was considered inappropriate by Kreht because of the inclusion of the other fibers mentioned. The fibers gathered from the eminentia granularis all appear to be myelinated in Proteus. In Triturus and Ambystoma small myelinated fibers are included among the unmyelinated ones of the lateral commissure; to these are added myelinated fibers of the ascending VIII root, forming an acousticolateral commissure. Judging from Kreht's figure of Proteus, VIII root fibers may be included, although they are not mentioned. Other myelinated fibers of this author's commissura cerebellaris appear to correspond to the intertrigeminal component of the commissura cerebelli of Herrick and myself in other urodeles. A spino-cerebellar component is not mentioned by Kreht and there is no indication in the sections illustrated of a corpus cerebelli, *sensu strictiori*. Since this subdivision is found in petromyzonts and in other urodeles, it is probably present, in rudimentary form at least, in Proteus.

In Salamandra maculosa, as described by Kreht (1930), both walls of the recessus lateralis consist of compact nervous tissue. The recess is covered with folded choroid membrane, but there is no such plexus at the apex of the recess and there is no anterior diverticulum. The posterolateral wall is said to be formed of the most anterior part of the acousticolateral area, while the anteromedial wall is continuous, medially, with the gray of the median part of the cerebellum and, behind the lemniscus fascicles, with the tegmentum. The gray layer of the anteromedial wall, in Kreht's illustrations, corresponds to the eminentia granularis as above defined in other urodeles, but appears to reach the cerebellar surface as in fishes.

The median part of the cerebellum, called the corpus cerebelli by Kreht, is a dorsocaudally tilted plate arching above the fourth ventricle and somewhat caudalward. It comprises an anterodorsal molecular layer which crosses the midline, and a posteroventral cerebellar layer which tapers toward the midline from either side but does not cross it. Except near the midline the median part of the cerebellum of Salamandra, in sagittal sections, resembles the cerebellum of small frogs.

Kreht differentiated two systems of commissural fibers in Salamandra. One, consisting of unmyelinated and thinly myelinated fibers, he regarded as corresponding to the commissura lateralis cerebelli of Herrick; the other, formed of myelinated fibers, he called the commissura cerebellaris. He says the two systems are sharply separated in the lateral region, on either side, but intermingle in the median part of the cerebellum. Kreht is vague regarding the origin of the fibers of the lateral commissure. In his figures of sagittal sections this commissure is situated at some distance beneath the dorsal margin of the cerebellum but between the more deeply located commissura cerebelli and this margin. It corresponds in position to the vestibular commissure of the frog, described below. Whether the commissure in Salamandra includes VIII root and secondary vestibular fibers, thus constituting the vestibular part of an acousticolateral commissure, as in Triturus and Ambystoma, is not clear in Kreht's figures, and no reference to an VIII root component is made in the text. The commissura cerebelli is described as formed of decussating fibers of the spino-cerebellar tract, but Kreht is uncertain of a trigeminal component. The corpus cerebelli, *sensu strictiori*, as in the frog (p. 170), is probably represented by the bilateral ventral regions of the median part of the cerebellum. These, however, do not fuse across the midline as in adult Anura.

THE FIBER CONNECTIONS

The afferent tracts. The origin and course of the ascending fiber tracts ending in the lateral lobule have been described, but their specific areas of distribution need further consideration. The lateral-line fascicles terminate in the neuropil beneath and anterior of the eminentia granularis in Triturus, the fibers spreading and branching (fig. 127). In Ambystoma the corresponding neuropil is situated more dorsally, owing to the upward turned and less rostrolateral projection of the lobule. A fascicle of VIII root fibers, in Triturus and midlarval Ambystoma, courses dorsomedially in the neuropil immediately medial of the eminentia, after passing beneath the cellular connection of the eminentia with the median gray substance. Many of its fibers distribute in the neuropil rostroventral of the eminentia, branching and intermingling with the terminal lateral-line fibers. Others turn dorsomedially into the cerebellar arch, forming a component of the acousticolateral commissure (fig. 127). In Cajal preparations of Triturus many fibers can be seen to branch into fine terminal threads that end in the fibromolecular layer. They appear to be terminals of the VIII root component of the acousticolateral commissure. Fibers from the commissural fascicle also end among the cells of the intereminential cell band by slender twigs having small terminal boutons. These possibly represent secondary vestibular fibers, but there is no certainty of their source. In Golgi preparations of Triturus I have

not found terminals in the intereminential cell band from the VIII root fascicle of the acousticolateral commissure, and Herrick does not mention such terminals in Ambystoma. They are numerous, however, in Cajal and heavily stained iron-hematoxylin series. Judging by the directions from which they enter the cell layer, they are chiefly ipsilateral in origin, but terminals of crossed fibers enter the median part of the cell band.

In Necturus, according to Herrick (1930), the ascending VIII root fascicle extends as far forward as the rostral end of the lateral lobule; in the lateral wall of the anterior diverticulum it turns dorsally among the fibers of the lateral commissure, but the fascicle could not be followed into the median part of the cerebellum. The ascending lateral-line fibers end farther caudally in the lobule.

Ascending fibers of tracts *a* and *b* to the neuropil of the lateral lobule have already been mentioned. In Cajal preparations of Triturus, fibers from tract *b* can be seen to distribute also among the cells of the eminentia granularis, ending in short branches with terminal boutons. The similar terminals in the intereminential cell band, above mentioned, may represent endings of tract *b* fibers, since this tract is closely associated with the ascending VIII fascicle as it turns dorsomedially from the acousticolateral area. The ascending tract *a* fibers appear to be secondary fibers related to the lateral-line system, but the ascending fibers of tract *b* are secondary vestibular fibers, as already noted.

A possible rudiment of the inferior olive and of fibers from it to the "auricle" are described in Ambystoma by Herrick (1948), but it is not clear if these fibers reach the more specific lobulus lateralis. According to Brodal (1940b) the flocculus and nodulus of the cat receive fibers from the rostral part of the medial accessory olive. This part of the olive was regarded by Kooy (1917) as the phylogenetically oldest part of the olivary complex. Some of the primitive olivary fibers of Herrick, therefore, possibly end in the eminentia granularis.

The remaining ascending fiber tracts of the cerebellum are related with the corpus cerebelli. The spino-cerebellar tract of Necturus, in association with the spino-tectal tract, ascends through the medulla oblongata with the spinal lemniscus. In the rostral region of the medulla oblongata the intermingled spino-cerebellar and spino-tectal tracts separate from the remainder of the spinal lemniscus complex and take a position lateral of the bulbar lemniscus. At the level of superficial origin of the V nerve the two tracts are indistinguishably intermingled, but at the level, anterior of the recessus lateralis, where the corpus cerebelli and the nucleus cerebelli merge, the mixed tract divides into its two components. The spino-

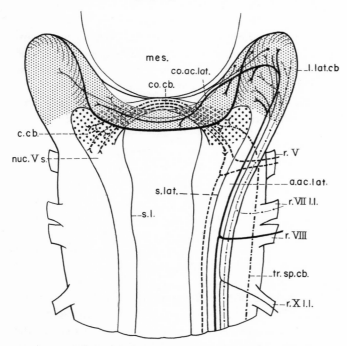

Figure 127. Diagram of cerebellum and its principal afferent connections in Triturus torosus.

158

cerebellar component spreads in part into the adjacent substance of the corpus cerebelli; part of it continues as a compact fascicle (figs. 124, 130A,C) which crosses the midline, forming a component of the commissura cerebelli (Herrick, 1914a). In Ambystoma the spino-cerebellar tract has the same general relations. As already mentioned, many of the fibers were observed by Herrick (1914b, 1948) to arise as collaterals of spino-tectal fibers. A fascicle described as the dorsal spino-cerebellar tract in Necturus (Herrick, 1914a), Ambystoma (Larsell, 1920), and Salamandra (Kreht, 1930) subsequently could not be confirmed, as Herrick (1948) states, by him or myself. In Golgi material of Ambystoma, however, he found that our earlier dorsal spino-cerebellar tract is a separate bundle of the spino-cerebellar tract which becomes mingled with ascending trigeminal fibers, continuing with the latter into the cerebellar commissure. In Triturus the spino-cerebellar and spino-tectal tracts separate from each other farther posteriorly than in Ambystoma. They are similar in other respects but I have failed to find collaterals from the spino-tectal tract entering the spino-cerebellar tract as Herrick found in Ambystoma.

Fibers that constitute a bulbo-cerebellar tract come from various parts of the medulla oblongata and accompany the spino-cerebellar tract of Triturus but their specific sources have not been ascertained. Some no doubt correspond to olivo-cerebellar fibers to the cerebellum in species of vertebrates that have well-defined olivary nuclei. Röthig (1927a) describes bulbo-cerebellar and spino-cerebellar tracts in Megalobatrachus. In Ambystoma Herrick (1948) found fibers from the sensory zone of the medulla oblongata and the nucleus of the dorsal funiculus of the cord joining the spino-cerebellar tract.

The tecto-cerebellar tract was described in Ambystoma tigrinum by Herrick (1925). I had seen indications of it in Ambystoma (1920) and described it in larval A. punctatum (1932a) and adult Triturus (1931); Röthig (1927a) and Kreht (1930) described the tract in Cryptobranchus (Megalobatrachus) and Salamandra, respectively. According to Herrick (1948), who made further observations on Golgi material of Ambystoma tigrinum, the tract originates chiefly in the posterior tectal nucleus. The dendrites of its neurons extend into the posterior border of the optic tectum and the axons pass through the anterior medullary velum as a compact fascicle of unmyelinated fibers in company with the mesencephalic V root. The fascicle turns ventralward at the anterior border of the cerebellum and the fibers spread in the anterior part of the corpus cerebelli (fig. 130D), some reaching the nucleus cerebelli, according to Her-

rick. Kashiwamura (1955) describes the tecto-cerebellar tract of Triturus as a single fascicle, in contrast with the frog and various other species of vertebrates in which two fascicles were found.

The mesencephalic V root (figs. 123C, 124) is prominent in all urodeles by reason of its heavily myelinated fibers. The mesencephalic V nucleus is conspicuous in larval stages of Ambystoma, consisting of large cells in the posterior tectal region and the anterior medullary velum. Although the fibers of the tract pass very close to the cerebellum there is little evidence that any enter it.

A mammillo-cerebellar (lobo-cerebellar) tract was tentatively described in Necturus by Herrick (1914a). In Ambystoma (1920) and Triturus (1931) I found fibers that appeared to represent a mammillo-cerebellar tract, and Herrick (1948) saw evidence of it in Ambystoma. The fibers are dispersed and no satisfactory description can be made from the observations recorded.

The efferent fibers. In urodeles, as in petromyzonts and fishes, internal arcuate fibers arise from the entire extent of the acousticolateral area. Some cross the midline to the opposite side before descending; others descend without crossing. In larval Ambystoma (Larsell, 1932a) arcuate-like fibers arise from the regions of the nucleus cerebelli, the corpus cerebelli, and also from the lateral lobule. Some of the fibers pass caudalward on the same side, others cross, and still others are directed forward into the midbrain. As the corpus cerebelli and nucleus cerebelli increase in volume and lateral extent, in later larval stages, the rostrally directed fibers assume a more medial course. In the larval stages the fibers from the cerebellar region to tegmentum and midbrain form indistinct groups. In adult Ambystoma, according to Herrick (1948), large numbers of fibers descend from the lateral lobule, the nucleus cerebelli, and the corpus cerebelli into the tegmentum. They pass ventrally, caudally, and rostrally as myelinated and lightly myelinated fibers radiating from the cerebellum.

A primitive brachium conjunctivum is formed by a rather compact fascicle of rostroventrally directed fibers. Herrick describes these fibers from Golgi material of adult Ambystoma as originating in cells of the nucleus cerebelli and the adjacent part of the corpus cerebelli. The fascicle passes rostrally and ventrally into the isthmus, some of the fibers decussating a short distance behind the fovea isthmi, and then enters a dense superficial neuropil lateral of the decussation. A tertiary visceral tract, which joins the brachium conjunctivum in the isthmus, also enters this neuropil. Uncrossed fibers pass into the neuropil related to the tegmentum of the isthmic region. There is no indication of a concentration of cells in relation to the brachium conjunctivum that could be regarded as an incipient nucleus ruber. Apparently the fascicle comes into functional relationship, in a diffuse manner, with the entire tegmentum on both sides of the isthmic region, as Herrick (1948) points out. In Triturus the brachium conjunctivum shows the same general relations as in Ambystoma, but details could not be followed, owing to less abundant and less favorably impregnated Golgi material.

In my earlier study of Triturus I interpreted fibers that arise in the lateral lobule and, apparently, in the cerebellar arch as corresponding to the cerebellomotor tract of Ariens Kappers (1906) in fishes. A review of my silver material of Triturus and comparison with the observations of Herrick on Ambystoma now incline me to the belief that at least some of the fibers of the cerebellar arch so interpreted belong to the acousticolateral commissure. Some fibers from the lateral lobule pass into tract *a* (fig. 122A) and many others into the arcuate system. The fibers from the eminentia granularis may correspond, in part, to direct flocculo-bulbar fibers of higher vertebrates, but it is unlikely that the uncinate bundle of Russell, which arises from the fastigial nucleus, is foreshadowed by these or by fibers entering tracts *a* and *b*. Descending fibers from the nucleus cerebelli, however, can be considered precursors of this bundle.

THE HISTOLOGY

The histological pattern of the urodele cerebellum can be described most simply in terms of the sensory zone of the medulla oblongata. Like the latter, the cerebellum comprises a layer of cells which faces the fourth ventricle and its lateral recess, and a superficial fibrous and molecular layer (figs. 128, 129). The dendrites and axons of the cells are directed outward, in general, into the fibromolecular layer. In Necturus and other lower urodeles, as already noted, the gray layer ends considerably short of the midline of the cerebellar arch except for a few cells of uncertain significance that accompany the commissures. In Triturus, Ambystoma, and Cryptobranchus the gray layer reaches the midline, a few cells forming a bridge across it. Purkinje cells are irregularly arranged among smaller elements in the gray layer but do not form so distinct a stratum as in most other vertebrates (fig. 128). The fibromolecular layer, consisting of fibers and neuropil, forms a primitive molecular layer which covers the entire external surface of the cerebellum. The cell layer, with its Purkinje cells, and the molecular layer together constitute a primitive cerebellar cortex. In some of the lower urodeles only myelinated commissural fibers have been described as crossing the median sagittal plane, but in Necturus and other species studied in silver preparations a definite zone of finer fibers, mostly

unmyelinated, crosses from one side of the cerebellum to the other. This zone increases in area, as seen in sagittal sections, in the higher urodeles.

Neurons of three sizes already have been mentioned in Triturus and Ambystoma. In Necturus Herrick (1914a) describes and illustrates relatively large cells in the "corpus cerebelli" that send dendrites forward and ventralward among terminals of the spino-cerebellar, tecto-cerebellar, mammillo-cerebellar, and perhaps other tracts; the axons of these cells enter the brachium conjunctivum. Herrick regards these cells as simplified Purkinje cells. Those most posteromedially situated evidently belong to the corpus cerebelli proper. Others in the posterior part of the medial wall of the anterior diverticulum possibly should be assigned to the eminentia granularis, but in Necturus there appears to be no boundary

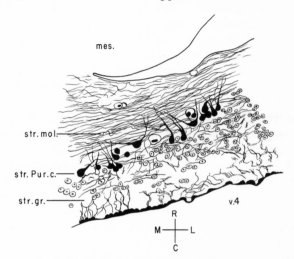

Figure 128. Horizontal section through part of cerebellum of Ambystoma tigrinum. Cajal method. ×125. (Larsell, 1920.)

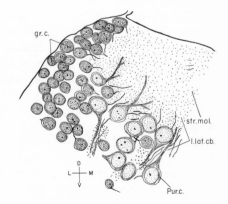

Figure 129. Portion of acousticolateral area and lateral cerebellar lobule, showing the two principal types of cells. Toluidine-blue and erythrosin. Camera lucida. ×283. (Larsell, 1931.)

between the eminentia and the corpus cerebelli in the medial wall of the diverticulum. Farther rostrally in the medial wall Herrick illustrates neurons whose dendrites branch among the fibers of the lateral commissure and clearly belong to the eminentia granularis. Also in the thin lateral wall of the diverticulum, which comprises only one to three layers of cells in addition to ependyma, flattened Purkinje cells are described with dendrites that spread widely in a thin white layer. The specific cells that give rise to the lateral commissure were not identified and no impregnated granule cells were found.

In Triturus and late larval Ambystoma dendrites from cells in the trigeminal tegmentum and the base of the corpus cerebelli extend toward the ascending V fascicle and the spino-cerebellar tract (fig. 130A). Many of these neurons give rise to ventrorostrally directed axons that appear to become part of the brachium conjunctivum; other axons pass caudalward. The axons arise from the dendrites, as do those of the neurons above mentioned in Necturus. Although neuropil is intermingled with the trigemino- and spino-cerebellar fibers, among which the dendrites extend, this zone of distribution cannot be considered as cortex and the neurons are not Purkinje cells.

In larval Ambystoma large cells of the eminentia granularis send elongated dendrites into the zone of fi-

bers and neuropil which separates the granular eminence from the medial gray layer. These dendrites branch chiefly among the fibers of the ascending VIII root fascicle and its related neuropil. Similar neurons occur in Triturus (fig. 131). These undoubtedly are primitive Purkinje cells. Dendrites also extend into the zone of fibers and neuropil beneath and anterior of the eminentia granularis. Cells in the dorsomedial part of the eminentia and in the intereminential cell band send their dendrites into the molecular layer of the cerebellum. These are definitive Purkinje cells.

The larger cells in the corpus cerebelli part of the cerebellar arch also send their dendrites into the molecular layer. These are similar to the Purkinje cells of the dorsomedial part of the eminentia and of the intereminential band.

Few smaller cells were found in Golgi preparations of Triturus, but in late larval Ambystoma numerous neurons of intermediate size and with short dendrites radiating in the eminentia granularis were seen. These appear to represent primitive stellate cells. Many of them give rise to axons that become part of the lateral commissure. Terminal branches of this commissure, ending among the cells of the eminentia granularis, apparently represent the endings of axons of contralateral stellate cells. Similar cells give rise to descending fibers of tract *b*.

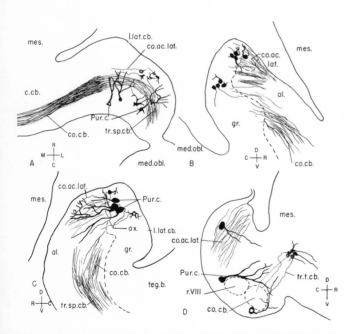

Figure 130. Triturus torosus. A. Horizontal section through lateral part of cerebellum. ×44. B. Sagittal section through lateral part of cerebellum. ×65. C. Sagittal section through lobulus lateralis cerebelli. ×65. D. Sagittal section through corpus cerebelli. Golgi method. ×86. (Larsell, 1931.)

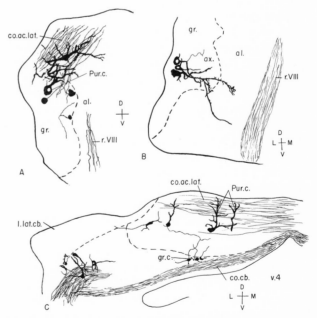

Figure 131. Triturus torosus. A. Transverse section through lobulus lateralis cerebelli. ×113. B. Transverse section through lobulus lateralis. ×183. C. Transverse section through cerebellum. ×68. Golgi method. (Larsell, 1931.)

Small cells that stain more intensively with iron-hematoxylin and toluidine blue have already been noted in the auricle proper of Triturus. These cells were not impregnated in Golgi preparations, so no specific axons can be associated with them. In toluidine blue and erythrosin sections, however, very fine axons can be followed a short distance into the molecular layer of the cerebellum, making it appear probable that the very fine fibers seen in Cajal and some Golgi material are derived from these and probably other granule cells.

Some small cells in the corpus cerebelli of Triturus suggest granule cells. Fine fibers pass from them into the molecular layer and several short dendrites radiate from the cell body. A few larger cells of stellate type were also encountered; their axons probably enter the cerebellar commissure.

ANURA

THE nervous system of anurans undergoes important modifications during metamorphosis from the aquatic larval stage to the land-adapted stage of the adults of most species. The lateral-line system disappears, except in the South American frog Xenopus, in which part of it remains in the adult. Part of the acousticolateral area is transformed into the sensory nuclei of a well-differentiated auditory organ. This comprises a tympanic membrane to an aperture equivalent to the oval window in man, but which opens into the sacculus above and lateral of the macula sacculi (McNally, 1929). The transformation of the nuclei of the acousticolateral area, described by Larsell (1934a), is accompanied by modifications of the connections with other parts of the brain and by development of specific auditory centers. The vestibular nuclei also differ, in metamorphosed Anura, from those of fishes and, presumably, of tadpoles in which they have not been studied in detail.

The disappearance of the lateral-line system is accompanied by changes in the connections of the homologue of the lateral lobule of urodeles and other Ichthyopsida. This part of the cerebellum and its related structures undergo considerable modification (fig. 132).

The strengthening of the paired appendages to bear the weight of the body and to provide for locomotion on land and a different manner of swimming than in Ichthyopsida is accompanied by the development of a larger number of neuromuscular spindles and a more widespread distribution than in urodeles.

Larval Stages
THE ACOUSTICOLATERAL AREA

The lateral-line system of frog larvae is similar in general to that of urodeles. The anterior lateral-line nerve has dorsal, medial and ventral roots, recognizable in the 9 mm long larva of Rana pipiens (fig. 133A) and prob-

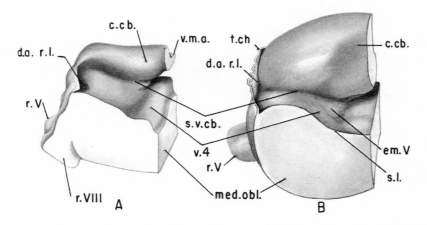

Figure 132. Views of models of left side of frog's cerebellum from behind and slightly from above, showing relations of cerebellar structures to recessus lateralis. A. Larval frog, 36 mm long, with well-developed legs. Hyla regilla. ×40. B. Adult frog, Rana pipiens. ×20. (Larsell, 1923.)

163

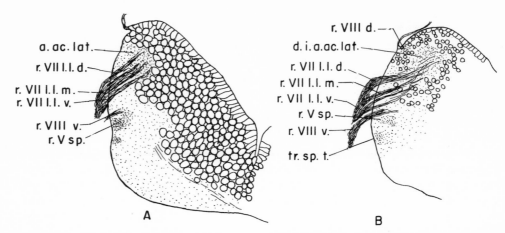

Figure 133. Transverse sections of medulla oblongata of Rana pipiens at level of entrance of lateral-line VII roots. A. Larva, 9 mm long. B. Larva, 14 mm long. Hematoxylin and orange G stain. ×156.

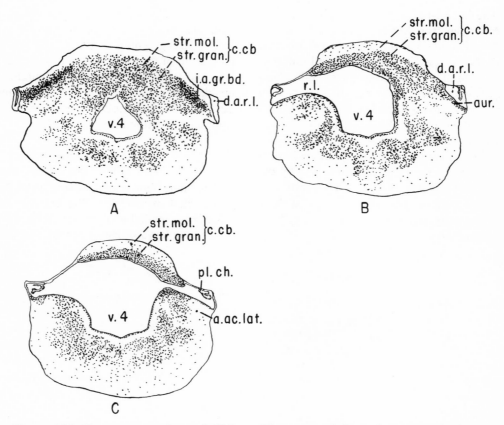

Figure 134. Transverse sections of Hyla regilla at completion of metamorphosis. A. Through the middle of corpus cerebelli. B. Level of the lateral recess (left side) and the anterior diverticulum (right side). C. Through caudal part of cerebellum.

ably earlier. Strong (1895) described two roots of this nerve in late stages of the frog tadpole, designating them roots VIIb1 and VIIb2. The first corresponds to the dorsal anterior lateral-line root of urodeles, the second to the medial and ventral roots of the earlier stages of the frog larva and some urodeles; these two roots have merged to a large extent in older tadpoles. All these roots enter the acousticolateral area and form ascending and descending fascicles as in urodeles. The posterior lateral-line root and the fascicles formed by it are also similar to the corresponding fibers in urodeles. Strong describes this root in the frog tadpole as composed of large myelinated fibers similar to those of the dorsal anterior lateral-line root. The posterior lateral-line nerve divides into two principal branches that distribute to pit organs on the body.

Dorsal and ventral roots of the VIII nerve were described by Strong (1895) and myself (1934a). The ventral root, entering the acousticolateral area beneath the anterior lateral-line roots, was found in the 9 mm larva of Rana pipiens (fig. 133A), the youngest stage I studied. Dorsal VIII root fibers were identified in the 12 mm larva, but probably occur at earlier stages. In the relatively much further developed 16 mm larva of Hyla regilla an ascending fascicle from the ventral root reaches the cerebellar region.

The acousticolateral area is fully developed in bullfrog tadpoles of 62–65 mm length. At these stages no limb buds have yet appeared and the lateral-line system shows no signs of the regressive changes that appear during metamorphosis (1925, 1934a). Consideration of the vestibular nuclei will be deferred until they have attained full development in the adult, but the lateral-line division of the area will be described in these tadpoles and as it appears in various stages of other species. Mauthner's cell, not found in metamorphosed frogs, is present in larval stages.

The acousticolateral area forms the floor of the lateral part of the fourth ventricle, as does its rostral part in urodeles (fig. 134). It comprises a layer of cells immediately beneath the floor, and a layer of fibers and neuropil situated ventral and ventrolateral of the cellular layer. In later stages of the larvae more cells have migrated into the fibrous layer than in urodeles, especially in the regions of the entering root fibers. The anterior lateral-line roots enter the fibrous layer, the dorsal root terminating in a small dorsomedially situated zone of mostly very fine and some coarse fibers (fig. 133B) that correspond to the "dorsal island" of Kingsbury in Necturus and to the nucleus dorsalis of petromyzonts, elasmobranchs, chondrosteans, and some other fishes already described. The ventral roots enter the more ventrolateral part of the fi-

brous layer, which is more or less continuous with the "dorsal island," and divide into ascending and descending fascicles. Cells scattered among these fascicles, although few, give this part of the fibrous layer a greater resemblance to the nucleus medialis of other Ichthyopsida than is true in urodeles. The ascending fascicles and associated neuropil pass beneath the "dorsal island," producing the effect of increasing its size. Behind the level at which the small "dorsal island" is recognizable the fibrous layer related to the ventral anterior and posterior lateral-line roots extends medialward for some distance. At the level of entrance of the ventral root of the VIII nerve larger cells represent the vestibular nucleus (fig. 139D).

THE LATERAL LOBULE AND THE VESTIBULO-LATERAL LOBE

As in urodeles an anterior diverticulum of the recessus lateralis extends around the posterolateral part of the base of the corpus cerebelli and into a rostrolateral projection which, as will appear, corresponds to the lateral lobule of urodeles and other Ichthyopsida (fig. 132). The diverticulum is covered laterally, dorsally, and dorsolaterally by a choroid membrane. The floor, medial wall, and ventral part of the anterior wall make up a granular mass which continues as an ear-like projection, rostrolaterally, and merges with the somewhat more loosely arranged cellular mass of the corpus cerebelli medially. In the 62 mm bullfrog tadpole the greater part of the ventromedial wall of the anterior diverticulum is continuous caudally with the cellular column of the nucleus medialis portion of the acousticolateral area (fig. 134). A smaller and more lateral aggregation of granules is continuous with a chain of cells which extends forward from the nucleus dorsalis, i.e., from the cells related to the "dorsal island." In sections of more anterior levels a similar fringe of cells is found beneath the principal cell mass and the attachment of the choroid tela.

The larger cell mass corresponds to the eminentia granularis of urodeles and fishes. If the fringe of granules be regarded as very rudimentary inferior and superior folds of a much reduced auricle, sensu strictiori, the eminentia granularis and auricle together correspond to the lateral lobule of Ichthyopsida. The anterior tip of the eminentia reaches the external cerebellar surface, but the exposed surface is very small compared with that of fishes. The greater part of the eminentia faces the anterior diverticulum (fig. 135) and is covered with ependyma, as in urodeles. The posterior part of the eminentia of many bony fishes also has an ependymal layer which forms the lining of a narrow recessus lateralis. In chondrosteans much of the primitive eminentia granularis faces the anterior diverticulum.

The eminentia granularis of the tadpole is continuous medially with a zone of closely packed granule-like cells which extends along the cerebellar margin, beneath a thin molecular layer, and eventually fuses across the midline with the contralateral zone. The bilateral zones correspond to the interlobular cellular band of urodeles and elasmobranchs. The cellular connections between the eminentiae in fishes is relatively shorter. A medial continuation of the interauricular granular band can be followed a short distance. Whether or not a string of rather scattered cells, in the 62 mm bullfrog larva, along the upward-tilted cerebellar margin should be regarded as

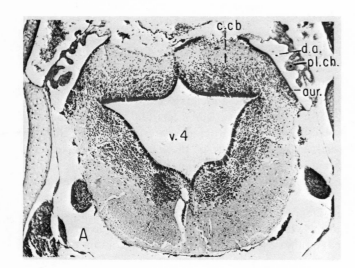

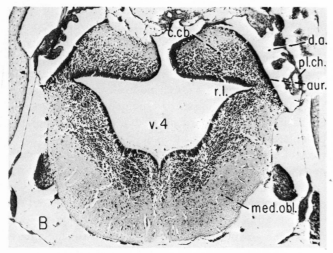

Figure 135. Transverse sections through cerebellum of bullfrog tadpole, 65 mm long. A. Through the middle of the cerebellum. B. Through caudal part of cerebellum. Hematoxylin-eosin stain.

a reduced version of this band is not clear. The eminentia granularis and the interlobular or intereminential band are continuous ventromedially and ventrally, respectively, with the granular layer of the corpus cerebelli, in which the cells are less closely arranged. In Hyla regilla, at completion of metamorphosis, the interlobular cellular band still forms a zone of closely packed cells along the lateral and caudal margins of the cerebellum, which is caudally tilted in this species. The band is less distinct than in tadpole stages, however, apparently owing to the greater crowding of the granules of the corpus cerebelli.

The lateral part of the ventral floor of the recessus lateralis, beneath which the small auricle is situated, disappears during metamorphosis. The lateral lobule is reduced as a result to the eminentia granularis which, as will appear, corresponds to the flocculus of birds and mammals and also to the flocculus of reptiles, described below.

THE CORPUS CEREBELLI

Medial of the rostral part of the acousticolateral area and in the floor of the recessus lateralis a rounded elevation has appeared in the 18 mm and 25 mm stages of Hyla regilla. This corresponds to the trigeminal eminence of Herrick in urodeles. Immediately in front of this elevation the rudiment of the corpus cerebelli tilts dorsalward, forming the medial wall of the caudal part of the anterior diverticulum. In the 25 mm Hyla tadpole the corpus has a broad base from which it continues rostromedially above the fourth ventricle. The bilateral rudiments presently fuse across the midline, beginning anteriorly. Each half becomes thickened so that a median groove results in the ventricular surface but a cellular layer crosses the midline (fig. 132).

Metamorphosed Anurans
THE MEMBRANOUS LABYRINTH AND THE ACOUSTIC NERVE

After the lateral-line system has disappeared, the modified part of the medulla oblongata which was the acousticolateral area in the larval stage receives only root fibers of the anterior or ventral and posterior or dorsal branches of the VIII nerve. The anterior branch of this nerve is distributed to the cristae ampullares of the anterior and lateral semicircular canals and to the macula utriculi. The posterior branch serves the posterior crista ampullaris, papilla lagenae, papilla basilaris, and papilla amphibiorum. The papilla neglecta, found in urodeles, is lacking in anurans according to de Burlet (1929); in Ichthyophis glutinosus, a caecilian, both papilla neglecta and papilla amphibiorum are present. The root of the posterior branch of the VIII nerve in anurans, accordingly, includes both vestibular and auditory fibers. It corresponds in part to the posterior VIII root of urodeles and other lower vertebrates, but the fibers from the macula sacculi of anurans join the anterior or ventral root instead of the posterior or dorsal root, as pointed out by de Burlet (1929) and Ariens Kappers (1947).

There is evidence, however, that the postero-inferior part of the macula sacculi is more closely related to the auditory than to the vestibular labyrinth. It has a perilymphatic space such as occurs in relation to the papilla basilaris and papilla amphibiorum, de Burlet (1934) states. According to McNally (1936) the sacculus of the frog responds to vibratory stimulation more than to movement or change of position; also, action currents related to vibratory stimuli were recorded from the saccular nerve. Ashcroft and Hallpike (1934) also reported reactions to auditory stimuli in the saccular nerve of the frog.

In the rabbit Versteegh (1927) found no changes in vestibular reflexes following destruction of one or both maculae sacculi. Jonkees (1950), however, concluded from further experimental studies on this animal that the sacculus possesses a vestibular function and responds to linear acceleration, acting from one ear to the other.

The threshold curve for sounds between 30 c.p.s. and 15,000 c.p.s. was determined by Kleerekoper and Sibabin (1959) in Rana pipiens and R. clavata. This much greater range at the high frequencies, as compared with fishes, must be related to the modifications of the peripheral and central auditory apparatus of anurans.

The papillae basilaris and amphibiorum are covered by tectorial membranes, as above noted, and the fibers leading from these papillae pass to the dorsal cochlear nucleus, described below. The macula lagenae, in common with the maculae sacculi and utriculi, has an otolithic membrane as in fishes. Many authors regard the lagena as auditory, whereas others consider it vestibular in function. Both lagena and sacculus appear to be sound receptors in fishes (Manning, 1924; von Frisch and Stetter, 1932; Vilstrup, 1951).

The cochlear and vestibular nuclei. As the lateral-line system disappears during metamorphosis, the nuclei of the dorsal part of the acousticolateral area become transformed into a predominantly small-celled dorsal VIII or acoustic nucleus and a ventral magnocellular acoustic nucleus, Larsell (1934a) points out. The small-celled nucleus occupies the position of the cellular elements that send their dendrites into the "dorsal island" of neuropil in larval stages. No degeneration of cells of this region was observed during metamorphosis, but nerve fibers from the papilla basilaris and papilla amphibi-

orum, as these auditory parts of the labyrinth differentiate, enter the acousticolateral part of the acousticolateral area in which these cells are situated.

The nucleus dorsalis of the acousticolateral area, when it loses its lateral-line function by degeneration of dorsal root anterior lateral-line fibers, is transformed by new connections from fibers of some of the auditory divisions of the labyrinth into the primordium of the dorsal acoustic nucleus. This nucleus becomes more extensive by migration of cells into the space of the degenerated fibers and neuropil and toward the entrance of the dorsal root of the VIII nerve. Most of its cells are small, but some of medium size also occur (fig. 139C,D).

The magnocellular acoustic nucleus is formed farther ventrally, some of its cells occupying the space left by degenerating fibers and neuropil of the ventral anterior and posterior lateral-line root fascicles. The nucleus expands, forming a large rounded zone in the acoustic area of the medulla oblongata.

The posterior branch of the VIII nerve enters the medulla oblongata by the posterior or dorsal root. This root includes fibers from the crista of the posterior ampulla and the papillae basilaris, amphibiorum, and lagenae. The majority of those from the posterior ampulla, which is vestibular, pass beneath the magnocellular acoustic nucleus and divide into ascending and descending branches (fig. 139D). According to Ariens Kappers (1947), these end in the nucleus of Deiters and its ascending continuations. The remaining fibers of the dorsal VIII root end in the acoustic nuclei. Fibers from the macula sacculi to the magnocellular acoustic nucleus have not been specifically described in the frog or toad. It is probable, however, that many reach this nucleus, but by way of the ventral instead of the dorsal root of the VIII nerve. In Ictalurus and Carassius, as already mentioned, Pearson (1936b) followed saccular fibers to the rostral part of the nucleus medialis of the acousticolateral area and to the eminentia granularis. The magnocellular acoustic nucleus, which is an enlarged modification of the anterior part of the nucleus medialis, presumably retains its saccular connections. Ariens Kappers (1947) says it receives both auditory and vestibular fibers.

The cells of the two acoustic nuclei give rise to internal and external fibers that pass to the superior olive, giving off collaterals to this nucleus. They then continue into the contralateral lemniscus lateralis, *sensu strictiori.* The superior olive constitutes a new feature in the anuran medulla oblongata. It develops in connection with the transformation of part of the central lateral-line apparatus into an acoustic system (Larsell, 1934a). Cells of the superior olive contribute their axons to the lateral lemniscus, which ends in the corpus posticum of the midbrain. According to Ariens Kappers (1947), some fibers of his lateral lemniscus pass to the nucleus of the VI nerve and others end in the optic tectum after sending collaterals into the nucleus isthmi.

The anterior or ventral VIII root, including fibers from the anterior and lateral cristae ampullares and the maculae utriculi and sacculi, divides into both ascending and descending fascicles. Many of the fibers of the descending fascicle make synaptic connections with the large cells of Deiters's nucleus; others synapse with the smaller cells of the caudal continuation from this nucleus. Some of the root fibers cross to the contralateral nucleus of Deiters, as found by Wallenberg (1907) and Schepman (1918). The descending fascicle continues into the ventral funiculus of the spinal cord, according to Deganello (1906), who observed degeneration in the cord after injury to the labyrinth in Rana. Wallenberg (1907) followed degenerating fibers to the sixth spinal segment. Ariens Kappers (1947) states that the fibers to the cord probably are utricular, serving the static reflexes of the extremities. The ascending fascicle of the ventral root comprises both utricular and saccular fibers. It distributes to the vestibulo-cerebellar nucleus, the flocculus, the lateral and dorsal marginal zone of the cerebellum, including the vestibular commissure, and ipsilaterally to the granular layer of the deep part of the corpus cerebelli. Utricular and saccular fibers probably become segregated as they distribute, but the regions that they respectively reach are not known. We shall return to the vestibular fibers that end in the corpus cerebelli.

The vestibular nuclear complex of metamorphosed anurans comprises large polygonal cells similar to those of Deiters's nucleus in other vertebrates, and aggregations of smaller cells that continue rostralward and caudalward from the large-celled group. As in elasmobranchs no tangential nucleus is differentiated, but some of the more laterally situated large cells send dendritic branches among the entering fibers of the ventral root of the VIII nerve. In silver preparations of the toad, more clearly than in the frog, an aggregation of small cells beneath the caudolateral part of the cerebellum appears to correspond to the vestibulo-cerebellar nucleus of reptiles and birds.

Secondary paths from the ventral VIII nucleus reach the spinal cord, midbrain, and cerebellum (fig. 136B). The more laterally situated large polygonal cells of the vestibular nuclear complex give rise to an ipsilateral vestibulo-spinal tract, these cells corresponding more strictly to Deiters's nucleus in other vertebrates. Other cells send their axons into the fasciculus longitudinalis medialis, ipsilateral and contralateral; the crossed fibers, especially, ascend to the oculomotor nuclei and some appear to continue into the posterior commissure of the cerebrum, Ariens Kappers (1947) states. Secondary fibers also reach the nucleus of the VI nerve which, in the frog, is situated behind the entrance of the VIII nerve.

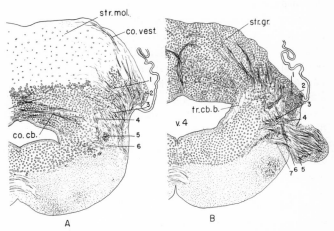

Figure 136. Transverse sections through cerebellum of adult Rana pipiens. A. Through middle region of cerebellum. B. Through caudal region of cerebellum. 1, tr. vestibulo-cerebellaris; 2, auricula; 3, tr. spino-cerebellaris; 4, tr. trigemino-cerebellaris; 5, tr. spinotectalis; 6, tr. visceralis ascendens. Cajal method. ×24. (Larsell, 1923.)

PROPRIOCEPTORS AND EXTEROCEPTORS

The neuromuscular spindles in the frog comprise one to many slender muscle fibers which are encircled by sensory nerve fibers that divide and frequently form coils. Sometimes a single large muscle fiber splits into three or more small ones near the sensory termination of the nerve fiber. A delicate sheath of connective tissue is separated from the spindle by a space, which, according to Jahn (1959), belongs to the lymphatic system because lymphocytes occur within it.

Neuromuscular spindles were first described and illustrated in the frog by Weismann (1861) and Koelliker (1862). The observations of these investigators constituted the real discovery of this type of terminations, although Leydig (1851) had seen them. Kuhne (1863a) confirmed and added to the description of the "muscle spindles," as he named them in the frog, and described similar spindles in the rat. Experimental studies by Sachs (1874) on the frog first suggested that these organs are sensory, and Ramon y Cajal (1888a) published a more detailed illustration of the spindle, including its motor innervation, from the sternocutaneous muscle of the frog. Huber and De Witt (1897) also described and illustrated muscle spindles in the frog but did not name the muscles from which they were taken. Muscle spindles appear to be lacking in the segmental muscles of the back in the frog (Byrnes, 1929).

Ramon y Cajal described the motor fibers to the spindles as derived from myelinated fibers that also innervate the ordinary or extrafusal muscle fibers, as did Sihler (1900). Electrophysiological studies by Katz (1948), and Kuffler and Hunt (1952) have confirmed such an origin of the motor fibers that reach the intrafusal muscle fibers. A specialized system of small nerve fibers was also described in the frog by Kuffler and Hunt which innervates chiefly the ordinary muscle fibers. Impulses conducted by these fibers produce local contractions that result in tension of the muscle fibers.

The unarmored skin of anurans presumably has a rich exteroceptive innervation. Impulses from the skin as well as the muscle spindles reach the corpus cerebelli by way of the spinal nerves and spinal cord tracts. Cutaneous impulses from the head, and also proprioceptive impulses, reach the corpus cerebelli through trigeminal connections.

The greater importance of the auditory apparatus and its refinement for the conduction of air-transmitted sound stimuli, and the large eyes of Anura, are correlated with the development of enlarged auditory and optic centers in the midbrain which send important tracts into the corpus cerebelli.

The much greater development and functional importance of all these sensory organs, the cerebellar connections of which are with the corpus cerebelli, coupled with the greater activity of frogs and toads as compared with urodeles, are correlated with the predominance of the corpus cerebelli in the cerebellum of Anura.

The Cerebellum

THE FLOCCULUS AND THE MARGINAL ZONE

The lateral lobule of the larva is reduced to a plate of cells, in the metamorphosed frog, which lies lateral of the corpus cerebelli and continues rostrolaterally as an ear-like projection (fig. 136B). Fascicles of vestibular fibers form a fibrous layer which separates the principal mass of the plate from the corpus cerebelli. Some of the fascicles continue into the plate and its projection, while others continue dorsally into the marginal part of the main body of the cerebellum. The ear-like projection is separated from the corpus cerebelli by a furrow which is the lateral segment of the posterolateral fissure. This projection, frequently torn off in removing the brain or its membranes, is well shown in brains sectioned in situ.

The floor of the anterior diverticulum, which is broad and cellular in the tadpole, undergoes atrophy as the lateral-line fascicles degenerate (fig. 132A,B). Also the

subtenial chains of cells, which correspond to the folds of the auricle, *sensu strictiori*, of urodeles disappear, the diverticular floor being reduced to a choroid membrane (fig. 137). When metamorphosis is completed there remains, of the lateral lobule of Ichthyopsida, only a modified eminentia granularis. The anterior diverticulum is reduced to a relatively narrow space with membranous floor and lateral wall and roof, the choroid epithelium of which is directly continuous with the ependymal layer of the eminentia (fig. 137).

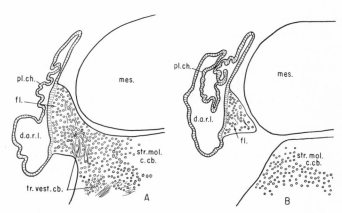

Figure 137. Transverse sections through flocculus of Rana pipiens. A. Rostral part of flocculus beyond base of cerebellum. B. Level rostral to A. Hematoxylin and orange G stain.

The modified eminentia granularis consists chiefly of granule cells. It is continuous with the granular layer of the corpus cerebelli, medially by similar cells interspersed among fascicles of fibers, above mentioned; dorsomedially it is continuous with the marginal zone, described below.

The vestibular connections of the modified eminentia granularis corresponds to the vestibular afferents of the flocculus of birds and mammals. Olivo-floccular fibers, in addition, have been demonstrated experimentally in mammals by Brodal (1940b). Possibly homologous connections are present in submammals; if present, the afferents to the eminentia of the frog are entirely similar to those of the flocculus of higher vertebrates. This homology and the morphological homologies of relations to corpus cerebelli, marginal zone, and the ear-like projection appear to justify the employment of the term flocculus for the modified eminentia granularis of Anura.

The interlobular or interreminential granular band of the tadpole is still recognizable in newly metamorphosed Hyla regilla by the more compact arrangement of its cells as compared with the corpus cerebelli (fig. 134A). In this species the cerebellum tilts caudalward more than in Rana, the granular band forming its lateral and caudal, instead of lateral and dorsal, borders. The band has merged with the granular layer of the corpus cerebelli in adult cerebella of both Hyla and Rana to such an extent that it can be differentiated from the corpus only in the vicinity of the flocculus. Vestibular fibers, both primary and secondary, continue dorsally and then medially from the fascicles between the corpus cerebelli and flocculus. Their course is parallel with the marginal surface, in general, but well beneath it (fig. 136). Many continue across the midline, forming a commissure. We shall return to the distribution of these fibers.

The two flocculi and the marginal zone constitute a unit which has greater similarity to the flocculonodular lobe of birds and mammals than to the vestibulolateral lobe of Ichthyopsida which is homologous only in part. There is no surface boundary between the marginal zone and the corpus cerebelli, however, and no nodulus is differentiated.

THE CORPUS CEREBELLI

The corpus cerebelli forms a massive, dorsally tilted plate above the rostral part of the fourth ventricle (figs. 132B, 136). A deep mesencephalo-cerebellar fissure separates it and the projecting part of the flocculus from the midbrain. The dorsal tilt is more pronounced in Rana than in Bufo or Hyla. In transverse sections the corpus appears as a thick arch above the fourth ventricle (fig. 136). It is partly divided into bilateral halves by a shallow median cleft which dips into the posterior surface and corresponds morphologically to the cerebellar ventricle of fishes. Sagittal sections show thick molecular and granular layers, a layer of Purkinje cells intervening between them (fig. 138). These layers all are continuous

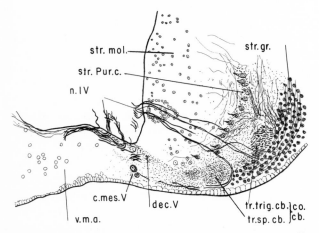

Figure 138. Section through ventral portion of cerebellum and part of anterior medullary velum of adult Rana pipiens, near midsagittal plane. Cajal method. ×110. (Larsell, 1923.)

across the midline, but the granular layer is reduced in thickness as it approaches the median sagittal plane. On either side of the median cleft the granular layer becomes thick and forms a rounded mass which projects into the fourth ventricle. These bilateral thickenings correspond to the granular masses of the narrower corpus cerebelli of teleosts that fuse across the midline, reducing the cerebellar ventricle to a cerebellar canal. Lateroventrally the corpus cerebelli is continuous with the medulla oblongata, on either side of the fourth ventricle, and with the anterior medullary velum rostrally.

There is no external indication of a boundary between the corpus cerebelli and the vestibular marginal zone above described. Three principal functional areas of the cerebellum, however, have been demonstrated experimentally by Goodman (1958). To these we shall return.

The nucleus cerebelli. The nucleus cerebelli (Larsell, 1923) of adult anurans is more definitely a part of the base of the cerebellum than in urodeles (fig. 139A). It comprises a group of cells which is delimited by fiber bundles from the vestibular nucleus, the trigeminal nucleus, and other neighboring nuclear masses. Ventromedially it merges with the tegmentum, but its cells are larger and the nerve fibers less numerous than those of the tegmentum. Golgi sections show that it consists of multipolar cells part of whose axons pass rostrally and medially into the midbrain as the brachium conjunctivum while others pass into the medulla oblongata. The dendrites of its cells extend into vestibular as well as spinocerebellar and other neighboring territory (fig. 143A), and it receives fibers from the corpus cerebelli. More clearly than in urodeles the nucleus cerebelli appear to represent the primitive cellular mass from which the several cerebellar nuclei of higher vertebrates are differentiated.

Rüdeberg (1961) was unable to distinguish a distinct nucleus cerebelli, in the adult frog, in the sense of a well-defined cell mass. In embryos of Rana arvalis, however, he found a cell migration A_2B from the columna dorsalis which he regards as corresponding to the nucleus cerebelli of Ichthyopsida, as described in the literature.

THE FIBER CONNECTIONS

The afferent tracts. The fiber connections of the cerebellum of adult Anura differ from those of the larvae and of lower vertebrates by the absence of tracts related to the lateral-line system. The vestibular tracts, however, are prominent and the dominance of the corpus cerebelli is reflected in the greater development of the tracts related to it.

The vestibular tracts, already partially described, com-

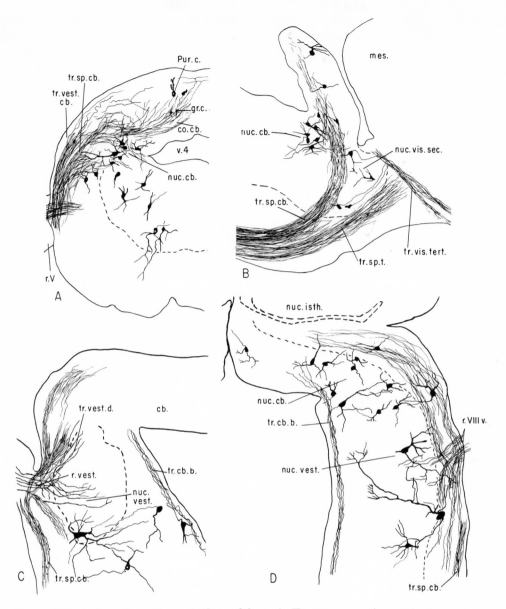

Figure 139. Sections through cerebellum of frog. A. Transverse section at the level of nucleus cerebelli. Hyla regilla of 10 mm tail length with well-developed legs. ×70. B. Sagittal section of cerebellum of Hyla regilla larva, 40 mm. ×65. C. Horizontal section at entrance of vestibular root, showing collaterals from the direct vestibulo-cerebellar fibers to vestibular nucleus. Hyla regilla of 1 mm tail length. ×95. D. Horizontal section through rostral region of medulla oblongata. Hyla regilla of 1 mm tail length. ×120.
Golgi method. (Larsell, 1923, 1925.)

prise a fascicle of root fibers and one of secondary fibers from the vestibular nuclei (figs. 136, 139, 142A). The root fibers include ascending saccular and utricular branches, but whether both reach the cerebellum and to what extent they may be segregated in distribution is unknown. Many of the ascending root fibers send collaterals to the nucleus cerebelli (fig. 139A). Most of them

continue to the flocculus and to the marginal zone, some apparently decussating in the commissure above mentioned.

The primary and secondary vestibular fibers that constitute the fascicles of the marginal zone distribute in this zone, as shown in Golgi and Cajal preparations. Many end among the granule cells (fig. 139A) but whether any terminate in the molecular layer is not clear. The commissure, which corresponds to the vestibular component of the acousticolateral commissure of urodeles, probably includes both secondary and root fibers.

A considerable number of vestibular fibers enter the ventral fiber mass of the corpus cerebelli, as Röthig (1927a) noted. This mass also includes fibers from several other sources, including the spinal cord. From it fibers distribute throughout the corpus cerebelli, many crossing the midline. The vestibular fibers are predominantly secondary and end contralaterally. I have been unable to follow primary vestibular fibers into the corpus cerebelli on the side opposite their entrance, but some end ipsilaterally.

This considerable contingent of vestibular fibers in the corpus cerebelli of the frog and toad is of special interest. It appears to correspond to the vestibular fibers that reach the lobulus posticus of elasmobranchs and the uvula of birds and mammals, which subdivisions also receive spino-cerebellar fibers. A fascicle from the fibrous layer of the pars medialis of the vestibulolateral lobe to the posteroinferior part of the corpus cerebelli of the salmon has also already been mentioned. In birds and mammals the uvula is the principal subdivision of the corpus cerebelli which receives vestibular fibers, in addition to those from the cord and inferior olive, although some also reach the ventral part of the anterior lobe. Considering the locomotor habits of the frog it is evident that a close correlation between vestibular and propriocep-

tive impulses is required. The extensive vestibular connections with the corpus cerebelli of anurans suggest that an incipient uvula, although not differentiated as a distinct lobule, is a predominant part of the corpus cerebelli of this class of vertebrates and facilitates such correlation.

The tractus spino-cerebellaris is the principal afferent tract of the corpus cerebelli in the frog and toad. It accompanies the spino-tectal tract through the medulla oblongata as far as the level of the trigeminal roots, the combined fascicles lying ventral of the descending trigeminal tract. The spino-cerebellar tract, on separating from the spino-tectal bundle, arches more dorsally and medially (figs. 136, 139), many of the fibers passing through the trigeminal root fascicles. The tract terminates in the granular layer, both ipsilaterally and contralaterally, the crossed fibers constituting the spino-cerebellar part of the commissura cerebelli (figs. 138, 143B). It appears to correspond to the ventral spino-cerebellar tract of birds and mammals.

Bulbo-cerebellar fibers in large numbers, probably derived in part from cells corresponding to the inferior olive, accompany the spino-cerebellar tract. The inferior olive is not represented by a distinct cell mass in amphibians, but fibers from the general region which it occupies in other vertebrates cross the raphe and become included in the bulbo-cerebellar assemblage which appears not to cross after entering the cerebellum.

Röthig (1927a) found both spino-cerebellar and bul-

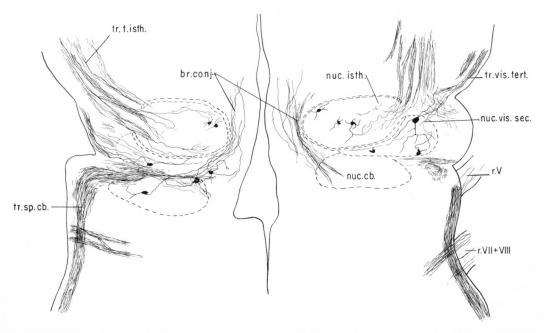

Figure 140. Horizontal section through ventral part of cerebellar region in Hyla regilla larva of 32 mm long, with well-developed legs. Golgi method. ×60. (Larsell, 1923.)

bo-cerebellar tracts in Weigert series of the frog and toad and also (1927b) in Marchi material of the frog. Wlassak (1887) described a dorsal spino-cerebellar tract from Weigert preparations of the frog, and Banchi (1903), in the toad, described "cordoni posteriori" as derived in part from the trigeminal, acoustic, glosso-pharyngeal, and vagus nerves. I have found the various components described by Wlassak and Banchi but none of them continues into the cord. Marchi preparations of frogs whose cords were hemisected immediately caudal of the medulla oblongata show degeneration along the course of the spino-cerebellar tract, but none could be followed into the cerebellum in a more dorsal course.

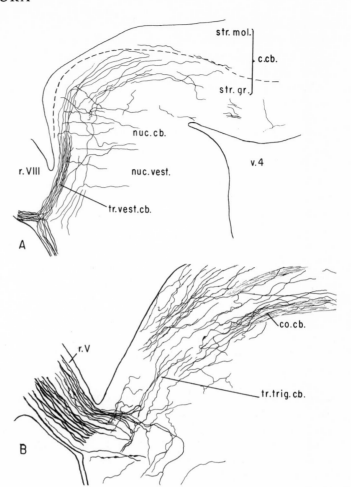

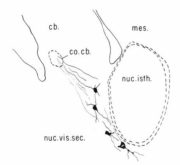

Figure 141. Sagittal section through secondary visceral nucleus, showing fibers from it to cerebellar commissure. Hyla regilla larva, 40 mm long. Golgi method. ×73. (Larsell, 1923.)

Trigemino-cerebellar connections are well defined in Anura. Small fibers of a fascicle in the rostral part of the root of the trigeminus bifurcate on entering the medulla oblongata, the finer ascending rami passing rostrome-dially into the corpus cerebelli (figs. 136, 142B). Wood-burne (1936) found a similar cerebellar bundle of direct trigeminal fibers in the frog. Many of the fibers cross in the commissura cerebelli (figs. 136, 138). Numerous fibers from the superior sensory nucleus of the trigeminus also enter the commissure, these corresponding to the intertrigeminal commissure of urodeles. The direct and secondary fibers together form the trigeminal element of the anuran cerebellar commissure. Röthig (1927a) also found trigemino-cerebellar fibers and an intertrigeminal commissure in the cerebellum of the frog and toad. Stieda (1870) describes fibers to the cerebellum which he believed to have their origin in the gasserian ganglion, and Banchi (1903) illustrates such fibers in the toad. My Golgi preparations of the frog clearly demonstrate that the greater proportion of fibers of the trigeminal commissure have their origin in cells of the superior sensory trigeminal nucleus. This nucleus, as described by Wood-burne (1936), is a fairly uniformly arranged group of

Figure 142. Horizontal sections through cerebellum and adjacent part of medulla oblongata of adult Rana pipiens. A. Section showing bifurcation of vestibular fibers to form the direct vestibulo-cerebellar tract. ×65. B. Section showing bifurcation of trigeminal fibers, with formation of a trigemino-cerebellar tract. Neighboring sections show more numerous fibers, but not so many that enter the cerebellar commissure. Golgi method. ×110. (Larsell, 1923.)

cells whose principal dendrites pass ventrolaterally and ventrally toward the entering sensory root of the trigeminus.

A group of cells situated ventrolateral and ventrorostral of the nucleus cerebelli appears to correspond to the secondary visceral nucleus of Herrick in teleosts. It receives secondary fibers from the nucleus of the solitary tract and gives rise to a tertiary tract which reaches the hypothalamus. The axons of some of the cells appear to pass into the base of the cerebellum and others are lost in the isthmus (figs. 140, 141). I can add nothing to my earlier (1923, 1925) descriptions of this nucleus and its connections, based on Golgi preparations. More recent

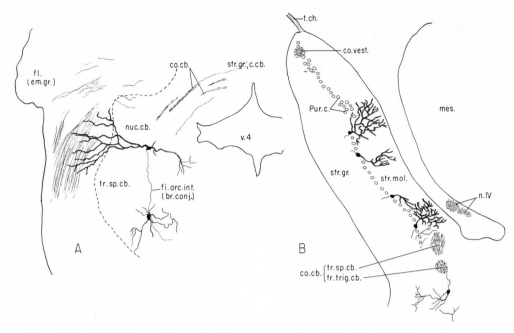

Figure 143. Adult Rana pipiens. A. Transverse section through cerebellar nucleus. ×40. B. Paramedian sagittal section (cells partly from other sections), showing Purkinje cells and the cerebellar commissures. Golgi method.

neurophysiological evidence of visceral connections with the cerebellum in mammals (see Dow and Moruzzi, 1958) is of interest in this connection.

The tecto-cerebellar tract of Anura is seen in sagittal sections as a series of small fascicles that sweep downward and caudally from the tectum and the corpus posticum and then arch upward into the cerebellum, in which some of the fibers cross. The deeper fascicles arch beneath the nucleus isthmi, while others pass medial of this nucleus. The tract was described briefly by Wlassak (1887) and Ariens Kappers (1920–21) in the frog. Röthig (1927a) differentiated postico-cerebellar and tecto-cerebellar fascicles in Weigert series of frog and toad, the fibers of tectal origin intermingling with those from the corpus posticum as they arch toward the cerebellum.

In my Golgi preparations of larval and adult Rana (1923) and adult Hyla (1925) fibers from small cells of the corpus posticum pass medial of the nucleus isthmi and arch ventrally and then dorsally into the corpus cerebelli. The cells of origin, so far as observed, were situated in territory receiving terminal fibers of the spino- and bulbo-tectal tracts. Herrick (1948) found cells of the tecto-cerebellar tract in the corresponding portion (nucleus posterior) of the midbrain of Ambystoma, their dendrites extending toward the optic tectum. The fibers arising in the corpus posticum of the frog correspond to part of the postico-cerebellar tract of Röthig. The cells

of origin of the fascicles extending toward the optic tectum were not observed in my frog material, but presumably they are situated in the deep gray layer of this part of the tectum. These fascicles probably are homologous with the anterior mesencephalo-cerebellar or tecto-cerebellar tract of fishes.

In order to examine the homology of the postico-cerebellar component of the tecto-cerebellar tract of anurans a brief comparison of the corpus posticum with the nucleus posterior of urodeles and the torus semicircularis of fishes is necessary. The corpus posticum of Anura is regarded by Herrick (1948) as corresponding to the nucleus posterior of the tectum mesencephali of urodeles, which is interpolated between the tectum opticum and the cerebellum. No sharp boundary exists between the optic tectum and the nucleus posterior, but the latter is distinguished by the absence of optic tract terminals, the entrance into it of a small primordial lemniscus lateralis, and by an efferent tractus tecto-bulbaris posterior. The nucleus posterior is the primordial inferior colliculus. The primordial lateral lemniscus is probably the precursor of the lateral lemniscus of land forms, first appearing in anurans as a differentiated tract in relation with differentiated peripheral auditory organs, namely, the papilla cochlearis or primitive cochlea, and the papilla amphibiorum (Larsell, 1934a). The posterior part of the tectum of anurans has enlarged under the influence of the well-developed lateral lemniscus and has become

174

folded into the aqueduct as the so-called corpus posticum. In some reptiles and in all mammals it reappears on the dorsal surface of the midbrain as the definitive inferior colliculus, Herrick (1948) states. The auditory function of the corpus posticum of the frog has been demonstrated by Aronson and Noble (1945). Their experiments revealed that after extensive destruction of this part of the brain the warning croak during mating was abolished, although complete ablation of the optic tectum, anterior part of the tegmentum, diencephalon, cerebral hemispheres, and cerebellum failed to produce such effects.

The degree to which the corpus posticum of the frog and toad corresponds to the torus semicircularis of teleosts is open to question. In bony fishes this part of the midbrain is a protrusion into the ventricle which is derived from the deep small-celled layer of the dorsomedial wall of the tectum, Ariens Kappers (1947) says. As already mentioned, it is the principal terminus of the acousticolateral lemnicus or fasciculus longitudinalis lateralis of teleosts, which Ariens Kappers calls the lateral lemniscus. The torus sends fibers to the nucleus lateralis valvulae, which is found only in fishes that have a valvula cerebelli, and this nucleus gives rise to the greater part of the posterior mesencephalo-cerebellar tract. This tract is predominantly related with the valvula, although a considerable contingent of fibers, already described as originating in the lateral nucleus of the valvula, passes into the corpus cerebelli. The various connections of this nucleus appear to have little in common with those of the corpus posticum of anurans, and it is very unlikely that the valvular part of the posterior mesencephalic tract of teleosts corresponds to any part of the tecto-cerebellar tract of anurans. The fibers, seen in silver sections of teleosts, that bypass the nucleus lateralis valvulae before joining the posterior mesencephalo-cerebellar tract appear to have their origin too far rostrally to correspond to those from the corpus posticum of anurans.

The elasmobranch homologue of the torus semicircularis is the nucleus tegmentalis lateralis of the midbrain (Ariens Kappers, 1947). A tractus mesencephalo-cerebellaris superior is formed in elasmobranchs by the convergence of fibers in the anterior dorsal part of the mesencephalic tegmentum, but the origin of the fibers is obscure. Some appear to derive from the rostral part of the optic tectum and to correspond to the tecto-cerebellar tract of teleosts. The fascicle may also include the homologue of the posterior mesencephalo-cerebellar tract in the opinion of Ariens Kappers, Huber, and Crosby (1936). Since no nucleus lateralis valvulae is found in elasmobranchs the latter tract, if represented, passes directly to the cerebellum. It does not seem prob-

able, however, that these correspond to the fibers derived from the posterior part of the corpus posticum of anurans, which is a phylogenically new elaboration of the posterior region of the tectum, as shown by Herrick's studies of the urodele brain.

In a comparative study of the tecto-cerebellar tract in lower vertebrates, Kashiwamura (1955) describes the tract as arising from the posterior part of the tectum and reaching the corpus cerebelli by two kinds of paths. In Triturus, Clemmys, Gecko, and Eumeces a single fascicle was found; in Rana, Bufo, and Elaphe dorsal and ventral fascicles characterized the tract. Kashiwamura states that the tecto-cerebellar tract has synaptic relations with the spino-cerebellar and secondary sensory trigeminal tract in the neuropil of the commissura cerebelli.

Irrespective of the homologies of these tracts in teleosts and elasmobranchs it appears clear that the so-called tecto-cerebellar tract of Anura includes a component related with the auditory system and one related with the optic tectum.

The efferent tracts. The brachium conjunctivum already has been mentioned. Its fibers have their origin in part from the nucleus cerebelli and in part as direct axons of Purkinje cells. They decussate in the posterior part of the midbrain, beneath the medial longitudinal fascicle, and continue rostroventrally to the mesencephalic tegmentum. According to Ariens Kappers, Huber, and Crosby (1936) they end in the region which gives rise to the nucleus ruber in higher vertebrates. Some fibers probably continue to the thalamus. Other fibers reach the medulla oblongata, constituting the cerebello-motor or cerebello-bulbar connections. These appear to include axons of Purkinje cells of the corpus cerebelli and probably of the flocculus and also axons of cells in the nucleus cerebelli. Crossed fibers were designated tractus cerebello-motorius cruciatus by Röthig (1927a, 1927b). A cerebello-spinal tract appears to be present, as Ariens Kappers and Hammer (1918) believed.

A cerebello-tectal tract was found by Goodman (1958), who employed the Nauta technique for degenerated unmyelinated fibers. This tract apparently corresponds to one Tuge (1935) found in the goldfish and similarly named.

Figure 144 gives diagrammatically a summary of the cerebellar connections in anura.

The experimental results of Goodman (1958) on unanesthetized and unrestrained bullfrogs with implanted electrodes are of great interest with reference to the functional organization of the anuran cerebellum. Stimulation of the flocculus and marginal zone (the dorsal fifth of the principal cerebellar mass) elicited a response characterized by rotation of the head with the contralat-

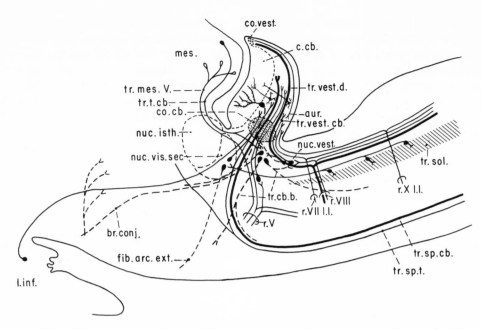

Figure 144. Diagram of cerebellum and its connections in frog, represented as projected on a plane about midway between midsagittal plane and lateral surface of cerebellum.

eral side down, slight concavity of the body contralaterally, extension and slight abduction of the ipsilateral hindlimb. This dorsolateral area pattern was reversed by stimulation of the ventral half of the corpus cerebelli. The resulting "ventral area pattern" was characterized by ipsilateral turning of the head and concavity of the body, ipsilateral forelimb flexion and protraction, with occasional adduction, ipsilateral hindlimb flexion, contralateral forelimb extension and abduction with occasional retraction, and contralateral hindlimb extension, protraction, and adduction.

From areas between the marginal zone and the ventral half of the corpus cerebelli, and in the region of the nucleus cerebelli, weak stimuli evoked first the "ventral area pattern" which, after two to four seconds of stimulation, would reverse to the "dorsolateral area pattern," the reversal occurring during the stimulus. Stronger initial stimuli evoked only the "dorsolateral area pattern" of response. Stimulation of the middle third of the brain stem and at the level of entrance of the VIII nerve elicited first the dorsolateral area posture which, during the stimulus reversed to the ventral area posture.

Three functionally different areas were thus demonstrated: a ventral, a dorsolateral marginal, and the region of the nucleus cerebelli. There were no movements of one side of the body without reciprocal movements of the other side. After unilateral extirpation of the labyrinth the resulting characteristic posture was superseded by modifications when the cerebellum was stimulated, in-

dicating cerebellar dominance over labyrinthine influences. Responses evoked by stimulation of the optic tectum, however, appeared to be dominant over cerebellar effects.

Goodman's experimental results (1958) support the conclusions from anatomical studies that the flocculi and marginal zone constitute a cerebellar unit, distinct from the corpus cerebelli, which is homologous with the flocculonodular lobe of birds and mammals, except that a nodulus is lacking. It also is homologous, in modified form, with the vestibulolateral lobe of Ichthyopsida, but the elements related to the lateral-line system have disappeared.

Although no furrows, except the lateral segment of the posterolateral fissure, divide the cerebellum of Anura into the lobes and lobules characteristic of many higher and some lower vertebrates, Goodman's results indicate areas of specific functional significance. The marginal zone, in addition to its functional differences from the corpus cerebelli, differs from the latter in the number of its fibers, in the arrangement of the fascicles parallel with the marginal surface, and in its purely vestibular nature. In sagittal section of the cerebellum this zone presents a modification of the picture seen in the corpus. The zone beneath this in the corpus cerebelli, in which both vestibular and spinal fibers are distributed, can be regarded as an incipient uvula. The distribution of trigemino- and tecto-cerebellar fibers within the cerebellum is not known in Anura. The tecto-cerebellar fibers enter the general fiber mass. Although this tract is large in the frog and toad, the effects of stimulation of the tectum in superseding cerebellar effects are possibly mediated through the tecto-spinal tract.

THE HISTOLOGY

The relations of the molecular layer, the layer of Purkinje cells, and the layer of granular cells already have been noted (figs. 136, 138). The finer structure of the granular layer will first be considered. This layer consists of small, rounded cells with short dendritic processes (fig. 145). Their slender axons pass into the molecular layer, where they bifurcate in the characteristic manner to form parallel fibers. Golgi type II cells were not found

the parallel fibers derived from the granule cells (fig. 145). These fibers pass through the dendritic branches of Purkinje cells. A small bundle of larger fibers, the vestibular commissure above described, extends from the flocculus of one side to the other. It passes through the granular layer on either side and then along the lateral and dorsal margins of the granular layer and, to some extent, in the adjacent molecular layer in the more dorsal regions of the cerebellum (fig. 143B). A similar bundle is apparent in Cajal and Weigert preparations of the toad. Some of the fibers are lightly myelinated, whereas others, though of larger caliber than the parallel fibers, possess no myelin sheaths. Small neurons in the molecular layer, shown in Cajal series, probably represent stellate cells, but in Golgi series these were not sufficiently well impreg-

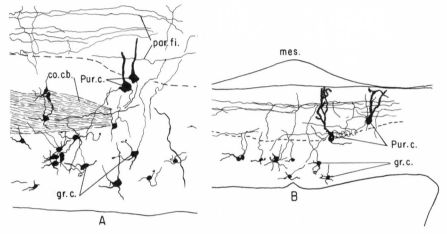

Figure 145. Horizontal sections of cerebellum. A. Granule cells and parallel fibers. Rana. Golgi method. ×73. B. Principal elements of cerebellum of Acris gryllus. Golgi method. ×73. (Larsell, 1923.)

in my earlier (1923) study of the frog cerebellum, and a survey of additional Golgi material has failed to reveal such cells. In view of their presence in more primitive and smaller cerebella one would expect to find Golgi cells in Anura. The granules are more crowded in the flocculus and, in newly metamorphosed frogs, in the marginal band than in the corpus cerebelli. In the ventral part of the corpus cerebelli the granular layer is separated from the Purkinje cells by a considerable layer of fibers (fig. 138), and a zone of fibers suggestive of the infraganglionic or tangential plexus of mammals is evident in most of the remainder of the corpus cerebelli. Numerous fibers scattered throughout the granular layer represent terminals of various entering tracts, but clear evidence of mossy fibers was not observed in my frog material although Banchi (1903) found fibers that resemble them in the toad.

The fibers of the molecular layer are predominantly

nated to reveal their type. No evidence of basket cells or of their characteristic fibers was found. The absence of basket-cell fibers and of baskets about the Purkinje cells in the frog has recently been confirmed by the Glees silver method (Glees, Pearson, and Smith, 1958).

The Purkinje cell layer forms a well-defined zone between the granular and molecular layers (figs. 138, 143B). The cells may occur as a single layer, but in many places two, three, or four layers are common, or the cells may be grouped into clusters. The Purkinje cells have a rounded or ovoid cell body averaging 11.3 μ in diameter (Glees, *et al.*, 1958) and a single dendritic stem. This soon divides into secondary and tertiary branches studded with gemmules (figs. 143B, 145B). As in higher vertebrates the dendritic spread is at right angles to the path of the parallel fibers. According to Glees and his coworkers the greater part of the molecular layer is filled with very thin branches of the Purkinje cell dendrites and larger fibers, some of which may be climbing fibers or other afferents to the layer. Climbing fibers reach the Purkinje cell dendrites from the fibrous zone between the granular layer and the Purkinje cells and twine about the dendrites in typical manner. Aside from the intimate contact between these fibers and the dendrites Glees and coworkers could find no definite histological basis for synaptic connections. Comparatively few ring-like boutons were found in contact with the basal part of the Purkinje cell dendrites, and the authors suggest that the principal type of synapse with these cells is the axo-dendritic connection between the climbing fibers and the dendrites. Ramon y Cajal (1909) found climbing fibers in Golgi preparations of the frog tadpole.

The axons of the Purkinje cells pass into the granular layer, where they are deflected ventrally. Many end in the nucleus cerebelli, but others continue into the brachium conjunctivum or the medulla oblongata.

REPTILIA I

THE cerebellum differs greatly in the several orders of reptiles. This is not surprising when the early divergence of the ancestors of the major groups from the primitive stem reptiles is taken into consideration. There also are striking differences in the form and relative size of the organ within some of the orders, as illustrated especially in the lizards and snakes. We shall return to a consideration of the various patterns and the apparent significance of the variations of form and size.

All reptiles have a corpus cerebelli which forms the predominant feature of the cerebellum, and a small flocculus. A vague groove, beginning at the flocculus, extends caudomedially for a variable distance in some species, probably representing the lateral segment of the posterolateral fissure (figs. 172, 173). Vestibular fibers in the margin of the cerebellum and more or less related with the flocculus indicate a vestibular marginal zone as in Anura. No morphologically posterior median enlargement such as the pars medialis of the vestibulolateral lobe of Ichthyopsida or the nodulus of birds and mammals is differentiated from the corpus cerebelli, *sensu strictiori*. The corpus cerebelli, however, is divided into a median and a bilateral anteroposterior zone (fig. 156). The median zone, which I called the pars interposita (1926, 1932b), and the lateral zone on either side, called the pars lateralis, are most prominent in the anterior part of the cerebellum, but extend posteriorly for an indeterminate distance. They involve both the granular and molecular layers of the cerebellum, but have no distinct boundaries either externally or internally, except possibly some longitudinally directed grooves in the walls of the fourth ventricle of turtles. As pointed out in my earlier contributions, these zones vary in relative thickness, especially of the granular layer, in correlation with the relative development of the extremities and trunk, respectively, and the significance of leg and trunk musculature in locomotion. The pars interposita of the limbless snakes is thick, whereas the pars lateralis is reduced (figs. 164A, 166B). In turtles, which present the greatest contrast with the snakes, the pars lateralis is enlarged and the pars interposita is reduced. The extremities of turtles are the sole organs of locomotion, the trunk musculature being atrophied. Other species present intermediate degrees of relative development of the anteroposterior zones and of the relative significance of the legs and trunk in propulsion.

A restudy of the material on which my earlier interpretations were based and further study of additional material confirms the pars interposita and pars lateralis, to which we shall return.

THE MEMBRANOUS LABYRINTH AND THE ACOUSTIC NERVE

The acoustic or VIII nerve of all reptiles has two peripheral branches, an anterior and a posterior, as in lower vertebrates. In snakes and lizards the anterior branch serves the anterior and lateral ampullary cristae and the macula of the utriculus. It also gives off a branch, in turtles and the crocodile, to the macula sacculi as described by Retzius (1881) and de Burlet (1929). The posterior branch serves the posterior crista ampullaris, a part of the macula sacculi, and the papillae neglecta, lagenae, and basilaris. According to de Burlet (1929) the macula sacculi of Crocodilia and turtles is served in part by the posterior branch and in part by a cochleosaccular branch which passes separately through a median acoustic foramen; in the chameleon the sacculus is served by an independent branch and in Iguana it is served by the posterior branch.

The papilla basilaris, which is the precursor of the organ of Corti, differs greatly in relative size from the snake to the crocodile, being smallest in snakes but even

179

relatively smaller in Sphenodon, Weston (1939b) states. If the pars basilaris is the only organ of hearing in reptiles, Sphenodon, snakes, and Iguana, these species, in which the ratio of area of the pars basilaris to the total area of the pars inferior of the labyrinth is the smallest, must have the most reduced auditory sense. If, in addition, other parts of the labyrinth serve hearing, the macula sacculi and macula lagenae would be the most likely subdivisions, according to Weston. The posterior branch of the VIII nerve, accordingly, has a component of cochlear fibers, the vestibular part forming the inferior part of the posterior or dorsal root. The auditory portion of the membranous labyrinth is relatively largest in crocodilians and the cochlear division of the VIII nerve is proportionately enlarged.

The ganglion cells of the posterior branch differ in size and position according to the distribution of the fibers arising from them (Beccari, 1912; Weston, 1938, 1939a). The cells of the ampullary fibers are large, those of the saccular and lagenar fibers are of medium size, and those of the fibers to the papilla basilaris are the smallest. According to Samano-Bishop (1946) the different types of cells are not regularly distributed in the acoustic ganglia of Sceloporus microlepidatus. The nerve fibers and their endings in the maculae differ somewhat from those of the cristae ampullares.

The VIII nerve enters the medulla oblongata by anterior or ventral, and posterior or dorsal roots. The posterior root may be divided into an inferior vestibular part and a superior part which is predominantly auditory in function (Ariens Kappers, 1947). All of the anterior root and the inferior part of the posterior root, according to Beccari (1912), contain both large and small fibers. The two roots are rather widely separated as they enter the medulla oblongata.

The variation in the sense of hearing suggested by the anatomy of the labyrinth is confirmed by other anatomical facts and by experimental evidence. In snakes and many lizards the eardrum is absent or rudimentary and the tympanic cavity has disappeared. The outer end of the stapes of snakes impinges on the quadrate bone and these creatures are sensitive to ground vibrations transmitted to these bones through the bones of the lower jaw, Bellairs (1960) points out. Prosser (1952) says there is evidence of electrical activity in the auditory nerve of snakes following ground vibrations but not after airborne sounds. Snakes and earless lizards are apparently influenced by airborne sounds only when these are of sufficient intensity to be conducted by the bones of the skull (Bellairs). Turtles are said to produce a variety of sounds when mating, and studies of electrical activity of the auditory nerve indicate different ranges of hearing in different species. In the painted terrapin, Chrysemys picta, Wever and Bray (1936) obtained responses to tones ranging from 120 c.p.s. to 1,000 c.p.s. Responses to low tones and noises were excellent but they declined rapidly in intensity above 500 c.p.s. and disappeared around 1,000 c.p.s., but in one case were obtained up to 3,600 c.p.s. The box turtles, which live chiefly on land, appear to be especially sensitive to notes of about 110 c.p.s. (Prosser, 1952). The alligator is said to hear sounds ranging from 50 to 4,000 c.p.s.

The vestibular nuclei and connections. The central connections of the acoustic nerve have been described in various species of reptiles by Holmes (1903), Beccari (1912), Ariens Kappers (1920), Frederikse (1931), Larsell (1926, 1932b), Weston (1936), and others. These contributions have been summarized by Ariens Kappers, Huber, and Crosby (1936) and by Ariens Kappers (1947). The central nuclei comprise a ventrally situated vestibular group and a dorsally placed cochlear group. Both groups are subdivided into a number of individual nuclear masses, forming a much more complex pattern than the relatively simple vestibular and cochlear nuclei of anurans.

Weston (1936) divides the vestibular complex into six nuclei: the nucleus vestibularis ventrolateralis, nucleus tangentialis, nucleus vestibularis ventromedialis, nucleus vestibularis descendens, nucleus vestibularis dorsolateralis, and nucleus vestibularis superior (fig. 146). The last named, which is distinct only in turtles, is a differentiation of the dorsolateral nucleus.

The ventrolateral or Deiters's nucleus consists of large cells situated at the level of entrance of the VIII nerve (fig. 146). It reaches its highest development in the alligator, Weston says. In all reptiles the neurons are large, multipolar, efferent-type elements having richly branching dendrites that spread to all parts of the vestibular region. These neurons are largest in the snakes but relatively less numerous than in other species. Weston suggests that fewer larger neurons, but with more numerous collaterals, are needed to supply the ventral horn neurons related to trunk muscles than are necessary for the functionally more specialized muscles of the extremities possessed by most other species of reptiles.

The tangential nucleus is represented by a collection of small and medium-sized cells among the entering fibers of the vestibular root. It is best developed in lizards and snakes, according to Weston, and least in the turtles, the degree of development being correlated with the relative development of the trunk musculature. This musculature is of great importance and its activity is well coordinated in the locomotion of snakes and lizards; the more sluggish activity of the trunk musculature of the alliga-

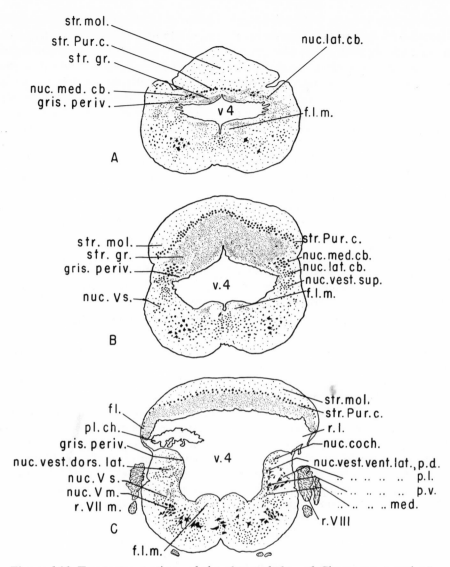

Figure 146. Transverse sections of rhombencephalon of Chrysemys marginata. A. Section through cerebellum at the rostralmost level of cerebellar nuclei. B. Section through cerebellum caudal to level A. C. Section through cerebellum just rostral to entrance of VIII nerve. ×10. (Weston, 1936.)

tor, Weston states, is related to the relatively smaller size of the tangential nucleus of Crocodilia. The absence of trunk movement in turtles is correlated with the great reduction of the tangential nucleus in this group of reptiles.

The ventromedial nucleus is situated medial of the ventrolateral nucleus near the inferolateral angle of the fourth ventricle (fig. 146). It consists of small cells, poorly delimited as a group. The nucleus receives the terminals of vestibular fibers, but fibers of passage from trigeminal, cochlear, and vagus centers also are found in it (Weston, 1936). The extent to which these contribute impulses to the nucleus is uncertain. According to Ariens

Kappers (1947) the ventromedial nucleus corresponds to the nucleus of Schwalbe in mammals.

The dorsolateral nucleus of Weston is the superior vestibular nucleus of Beccari (1912) in the lizard, and probably corresponds to part of the nucleus vestibularis anterior of van Hoevell (1916) in Caiman sclerops. It was called the superior vestibular nucleus by myself (1926) and by Hindenach (1931). Ariens Kappers (1947) considers it homologous with the nucleus of Bechterew. Caudally there is little difference between the cells of this nucleus and the smaller elements of the ventrolateral nucleus, with which it is continuous. Rostrally there is little difference between its cells and those of the superior vestibular nucleus of Weston and also those of the cerebellum, according to Weston. The cells are of medium size and multangular form, many smaller cells being scattered among those of medium size, especially caudally.

The superior vestibular nucleus (fig. 146), as defined by Weston, who found it only in turtles, is similar to the superior vestibular nucleus of Sanders (1929) in birds (p. 221). The cells resemble those of medium size in the dorsolateral vestibular nucleus and also those of the lateral cerebellar nucleus, Weston points out, but the multangular type predominates, giving the nucleus a greater similarity to the vestibular nucleus.

The coarse fibers of the anterior VIII root, distributed peripherally to the anterior and lateral ampullae, end in the ventrolateral part of the tangential nucleus. Those of the posterior root that pass to the posterior ampulla and papilla neglecta end centrally in the anterodorsal part of this nucleus. According to Beccari (1912) all these fibers have spoon-like terminals on the nuclear cells. Ampullary fibers appear not to have cerebellar connections.

The smaller fibers from the utriculus, or their collaterals, end in large part in the ventrolateral (Deiters's) nucleus and in the ventromedial (Schwalbe's) nucleus, according to Ariens Kappers (1947). Others bifurcate, their descending branches forming a descending root of the VIII nerve; the ascending branches reach the dorsomedial (Bechterew's) nucleus and the cerebellum.

According to Weston (1936), silver series of Chrysemys show many fibers of the vestibular root passing into the bulbar commissure and becoming intermingled with a larger number of secondary fibers. The direct fibers may cross the midline to reach the contralateral vestibular nuclei; they may enter the ipsilateral or contralateral fasciculus longitudinalis medialis, continuing either rostrally or caudally within it; or they may turn ventrally, beneath the inferolateral angle of the fourth ventricle, into the ipsilateral reticular formation. Many fibers are said to turn caudolaterally and slightly ventrally to form the descending vestibular root which, Weston states, constitutes part of the vestibulo-spinal tract. The descending vestibular root is closely related to the inferior (descending) vestibular nucleus throughout the extent of the nucleus, forming in turtles a large fascicle. Most of the fibers appear to end in the caudal part of the ventrolateral nucleus and in the inferior nucleus. The existence of root fibers beyond the caudal limit of the inferior nucleus is regarded as questionable by Weston. Beccari (1912), in the lizard, had described a direct vestibulo-spinal tract.

The principal efferent connections of the vestibular area are made through the fasciculus longitudinalis medialis, the vestibulo-spinal tract, and a vestibulo-cerebellar path. The medial longitudinal fascicle includes fibers from the ventrolateral, tangential, and inferior nuclei, according to Weston, which are largely crossed and descend to the cord. Others, from the dorsolateral nucleus, probably cross and ascend in the medial longitudinal fascicle. The vestibulo-spinal tract arises chiefly from the ventrolateral vestibular nucleus, with possible contributions from the inferior nucleus. Weston says that a dorsolateral vestibulo-spinal path is found in all reptiles. It becomes intermingled with the spino-vestibular tract. A second tract, which is strictly vestibulo-spinal only in lizards, lies a little ventrolateral of the inferolateral angle of the ventricle. In this region, in all reptiles other than lizards, numerous vestibulo-reticular fibers issue from Deiters's nucleus. According to Weston, these may synapse with reticular cells that give rise to reticulo-spinal fibers reaching motor cells of the cord. The vestibulo-reticulo-spinal pathway so formed, Weston suggests, mediates the slow and clumsy limb movements of turtles and crocodilians on land, whereas the rapid locomotion of lizards is served by the direct vestibulo-spinal tract. The interesting possibility presents itself that the much more rapid and better coordinated movements of turtles and crocodilians in the water are mediated by the direct vestibulo-spinal tract and, in Crocodilia which swim by trunk and tail movements, by fibers from the tangential nucleus that reach the cord by way of the medial longitudinal fascicle.

The vestibulo-cerebellar fibers are said by Weston to arise chiefly from the dorsolateral vestibular nucleus and to be joined by fibers from the nucleus laminaris (cochleo-vestibulo-cerebellar), and some direct vestibular root fibers. Scattered cells of the dorsolateral nucleus accompany the fascicle in its rostral course and probably add to its fibers. The fascicle of secondary fibers continues above the superior vestibular nucleus of turtles and into the cerebellum. My own observations in reptiles (1926, 1932b) are in general accord with Weston's. Voris and Hoerr (1932), however, in normal fiber preparations of the opossum, and Brodal and Pompeiano (1957), in experimental studies on the cat, found fibers to the cerebellum arising only in the medial and spinal vestibular nuclei, corresponding respectively to the ventromedial and inferior (descending) nuclei of reptiles.

The cochlear nuclei. The cochlear nuclei include the nucleus angularis, which is homologous with the tuberculum acusticum of mammals (Ariens Kappers, 1947), and the nucleus dorsalis magnocellularis, which is the homologue of the mammalian ventral cochlear nucleus.

The nucleus laminaris is regarded as cochlear by some authors, vestibular by others, and mixed by still others.

The dorsal magnocellular nucleus consists of quite large cells that are only slightly angular in form. It corresponds to the dorsal magnocellular nucleus of Anura. The nucleus angularis is situated in the dorsal margin of the medulla oblongata. Its cells are smaller than those of the magnocellular nucleus.

The nucleus laminaris is best developed in Crocodilia. It has been described in the alligator by Holmes (1903), Huber and Crosby (1926), and Weston (1936); in Caiman sclerops by van Hoevell (1916), and in the crocodile by de Lange (1917), Ariens Kappers (1921), and Ariens Kappers, Huber, and Crosby (1936). In other reptiles, studied by Holmes, the laminar nucleus is described as variously developed, but it is not mentioned in snakes, in which the entire region of the cochlear nuclei is reduced. Weston (1936) describes a dorsal nucleus in Chrysemys at approximately the level of the middle part of the ventrolateral vestibular nucleus, regarding it as corresponding to the nucleus laminaris of Holmes in Testudo and Chelonia. It becomes increasingly diffuse rostralward and cannot be delimited from the remainder of the cochlear gray mass. Behind the ventrolateral vestibular nucleus it includes large oval cells similar to those of the dorsal magnocellular nucleus. Ventrally it is separated from the vestibular nuclei by a well-defined mass of longitudinal and transverse fibers. The cells of the nucleus are of medium size and spindle-like or of multangular form, small cells being intermingled. Most of the cells are said to be so oriented that one of the two principal processes extends dorsalward and the other ventrally.

The laminar nucleus appears to vary most greatly in the lizard. Beccari (1912) was unable to identify a comparable nucleus in Lacerta muralis. A gray mass was found by Weston (1936), in the smaller species of lizards, which corresponded to the laminar nucleus in position but at some levels was situated farther laterally. Shanklin (1930) identified as nucleus laminaris, in Chameleon, a mass of small and medium-sized cells that were separated into groups by fascicles of fibers. This mass is said to have the same relations as the laminar nucleus of crocodilians. In the larger lizards Weston (1936) describes a nuclear mass similar to that of the laminar nucleus of Chrysemys and of turtles, as described by Holmes, but not so well developed. Weston notes that in lizards both the laminar nucleus and the cochlea are most variable in development, pointing to a chiefly cochlear function of the nucleus. He was unable to delimit a definite nucleus laminaris in snakes. Ariens Kappers (1947) regards the laminar nucleus as secondary to the nucleus magnocellularis and the nucleus angularis, beneath which it is situated.

A superior olivary nucleus, also secondary, has been described in reptiles by Schepman (1918), Ariens Kappers (1920–21), Huber and Crosby (1926), Shanklin (1930), and others. Ariens Kappers, Huber, and Crosby (1936) have summarized these accounts. A small-celled portion of the superior olive is situated dorsally, embedded among arcuate fibers arising in the laminar nucleus. A more ventral part of the olive which, however, is continuous with the dorsal part, is situated along the lateral lemniscus. Detached masses of cells along the lemniscus lateralis are regarded as homologous with the ventral nucleus of the lemniscus. According to Ariens Kappers (1947), the superior olive receives collaterals from ipsilateral and contralateral fibers arising in the primary cochlear nuclei and reaching the olive through the lateral lemniscus. Both superior olive and laminar nucleus also are said to receive axons from these nuclei.

The fibers of the posterior VIII root whose peripheral distribution is to the auditory part of the labyrinth also bifurcate on entering the medulla oblongata. In snakes, the smaller lizards, and Crocodilia, according to Weston (1936), the cochlear root fibers are smaller than those of the vestibular root; they are said to be approximately equal in size in Varanus and Heloderma. Their distribution within the medulla oblongata has been studied by Holmes (1903), Beccari (1912), Ariens Kappers (1920–21), Huber and Crosby (1926), and others. Most authors agree that the root fibers pass to the nucleus dorsalis magnocellularis, nucleus angularis, and nucleus laminaris. Beccari emphasizes direct cochlear root fibers to the cerebellum. According to Holmes, secondary cochlear fibers form a component of his tractus acustico-cerebellaris, but direct cochlear fibers were not excluded, although not recognized with certainty. Ariens Kappers (1921), Huber and Crosby (1926), Shanklin (1930), and Frederikse (1931) describe secondary cochleo-cerebellar fibers, and I also found them (1926, 1932b). Weston (1936) describes cochlear root fibers to all the cochlear nuclei of the turtle, but chiefly to the dorsal magnocellular nucleus. Near the nuclei, however, the root fibers become so intermingled with secondary cochlear and vestibular fibers that their further course was obscured. Unquestionable root fibers, reaching the base of the cerebellum, according to Weston (1936), were found in a silver series of a 3-day-old (after hatching) specimen of Chelydra serpentina. They were relatively few and were accompanied by a much larger number of secondary fibers from the laminar nucleus.

The magnocellular and laminar nuclei give rise to arcuate fibers that pass ventrally and, after partial decussation beneath the medial longitudinal fascicle, continue to a position dorsal of the most ventral part of the superior olive. After giving off collaterals to the olive the fibers continue as the lateral lemniscus. Fibers from the laminar nucleus are said to come into relation with the dorsal part of the superior olive, some synapsing and others continuing into the lateral lemniscus. The laminar nucleus also gives rise to fibers, already mentioned in the turtle, that enter the base of the cerebellum. These correspond to a lamino-cerebellar tract, described by Shanklin (1930) in Chameleon. Ariens Kappers (1947) refers to cerebellar fibers from the laminar nucleus as joined by secondary fibers from Deiters's nucleus and by VIII root fibers to the cerebellum. He calls the fascicle so formed the cochleo-cerebellar tract.

The nucleus angularis gives rise to fibers that pass ventralward, beneath the surface of the medulla oblongata, and come into relation with the ventral part of the superior olive, both ipsilateral and contralateral. Some of these fibers synapse and others continue into the lateral lemniscus. It is uncertain if cells of the superior olive contribute fibers to the lemniscus.

The lemniscus lateralis includes both ipsilateral and contralateral fibers. It terminates entirely in the posterior bigeminal body, which is a further development of the torus semicircularis of lower vertebrates, and in the nucleus isthmi, Ariens Kappers (1947) states.

INNERVATION OF THE SKIN

Reptiles, in common with all other vertebrates, have dermal networks of nerve fibers. Merkel (1880), in material prepared with osmic acid, found simple "Kolbenkörperchen" in the skin of the entire body of Lacerta agilis. In segments of the tail of Anolis roquet, stained by a modification of the Cajal method, May (1954) observed numerous small nerves individually directed toward the subdermal region. Intradermal fibers, derived from these nerves, terminate as free endings near the chromatophores. Other endings, in the form of small spindles, also were found near the chromatophores. Recently Liu and Maneely (1962) have described many types of nerve endings in the skin of the soft-shelled turtle, Trionyx sinensis.

The skin of Trionyx, according to these authors, is divided into four zones: I, epidermis; II, subepidermis; III, dermis; and IV, hypodermis. Free nerve endings occur both in the subepithelial connective tissue layers and in the stratified squamous epithelium. End coils, with many variations of form, are widely distributed at different levels in the subepithelial connective tissue. Complex endings, possibly representing a primitive type of neurotendinous end organ, are also described.

With reference to specific areas, the skin of the limbs and neck shows free nerve endings, nerve coils, and complex coiled terminal arborizations. The pads have free endings in zones II and III, and encapsulated simple coils in zone III. A more complex type occurs near the blood vessels. Zones I and III of the digits have free endings. In the snout, zone III is very rich in free endings and the Malpighian layer has a rich supply of nerve fibrils and small bifurcated intercellular endings. The leathery carapace has a cutaneous covering which includes all four zones. The nerves pass upward from zone IV and penetrate zone III, following the course of the blood vessels perpendicularly. The fibers terminate in zones II and I as unencapsulated free endings that lack terminal expansions. End organs of the Pacini and Meissner types were not found in any region of the skin. The specific types of sensibility served by the many types of nerve terminations are unknown.

The forked tongue of the snakes and some lizards, used in exploring their path, is usually described as a delicate tactile and, in part, accessory olfactory organ. Ditmars (1910) also ascribes to it a vibratory receptor function.

THE NEUROMUSCULAR SPINDLES

The neuromuscular spindles of reptiles are encapsulated, but are said to lack a lymphatic space. The number of intrafusal fibers varies from one, in snakes and lizards as found by Huber and De Witt (1897), Sihler (1900), Regaud and Favre (1904–05), Kulchitsky (1924), Tiegs (1932a, 1932b), to as many as eight in the turtle as described by Huber and De Witt (1897). The sensory nerve fibers give rise to branches that encircle the intrafusal muscle fibers less regularly than in mammals but sometimes form typical annulospiral terminations, Perroncito (1902) points out. These usually derive from one coarse myelinated fiber, although two are sometimes involved. Motor endings on the intrafusal fibers may be quite numerous in the lizards. They are sometimes found attached to branches of the large motor fibers that pass to extrafusal muscle fibers. Tiegs (1932a, 1932b, 1953) has demonstrated by degeneration methods that these fibers are related to the somatic motor system.

Impulses from cutaneous receptors of the body, tail and limbs, neuromuscular spindles and other proprioceptors, of which little is known in reptiles, undoubtedly are transmitted by the spinal nerves, those reaching the cerebellum being relayed by the spino-cerebellar tracts. The trigeminal nerve serves the corresponding receptors in the head. This nerve, especially the sensory root, is hypertrophied in crocodilians, in which it innervates the surface of the large snout. In snakes the motor and mesencephalic V roots are hypertrophied in correlation with the relatively greater development of the jaw muscles and their proprioceptive innervation. The axons of the mesencephalic V cells, according to Ariens Kappers (1947), enter the motor V and perhaps the VII nucleus. Some fibers are said to enter the anterior part of the corpus cerebelli.

Root fibers from the sensory ganglion of the V nerve bifurcate, after entering the medulla oblongata, into descending and ascending branches. Whether some ascend without branching, as in mammals, is not known. The ascending branches end chiefly in the superior V nucleus, but some continue into the anterior part of the cerebellum. Such fibers, to which we shall return, have been found in many species of reptiles representing all the living orders and with secondary trigemino-cerebellar fibers, must be considered well established. The descending or spinal tract of the V root fibers terminates in the nucleus of the spinal V tract, which is continuous with the gelatinous substance of the dorsal gray column of the spinal cord. A large number of V root fibers reach the cerebellum of snakes, and in lizards there are indications of such fibers intermingled with fibers of the ventral spino-cerebellar tract. Banchi (1903) described them in lizards as well as in snakes and turtles, and Weston (1936) found them in the horned toad and snake. Woodburne (1936) also reported V root fibers to the cerebellum in reptiles. In Golgi series of adult turtles I observed (1932b) V root fibers entering the base of the cerebellum, and in a Cajal series of an embryo of Chrysemys marginata I followed an ascending fascicle from the V root into the cerebellar commissure, finding that many of the fibers cross the midline. Ariens Kappers (1947) mentions direct V root fibers accompanying secondary fibers from the superior V nucleus to the cerebellum in Boa constrictor and the crocodile.

A secondary trigemino-cerebellar tract is well shown in turtle embryos (fig. 151) and also in Caiman. It enters the cerebellar commissure. According to Ariens Kappers (1947), the superior V nucleus is especially well developed in the crocodile and Boa and gives rise to the secondary cerebellar tract already mentioned. Other secondary fibers continue rostralward, but their distribution is not known. Shanklin (1930) found a small fascicle from the superior V nucleus to the cerebellum of Chameleon, but makes no mention of direct V root fibers.

TESTUDINATA

The turtles represent an early side branch of the Cotylosauria or stem reptiles which, in most respects, were little advanced beyond their amphibian ancestors and relatives, Romer (1945) states. Since the development of a protective shell of bone and horn, further structural advances have been limited. The muscles of the back are present in turtle embryos, and side to side movements of the trunk have been observed in young stages as in amphibian larvae. As the carapace develops the back muscles regress and such movements cease (Smith and Daniel, 1947).

The cerebellum of the 10 mm carapace-length stage of Chrysemys marginata (fig. 147) is represented chiefly by paired, thickened rudiments of the corpus cerebelli that are connected across the midline by a thin layer forming the floor of a deep sagittal fissure. The organ is tilted dorsocaudally from its anterior base, as in Anura. At the angle between the lateral part of the cerebellar base and the vestibular region of the medulla oblongata there is a small flocculus, but this does not project beyond the general lateral surface of the corpus cerebelli. In the newly hatched turtle the median sagittal furrow persists dorsally, but the fusion of the rudiments of the corpus cerebelli is more advanced anteroventrally. A

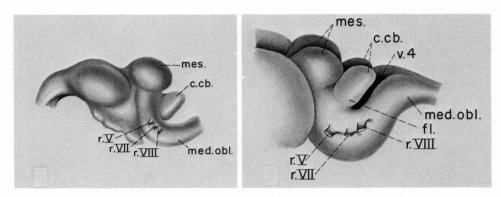

Figure 147. Lateral view of brain of embryonic Chrysemys marginata of 10 mm carapace length. × ca 20. *Figure 148.* Lateral view of brain of newly hatched Chrysemys marginata. × ca 15. (Larsell, 1932b.)

thin zone along the lateral and dorsocaudal cerebellar margins, beginning at the flocculus, affords attachment for the taenia of the roof of the fourth ventricle (fig. 148).

THE CORPUS CEREBELLI

The corpus cerebelli of the adult turtle has a broad base of attachment to the anterior medullary velum and the dorsolateral part of the anterior region of the medulla (fig. 152). The form of the corpus varies in different species. In the box turtle, Terrapene carolina, which attains a length of about six inches, the cerebellum forms a broad arch, above the fourth ventricle, which has thick lateral walls, anteriorly, and a thinner median roof. Sag-

pus cerebelli forms a high dome connected with the cerebellar base by tall anterior and lateral nearly vertical walls (fig. 153). The upper part of the anterior wall tilts forward so that, to some extent, it overhangs the midbrain. A shallow transverse groove at the transition from the vertical to the rostrally tilted part of the anterior surface was called the sulcus anterior by Ingvar (1918). The high lateral walls of the corpus cerebelli are more extensive than the dome, and the granular layer is thicker. An anteroposterior ventricular groove at the transition from lateral wall, on either side, to the dome appears to represent a boundary between pars interposita and pars lateralis. A ventricular groove, the dorsal internal floccular sulcus delimits the pars lateralis from the floc-

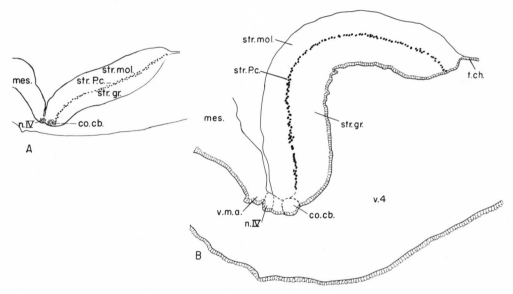

Figure 149. A. Midsagittal section of cerebellum of Cistudo carolina. Weigert stain. ×8. B. Midsagittal section of cerebellum of adult Chrysemys. Toluidine-blue stain. ×16. (Larsell, 1932b.)

ittal sections show the roof sloping gradually dorsalward from the anterior base to the dorsocaudal cerebellar margin. The caudal part of the arch is flattened and nearly uniform in thickness. In Chrysemys marginata, which grows to a length of about eight inches, the corpus cerebelli arises vertically from its anterior base and then turns sharply caudalward, assuming a helmet-like form. The ascending segment in median sagittal section (fig. 149B) is somewhat thicker than the caudally directed horizontal segment, but on either side of the pars interposita the granular layer of the pars lateralis forms a greatly increased mass which projects into the fourth ventricle (fig. 150).

In Chelonia midas, which attains a length of three to four feet and may weigh as much as 850 pounds, the cor-

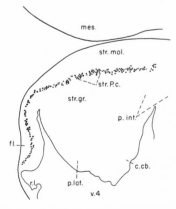

Figure 150. Horizontal section through corpus cerebelli and flocculus of adult Chrysemys marginata. Toluidine-blue stain. ×16. (Larsell, 1932b.)

culus (fig. 153). The dome of the corpus cerebelli turns sharply caudalward from the anterior and anterolateral walls. It is broad anteriorly, but the caudally directed horizontal part gradually becomes reduced to a relatively thin-walled and narrow inverted trough above the fourth ventricle. A choroid membrane is attached to the ventrally directed tenial border on each side and extends to the taenia of the medulla oblongata. This membrane also is attached to the caudal margin of the cerebellum and extends caudally and ventrolaterally as the roof of the fourth ventricle.

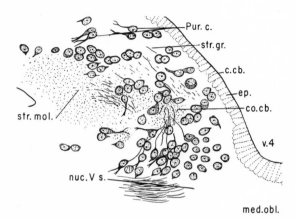

Figure 151. Parasagittal section through cerebellar region of Chrysemys marginata, embryo at stage of 9.8 mm carapace length, showing origin of cerebellar commissural fibers from cells of the superior V nucleus region. Iron-hematoxylin stain. ×530. (Larsell, 1932b.)

The ventricular cavity is greatly expanded beneath the cerebellum of most turtles. In the smaller species there is no subdivision of the cavity, but in Chelonia the dorsal extension of the space into the dome of the corpus cerebelli is so great that the dorsal part may well be called the cerebellar ventricle (fig. 153).

The cerebellum of the soft-shelled turtle, Trionyx japonicus, described by Fuse (1920), resembles in some features the same organ in Chelonia. The anterior part of the corpus cerebelli rises vertically and projects slightly forward. The remainder extends caudalward as a horizontal ovoid mass above the fourth ventricle. Like the corresponding horizontal part in Chelonia it forms an inverted trough but is so compressed from side to side that the cavity is a narrow vertical slit.

According to Fuse, many specimens of Trionyx have a fold of granular layer suspended in the ventricular cavity from the roof so that in transverse sections it resembles a pendulum. This "pendulum" of Fuse's becomes shorter, dorsoventrally, and broader from side to side, at successively more rostral levels, until it merges with the

granular layer of the anterior wall; caudally it gradually disappears by merging with the granular layer on either side. Where most evident, as illustrated by Fuse, the "pendulum" is separated from the lateral walls of the ventrical by a deep ventricular cleft on either side. This appears to represent a greatly exaggerated ventricular furrow corresponding to that mentioned above in Chelonia as delimiting the pars interposita from pars lateralis. The "pendulum" of Trionyx appears to represent a median, thickened ridge of the granular layer which has become compressed from side to side, in the narrow and elongated cerebellum of this species, so that it projects into the ventricle. It is the granular layer of the pars interposita, corresponding to that of the roof of the ventricle in Chelonia, but increased in relative mass and fused across the midline. One can only suggest that the increase of the granular layer of the pars interposita in Trionyx is correlated with the extensive sensory innervation of the carapace and plastron, described by Liu and Maneely (1962), and possibly by retention to a greater degree of the dorsal musculature than in hard-shelled turtles.

THE FLOCCULUS

The massive architecture of the testudinate cerebellum obscures the flocculus. The principal fascicle of vestibulo-cerebellar fibers, described below, passes into the base of the cerebellum. At the posterior border of the junction

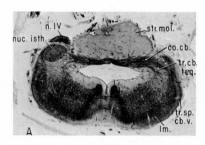

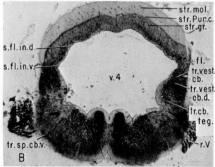

Figure 152. Transverse sections of cerebellum and medulla oblongata of Cistudo carolina. A. Section through base of cerebellum. B. Section at the level of V roots of same series. Weigert stain. (Larsell, 1932b.)

of this base with the medulla oblongata a relatively thin posterolateral continuation of both the granular and molecular layers is entered by a smaller distinct vestibular fascicle. This thinner part, although it has no external boundary from the corpus cerebelli and does not project laterally or rostrolaterally in most turtles, I regard as the flocculus (figs. 152, 153). In some smaller species it pro-

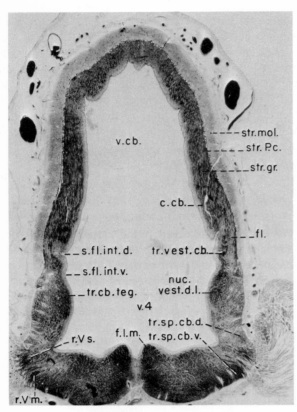

Figure 153. Transverse sections of cerebellum of Chelone midas at the level of V root. Pal-Weigert stain. (Larsell, 1932b.)

jects slightly lateralward and in Trionyx japonicus, as shown in Fuse's illustrations (1920), both a lateral projection and a deep furrow are present. The furrow appears to correspond to the lateral segment of the posterolateral fissure in Crocodilia, described below. In other species of turtles the flocculus is continuous with a relatively thin marginal zone which extends posteromedially but ends short of the midline. It includes both granular and molecular layers. In my 1932 contribution I included this marginal band and the flocculus under the term floccular lobe. The anterior part corresponds more specifically to the flocculus of other reptiles.

RHYNCHOCEPHALIA AND LACERTILIA

A branch of the ancestral Cotylosaurs led to the Squamata, including lizards and snakes, and also to the Rhynchocephalia. This branch divided, in the Mesozoic Era, into the two orders. The Rhynchocephalia are now represented only by Sphenodon punctatum, a lizard-like species of New Zealand. The Squamata, comprising the suborders Lacertilia and Ophidia, are represented by numerous species widely distributed.

The cerebellum of Sphenodon is so similar in type to that of lizards that it will be included with the description of the organ in this suborder. In Ophidia, however, the cerebellum differs so greatly from that of most lizards that separate consideration is necessary.

The lacertilian cerebellum is typically tilted upward and forward so that the granular layer is everted and the molecular layer faces rostrally and, in many species, rostroventrally (figs. 154, 155). In the lizard-like Sphenodon, the cerebellum, described by Hindenach (1931), is of this type. It presents a semicircular fold, as seen in sagittal sections, all of which lies behind the optic tectum. In Heloderma the external surface of the organ describes approximately three fourths of a circle, in median sagittal section, and the rostral margin lies above the caudal part

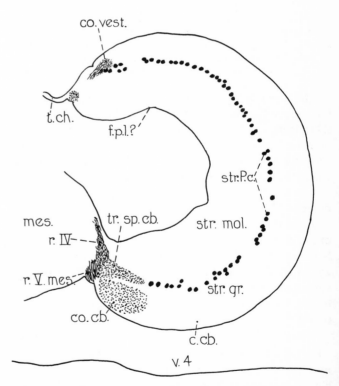

Figure 154. Paramedian sagittal section of the everted cerebellum of Heloderma, showing cerebellar commissures. Pyridine-silver stain. ×50.

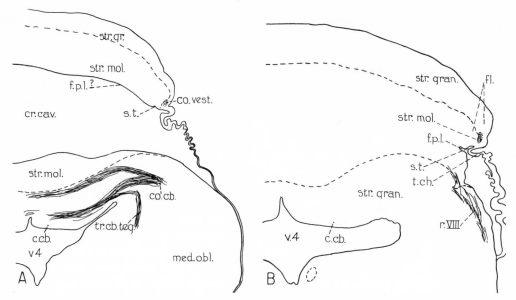

Figure 155. Transverse sections of cerebellum of Heloderma. A. Section at the level of cerebellar commissure. B. More caudal level. Pyridine-silver stain. ×38.

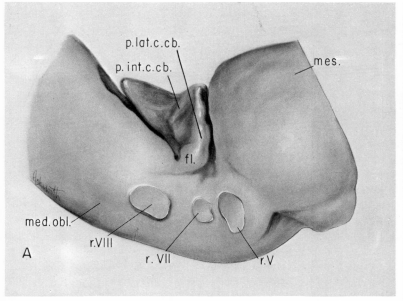

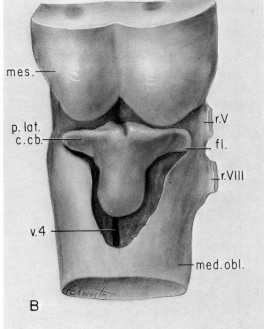

Figure 156. Model of cerebellar region of brain of Gerrhonotus principis. A. Lateral view. B. Dorsal view.

of the optic tectum (fig. 154). Sceloporus and Phrynosoma have a relatively larger but thinner and somewhat shield-like plate which extends farther rostralward above the tectum (fig. 163). In some species of Varanus the plate is first directed dorsocaudally from its base and then turns forward, extending a considerable distance above the midbrain. The lateral and anterodorsal marginal region of the plate is much thinner than the remain-

der, in most species, a shallow furrow in the surface of the granular layer suggesting a boundary. The lateral margin is continuous, ventrally, with a small flocculus, but the furrow just mentioned cannot be regarded as the posterolateral fissure since this, in all other vertebrates, is external, indenting the molecular layer.

The everted type of cerebellum is combined with a caudal, more or less tongue-like projection in Gerrhono-

189

tus coeruleus principis and some other species (figs. 156, 157). This projection is an enlargement of the pars interposita, the anterior portion of which is flanked on either side by a reduced pars lateralis. The flocculus of Gerrhonotus forms an externally rounded but small projection at the lateral junction of the cerebellum with the medulla oblongata (fig. 156).

THE CORPUS CEREBELLI

The thin marginal zone of the cerebellum, on the basis of fiber connections so far as these have been established in normal fiber-stained preparations, appears to be related to the vestibular system. The remainder of the cerebellum, excluding the flocculus, comprises the pars interposita and the bilateral pars lateralis. The greatest contrast between pars interposita and pars lateralis, among the lizards studied, was found in the alligator lizard, Gerrhonotus (fig. 156).

The pars lateralis is reduced in Gerrhonotus, as compared with Sceloporus and other species with strong legs.

It is directed dorsalward and the granular layer is everted, facing caudally and dorsally, whereas the molecular layer faces anteriorly (fig. 157). The pars interposita is more massive; anteriorly it tilts dorsalward, but lies entirely behind the midbrain. Its rostral surface is divided by a vertical cleft in the median sagittal plane, the anterior cerebellar surface swelling forward on either side of the cleft (fig. 158). The most striking feature of the Gerrhonotus cerebellum, however, is the caudal tongue-like projection above noted (fig. 157B,C). It represents an hypertrophy of the pars interposita, the lateral and ventral surfaces of which are formed by a posterior continuation of the granular layer. The dorsal portion of the pars interposita consists of a thick molecular layer which continues to the dorsocaudal tip of the cerebellum. The molecular layer of part of the caudal projection is covered dorsally, laterally, and ventrally by a thick layer of granules (fig. 157B). This anomalous arrangement would result if the fully everted type of cerebellum were reduced laterally and an elongated pars interposita were folded

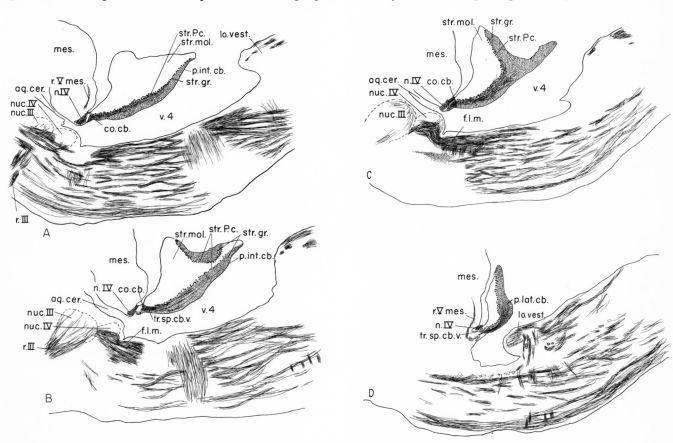

Figure 157. Sagittal sections of cerebellum of Gerrhonotus principis. A. Section close to midplane. B. Section showing beginning of transitional zone, described in text. C. Section showing lateral part of transitional zone. D. Section through lateral part of cerebellar region. Iron-hematoxylin and orange G stain. ×24.

caudalward into the fourth ventricle instead of ventralward. The granular layer of the everted pars lateralis would thus become arched onto the sides and inferior surface of the rostral part of the tongue. Near the caudal end the granular layer would become entirely ventral in position. There are variations in the caudal extent of the pars interposita and in other features of the cerebellum in individual specimens of Gerrhonotus. Other species also show many variations of the organ, also mentioned by Hindenach (1931) in Sphenodon. The Gerrhonotus

rected plate. He calls the granular part of the caudal projection the "pars medialis" of the granular layer and the more lateral granular mass the "pars lateralis cerebelli." These correspond, respectively, to the granular layer of the pars interposita and pars lateralis of Gerrhonotus. In Heloderma the two layers are thinner on either side than in the median part of the corpus cerebelli. The cerebellum of Sphenodon, Hindenach says, thickens on each side of the midline, gradually tapering to the lateral borders. His illustrations of transverse sections

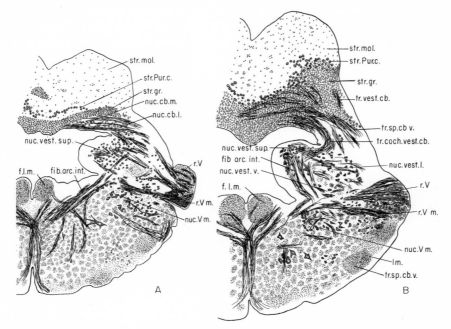

Figure 158. Transverse sections of cerebellum of Gerrhonotus principis. A. Section at rostral level of V nerve roots. B. Section at caudal level of V nerve roots. Iron-hematoxylin stain. ×38. (Larsell, 1926.)

cerebellum, however, shows a combination of lacertian and ophidian characteristics not found in other species of lizards except Anniella, in which, however, they take a somewhat different pattern.

A caudal but much shorter swelling of the ventral region of the pars interposita is seen in the strongly everted cerebellum of Phrynosoma, and in Frederikse's (1931) figures of external views of the cerebellum of Lacerta vivipara a similar but less pronounced caudal projection appears. A small caudal projection is also illustrated in Krabbe's (1939) illustration of the brain of a chameleon embryo. The pars lateralis of Phrynosoma and other species, however, is not reduced as in Gerrhonotus. Frederikse's description is brief, but his photomicrographs of transverse and sagittal sections of Lacerta vivipara indicate a pattern somewhat intermediate between Gerrhonotus and species with a more strongly dorsorostrally directed

show a much more massive development of the lateral part of the organ, on either side, than of the median region, but he does not subdivide the corpus cerebelli.

In Sceloporus the granular layer projects into the ventricle on both sides of the midline (fig. 163); and in Lacerta vivipara, as illustrated in the photomicrographs of Kawakami (1954), a more pronounced ventral projection involves both granular and molecular layers. I have observed similar projections in several other species of lizards, distinctly bilateral in some and more or less fused in others. It is probable that these projections correspond, in less extreme form, to the pendulum of Fuse, and represent a thickening of the granular layer of the pars interposita.

The variations of the granular layer in the pars lateralis of different species have already been mentioned, and the correlation between the thickness of this part of the layer and the relative importance of the extremities has been noted.

In lizards having strong legs but in which the dorsal musculature also plays an important role in progression, there appears to be little difference in the thickness of the median and the lateral parts of the cerebellum except in the lateral and anterodorsal margins. The granular layer of the ventral part of the pars interposita of Sceloporus, however, is increased by bilateral projection of this region into the fourth ventricle. In Kawakami's (1954) photomicrographs of transverse sections of this region in Lacerta vivipara a similar but more pronounced projection, instead of being distinctly bilateral, also has a median zone of molecular layer, only a slight ventricular notch appearing at the midline of the granular layer.

These projections, varying in different species of lizards, appear to represent different degrees of develop-

ment of the pars interposita, reaching the maximum in the caudally projecting tongue, comprising both granular and molecular layers of Gerrhonotus (fig. 157B).

The cerebellum of the legless lizard, Anniella nigra, is the smallest and simplest I have found among reptiles. Undoubtedly it represents a retrogressed form of the organ. In this lizard the cerebellum is almost hidden in a cavity between the midbrain, rostrally, and the VIII nerve roots and nuclei, laterally and caudally (fig. 159).

The corpus cerebelli is massive throughout (fig. 160), but a notch at the midline of the dorsocaudal border reduces its size in median sagittal section (fig. 162). On both sides of the midline it expands into a dorsocaudally tilted half of the pars interposita, the constriction in the median sagittal plane indicating the bilateral origin of this anteroposterior division. The granular layer, thicker on each side of the midline than in the median plane (fig.

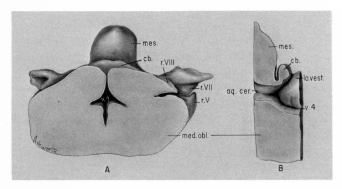

Figure 159. Model of cerebellar region of Anniella nigra. A. Viewed from the rear and slightly from above. B. Model seen in midsagittal section. ×25. (Larsell, 1926.)

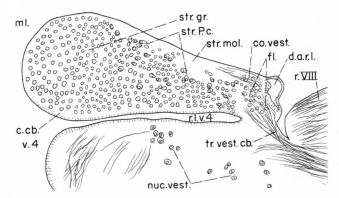

Figure 161. Transverse section through right half of cerebellum of Anniella principis at the level of lateral recess of fourth ventricle. ml, midline. Iron-hematoxylin stain.

162A,B), faces ventrally and caudalward, and its molecular layer faces the caudal surface of the midbrain. The pars lateralis has a nearly horizontal dorsal surface, formed by the molecular layer. The granular layer, much reduced in thickness compared with this layer in the pars interposita, faces ventrally (fig. 162C). The entire pars lateralis is greatly reduced compared with the pars interposita (fig. 161). A small collection of granules, somewhat separated from the granular layer of the pars lateralis and facing an anterior diverticulum of the lateral recess of the fourth ventricle, represents a much reduced flocculus (fig. 161).

Shallow transverse grooves in the concave anterior surface of the strongly everted cerebellum of some species of lizards were described by Hausman (1929) as dividing the organ into three more or less equal segments and suggesting the sulcus anterior and sulcus posterior of crocodilians (p. 199). These grooves, however, are so

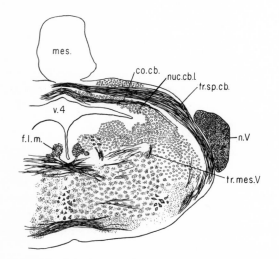

Figure 160. Transverse section through cerebellar region of Anniella nigra at the level of lateral recess of fourth ventricle. Iron-hematoxylin stain.

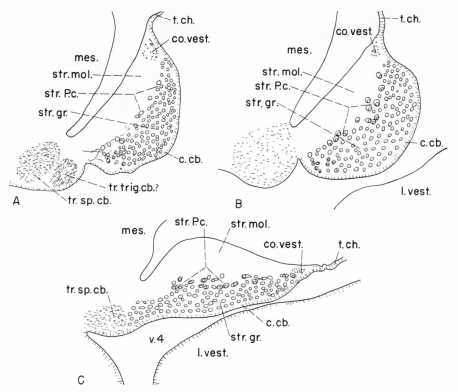

Figure 162. Sagittal section of cerebellum of Anniella nigra. A. Midsagittal section. B. Section midway between midplane and lateral cerebellar margin.
C. Section lateral to the level of B. Iron-hematoxylin stain.

inconstant that I regard them as wrinkles, probably representing artifacts rather than incipient cerebellar fissures. A shallow groove in the granular layer, parallel with the thin marginal zone, which it appears to delimit, seems to correspond to the dorsal internal floccular sul-

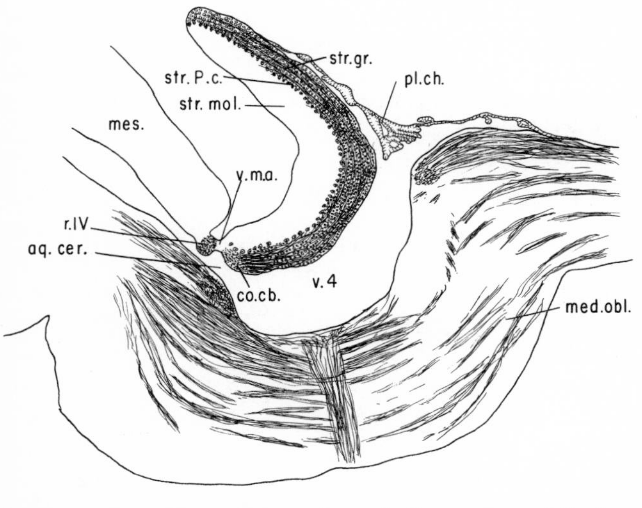

Figure 163. Sagittal section of cerebellar region of Scelopus biseriatus. Cajal method. ×25. (Larsell, 1926.)

cus of some species of turtles. It is most prominent in Varanus.

THE FLOCCULUS

The flocculus of all lizards is small, as already noted, and situated at the transition from the dorsorostral part of the medulla oblongata to the lateral part of the cerebellum. In Gerrhonotus a slight furrow between the laterally projecting rounded flocculus and the dorsolateral surface of the medulla oblongata represents a short lateral segment of the posterolateral fissure which disappears on the anterior surface of the cerebellum. Hindenach (1931) describes a furrow between the body of the cerebellum and the "auricle" (flocculus) of Sphenodon. Suggestions of a furrow in the molecular layer which may indicate the boundary between corpus cerebelli and flocculus appear in Heloderma (fig. 154) and Varanus, but in these and other species with a strongly everted cerebellum the posterolateral fissure is uncertain. Also in these species the flocculus is difficult to identify because of its small size and the distortions of the granular layer at the lateral base of the cerebellum. In my 1926 account of the cerebellum of Anniella I stated that there is no sign of an "auricular lobe," that is, of the flocculus of my

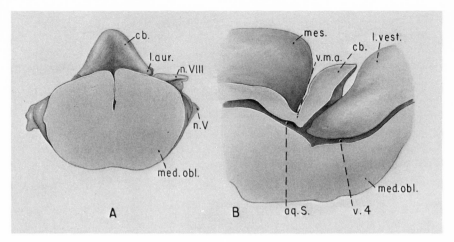

Figure 164. Model of cerebellar region of Thamnophis (probably T. leptocephala). A. Viewed from the rear and slightly above.
B. Seen in midsagittal section. ×20.

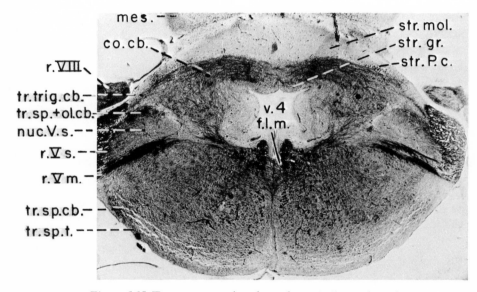

Figure 165. Transverse section through cerebellar region of snake, Thamnophis. Weigert stain.

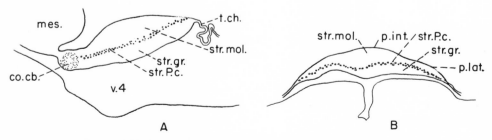

Figure 166. Garter snake, Eutania sirtalis. A. Midsagittal section.
B. Transverse section. ×30.

present terminology. A restudy of the material on which the earlier description was based has convinced me, however, that a small flocculus is represented by a reduced lateral aggregation of granules in which a fascicle of vestibular fibers distributes (fig. 161).

In Sceloporus vestibular fibers can be followed in the lateral margin of the cerebellum toward the rostrodorsal apex. They distribute laterally and dorsally in the granular layer, but a small, compact fascicle crosses the midline, evidently corresponding to the vestibular commissure of the frog. A compact fascicle continues beneath the lateral and anterodorsal margins of the cerebellum and crosses the midline also in Heloderma and Varanus (fig. 154). It accompanies the thinner marginal zone and can be followed ventralward to the region of the flocculus. This fascicle appears to be related to VIII root fibers, but could not be traced to this root with certainty. In Anniella fibers continue dorsomedially from the base of the flocculus, in the lateral and dorsal margins of the cerebellum, some crossing the midline. Other fiber connections of the lizard cerebellum are described below.

OPHIDIA

THE CORPUS CEREBELLI

The corpus cerebelli of the snakes tilts caudally and dorsally from a broad base (fig. 164). The angle of its median axis varies in different species. As illustrated by de Lange (1917) the dorsal surface of the corpus cerebelli of Eunectes murinus is nearly horizontal. In Thamnophis it is tilted strongly dorsalward in its position between the large optic tectum and the lobe-like mass formed by the vestibular nuclei (fig. 164B). It tapers from the ventro-anterior base to the dorsoposterior tip, forming a tongue-like projection. The molecular layer forms its dorsal or anterodorsal surface and the granular layer is ventrally or posteroventrally situated, facing the fourth ventricle (fig. 165). Both layers are thick medially but reduced laterally on each side. The pars interposita and pars lateralis accordingly are well shown in snakes, as already noted.

A transverse mass of fibers extends from one side to the other of the cerebellar base (figs. 165, 166A). It includes fascicles from the spino-cerebellar, trigemino-cerebellar, and vestibulo-cerebellar tracts. The spino-cerebellar and the trigemino-cerebellar tracts decussate across the midline, in part, thus corresponding to the commissura cerebelli of Amphibia. Secondary vestibular fibers enter the cerebellar base from the vestibular nuclei by arching around a dorsolateral cleft-like extension of the fourth ventricle. Most of these fibers end ipsilaterally in the granular layer, but some appear to cross the midline. Fibers from the commissura cerebelli and also from the vestibular and other bulbar fascicles that enter the base of the cerebellum extend into the caudally tilted part of the organ. The distribution of these fibers appears to resemble that in the cerebellum of the frog, but I have not observed, in adult snakes, a fascicle corresponding to the vestibular commissure of anurans.

THE FLOCCULUS

A very small lateral projection, which receives a small fascicle of vestibular fibers, represents the flocculus.

REPTILIA II

CROCODILIA

THE alligators and crocodiles represent a surviving aberrant branch of the Archosauria and are far removed from the Cotylosauria or stem reptiles (Romer, 1945). Many of their anatomical features are said to be shared with birds which derived from archosaurian relatives of the crocodilian branch. These considerations have a bearing on the pattern of the cerebellum of Crocodilia which, fundamentally, resembles the avian type more than that of other groups of reptiles.

The Development of the Cerebellum

The crocodilian cerebellum undergoes so much transformation during development and post-embryonic growth that consideration of its morphological features and comparison with those of other reptiles and of birds can best be approached by describing some embryonic stages. According to Krabbe (1939) the rudiment of the cerebellum in 19 mm and 24 mm length alligator embryos consists of two lateral plates that are thickest medially but are connected across the midline by a thin bridge. His illustration of a section of the cerebellum of the 19 mm embryo shows a shallow lateral groove beyond which flares a marginal zone comprising a thin cellular layer overlying a relatively thick layer of ependyma. The position and relations of the lateral groove are similar to those of the posterolateral fissure of other vertebrates, and the marginal part of Krabbe's lateral plates appears to represent a cerebellar continuation of the vestibular rhombic lip, although not described as such by the author.

An alligator embryo somewhat beyond Reese's stage XIX, and considerably more advanced than Krabbe's 24 mm specimen, shows the vestibular part of the rhombic lip turned sharply dorsalward, above the root of the V

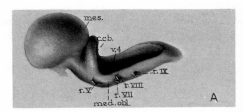

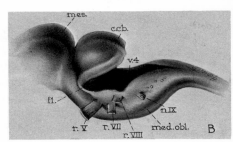

Figure 167. Brain stem of Alligator missisippiensis. A. Embryo at Reese's stage XIX+. ×7. B. Embryo at Reese's stage XXI+. ×7. (Larsell, 1932b.)

nerve and continuing medially, as the posterodorsal margin of the cerebellum, toward the midline (fig. 167A). A bridge of ependyma and cells, still relatively thin, connects the bilateral halves of the organ. The rudiments of the corpus cerebelli have enlarged greatly on either side of the midline but are separated, except by cells above the ependyma of the connecting bridge, by a superficial sagittal fissure which ends as a posterior notch. The cerebellum of the alligator embryo at Reese's stage XIX+ is very similar to that of the newly hatched turtle, allowing for the more caudal tilt of the latter which is due to the greater curvatures of the medulla oblongata (cp. figs. 147B, 167A, 168).

At Reese's stage XXI+ the cerebellum of the alligator is expanded into a more caudally tilted plate which is arched anteroposteriorly and also from side to side (fig. 167B). It still has a medial sagittal fissure which widens posteriorly and ends as a notch. A band along the lateral and caudal cerebellar borders arches ventralward and anteriorly, around a lateral recess of the fourth ventricle, and then posteriorly to become continuous with the rhombic lip. This marginal band is delimited from the rounded surface of the corpus cerebelli by a furrow whose rostral continuation separates the ventrally arching part of the

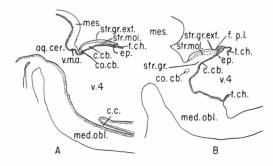

Figure 168. A. Midsagittal, B. parasagittal sections through cerebellar region of alligator embryo at Reese's stage XIX+. × ca 10. (Larsell, 1932b.)

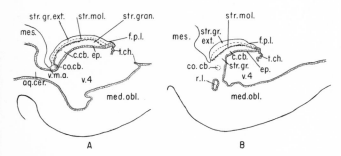

Figure 169. A. Midsagittal, B. parasagittal section through cerebellar region of alligator embryo at Reese's stage XXI+. × ca 10. (Larsell, 1932b.)

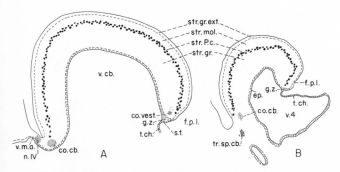

Figure 170. A. Midsagittal, B. parasagittal sections through cerebellar region of alligator embryo at Reese's stage XXII+. × ca 10. (Larsell, 1932b.)

band from the anterior part of the corpus cerebelli. The rostrolaterally projecting arch of the band is the rudiment of the flocculus, and the furrow is the lateral segment of the posterolateral fissure; posteromedially the furrow disappears short of the midline (fig. 167B). The entire cerebellum at stage XXI+ of the alligator is very similar to that of the chick embryo at 8 days of incubation. Both have a flocculus, a marginal band, and an arched corpus cerebelli, the dorsal surface of which is rounded but also divided into bilateral halves by a sagittal fissure. In the chick's subsequent development a bilateral rudiment of the nodulus appears in the marginal band, on both sides of the midline (p. 226), gradually merging to form an unpaired fold of cortex. A distinct corresponding structure does not appear either in embryonic or in adult crocodilians, but a small fascicle of fibers follows the vestibular margin, in embryos, and crosses the midline posteriorly. This fascicle could not be followed with assurance to its sources, but it appears to represent vestibular fibers that form a small vestibular commissure. The bilateral flocculi, marginal bands, and the small commissure connecting them appear to constitute a unit which is the precursor of the flocculonodular lobe of birds and mammals. In the alligator embryo and, as will appear, in postembryonic crocodilians, all the elements of this lobe are represented except a differentiated nodulus.

At Reese's stage XXI+ the posterior margin of the cerebellum is the actual caudal as well as morphological end of the organ (fig. 169). Subsequent growth greatly increases the size and dorsal arching of the corpus cerebelli. Sagittal sections at Reese's stage XXII+ show ascending, horizontal, and descending segments of an irregular dome, the external surface of which has a roughly semicircular outline (fig. 170). The marginal zone has thickened and shows a thin molecular layer laterally, and a small vestibular commissure medially. A faint groove in the surface of the molecular layer, disappearing medially, represents the lateral segment of the posterolateral fissure (fig. 170).

The Postembryonic Cerebellum

Continued growth and differentiation of the cerebellum after hatching results in the disappearance of the external sagittal fissure by completion of the fusion of the bilateral halves of the corpus cerebelli (figs. 171, 172). The organ expands most rapidly dorsally and dorsocaudally and folds more strongly both anteroposteriorly and from side to side. Sagittal sections of the cerebellum of a young alligator show the horizontal segment of the late embryonic stage now turning sharply caudalward from the ascending segment, its caudal part forming the dorsal portion of a dorsocaudal projection (fig. 173). The ventral part of this projection is formed by the now elongated and anteroventrally directed descending segment of the embryonic cerebellum. The anteriorly directed margin of this ventral part pinches off a cerebellar ven-

tricle, from which a posterior recess extends into the dorsocaudal projection.

A transverse thickened zone of the molecular layer of the dorsal cerebellar surface in the juvenile stages foreshadows a faint furrow in the 38-inch-long alligator, the largest available, but it disappears on the lateral surface (figs. 171, 172A). In specimens of Caiman sclerops averaging about 16 inches long, the dorsal furrow is deep and continues onto the lateral cerebellar surface, where it varies from a thickening of the molecular layer to a broad rounded groove, anteriorly, between the median cerebellar mass and a ventrolaterally flared margin of the posterior lateral part of the cerebellum. In some cerebella a superficial groove is visible from the lateral part of the deep dorsal fissure to the anterior end of the outflared margin.

The molecular layer of the anterior cerebellar surface also is thickened in a transverse zone in the juvenile alligator. This thickened zone corresponds in position to a relatively deep but narrow and transversely short fissure in young caymans. Only a suggestion of the groove was found on the anterior cerebellar surface of the 38-inch alligator (fig. 172A).

Ingvar's (1918) reproduction of a photograph of the brain of a presumably adult cayman shows two prominent fissures in the cerebellar surfaces. Sagittal sections of the cerebellum of the same species, illustrated by de Lange (1917) and Ariens Kappers (1921), show both fissures penetrating deeply into the organ; two corre-

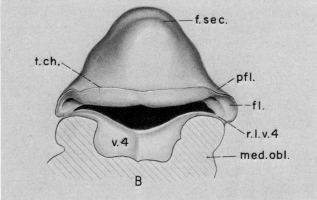

Figure 171. Brain of Alligator missisippiensis, 30 cm long.

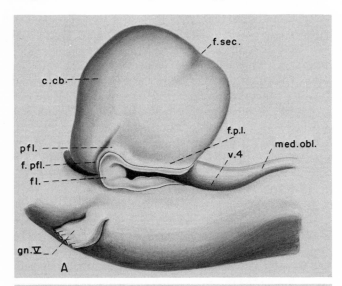

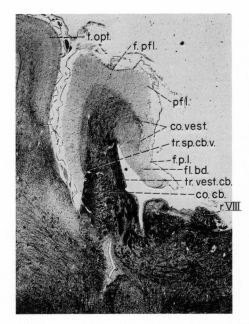

Figure 172. Cerebellum of Alligator missisippiensis, 1 m long. A. Lateral view. B. Posterior view, tilted upward.

Figure 173. Parasagittal section through cerebellum of young alligator. Pal-Weigert method. ×14. (Larsell, 1932b.)

sponding deep fissures are also shown in a photograph of a sagittal section of the Nile crocodile by Ziehen (1934a). The two fissures were called the sulcus anterior and sulcus posterior by de Lange (1917) and by Ingvar (1918). One may be permitted to wonder if the shallowness of the furrows in the 38-inch alligator, which had been confined to a laboratory tank for a long period during growth, is related to the inactivity of the animal throughout this period.

In my 1932 description of the cerebellum of a young alligator, smaller than specimens subsequently available, I labeled as fissure x a groove between a relatively small apical projection of the corpus cerebelli and a larger caudoventrally elongated division. In a later paper (1934b) this furrow was interpreted as corresponding to the fissura prima of mammals. No furrow situated so far forward, relatively, on the dorsal cerebellar surface has been found, however, either in subsequent dissections or in sagittal sections of larger specimens. Other features of the cerebellum of the small specimens indicate a considerably earlier phase of development of the cerebellum than in the remaining preparations studied. The anterior apical projection in the small specimen may represent an early stage of expansion of the medial lobe of Ingvar, and the elongated posterior part possibly represents the posterior lobe after ventral folding of the lateral part of the embryonic plate has occurred but before anteroventral folding has progressed very far. If so, fissure x would correspond to the posterior sulcus of Ingvar, although relatively more prominent than in other young alligators. Lack of additional juvenile growth stages has forestalled further study of these possibilities. Dissections and sections of larger alligators make it clear that the zones of thickened molecular layer in the anterior and dorsal surfaces (fig. 174) correspond, respectively, to the sulcus anterior and sulcus posterior of de Lange (1917) and Ingvar (1918).

Interpretation of these fissures in terms of avian and mammalian cerebellar anatomy was made by Ingvar only by implication through his division of the crocodilian cerebellum into anterior, medial, and posterior lobes, corresponding to his three lobes of birds and mammals. The sulcus anterior, on this basis, corresponds to his sulcus x or primarius of birds, which was regarded as homologous with the fissura prima of mammals. The sulcus posterior of Ingvar in crocodilians corresponds to his sulcus y of birds which is homologous with the mammalian fissura secunda (Larsell, 1948; p. 226), rather than with the prepyramidal fissure, as Ingvar regarded it. The terms fissura prima and fissura secunda are inappropriate in crocodilia with reference to their order of appearance in the corpus cerebelli. The sulcus anterior or fissura prima, however, seems to correspond to the sulcus anterior in Chelonia, above mentioned, which is the first transverse furrow found among reptiles. The two terms will be used for the sake of ready comparison of homologies.

The anterior, medial and posterior lobes of Ingvar in birds and mammals, as is well known, are subdivided into secondary folds of cortex of which there is no suggestion in Crocodilia. The anterior lobe of Crocodilia corresponds to the anterior lobe of all authors who have defined it in birds and mammals, in which it becomes differentiated into folia I–V and lobules I–V, respectively (Larsell, 1948, 1952). The medial lobe, between the fissura prima and fissura secunda, appears to correspond to Elliot Smith's medial lobe and Bolk's lobule c in mammals, and to folia VI–VIII of birds and lobules VI–VIII of mammals (fig. 175). Considering Ingvar's posterior sulcus as the fissura secunda instead of the prepyramidal fissure, the undifferentiated pyramis (folium or lobule VIII) would be included in the medial instead of the posterior lobe. The posterior lobe of Ingvar in crocodilians corresponds to the posterior lobe of Elliot Smith, lobules

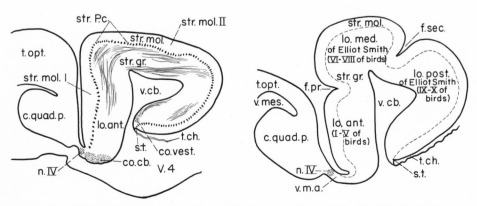

Figure 174. Midsagittal section of cerebellum of Alligator missisippiensis. *Figure 175.* Sagittal section of the cerebellum of Crocodilus niloticus. (Modified from Ziehen, 1934a.)

a and *b* of Bolk, and folia or lobules IX and X, plus a laterorostral continuation, in both birds and mammals, which represents part of the paraflocculus.

The granular layer of the median part of the corpus cerebelli is thicker than that of the lateral parts of the medial and posterior lobes, differentiating these lobes into pars interposita and bilateral pars lateralis. These longitudinal zones are difficult to distinguish in the anterior part of the medial lobe and in the anterior lobe, but experimental evidence, cited below, shows that the pars lateralis is distinct rostrally also. Presumably the pars interposita is represented anteriorly by the large granular mass which separates the two forward continuations of the bilaterally represented pars lateralis.

A rostrolateral projection from the ventral part of the cerebellum of crocodilians was called the auricle by Ingvar, who recognized its continuity with his posterior lobe. It is formed in part by a ventrolateral extension of the granular layer of the pars lateralis of the posterior lobe, covered by molecular layer, and in part by the flocculus (figs. 171, 172). By virtue of these two components the crocodilian "auricle" resembles the "avian auricle" (p. 234), which also represents the flocculus and part of the corpus cerebelli of birds. As will appear, the lateral projection of the corpus cerebelli which contributes to the "avian auricle" is not strictly identical with that of crocodilians. In both groups, however, they are homologous with subdivisions of the mammalian paraflocculus. The parafloccular complex of marsupial and placental mammals comprises a dorsal and a ventral paraflocculus; in most species the accessory paraflocculus of Jansen, which is related to the ventral paraflocculus, is also recognizable. The fissura secunda separates the dorsal and ventral parafloculi, but they are continuous with each other around the end of this fissure, as is well shown in embryos and, in many species, also in the adult cerebellum.

The component of the crocodilian auricle which is related to the corpus cerebelli is situated lateral of the fissura secunda (figs. 171, 172) and is a continuation of the part of the posterior lobe which, in birds and mammals, including monotremes, has differentiated into folium or lobule IX, the uvula. Ornithorhynchus has a prominent "auricle" comprising a flocculus and a foliated extension of lobule IX. This lies behind the lateral continuation of the fissura secunda, as does the simpler lateral extension of the posterior lobe of Crocodilia and the ventral paraflocculus of marsupials and placental mammals. There is no sign of a lateral projection of the corpus cerebelli, in crocodilians, which corresponds to the dorsal paraflocculus, and very little which can be so interpreted in Ornithorhynchus. It appears justified to consider the lateral continuation of the corpus cerebelli into the "auricle" of crocodilians as representing an incipient and primitive ventral paraflocculus only. In birds it corresponds in morphological relations to the accessory paraflocculus of Echidna, the posterior part of the cerebellum differing in important features in the spiny anteater from that of the platypus, as described below.

THE FLOCCULUS

The flocculus, in both Alligator and Caiman, forms the granular floor and anterior and medial walls of a laterorostral recess of the fourth ventricle (figs. 171, 172). It is covered laterally by choroid plexus, which is attached to the tenial margins and is continuous, caudomedially, with the roof of the fourth ventricle. Dorsally and anteriorly the flocculus is enclosed by the paraflocculus (figs. 171, 172). Medially it is partly separated from the granular layer of the rudimentary paraflocculus by a gap, in cell-stained preparations, which in pyridine-silver and Weigert series shows vestibular fibers that enter the flocculus in large numbers. Both primary and secondary fibers are included. Secondary vestibular fibers probably enter the paraflocculus, but could not be differentiated from others with certainty. Posteromedially the flocculus is continuous with the granular layer of the ventrolateral margin of the posterior lobe, more closely arranged granules immediately beneath the taenia possibly indicating an incipient nodular rudiment on each side. A shallow furrow in the molecular layer, parallel with the tenial border but not reaching the midline, appears to represent the relatively more prominent posterolateral fissure of the late embryo (fig. 172A). It is obliterated, or nearly so, dorsal of the flocculus, as in some birds (p. 256). My earlier statement (1932b) that the posterolateral fissure crosses the midline posteriorly in the young alligator I have been unable to confirm. Study of additional series of sagittal sections of cerebella from specimens varying in size has yielded no evidence of a posterior groove except the sulcus taeniae. Review of embryonic material has led to the same conclusion.

The cerebellar nuclei. Banchi (1903) and Edinger (1908) briefly describe a cerebellar nucleus in reptiles which, since the studies of van Hoevell (1916) in Caiman sclerops, has generally been regarded as comprising two cell groups called the nucleus lateralis and the nucleus medialis cerebelli. The nucleus medialis of reptiles, in general, is characterized by relatively large, dark-staining cells of oval, polygonal, or triangular form, but many small cells are interspersed among the larger ones. The nucleus lateralis, by contrast, consists chiefly of small and medium-sized cells, oval or bipolar in form (fig. 176). According to Weston (1936), the lateral cerebellar nucleus of van Hoevell is part of the smaller-celled component of the medial nucleus, such cells being continuous between the two nuclei. The lateral nucleus is closely related in position to the superior vestibular nucleus of Weston, who regards the caudal part of the lateral nucleus as the cell mass labeled anterior vestibular nucleus by van Hoevell.

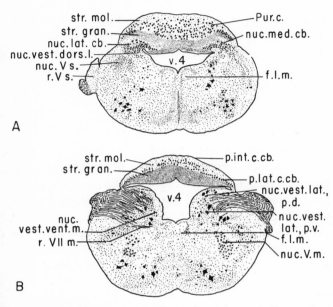

A

B

Figure 176. Transverse sections through cerebellar region and cerebellar nuclei of Thamnophis sirtalis. Toluidine-blue stain. ×20. (Weston, 1936.)

Lateral and medial cerebellar nuclei were described in various reptiles by Ariens Kappers (1921), myself (1926, 1932a), Shanklin (1930), Hindenach (1931), Weston (1936), and others. They are most distinct from each other in Crocodilia. In Sphenodon, Hindenach states, the cell mass is continuous and differentiation into two nuclei was made only on the basis of fiber connections. In the smaller lizards and in snakes a distinct division into two nuclei is difficult or impossible to recognize. The larger lizards have a more distinct lateral nucleus, as in Crocodilia. Intergradations between a single cell mass and two nuclei were confirmed by Stefanelli (1943) and Stefanelli and Pietrogrande (1944).

The rudiment of the cerebellar nuclei, according to Ariens Kappers, Huber, and Crosby (1936), probably is subcerebellar, Ariens Kappers (1947) describing it as having a ventrolateral position in the subcerebellar eminence and as derived from the vestibular nuclei. True cerebellar nuclei, according to him, are not found in turtles, lizards, and snakes; only in Crocodilia are the cells drawn, under neurobiotactic influences, to a supraven-

tricular position, forming the medial and lateral nuclei. As illustrated in figures 146, 158, and 176, and as shown by Weston and other authors, however, the medial nucleus of turtles, lizards, and snakes is situated in the cerebellar arch and is supraventricular. The lateral nucleus lies lateral of the angle of the fourth ventricle and above the lateral part of the ventricle. It is not clear if this region corresponds to the subcerebellar eminence of Ariens Kappers or if the latter is homologous with the eminentia cerebellaris ventralis of Herrick in urodeles, which Herrick (1948) described as the primordium of the deep cerebellar nuclei.

In embryos of Chrysemys picta and Gorgylus ocellatus, according to Rüdeberg (1961), a migration A_2 is derived from migration A of the cerebellum and probably receives a contribution of cells from migration B. The combined cell mass presumably develops into the cerebellar nuclei as in other vertebrates, but Rüdeberg does not describe its later history in reptiles. Although the lateral cerebellar nucleus of adult reptiles is closely related in position to the superior vestibular nucleus of Weston, it appears very doubtful if either this or the medial nucleus derives from the vestibular nuclei.

Considering the medial nucleus first in turtles, toluidine-blue series of Chrysemys marginata and neutral red series of Terrapene carolina show it as quite distinct dorsally, but joined with the lateral nucleus by a bridge of cells ventrally (fig. 146). In Chrysemys the medial nucleus has an oblique position in the deep part of the cerebellum, its rostral part extending nearly to the midline. My observations, in accord with those of Weston (1936) in Chrysemys, indicate that the medial nucleus of turtles is supraventricular and cerebellar. The typical cells of this nucleus in turtles are approximately equal to the Purkinje cells in size, some appearing slightly larger. Numerous smaller cells are typically scattered among the large ones.

As shown in Golgi sections, the fibers arising from the medial nucleus extend rostrally, rostromedially, medially, and caudally. Those directed rostrally, rostromedially, and medially are diffuse and resemble arcuate fibers, but some of the rostral fibers may become included in the brachium conjunctivum. The caudally directed fibers pass toward the vestibular nuclei, in which some terminate, while others continue into the bulbar tegmentum. A bundle of fibers which takes a caudal course close to the lateral part of the floor of the fourth ventricle undoubtedly corresponds to the uncinate bundle of Russell, as de Lange (1917) and Ariens Kappers (1921) believed. Numerous fibers also pass directly to the reticular formation, both rostrally and caudally.

The medial nucleus of lizards, both large and small,

has essentially the same relations as in turtles, in accord with Weston (1936). It is less compact and cells are scattered laterally in the granular layer. In Anniella and Gerrhonotus it is smaller than the lateral nucleus, from which it is poorly differentiated. In snakes it is similar to that of the small lizards, as Weston also found (fig. 176). The large cells are relatively few and are intermingled with the granule cells, at least in Thamnophis. Shanklin (1930) reverses the description of the cells of the two nuclei in Chameleon. His identification of the individual nuclei is made uncertain by this and other features of his account.

The medial nucleus of the crocodilians (fig. 177) resembles that of turtles, but does not reach so far rostralward. It has been described in Caiman sclerops by van Hoevell (1916), briefly in crocodilians by Ariens Kappers (1921), and in Alligator missisippiensis by Weston (1936). My own observations on the alligator and cayman add nothing to those of the authors named. The large cells, as in lizards, are scattered among the deeper cells of the granular layer and are larger, as a rule, than the Purkinje cells. In addition to the large cells the medial nucleus, as in turtles, includes numerous small cells that are very similar to those of the lateral cerebellar nucleus, as already mentioned.

The lateral cerebellar nucleus in Chrysemys, according to Weston (1936), who described it in greater detail than I did in Chrysemys and Terrapene (1932b), forms a dense group of cells situated at the rostralmost level of the trigeminal roots, immediately lateral of the fourth ventricle, and at about the middle of the peduncular connection between cerebellum and medulla oblongata (fig. 146). The medial nucleus lies dorsal of it and the vestibular nucleus lies ventral; its lateral limit is formed by the fiber tracts to the cerebellum. Followed rostralward, the nucleus assumes an increasingly dorsal position so that its anterior portion lies above the fourth ventricle, from the surface of which it is separated by a layer of small cells that probably are granules. Medially the nucleus lateralis is continuous with the nucleus medialis (fig. 146A), as in Cistudo carolina (fig. 178).

In the smaller lizards the lateral cerebellar nucleus is more difficult to delimit because of its reduced size and greater diffusion and also because the eversion of the cerebellum has displaced the cerebellar nuclei ventralward. The larger lizards, however, show it as similar to the nucleus medialis and its relations are much like those in Chrysemys. In Varanus, according to Weston, it resembles the nucleus lateralis of the alligator more than

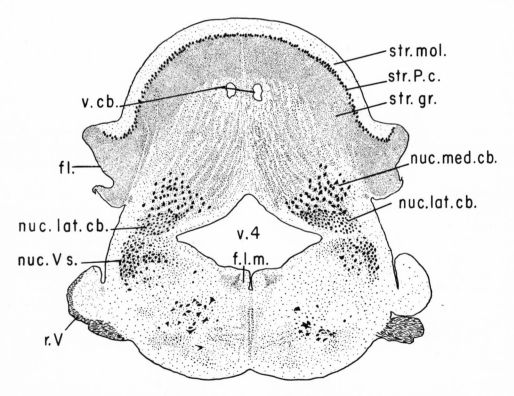

Figure 177. Transverse section through cerebellar nuclei of Alligator missisippiensis. Toluidine-blue stain. ×10. (Weston, 1936.)

that of turtles. The cells are mostly of medium size but many small cells are scattered throughout.

The nucleus lateralis of the crocodilians (fig. 177) is larger than in turtles but its relations are similar. As already noted, it extends farther rostralward than the medial nucleus. Weston regards as part of the lateral nucleus a cell mass which van Hoevell (1916) designated nucleus vestibularis anterior in Caiman sclerops.

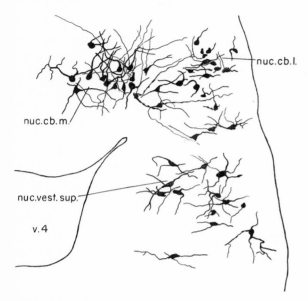

Figure 178. Cerebellar and vestibular nuclei of Cistudo carolina. Combined drawing from two adjacent sections in horizontal series. Golgi method. ×48. (Larsell, 1932b.)

The nucleus lateralis in reptiles must not be confused with the nucleus lateralis of Weidenreich (1899), Brunner (1919), and Demole (1927), who applied the term to the nuclear mass of subprimates and monkeys which enlarges into the nucleus dentatus of the higher primates. In order to avoid confusion the nucleus lateralis of the above-cited authors in mammals will be called the nucleus lateralis (dentatus).

Van Hoevell (1916), Ariens Kappers (1921), and Ariens Kappers, Huber, and Crosby (1936) describe a small mass of rather scattered cells situated above the fourth ventricle and ventral of the nucleus medialis, and extending toward the midbrain in the anterior medullary velum. It is called the nucleus of the brachium conjunctivum, but its fiber connections are not known.

On the ground of their relative positions and their fiber tract connections it appears permissible to regard the nucleus medialis as homologous with the fastigial nucleus of mammals, and the nucleus lateralis as corresponding to a portion, at least, of the nucleus intermedius or interpositus. The nucleus lateralis of reptiles, which

sends its axons rostralward almost exclusively, gives rise to the greater part of the cerebello-mesencephalic tegmental tract or brachium conjunctivum. Some neurons situated between the main masses of the lateral and the medial nuclei give off ventrally and ventrolaterally directed axons. These cells may be considered as having less specific connections than those of the lateral nucleus proper. The greater differentiation of connections of the deep cerebellar nuclei, carrying with it greater specificity of function, has advanced considerably among the reptiles as compared with amphibians.

THE FIBER CONNECTIONS

The afferent tracts. Ascending root fibers of the VIII nerve to the cerebellum were described by Beccari (1912) in the lizard, by Ingvar (1918) in the alligator, and by myself (1926, 1932b) and Weston (1936) in turtles, lizards, snakes, and crocodilians. As in Amphibia and Ichthyopsida these are branches of bifurcated root fibers. In lizards and snakes a small fascicle of root fibers, accompanied by secondary vestibular fibers, passes to the lateral angle between the medulla oblongata and cerebellum and turns dorsolaterally into the reduced flocculus (fig. 161). Golgi preparations of the turtle show vestibular root fibers passing around and beneath the recessus lateralis of the fourth ventricle to the flocculus, accompanied by secondary fibers. Though the majority of root fibers appear to terminate in the flocculus, others pass dorsolateral of the nucleus vestibularis superior, probably sending collaterals into this nucleus, and continue into the fiber mass behind and distinct from the commissura cerebelli proper. Root fibers, accompanied by secondary fibers, pass beneath the floor of the lateral recess in crocodilians, distributing to the flocculus. Others pass through the rudimentary inferior cerebellar peduncle of Crocodilia into the more posterior fiber mass in the base of the cerebellum (fig. 173).

According to Kawakami (1954), the vestibulo-cerebellar connections are grouped into two fascicles in some species of reptiles and into three in others. The entire tract is smaller in snakes, relatively, than in turtles, lizards, or crocodilians.

The secondary vestibulo-cerebellar fibers first gather into small fascicles from their cells of origin and become more compactly arranged as they ascend toward the cerebellum. In lizards and snakes a small fascicle passes to the reduced flocculus and a larger fascicle arches around the lateral angle of the fourth ventricle, turning dorsomedially into the cerebellum (fig. 179). The numerous small fascicles in turtles continue into the attachment of the posterior lateral part of the cerebellum to the medulla oblongata. In crocodilians they continue into the primitive inferior peduncle, where they are intermingled with other fibers. On entering the cerebellum they lose their fasciculated arrangement.

The vestibular fibers distribute in the granular layer of the small flocculus and of the thin marginal zone of the remainder of the cerebellum of lizards and snakes. The marginal fibers may include VIII root fibers but this is conjectural. A small compact fascicle is gathered together beneath the dorsal margin of the cerebellum and, as above noted, crosses the midline in Sceloporus, apparently corresponding to the vestibular commissure of the

fascicle turns dorsomedially from the vestibular nuclear gray and enters the large fiber mass in the anterior base of the cerebellum, in which it becomes lost. Weston, in Chrysemys, labels a corresponding fascicle the tractus cerebellomotorius bulbi, but in the box turtle it appears to include ascending fibers, corresponding to the dorsomedial vestibulo-cerebellar fascicle of lizards and snakes. Numerous fascicles of vestibulo-cerebellar fibers ascend through the primitive inferior peduncle of the alligator and cayman. These distribute chiefly in the ventral and lateral parts of the posterior lobe. Vestibular fi-

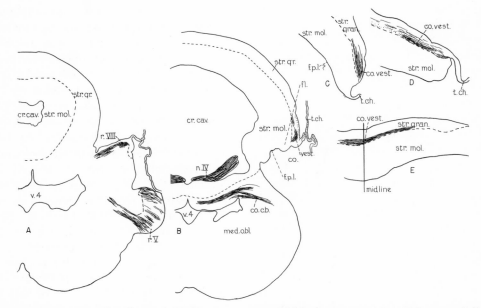

Figure 179. Five transverse sections of cerebellar region of Varanus, A to E in rostral direction, showing trigeminal and vestibular fibers, respectively, to cerebellar and vestibular commissures. Golgi method.

frog. A similar small, compact fascicle follows the cerebellar margin, in Heloderma and Varanus, from the base of the flocculus to the forward-tilted tip of the cerebellum, crossing the midline (figs. 170, 179). More diffuse fibers accompany it along the cerebellar margins. A small fascicle, already mentioned, in embryos of Thamnophis, appears to correspond, but in adult snakes, including Thamnophis, Boa, and Tropidonotus, no compact fascicle was observed.

In the turtles the vestibulo-cerebellar fibers distribute in the granular layer of the lateral and posterior parts of the organ (figs. 152, 153), in addition to the flocculus, but no decussating fascicle was observed. Individual fibers or small groups of fibers, however, cross the midline of the caudal part of the cerebellum. The lateral and caudal distribution of the vestibular fibers in the turtle was also described by Weston (1936). In Terrapene a

bers also pass close to the nucleus medialis of the cerebellum and some may enter it, as Weston (1936) believed. So many fibers, originating in the cerebellar nuclei and probably also from Purkinje cells, descend in company with the ascending vestibular fascicles that terminal fibers of the latter to the nuclei are uncertain. The lateral and caudal spread of the vestibular fibers was also noted in the crocodile by Ingvar (1918) and by Weston in reptiles generally. Some of the fibers pass into the large mass of fibers, behind and above the cerebellar commissure proper, which includes dorsal spino-cerebellar and other afferents. Vestibular fibers may decussate in this mass and some may possibly extend to the ventral part of the anterior lobe, as found in mammals, but vestibular fibers to the anterior part of the cerebellum have not been described in crocodilians or other reptiles.

A rather diffuse fascicle becomes separated from the

principal mass of vestibular fibers as they turn caudalward into the posterior lobe and follows the margin of this lobe as it turns medially beneath the dorsocaudally projecting part. As this fascicle approaches the midline some of its fibers gather into a more compact fascicle, which crosses the median sagittal plane in the cayman; in pyridine-silver preparations of the alligator only individual fibers were seen to cross. The course of the marginal fascicle, parallel with the tenial margin, corresponds to that of the fibers leading to the vestibular commissure of other species, but decussating fibers are relatively few in crocodilians.

Regarding the nuclei of origin of the secondary vestibular fibers there is little agreement in the literature. Many authors, including myself (1926), have described these fibers as arising chiefly in the superior vestibular nucleus. In Thamnophis I described some as derived from the lateral nucleus. According to Weston (1936) the ventrolateral (Deiters's) and dorsolateral vestibular nuclei give rise to the vestibulo-cerebellar fibers. Ariens Kappers, Huber, and Crosby (1936) and Ariens Kappers (1947) limit the origin of the vestibular fibers proper to the ventrolateral nucleus. None of these nuclei, however, corresponds either to the nucleus medialis or to the nucleus inferior (descendens) of mammals, from which Voris and Hoerr (1932) in the opossum, and Brodal and Pompeiano (1957) in the cat, derived the vestibulo-cerebellar fibers, the last-named authors employing experimental methods. My own more recent observations on reptiles are inconclusive except with reference to the cochlear component of the complex. Favorable Golgi preparations or experimental methods are needed to clarify the problem in reptiles. Possible crossed fibers from the nucleus vestibularis inferior and nucleus tangentialis are mentioned by Weston, but are considered insignificant if present.

The secondary vestibular tract is joined by fibers from the nucleus laminaris, as noted by de Lange (1917) in the alligator, by Shanklin (1930) in the chameleon, by myself in turtle and alligator (1932b), and confirmed by Weston (1936) in various reptiles. Fibers that arise in the laminar nucleus are included by Huber and Crosby (1926), Ariens Kappers, Huber, and Crosby (1936), and Ariens Kappers (1947) in a tractus cochleo-vestibulo-cerebellaris (fig. 158). Shanklin calls the fascicle the tractus lamino-cerebellaris. As already mentioned, Beccari (1912) describes direct cochlear fibers to the cerebellum of the lizard, and Weston (1936) found direct cochlear fibers ending at the junction of the base of the cerebellum with the medulla oblongata in a very young turtle. In adult Chrysemys and Terrapene a continuation of the molecular layer of the cerebellum extends a short distance onto the surface of the rhombic lip, as pointed out in my 1932 contribution. It appears possible that this transition zone represents a cochlear part of the reptilian cerebellum, but the evidence is only suggestive. According to Weston (1936) primary and secondary fibers of the cochleo-vestibulo-cerebellar tract accompany the vestibular fibers to the floccular lobe of my earlier terminology. I have been unable to differentiate distributing cochlear fibers from those arising in the vestibular nuclei, although the initial tract is distinct.

As already noted, the laminar nucleus varies greatly in different groups of reptiles, as apparently the sense of hearing also does. Both in birds, however, which have a laminar nucleus, and in mammals, which have not, the only pathway for auditory impulses to the cerebellum so far established is the tecto-cerebellar tract.

The spino-cerebellar connections of reptiles have been described by many authors, most of whom recognize dorsal and ventral tracts. The ventral spino-cerebellar tract was described in turtles by myself (1932b), Weston (1936), and Kawakami (1954). It is situated immediately beneath the lateral surface of the medulla oblongata, ventral of the spinal V tract (figs. 152, 153). Rostrally it passes through the fascicles of the sensory V root and arches dorsally and medially into the base of the cerebellum, immediately behind the attachment of the anterior medullary velum. It decussates extensively, together with root fibers of the V nerve, forming the anterior cerebellar commissure or commissura cerebelli (figs. 154, 155). Fibers from the commissural mass distribute to the granular layer of the cerebellum. In its course through the medulla oblongata the tract is closely related to the spino-tectal tract. In this respect as well as in its relations to the sensory V roots, as it turns toward the cerebellum, and to the anterior medullary velum and the cerebellar commissure, it corresponds to the spino-cerebellar tract of Anura in which only one tract passes from the cord to the cerebellum. As will appear, similar relations also hold true in other reptiles and for the ventral spino-cerebellar tract of birds and mammals. This tract, accordingly, is, phylogenically, the older of the two spino-cerebellar tracts.

The ventral spino-cerebellar tract of lizards and snakes is similar to that of turtles in course and relations (figs. 158, 165). It is relatively large in lizards and its decussation in the base of the cerebellum forms the greater part of a rather large cerebellar commissure. In Anniella the ventral tract appears to be the principal afferent connection of the cerebellum. It is large also in snakes, in which Weston (1936) indicates both dorsal and ventral spinocerebellar tracts but Kawakami (1954) found only one tract, corresponding to the ventral. We shall return to the ventral spino-cerebellar tract as represented in Crocodilia after consideration of the dorsal tract.

The dorsal spino-cerebellar tract is mentioned by Ariens Kappers (1921) and is described by myself (1926, 1932b), Shanklin (1930), Weston (1936), and Kawakami (1954) in various reptiles. In turtles the tract begins to separate from the ascending spino-cerebellar system by a lateral deflection of some of the more dorsally situated fibers, commencing a little rostral of the entering X roots. The fibers pass around the descending V root, and assume a position dorsal of this root (fig. 153), increasing in number rostralward and accompanied by bulbo-cerebellar fibers (Weston). Immediately caudal of the level of entrance of the V root they turn dorsalward into the cerebellum, which they enter more laterally than the ventral tract. The fibers distribute to the granular layer of the lateral part of the cerebellum chiefly, but do not reach the lateral and caudal marginal zones. It is possible that both ventral and more specifically dorsal tract fibers are intermingled in this posteriorly entering fascicle, as in crocodilians, described below, but in turtles only bulbo-cerebellar fibers have been recognized as accompanying it.

In the lizard, according to Banchi (1903), the dorsal tract has an origin in the spinal cord resembling that in mammals, in which the fibers arise from cells of the dorsal column of Clarke. It is so intermingled with bulbo-cerebellar fibers in lizards and snakes that a spinal component of the complex is uncertain in Thamnophis, at least, in which I have studied the spino-cerebellar connections most intensively in snakes. Weston indicates a dorsal as well as a ventral spino-cerebellar tract in Natrix as well as in lizards. The dorsal tract in most Lacertilia blends with the ventral tract in the posterior part of the medulla oblongata, but can be followed rostralward, among the bulbo-cerebellar fibers, to its entrance into the cerebellum. This entrance is posterior and lateral to that of the ventral spino-cerebellar tract and the fibers distribute chiefly to the granular layer of the lateral part of the cerebellum, as also illustrated by Weston in Phrynosoma. A dorsal spino-cerebellar or bulbo-cerebellar tract was described in Anniella in my 1926 contribution, with the statement that its identity is lost in the caudal part of the medulla oblongata. It now appears probable that no spinal fibers are included in the complex and that this is formed entirely of fibers originating in the bulb. A Cajal series of Gerrhonotus makes the dorsal tract fibers fairly certain in this species.

In the alligator Huber and Crosby (1926) included all the fibers from cord to cerebellum under the term spino-cerebellar tract, noting that a relatively small number of fibers associated with the spino-mesencephalic

fascicle suggests a ventral spino-cerebellar tract. These enter the anterior base of the cerebellum. It is not clear whether the fibers arising in the cervical part of the cord of Crocodilia, and perhaps other reptiles, should be included in the dorsal or the ventral spino-cerebellar tract. In Crocodilia the cervical fibers assume a position ventral of the principal part of the dorsal tract. In the rhesus monkey Yoss (1952) found that the ventral tract is augmented in the cervical cord and he inclined to the belief that dorsal tract fibers do not arise above the thoracic segments. Recently Marion Smith (1961) has shown that, in man, the great majority of spino-cerebellar fibers, including those of the ventral tract, enter the cerebellum through the inferior peduncle. This is in accord with the observations of Huber and Crosby in the alligator and suggests that a considerable proportion of the fibers in the primitive inferior cerebellar peduncle of Crocodilia are ventral rather than dorsal tract fibers. The phylogenic gap between crocodilia and primates, however, is so great that this suggestion must be tested by experimental or other methods.

The ventral spino-cerebellar fascicle which accompanies the spino-mesencephalic fibers in Crocodilia turns dorsomedially and forms most of the cerebellar commissure in the base of the anterior lobe (figs. 170, 173). The dorsal tract and the apparently accompanying ventral spino-cerebellar fibers, and also other fibers described below, continue forward and join the anterior fiber mass which extends dorsalward from the commissure. The combined mass, in which no distinction can be made between dorsal and ventral tract fibers, distributes chiefly to the granular layer of the anterior and medial lobes, but a posteriorly directed branch of the principal fiber mass, on either side of the cerebellar ventricle, extends into the posterior lobe. Fibers from this branch also extend into the posterior part of the medial lobe and some fibers perhaps reach the incipient paraflocculus; the latter probably correspond to spino-cerebellar fibers that Kawakami (1954) describes as reaching the "flocculus" in Crocodilia. Spinal origin of fibers to the incipient paraflocculus, however, is uncertain.

Considering the anterior, medial, and posterior lobes of Crocodilia as the phylogenetic antecedents of folia or lobules I–V, VI–VIII, and IX and X, respectively, of birds and mammals, the distribution of the spino-cerebellar tracts corresponds, in general, to the pattern found by Ingvar (1918) and Whitlock (1952) in the pigeon, by Beck (1927) in the cat, and by Anderson (1943) in the rat. Ingvar did not subdivide the spino-cerebellar system into dorsal and ventral tracts in the pigeon, although Friedländer (1898) had done so, and Whitlock confirmed such a subdivision. All these authors employed the Marchi method. Both Ingvar and Whitlock found degeneration of spino-cerebellar fibers in the pigeon extending chiefly into the anterior lobe (folia II–V) and the rostral part of the medial lobe (subfolia VIa and VIb). Whitlock found none to VIc or to folium VII, but some to folium VIII, the pyramis, and a considerable distribution to the subdivisions of folium IX, the uvula. Although dorsal and ventral tracts are recognizable in the cord and medulla oblongata, no difference in their cerebellar distribution was observed. In the rat Anderson (1943) observed degenerated ventral tract fibers in lobule VI and more in lobule VIII, in addition to those in the anterior lobe (lobules I–V), but none elsewhere. Degenerated dorsal tract fibers were found in all parts of the anterior lobe, in lobules VI and VIII, and some in lobule IX and the lobulus paramedianus (HVIIB + HVIIIA). According to Anderson the ventral tract fibers occur in greatest number near the midline, whereas the dorsal tract fibers are distributed on either side of the median zone. In crocodilians and other reptiles the topographically dorsal tract enters the cerebellum somewhat lateral as well as caudal of the entrance of the ventral tract, but in normal fiber preparations the distribution of the two tracts cannot be differentiated. The fibers appear to be intermingled, not only to the anterior part of the cerebellum but also to the posterior lobe of crocodilians.

According to Ariens Kappers, Huber, and Crosby (1936) some of the spino-cerebellar fibers in the alligator appear to end in the "roof nuclei" of the cerebellum, and Weston (1936) notes that in Chrysemys marginata some of the fibers come into close relations with the cerebellar nuclei. In Golgi preparations of turtle cerebella, however, I have found no evidence of termination of spinocerebellar fibers in either of the cerebellar nuclei. Studies by the Marchi method in birds (Whitlock, 1952) and in mammals (Anderson, 1943, and others) likewise failed to show spino-cerebellar fibers ending in the cerebellar nuclei.

Trigemino-cerebellar fibers, both direct and secondary, have been demonstrated in various reptiles. Direct fibers were described by Banchi in lizard embryos. According to de Lange (1917) root fibers of the V nerve to the cerebellum appear to be present in the crocodile, as Ingvar (1918) confirmed. Huber and Crosby (1926) found direct fibers accompanying crossed and uncrossed secondary trigemino-cerebellar fascicles. In Golgi series of turtle cerebella I found direct V root fibers to the base of the cerebellum (1932b) and in a 7 mm embryo of Chrysemys marginata, prepared by the Cajal method, ascending fibers clearly continued directly into the cerebellar commissure, some crossing the midline. Direct V root fibers enter the cerebellum in considerable number in the

snake, although in my earlier (1926) study I failed to identify them. Weston (1936) found V root fibers to the cerebellum in Chrysemys, Phrynosoma, snake and, in relatively smaller number, in the alligator.

Secondary trigemino-cerebellar fibers were found in Cajal preparations of the alligator brain by Huber and Crosby (1926). Uncrossed fibers, forming a "dorsal trigemino-cerebellar tract," pass dorsomedially from cells in the chief sensory V nucleus to the cerebellum. Crossed or ventral trigemino-cerebellar fibers pass beneath the ventricular floor, according to these authors, to the opposite side of the cerebellum. Fibers arising from the spinal V nucleus, at various levels, are said to contribute to the dorsal spino-cerebellar tract. Fibers from the spinal V nucleus, already mentioned as the ventral trigemino-cerebellar tract of Huber and Crosby (1926), apparently relay not only impulses from the descending or spinal V tract, but also impulses from somatic sensory fibers of the IX and X nerve roots which Huber and Crosby followed into the spinal V tract of the alligator.

Weston (1936) confirmed the various secondary connections. In the chameleon Shanklin (1930) describes a small fascicle from the chief sensory V nucleus to the granular layer of the cerebellum, and Woodburne (1936) observed fibers in Anolis that he interpreted as crossed and uncrossed trigemino-cerebellar connections. Turtle embryos, in which other cerebellar fibers are less profuse, show the secondary fibers from the superior V nucleus more clearly (fig. 151). They form an intertrigeminal component of the commissura cerebelli, as in amphibians. Golgi series of adult turtle brains show many cells in the superior V nucleus whose dendrites extend ventrolaterally, as in amphibians, and whose axons enter the cerebellar commissure.

The trigemino-cerebellar tract is relatively large in snakes, according to Juh Shen Shyu (1939), as I have confirmed (fig. 165). Kawakami (1954) found the tract in snakes, lizards, turtles, and crocodilians, describing it as joining the ventral spino-cerebellar tract in the commissura cerebelli. Protargol preparations of Caiman sclerops show both V root and secondary V fibers entering the cerebellar commissure, in which some cross. It is difficult to distinguish trigeminal fibers from those of the spino-cerebellar tracts as they distribute in the cerebellar cortex. The trigeminal fibers, however, appear to end in the medial lobe in Caiman. Whitlock (1952) found the trigemino-cerebellar tract distributed to folia VI and VII in Marchi preparations of the pigeon.

The mesencephalic V root passes through the region of the cerebellar base in reptiles, fibers extending from it into the cerebellum, as Weston (1936) noted. In embryos of turtle and alligator I found (1932b) numerous cells of mesencephalic V type as far caudally as the base of the cerebellum. The number of such cells within the cerebellum itself is small in reptiles, as in all other species in which such cells and related fibers have been described in the organ, and their functional significance is obscure.

The bulbo-cerebellar system of amphibians is represented in reptiles by fibers that can be followed into more specific nuclei of origin, as a rule. Weston (1936) calls it the nucleo-cerebellar system. In addition to fibers from the spinal V nucleus, already mentioned, it includes ventral superficial arcuate fibers, reticulo-cerebellar fibers, and, probably, olivo-cerebellar fibers from diffusely scattered olivary cells.

Banchi (1903) describes a ventral superficial arcuate system in the lizard. According to Weston such fibers have their origin in the nuclei of the posterior funiculus and from the reticular nuclei, arching ventrally and, after crossing the midline, continuing to the cerebellum with the dorsal spino-cerebellar tract. In view of more recent studies of various mammals, which have shown that the lateral cuneate nucleus is the source of fibers from the dorsal nuclear group to the cerebellum, it is possible that a more restricted localization prevails also in reptiles. Bulbo-cerebellar fibers, in snakes, possibly accompany a dorsal spino-cerebellar tract, but this tract is uncertain and may be entirely absent.

Many authors, including myself (1926, 1932b), have described an olivo-cerebellar tract in reptiles. According to Kooy (1917) the inferior olive is represented only by scattered cells in this class of vertebrates. Shanklin (1930), however, described an inferior olive and an olivo-cerebellar tract in Chameleon. A more or less well-defined group of cells, corresponding to the inferior olive in position, is described by Weston (1936), but, according to him, it may be a group of reticular cells. This group apparently corresponds to what I regarded as the inferior olive in my earlier contributions. Weston expresses uncertainty regarding an olivo-cerebellar tract and Tuge (1932) could not identify such a tract satisfactorily in Chrysemys. Kawakami (1954) also was uncertain of the existence of an olivo-cerebellar tract in reptiles.

According to Ariens Kappers (1947), in crocodilians an increase in the number of cells in the region corresponding to the inferior olive of birds gives some resemblance to this avian nucleus. A poorly developed crossed olivo-cerebellar tract is said to accompany the dorsal spino-cerebellar tract. Sections of Caiman, stained with toluidine blue, show an aggregation of cells which apparently corresponds to the lateral part of the olive in birds. In protargol series small, scattered fibers pass dorsomedially toward the midline and in a rostral direction, probably representing a diffuse olivo-cerebellar fascicle.

The tecto-cerebellar tract was first described in reptiles by Huber and Crosby (1926), who found it in Chrysemys marginata. Later in the same year I described it in Sceloporus and Gerrhonotus (1926) and subsequently (1932b) confirmed it in turtles. Shanklin (1930) described the tract in Chameleon, as comprising a crossed and an uncrossed component. These components were confirmed by Huber and Crosby (1933). Hindenach (1931) found the tecto-cerebellar tract in Sphenodon and Weston (1936) verified it in lizards, snakes, turtle, and alligator, describing crossed and uncrossed fibers. He regards the tract as especially well developed in reptiles because of the dominant role of the optic tectum. Juh Shen Shyu (1939) and Kawakami (1954) also describe the tract in various reptiles. Kashiwamura (1955) says it consists of a single fascicle in Gecko, Clemmys, and Euneces, but in Elaphe it includes dorsal and ventral fascicles, as in Anura.

According to my own observations in Caiman, which confirm those of Weston in the alligator, the tecto-cerebellar tract comprises both crossed and uncrossed fibers. The fibers emerge from the deep white layer of the tectum and, after passing beneath the decussation of the IV nerve, continue in the dorsal part of the anterior medullary velum to the cerebellum. Some enter the cerebellar commissure; others, Weston states, become lost in the region of the nucleus medialis, and still others pass into the granular layer. Coarser fibers from the deep white layer of the tectum follow a similar course. Small myelinated fibers from the deep white layer cross in the caudal part of the tectum and mingle in the anterior medullary velum with the uncrossed fibers, distributing with the latter. This description I have confirmed in Caiman and can only add that in this species, in which the medial lobe of Ingvar is well defined, fine fibers of the tecto-cerebellar tract appear to enter this lobe.

A superficial layer of fine fibers in the anterior medullary velum, followed into the superficial gray and white layers of the tectum by Huber and Crosby (1933) in Weigert preparations, was considered a cerebello-tectal tract by Weston, who verified it in silver material of the larger lizards, turtle, and alligator. I have observed these fibers in Caiman but can add nothing regarding their origin and termination, concerning both of which Weston was uncertain.

Owing apparently to a too general comparison of the afferent cerebellar tracts of amphibians and reptiles which I made in a brief paper (1934b), Ariens Kappers (1947) ascribes to me a lobo-cerebellar tract in reptiles. I have found such a tract only in Ichthyopsida. A strio-cerebellar tract is mentioned by Ariens Kappers (1947) but appears doubtful.

The efferent tracts. The efferent fibers of the reptilian cerebellum have been described under various names. A brachium conjunctivum, corresponding in general to the rostrally directed cerebellar efferent fibers of other vertebrates, was described by Ariens Kappers (1921) in the alligator; by myself (1926, 1932b) in lizards, snake, turtle, and alligator; and by Papez (1929), Shanklin (1930), Hindenach (1931), and Frederikse (1931) in various reptiles. Huber and Crosby (1926) and Kawakami (1954) described these fibers under the term tractus cerebello-tegmentalis mesencephali. Weston (1936) regards the cerebellar efferents, except those to the vestibular nuclei and a cerebello-tectal tract, already mentioned, as forming a continuous cerebello-tegmental fiber system. This he divides into a tractus cerebello-motorius et tegmentalis bulbi and a tractus cerebello-motorius et tegmentalis mesencephali. The latter includes fibers that connect the cerebellum, after decussating, with the primitive red nucleus of reptiles, thus corresponding to part of the brachium conjunctivum of birds and mammals. The remaining fibers of the mesencephalic and bulbar cerebello-tegmental tracts lead to the motor nuclei of the cranial nerves and the tegmental region, Weston states. The tract has its origin chiefly from the nucleus lateralis but is augmented by fibers from the nucleus medialis, those from the latter source passing more especially into the bulbar tegmentum. It also receives fibers from the base of the cerebellum which probably represent direct axons of Purkinje cells as in fishes and amphibians. Although many fibers decussate, including those to the primitive nucleus ruber, there is a large ipsilateral element. According to Kawakami (1954), a tractus cerebello-tegmentalis arises in the nucleus medialis cerebelli and runs ventromedially, decussating beneath the fasciculus longitudinalis medialis.

Cerebello-thalamic connections have not been observed in reptiles. Ariens Kappers (1947) remarks that this is not surprising since the cerebello-thalamic fibers of mammals arise in the nucleus lateralis (dentatus) and terminate in the ventrolateral thalamic nucleus which projects to the motor and premotor cerebral cortex.

A tractus cerebello-spinalis et cerebello-vestibularis, arising from both medial cerebellar nuclei, with additional fibers directly from Purkinje cells, is described by Weston. As it passes posteriorly through the vestibular region fascicles leave the tract, their fibers spreading in the vestibular gray, some extending farther ventrally into the reticular gray substance. The tract comes into especially close relation with the dorsal part of the ventrolateral vestibular nucleus, according to Weston, and appears to receive a small vestibulo-spinal addition from this nucleus. Although the tract could not be followed separately into the spinal cord, it appeared to reach the cord, an assumption which however needs experimental confirmation. Weston regards this tract as the reptilian representative of the uncinate fascicle of Russell in mammals. Other authors, as Ariens Kappers (1921) and Larsell (1932b), have included the fascicle in the cerebellomotor or cerebello-tegmental distribution of fibers. According to Weston it is most distinct in the turtles.

In Golgi series of both Chrysemys and Terrapene, which I have re-examined, the tract emerges from the commissural fiber mass as a fairly compact fascicle and passes caudalward close to the ventricle. More widely dispersed fibers from the medial cerebellar nucleus pass rostrally, medially, and caudally to the tegmentum and to the reticular formation of the bulb. The ascending fibers probably are the precursors of the "ascending limb of the uncinate fascicle" of Rasmussen (1933) in the cat.

In addition to the afferent and efferent tracts described, a fascicle situated near the median sagittal plane and directed anteroposteriorly in general dips beneath the fissura secunda and appears to interconnect the medial and posterior lobes of crocodilians. The fibers spread from both ends of the fascicle into the median zone of the granular layer of the medial and posterior lobes of Ingvar, respectively. No cells of origin of individual fibers could be identified in protargol series of Caiman, but the impression gained was that fibers arise in each lobe and distribute to the other. The aggregation of fibers appears to constitute an association fascicle, distinct from the spino-cerebellar and other fibers that distribute in the two lobes.

THE HISTOLOGY

Stieda (1875) first pointed out that the cerebellum of reptiles comprises the three typical layers — molecular, Purkinje cell, and granular — that characterize the organ in other vertebrates. The variation in position of the molecular and granular layers in the different types of cerebellum, and also the variations in their thickness, have already been described. The Purkinje cell layer, which typically is situated between the other two, is several cells thick in lizards and snakes and also as a rule in the smaller turtles (figs. 146, 150). In Chelonia midas there is but one layer of Purkinje cells (fig. 153). One to several layers occur in Crocodilia (fig. 177), a single layer being found most characteristically in the deep walls of the fissura secunda. Sections of the cerebellum of Gerrhonotus at certain levels show many layers of these cells, an appearance due to the curves of the cerebellar surface in the zone of transition from pars interposita to pars lateralis.

Neurons and fibers. The cerebellar neurons of lizards

were described by P. Ramon y Cajal (1894, 1896) and are summarized by S. Ramon y Cajal (1909–11). Valuable observations were added by Ochoterena (1932) on the cerebellar cells of Phrynosoma. The present description is based primarily on the turtle cerebellum, extensive Golgi material of which has been available.

The Purkinje cells vary in size and in complexity of dendritic branching in the different types of reptiles. According to S. Ramon y Cajal (1909–11) they are larger and their dendrites branch more freely in the chameleon than in amphibians, but they have fewer dendrites than in birds. Ochoterena (1932) describes the Purkinje cells of Phrynosoma as arranged in an irregular layer and having a relatively simple arborization. In Golgi series of the turtle cerebellum the most striking feature is the great number of Purkinje cells and their widespreading dendrites. In well-impregnated series these dendrites, among which cells of several other types, described below, are interspersed, form a jungle of branches in the molecular layer (fig. 180A).

The bodies of the Purkinje cells are flask-shaped, in general, but in Golgi preparations of turtles they may vary from this form. In Phrynosoma and Crocodilia they appear to be more uniformly flask-shaped. Nissl granules are distributed in the cytoplasm and, in toluidine blue preparations of Phrynosoma, according to Ochoterena, the nuclei of the cells show a single characteristic nucleolus and radially arranged chromatin granules. Cajal preparations show neurofibrils in the cell body and extending into the dendrites.

The dendritic branches of the cells arise from one or more primary dendrites in turtles. These ramify into horizontally and vertically directed branches of the second order which, in turn, may subdivide into additional vertical branches. All branches are studded with gemmules, but these are lacking on the primary dendrites (fig. 180). The greatest spread of the dendrites is anteriorly and posteriorly, the lateral spread being slight. In the molecular layer of the flocculus the dendritic spread is very wide from shortened primary dendrites.

Climbing fibers follow the dendrites and their branches (fig. 180B). Ochoterena describes climbing fibers in Cajal preparations of Phrynosoma as being characteristically related to the body and the dendrites of the Purkinje cells, and terminating as small varicosities or multiple rings. In protargol series of Caiman fine fibers accompanying the Purkinje cell dendrites appear to be climbing fibers, but the preparations were lacking in detail.

The axons of the Purkinje cells are directed more or less obliquely into the granular layer. Apparently they have but one recurrent collateral in turtles, and Ochoterena found only one in Phrynosoma.

The granule cells are small elements, 3 μ to 4 μ in diameter in Phrynosoma, according to Ochoterena. They are characterized by the typical chromatic structure of the nucleus and by three or four short dendrites that radiate from the cell. These dendrites end as tufts of short branches that are suggestive of the "claws" of mammalian granule cell dendrites but are less elongated (fig. 184A). The tufts come into synaptic relation with similar tufts on lateral branches of mossy fibers in the granular layer (fig. 184B). These fibers are numerous but have fewer tufted terminals than the mossy fibers of mammals. The axons of the granule cells are slender fibers that enter the molecular layer and divide in typical fashion to form parallel fibers (fig. 184A).

Cells, larger than the granules, are scattered through-

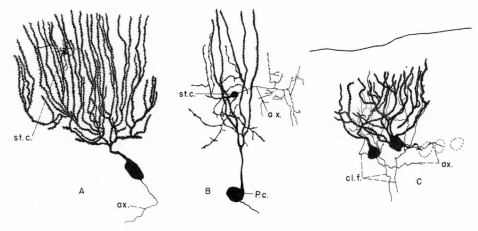

Figure 180. A. Purkinje cell from turtle. B. Purkinje cell and Golgi type II cell from turtle cerebellum. Golgi method. ×125. C. Purkinje cells and climbing fibers in Cistudo. Golgi method. × ca 150. (Larsell, 1932b.)

out the granular layer. Ramon y Cajal labels them star cells in Lacerta. Some may represent Golgi type II cells (fig. 181), but I have not found any in turtles with the characteristic axons of such cells.

The molecular or plexiform layer includes great numbers of fine horizontal or parallel fibers. These extend laterally, in either direction, from their points of origin as branches of granule cell axons, and end by branching into small twigs with terminal boutons. In Phrynosoma, according to Ochoterena, parallel fibers give rise to a few fine collaterals that terminate in one or two varicosities which, evidently, are terminal boutons.

Several types of star cells are present in the molecular layer (fig. 181). Some have both dendrites and axons which are confined entirely to the molecular layer. The dendrites are long and slender, spreading widely in all directions, whereas the axons are short and end as a tuft of branches. Such cells characteristically are found among the Purkinje cell dendrites, as shown in figure 180B. Several subvarieties are recognizable (fig. 181). One of these has dendritic processes of limited extent which spread toward the cerebellar surface. Such cells are found at various levels of the molecular layer. Another subvariety

has primary dendrites of great lateral spread, with secondary branches arising at nearly right angles from the primary dendrites and extending toward the cerebellar surface (fig. 181B). The axons of neither subvariety can be followed far; they are of small diameter and ramify within the molecular layer, frequently very close to the layer of Purkinje cells. Many of these axons and their collaterals come into relation with the dendrites of the Purkinje cells.

A second type of cell in the molecular layer, differing from the star cells just described and less numerous than them, is illustrated in figure 181C. Cells of this type lie near the external surface of the molecular layer, their major axes being parallel with the surface. The dendrites do not spread widely but extend, in general, nearly parallel with the major axis of the neuron. The axon is short, with only a few short collateral branches. These cells correspond, in general, to the superficial stellate cells of Ramon y Cajal in mammals.

A third subvariety in the molecular layer must be regarded as a primitive basket cell (fig. 182B). Some of these neurons lie a considerable distance from the layer of Purkinje cells but their axons extend toward this layer

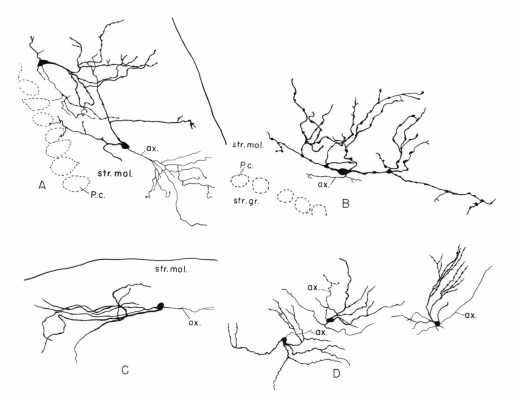

Figure 181. Turtle cerebellum. A. Golgi type II cells in molecular layer. ×325. B. Modified Golgi type II cell, with wide spreading dendrites and short axon in molecular layer. ×155. C. Stellate cell in molecular layer. ×155. D. Stellate cells in molecular layer. Golgi method.

and branch into short twigs that end by terminal boutons on the bodies of the Purkinje cells. In no case have I observed branches from any one basket cell reaching more than two or three Purkinje cells. The dendrites extend toward the cerebellar surface, between the dendrites of Purkinje cells. In the chameleon, as illustrated by Ramon y Cajal (1909–11) from Golgi preparations, the basket cells give rise to two groups of dendrites, one group radiating outward into the molecular layer, and the other directed toward the Purkinje cells and apparently ending in relation to them by short terminal branches (fig. 183). A slender axon of tortuous course branches into collaterals that form pericellular arborizations about the Purkinje

cell bodies. Ochoterena's illustrations of basket cells in Golgi and Cajal preparations of Phrynosoma also represent the terminations about the Purkinje cells as end process of fibers that have the appearance of dendritic branches of the cells. Some terminations may be end processes of more slender fibers that have a greater resemblance to axons, but neither type is labeled. Further investigation is needed to clarify the apparent differences between some of the dendrites of the primitive basket cells of lizards as compared with those of turtles and mammals. The cell body and dendrites of the basket cells of turtles are very similar to those of the star cells above described; the cells differ chiefly by virtue of the fact that

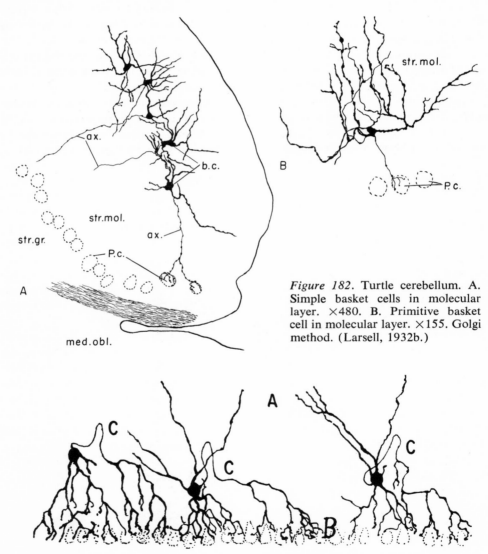

Figure 182. Turtle cerebellum. A. Simple basket cells in molecular layer. ×480. B. Primitive basket cell in molecular layer. ×155. Golgi method. (Larsell, 1932b.)

Figure 183. Anteroposterior section of cerebellum of Chameleo vulgaris, showing basket cells. A. Molecular layer. B. Layer of Purkinje cells. C. Axons broken up into free branches having for the most part contact with Purkinje cells. Golgi method. (Ramon y Cajal, 1909–1911.)

212

their axons end on the Purkinje cells instead of branching and terminating within the molecular layer.

The thin-walled flocculus and caudally continuing marginal zone of the turtle include cells whose dendrites spread rostrocaudally at right angles to the parallel fibers. The cells are similar to star cells elsewhere whose dendrites spread in all directions.

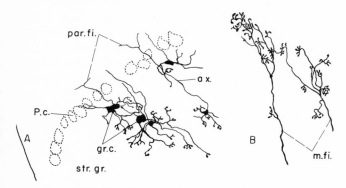

Figure 184. Cerebellum of Cistudo. A. Granule cells. B. Mossy fibers. Golgi method. ×270.

The neuroglia of the cerebellum of Lacerta stirpium was described by Ramon y Cajal (1909–11) from Golgi preparations and Ochoterena studied it in Phrynosoma by the method of Rio-Hortega. According to Ochoterena the neuroglia is localized exclusively in the granular layer of the simple lacertian type of cerebellum; no elements enter the molecular layer except some prolongations of the cells of Bergmann. The feet of these processes are located in the external part of the granular layer and the bodies much resemble the Müller cells of the retina.

Comparison of the Types of Reptilian Cerebellum

Returning to the morphological features of the cerebellum, the differing patterns of the organ in turtles, lizards, and crocodilians undoubtedly reflect the divergent phylogenic ancestry of these groups. The cerebellum of the turtles is the most primitive among reptiles. The Cotylosauria, from which the turtles branched very early, were archaic and in most respects were no more advanced than their amphibian ancestors and relatives (Romer, 1945). According to Romer they were clumsy and their limbs sprawled sideways from the body; the turtles are similar in gait, except several marine species which have paddle-like limbs.

Although the features of the cerebellum of Cotylosauria are unknown, the corpus cerebelli was presumably massive as in Anura and in turtles, and the vestibular part of the organ was probably reduced. The anurans are far removed from the amphibian ancestors of the reptiles and also have a specialized mode of propulsion but comparison of the cerebellum of Rana with that of the small box turtle, Terrapene carolina, is illuminating. In both species the corpus cerebelli is a broad plate, similar in general form and fiber tract connections. In Terrapene, however, the plate is inclined caudalward to such a degree that it forms an arch above the fourth ventricle and its granular layer faces ventralward, instead of caudally, while the molecular layer is dorsal instead of anterior. The flocculus is reduced in both species; in the box turtle it lies in the angle between the medulla oblongata and the caudally inclined corpus cerebelli, instead of forming an ear-like projection. Other species of turtles show various modifications of the Terrapene cerebellum, the most pronounced being represented in Trionyx and Chelonia. A definite testudinate pattern, however, is recognizable in all.

The Rhynchocephalia and Squamata differentiated from a common stem which branched from the reptilian stock at a much later period than the turtles. The typically everted pattern of the lacertilian cerebellum is shared by Sphenodon, although this species is a rhynchocephalian. Whereas snakes and lizards represent suborders of the Squamata, the ophidian cerebellum has a very different pattern than the lacertilian type (cp. figs. 156, 164).

The body form and extremities of most lizards and of Sphenodon are similar, in general, whereas the elongated body of the legless snakes differs greatly from both. The modifications, seen in Gerrhonotus and Anniella, from the typical lacertilian toward the ophidian type of cerebellum appear to be correlated with the different methods of propulsion in these lizards, as compared with the species in which the legs play an important role.

The Crocodilia, as already noted, represent an aberrant branch of the Archosaur stock, another branch of which evolved into birds. The crocodilian cerebellum differs from that of all other reptiles in being divided by transverse fissures into three lobes (fig. 174). Among other reptiles a transverse furrow, the sulcus anterior of Ingvar, has been described only in Chelonia midas, although a suggestion of this furrow is also shown in Ingvar's figure of the cerebellum of Chelonia imbricata. As already noted, the sulcus anterior appears to correspond to the fissura prima of Crocodilia and to delimit the anterior lobe from the undivided remainder of the cerebellum. The three lobes of the crocodilians correspond, in a more primitive stage of development and differentiation, to the similarly delimited subdivisions of the corpus cerebelli of birds.

The vestibular marginal zone of the posterior lobe of crocodilians, however, has differentiated in birds into the nodulus and its continuations with the flocculus on either side. The flocculonodular lobe, so formed on the base of the vestibular cerebellar margin, is a hypertrophy of this margin due to the resurgent importance of the vestibular part of the cerebellum in birds. Vestibular fibers also distribute to the caudal part of the uvula of birds, as of mammals, as they do to the inferior part of the posterior lobe in crocodilians. The pattern of transverse lobes, shared by Crocodilia and birds, presumably reflects the Archosaur ancestry which these two groups of vertebrates have in common.

The modifications of the ordinal types of cerebellum evidently reflect the influence of other factors than phylogenic relationships. One of these is the form of the skull and the cranial cavity, a subject which must here be set aside; another, already mentioned, appears to be the method of propulsion and the relative significance of the trunk and limbs, respectively, in locomotion and other movements.

Propulsion in turtles, both in walking and in swimming, is accomplished entirely by action of the extremities, the atrophied trunk musculature in the rigid shell playing no part. The sprawling legs also raise the body from the ground. Proprioceptive and exteroceptive impulses from the extremities undoubtedly are transmitted to the pars lateralis of the cerebellum in much larger numbers than are similar impulses to the pars interposita from the trunk, head, neck, and tail. In keeping with the tenets of comparative neurology such quantitative differences would account for the greater thickness and, therefore, volume of the pars lateralis in comparison with the pars interposita. The increase of the pars interposita in Trionyx, represented by the "pendulum" of Fuse, is perhaps correlated with the relatively rich cutaneous innervation of the carapace and plastron described by Liu and Maneely (1962).

The gliding progression of snakes, on the other hand, is accomplished by action of the trunk musculature alone. Proprioceptive and exteroceptive impulses to the cerebellum have their origin in the trunk and head only, since extremities are lacking. The contrast between the reduced pars interposita of turtles and the prominence of this zone in snakes already has been noted, as has the contrast between the well-developed pars lateralis of turtles and the reduction of this zone in snakes (cp. figs. 146, 165).

Gerrhonotus, the alligator lizard, which combines features of the ophidian cerebellum with others that are more typically lacertilian, walks on weak legs but is aided in forward propulsion by snake-like movements of the trunk and tail which involve proprioceptors in the trunk musculature as well as exteroceptors in the skin. The pars interposita, as above described, is enlarged and elongated caudalward, and the pars lateralis is reduced. The trunk musculature alone must account for propulsion in the legless burrowing lizard Anniella nigra; in this species the pars interposita is the predominant feature of the cerebellum.

The lizards that have a fully everted and rostrally tilted cerebellum show significant differences, from species to species, in locomotor habits. Heloderma, which has a heavy and stout body, relatively short but stout legs and short tail, walks slowly and clumsily but is capable of swift thrusts; this lizard is also said to be a powerful digger and can climb. Phrynosoma has a stout and heavy body and relatively short tail. When walking, the legs raise the body from the ground and the creature is capable of very rapid movements, darting away like a mouse when frightened. It is difficult to judge the respective roles of the trunk and limb musculatures of these two species, but both trunk and extremities appear to be involved in propulsion. The granular layer is thickened ventromedially and, in Phrynosoma, also projects somewhat beyond the posterior surface of the everted part of the corpus cerebelli but much less prominently than the pars interposita of Gerrhonotus. The granular layer of the pars lateralis of Heloderma and Phrynosoma does not differ greatly from the pars interposita in the everted cerebellum of these species.

Sceloporus and many other species of lizards dart rapidly on strong legs, the tail raised from the ground but its tip probably serving as a rudder. The monitor lizards can progress rapidly on land and all except the desert species Varanus griseus, are excellent swimmers (Ditmars, 1944). The varanids, some of which attain a length of ten to twelve feet, use the tail for propulsion in the water, the limbs being folded against the body (Ditmars). On land the strong limbs raise the body well above the ground. Yet the cerebellum of this lizard family is strongly everted, as in most other lacertilians, instead of massive and folded as in Crocodilia.

Owing to the dorsorostral as well as side-to-side curvatures of the strongly everted cerebellum of varanids and other lizards that use both trunk and strong legs in locomotion, the pars interposita blends into the pars lateralis, on both sides, and there appears to be little difference in the thickness of the granular layer. Both the granular and molecular layers, however, are reduced in the marginal zone.

The walking movements of Crocodilia are slow and clumsy, but the body is said to be carried high off the ground, only the tip of the tail dragging. Crocodilians can lunge forward very rapidly, however, and the tail is used as a powerful weapon of defense. Swimming is accomplished by undulating movements of the trunk and tail.

In Crocodilia, as already noted, the granular layer of

the pars interposita is considerably more massive than that of the pars lateralis. The "pendulum" of Fuse, sometimes encountered in crocodilians according to Fuse (1920) as well as Kawakami (1954), but which I have not observed, also appears to be another manifestation of increase of the granular layer of the pars interposita. In turtles, snakes, and most lizards the two zones are most distinct in the anterior part of the cerebellum, their caudal extent being indeterminate. In Crocodilia, however, they are recognizable also in the posterior lobe except the dorsocaudal tip.

The morphological evidence of a pars lateralis and pars interposita in crocodilians is substantiated by the electrophysiological studies of Goodman and Simpson (1960) on Caiman sclerops. Light is also thrown on the physiological significance of these zones by the results obtained.

Using unanesthetized and unrestrained young animals with electrodes implanted in the cerebellum and optic tectum at various loci, these authors observed that electrical stimulation of the medial two thirds of the medial lobe and the medial half of the posterior lobe evoked a "medial-area pattern" of response. This consisted of "ipsilateral forelimb flexion, adduction and protraction; ipsilateral hindlimb flexion, adduction and retraction; contralateral forelimb extension, abduction and occasional retraction; and contralateral hindlimb extension, abduction and occasional protraction." The body and tail became concave toward the side stimulated and the head turned ipsilaterally. Stimulation of the lateral part of the anterior lobe, the lateral third of the medial lobe, the lateral and caudal portions of the posterior lobe and the flocculus-paraflocculus region evoked the "lateral-area pattern," which was a mirror image of the first. The lateral zone of the corpus cerebelli from which the "lateral-area postural pattern" was evoked is said to conform rather closely to the pars lateralis as I had defined it on morphological grounds in the alligator. The medial area of the anterior lobe, which is largely hidden on the anterior cerebellar surface, was not included in the descriptions of Goodman and Simpson.

Both postural patterns could be evoked from the same electrode placement in certain parts of the cerebellum. At some loci the lateral pattern was first elicited by a weak stimulus but as the strength of the current was increased by small increments the response was reversed after two to four seconds of continued stimulation. At other loci stimulation first evoked the medial area pattern, followed by the lateral area pattern in the same manner.

Part of the zone from which the lateral-area pattern could be evoked is, according to Goodman and Simpson, localized in the flocculus and caudolateral region of the posterior lobe. This part is compared by the authors with the flocculus and dorsal rim area of the frog, in which Goodman (1958), using the same methods of investigation, had observed a postural pattern of response said to be identical with the lateral area pattern in Caiman. No evidence of somatotopic localization in the cerebellum was observed in the experiments on the caymans.

Goodman and Simpson (1960) further observed that a stimulus applied to a locus in the lateral part of the optic tectum of Caiman elicited a response identical with that evoked from the lateral area of the cerebellum. Response to stimulation of the medial region of the tectum was similar, in most respects, to that of the "medial-area pattern" evoked by stimulation of the cerebellum, but the head turned contralaterally instead of ipsilaterally.

Stimulation of the tectum undoubtedly involved the tecto-spinal as well as the tecto-cerebellar tract. The distribution of the latter within the cerebellum is imperfectly known but appears to be chiefly in the anterior and medial lobes, as above described. The medial lobe, at least, does not seem to be reached by vestibular fibers. So far as the responses evoked from loci in the cerebellum resulted from stimulation of fibers, rather than of the Purkinje cells directly, or of the granular layer, the tecto-cerebellar and spino-cerebellar tracts must have been involved in the anterior and medial lobes, and the vestibulo- and spino-cerebellar tracts in the posterior lobe. One can only speculate regarding the roles played by each of these tracts in the two patterns of response and by the granular layer in reversal from one pattern to the other. The total responses, evoked by stimulation of the tectum, so far as they were mediated by the tecto-cerebellar tract, presumably involved impulses relayed from the medial to the posterior lobe through the fascicle of association fibers above described. Total responses evoked from loci in the posterior lobe, on the other hand, presumably involved not only the spino-cerebellar tracts but also impulses from the posterior to the medial and, possibly, the anterior lobe by way of the association fibers.

There are indications that the ventral spino-cerebellar tract distributes chiefly medially, and the dorsal tract laterally, in crocodilians and other reptiles; but normal fiber preparations leave the distribution uncertain. In Marchi preparations of the rat (Anderson, 1943) and of the cat (Beck, 1927) the dorsal tract fibers extend farther laterally than those of the ventral tract, the latter being limited to the region adjacent to the midline. A similar lateral distribution of dorsal tract fibers was observed also in the human cerebellum by Brodal and Jansen (1941). In the cat Grundfest and Campbell (1942) recorded action potentials from the median part of the anterior lobe and also laterally, following stimulation of the dorsal spino-cerebellar tract. According to Brodal and Jansen (1954) it seems likely that the most lateral fibers of the dorsal tract are distributed to the pars intermedia. Recently Lundberg and Oscarsson (1962) have demonstrated that identified ventral tract fibers conduct impulses to longitudinal zones, in the cat, consisting of a lateral strip of vermian cortex and a medial strip of intermediate cortex.

Postural patterns of response similar to the lateral-area pattern in Caiman were reported by Goodman and Simpson (1959, 1960) in rats, subjected to the same method of investigation, the electrodes being implanted in the pars intermedia of Jansen and Brodal (1942). Similar results, with electrodes implanted in the paramedian lobule of the cat (lobule HVIIB + HVIIIA), had been obtained by Clark (1939).

There seems to be little question that the pars lateralis of reptiles corresponds to the mammalian pars intermedia. It also is probable that the dorsal spino-cerebellar tract distributes, perhaps preponderantly, in the pars lateralis, but ventral tract fibers cannot be excluded either on the basis of observation of the reptilian tracts or of the two tracts in mammals.

The pars intermedia of mammals is the medial portion of the cerebellar hemisphere. The corresponding pars lateralis of reptiles, accordingly, may be considered an incipient hemisphere, the lobules of the lateral part of the hemisphere being added in mammals. Chambers and Sprague (1955a, 1955b) emphasize the longitudinal zones represented by the pars intermedia and the vermis, in the restricted sense, and the cerebellar nuclei to which these zones project, respectively, as the fundamental functional divisions of the mammalian cerebellum. This conception could well apply also to the organ in adult reptiles, assuming that the nuclear connections of pars interposita and pars lateralis correspond to those of homologous parts of the mammalian cortex. The development of the organ, both comparative and ontogenic, however, must be taken into consideration for an understanding of the morphology of its subdivisions. It has often been emphasized that function is based upon structure, a relation as significant with respect to the cerebellum as to other parts of the nervous system and of the body in general. The subdivision of the cerebellum into transverse segments and the increased size and further subdivision of these segments to form the folia and lobules of birds and mammals indicates that the receptive areas of the cerebellum have the dominant role in organizing the efferent impulses that pass through the Purkinje cell axons and the paths from the cerebellar nuclei.

Considered from the point of view of phylogenic and ontogenic development, the cerebellum is a rostral and "suprasegmental" continuation of the general and special somatic sensory columns of the medullary oblongata. These columns, however, turn medially from either side and fuse across the midline, as is most simply illustrated in petromyzonts and urodeles, forming the transverse vestibulolateral lobe and corpus cerebelli. The distinct and specific afferent fiber connections and the individual commissures of these two divisions appear to justify considering them as the fundamental functional divisions of the cerebellum. The great increase in the size and functional importance of the corpus cerebelli, beginning with Anura, and the relative reduction of the vestibular part of the cerebellum in adult anurans and reptiles, obscures the transverse pattern of the organ. It is recognizable, however, by the commissura cerebelli and, in embryonic stages, by the gradual fusion of the bilateral rudiments of the corpus cerebelli, and also by the marginal zone and its vestibular connections in both anurans and reptiles. The cerebellar representation of the somatic sensory column expands so greatly that the reduced vestibular part of the organ is overshadowed and the flocculus is displaced farther laterally, relative to the midline, than in Ichthyopsida. The primitive relations are thus hidden. In the alligator embryo the commissura cerebelli and the transverse arch, the bilateral rudiments of which this commissure connects, and also the vestibular marginal band, extending toward the posterior midline, are recognizable before the granular layer can be subdivided into a thickened pars interposita and a thinner pars lateralis. As already mentioned, there is no distinct transverse division in reptiles corresponding to the nodulus of the flocculonodular lobe of birds and mammals. In some reptiles, however, a vestibular commissure is recognizable which, with the adjacent but thin marginal part of the granular layer, may be considered the precursor of the nodulus. In crocodilians the massive median part of the posterior inferior margin of the posterior lobe appears to represent a portion of the uvula and the precursor of the nodulus, as above described. Further studies on the morphogenesis of the reptilian cerebellum are needed before final conclusions can be reached. The observations so far recorded, however, appear to indicate that the transverse divisions whose foundations are the commissura cerebelli and the reduced (as compared with urodeles) or diffuse crossing fibers of the vestibular margin respectively correspond to the earliest morphological and functional divisions of the cerebellum in Ichthyopsida.

AVES I

THE cerebellum of birds has been studied morphologically and by experimental-anatomical methods by many authors, beginning with Carus (1814). It is relatively narrow from side to side, except posteroventrally, but in most species it is arched strongly dorsalward, forming a more or less dome-like structure. The dome is divided into anterior and posterior parts by a usually cleft-like cerebellar ventricle. The immediate posterior wall of the ventricle consists of a sheet of medullary substance which is continuous, above the ventricular apex, with a similar sheet in the anterior wall. The ventral part of the anterior sheet is separated from the ventricular surface by a zone of cells and more loosely arranged fibers which are related with the deep cerebellar nuclei. The medullary sheet so folded around the cerebellar ventricle represents the deep white substance of the cerebellum. It gives off sheet-like branches which, in sagittal sections, constitute the medullary rays. These branches are covered with a layer of cerebellar cortex which, together with the respective medullary sheets, form more or less leaf-like folds called the cerebellar folia.

Carus (1814) described the folia and their variations in a number of species of birds, and Leuret and Gratiolet (1839, 1857) concluded that the number of these folds is proportional to the volume of the cerebellum. This is described as relatively greater in birds than in lower vertebrates. Turner (1891) and Herrick (1893) published good illustrations of the surface features of the folia in a number of species, and Brandis (1894) analyzed them and their medullary rays in a large number of birds. This author also studied the fiber tracts and nuclei of the avian cerebellum and attempted to establish a morphological basis in the organ for a systematic classification of birds. Although he included more than two hundred species in his investigations no important results were obtained with reference to classification. Brandis emphasized,

however, the relation between body size of individual species and the number of folia.

Leuret and Gratiolet describe a small lateral appendage, on either side of the cerebellum, which they compare with the lateral part of the dogfish cerebellum. Turner called this projection the flocculus and Brouwer (1913) classified it, as represented in different species, into several types. Ingvar (1918), who called it the auricle, showed that this projection includes two components, one of which he recognized as the flocculus proper and the other he called the paraflocculus. My study of the bird cerebellum (1948) confirmed the two components both developmentally and in the adult organ. In order to differentiate this projection in birds from the auricle of lower vertebrates, as the flocculus of anurans and reptiles and the vestibulolateral lobe of Ichthyopsida were then usually designated, I called the projection in birds the "avian auricle." The term remains useful and will be retained.

Returning to the median part of the cerebellum, Shimazono (1912) divided it into anterior and posterior vermis, separated by the cerebellar ventricle but merging above this cavity. Brouwer (1913) divided the cerebellum into pars anterior, pars media, and pars posterior. The first and second are separated by a furrow which he called fissure x, and the second and third by fissure y. On the basis of development in the chick embryo Ingvar (1918) divided the organ into lobus anterior, lobus medius and lobus posterior, Brouwer's fissures x and y forming the anterior and posterior boundaries, respectively, of the medial lobe. Fissure x was regarded by Ingvar as corresponding to the sulcus primarius of Kuithan (1895) or fissura prima of Elliot Smith (1902) in mammals, and fissure y to the mammalian prepyramidal fissure. The anterior lobe was considered homologous with the mammalian anterior lobe of Elliot Smith. The medial and posterior lobes of Ingvar, however, differ from those of the British author because they include three subdivisions in the posterior lobe, considered homologous with the pyramis, uvula, and nodulus of mammals. The first two are separated by a furrow called *z* by Ingvar, and the uvula and nodulus by fissure *un*. Fissure *z* was considered homologous with the fissura secunda of Elliot Smith and fissure *un* with the uvulonodular fissure of Bolk (1906). Elliot Smith's fissura secunda, however, divides his medial lobe from his posterior lobe in mammals, and the pyramis is included in his medial lobe.

Ingvar's prepyramidal fissure corresponds to the fissura secunda of Elliot Smith, as Ariens Kappers, Huber, and Crosby (1936) interpreted it in the newly hatched ostrich, and his fissure *z* subdivides the uvula, as I pointed out in my 1948 contribution, in which this furrow was named uvular sulcus 1. The fissure *un* of Ingvar corresponds not only to the uvulonodular fissure but also to the vermal segment of the posterolateral fissure of mammals.

Ingvar's three lobes of the entire cerebellum of birds correspond to his three lobes of the crocodilian cerebellum, in which he also called the furrow dividing his medial from his posterior lobe sulcus *y*, as already noted. The nodulus and the uvula of birds are deeply separated, however, by the posterolateral fissure, whereas in crocodilians the nodulus is part of a uvulonodular segment of the cerebellum which has not differentiated into two divisions.

On the basis of its development in chick and duck embryos I divided the cerebellar cortex into ten primary folds which I called folia I–X (1948). Subsequently (1952, 1953a, 1953b, 1954) I divided the cortex of the developing cerebellum of the rat, cat, and pig into ten primary folds which were called lobules. Close comparison of the folia of embryonic and adult birds and their delimiting fissures, with the lobules and fissures of mammals, embryonic and adult, led me to conclude that lobules I–X of mammals are homologous, respectively, with folia I–X of birds. The lobules of mammals are relatively more massive than the folia of birds and subdivide into larger secondary and tertiary divisions. The ten primary divisions of the embryonic cortex in both birds and mammals are recognizable as the primary folia and primary lobules, respectively, in later embryonic and adult cerebella of both classes. As development progresses and the principle of unequal growth asserts itself they become grouped into lobes.

Folia I–V of birds are included in the anterior lobe of Ingvar (1918). In my 1948 contribution I regarded folium I as corresponding to the lingula of the mammalian cerebellum and folia II and III to the lobulus centralis,

as these terms are used by many authors. Ingvar appears to include both folia I and II in his lingula of the pigeon; folium III is labeled lobulus centralis and folia IV and V are included in the culmen. This corresponds to my present concepts of the homologies of these folia with the lobules of the anterior lobe of mammals as defined in my subsequent analysis of the mammalian and human cerebellum (1952, 1953a, 1953b, 1954). We shall return to the basis of the revised conceptions in connection with comparisons of the development of the cortical folds in birds and mammals and of the fiber tracts, as shown in Marchi preparations.

Folia VI–IX, situated between the fissura prima and the posterolateral fissure, could be regarded as two groups separated by the deep fissura secunda, one group comprising folia VI–VIII and the other folium IX, with its large subdivisions. The fissura secunda appears early in embryonic development and in most adult birds is the deepest and most prominent of the cerebellar fissures. Also, folium IX is the largest of the primary folia in the majority of species. On the grounds of development of this folium, described below, I regard it as part of the posterior lobe of the corpus cerebelli, folia VI–VIII forming the remainder. So considered the posterior lobe of birds corresponds to the posterior lobe of the corpus cerebelli of mammals which comprises lobules VI–IX.

Folium X is continuous with the flocculus proper on both sides. The two flocculi and the nodulus are delimited from the medial principal mass of the cerebellum by the posterolateral fissure which is continuous from the dorsolateral surface of one side of the medulla oblongata to the other, as I showed in the embryonic and adult cerebellum (1948). In reptiles, Anura, and most Ichthyopsida the median cerebellar mass is also larger than the lateral flocculi or vestibulolateral lobes and constitutes the corpus cerebelli, as it also does in birds. Folium X (the nodulus) and the paired flocculi of birds form a well-defined flocculonodular lobe.

Ramon y Cajal (1909–11) refers to a small lateral cerebellar hemisphere in birds but apparently he so regarded the "avian auricle," already mentioned. No evidence of a cerebellar hemisphere was found by Brouwer (1913) in twenty-five species of birds that he studied. In 1948 I described an area of unfoliated or only slightly foliated cortex which forms the ventrolateral surface of the cerebellum on either side, suggesting that it corresponds to a substrate from which the hemisphere developed in the mammalian line of evolution. Brodal, Kristiansen, and Jansen (1950) demonstrated, by the Brodal-Gudden method, two small pontine nuclei, a medial and a lateral, on either side of the anterior part of the medulla oblongata of the chicken. From these nuclei, fibers project to the ventrolateral unfoliated area of the cerebellum to the parafloccular part of the "avian auricle," and to folia VI–VIII and part of folium IX. The cerebellar projections of the lateral pontine nucleus were found to be chiefly ipsilateral, while those of the medial nucleus were chiefly contralateral. The crossed fibers project predominantly to the ventrolateral area of cerebellar cortex, some reaching the "avian paraflocculus." The ventrolateral area was regarded by Brodal, Kristiansen, and Jansen as a rudimentary cerebellar hemisphere. Whitlock (1952) confirmed the observations of these authors in the adult pigeon, but did not attempt to determine the distribution of the ponto-cerebellar fibers in specific areas of the cerebellum.

My earlier (1948) account of the avian cerebellum has been supplemented by descriptions of additional species, both with respect to early development and to adult pattern (Whitlock, 1952; Larsell and Whitlock, 1952; Saetersdal, 1956a, 1956b), and by study of the penguin cerebellum, described below. In my own studies I have paid special attention to fifteen species, representing nine orders of birds. These species range in size from the small hummingbirds to the large emperor penguin. They also present great diversity of methods and organs of propulsion, variations in visual and, probably, auditory acuity, and in the size and relative importance of the trigeminal nerve and its branches.

Though most birds have the capacity of flight this varies greatly in different species, as do the combinations of wing development with ability to use the legs in walking and swimming or both. No strictly cursorial species have been included in my personal investigations, but Ingvar (1918) published excellent illustrations of the cerebellum of the South American ostrich, Rhea americana, which serve well for comparisons, and Craigie (1930) has provided a brief description of the cerebellum of the Kiwi, Apteryx australis. The penguins have provided comparisons of the cerebellum in birds whose wings are modified into flippers which are the chief organs of propulsion and are used for "flying in the water." Whitlock (1952) supplemented a restudy of the fiber tract in embryonic and adult cerebella by neurohistological techniques, with investigations by electrophysiological methods. The results obtained make possible a close comparison of most of the subdivisions of the avian vermis with those of the vermis of mammals from the standpoint of afferent connections and somatotopic relations.

Before I review the morphological and experimental observations, the principal sensory system and nerves related to the cerebellum should receive attention. As in reptiles these are the labyrinth and acoustic nerve; the trigeminal nerve and its receptors, cutaneous and proprioceptive; and the exteroceptors and proprioceptors, impulses from which reach the cerebellum by way of spinal nerves and the spino-cerebellar tracts. The bulbar centers of the stato-acoustic nerve are also described as in reptiles and lower vertebrates.

THE ACOUSTIC NERVE

The acoustic nerve of birds is similar to that of reptiles but in several respects its peripheral distribution resembles that of lizards and snakes rather than of crocodilians. The anterior branch, according to Retzius (1884), serves the anterior and lateral ampullae and the utricle in most species. The posterior branch serves the crista of the posterior ampulla, the papilla neglecta, macula sacculi, papilla basilaris, and macula lagenae. The papilla neglecta, according to de Burlet (1928), is derived from the posterior ampullary crista and is regarded by Benjamins (1913) as a crista. As in lizards and snakes a cochleo-saccular branch of Hardy of the VIII nerve is lacking in birds although present in crocodilians (Weston 1937, 1939c).

According to Federici (1926) and Weston (1939a), the large cells of the VIII ganglion are intracranially, rather than intra-otically situated, and their peripheral processes pass to the ampullary cristae and the crista or papilla neglecta. Medium-sized cells, also intracranial, send their fibers to the maculae utriculi and sacculi, but others of medium size, whose fibers pass to the lagena, are intraotic in position.

The lagena of birds is a fleck-shaped enlargement, distal of the papilla basilaris, which has a distinct macula lagenae; the papilla basilaris alone corresponds to the organ of Corti of mammals, Weston (1939a) points out, but is not coiled. According to Weston (1939c) the nerve fibers to the papilla basilaris are processes of small intraotic cells that approach the sensory epithelium more closely than the cells related to the macula lagenae.

The anterior or ventral root of the VIII nerve is purely vestibular and the posterior or dorsal root is mixed. As in reptiles the latter root divides before entering the medulla oblongata, the cochlear fibers entering dorsal of the vestibular roots. The lagener fibers join the vestibular division of the posterior root, according to Federici (1926), an observation of interest because the lagena of birds is said to contain a papilla which is vestibular in function (Ariens Kappers, 1947). According to Weston (1939a), anatomical data also suggest an auditory function, in part at least, for the lagena, and von Frisch (1938) regards the avian lagena as auditory.

The vestibular reflexes of birds were studied by Groebbels (1927, 1928), and their auditory perception by Wever and Bray (1936), Brand and Kellogg (1939), and others. We shall return to some of the vestibular responses, but it may be mentioned at this point that the upper limit of the auditory range in most birds is about 10,000 c.p.s., although in the starling a range up to 15,000 c.p.s. has been recorded, according to Sturkie (1954). The low range is 40–400 c.p.s. The pigeon is said to have a range of 200–7,500 c.p.s. and the horned owl a range of 60–7,000 c.p.s. (Brand and Kellogg, 1939). Wever and Bray (1936), by electrophysiological methods, reported a range of 100–10,000 c.p.s. from the lagena of the pigeon.

The vestibular nuclei. The vestibular nuclei and their connections in birds have been investigated by Wallenberg (1898, 1900), Holmes (1903), Ramon y Cajal (1908a, 1908b), Bartels (1925), Craigie (1928, 1930), Sanders (1929), and others. The interpretations of the cell masses by various authors and the terminologies employed differ so greatly that much confusion has resulted. The contributions above cited were reviewed by Ariens Kappers, Huber, and Crosby (1936), who employed the terminology of Sanders, and more briefly by Ariens Kappers (1947). The subsequent literature appears to be silent on the anatomical aspects of the nuclei in birds.

As defined by Sanders (1929), the vestibular nuclei and their subdivisions are based upon cytoarchitectonic differences as shown in toluidine blue preparations of the sparrow. These were supplemented by silver preparations showing the connections of the nuclear subdivisions. Adoption of the subdivisions of the vestibular complex and the terminology of Sanders and also following her comparisons of these subdivisions with those of other authors will, to some extent, simplify the presentation of a complex subject.

The vestibular nuclear mass is divided into the following six principal nuclei: (1) nucleus vestibularis tangentialis, (2) nucleus vestibularis ventrolateralis, (3) nucleus vestibularis descendens, (4) nucleus vestibularis dorsomedialis, (5) nucleus vestibularis dorsolateralis, and (6) nucleus vestibularis superior.

The tangential nucleus of Sanders corresponds to that of Ramon y Cajal (1908a), Ariens Kappers (1921), Bartels (1925), Craigie (1928), and others. It consists of relatively small, oval cells situated among the entering fibers of the anterior root of the VIII nerve. Root fibers terminate on the cells by spoon-like or calyciform endings, as in fishes and other lower vertebrates.

The ventrolateral nucleus corresponds to Deiters's nucleus of Wallenberg (1898, 1900), Ramon y Cajal (1908b), and Craigie (1928). It is called the ventral nucleus of Deiters by Bartels (1925). This nucleus is large, but secondary groups of cells, described by Bartels, were not observed by Sanders. The cells are large, multipolar elements situated among the ventral vestibular fibers medial of the tangential nucleus and beneath the dorsal VIII root fibers. According to Sanders and others, the ventrolateral nucleus is homologous, as a whole or in part, with the lateral vestibular or Deiters's nucleus of mammals.

The descending or inferior nucleus appears in a plane of section passing through the rostral ends of the laminar and magnocellular nuclei of the cochlear nerve. It extends caudalward but a short distance, in the sparrow, before disappearing. According to Ariens Kappers (1947), it reaches from Deiters's nucleus to the calamus scriptorius. The cells are similar to those of the ventrolateral (Deiters's) nucleus but smaller. This nucleus has been recognized by most authors, but in Apteryx it is not clearly differentiated, according to Craigie (1930).

The dorsomedial nucleus, called the nucleus triangularis by some authors, and described by Wallenberg (1900), Holmes (1903), and others, is not included by Ramon y Cajal (1908b) with those receiving vestibular root fibers. Doubt about its position as a vestibular center was thus raised. Wallenberg, Craigie (1928), and Sanders, however, believed that such fibers reach the cell mass. The last-named author regards the nucleus as probably homologous with the medial vestibular nucleus of mammals.

The dorsolateral vestibular nucleus of Sanders, comprising a group of cell masses, is called the dorsal nucleus of Deiters by Bartels (1925), the ventrolateral nucleus, as above noted, corresponding to the ventral nucleus of Deiters in Bartels's terminology. On the basis of cytoarchitecture and fiber connections Sanders subdivides the nuclear mass into medial, intermediate, and lateral divisions.

The medial division is further subdivided into three parts: (1) a small-celled part, corresponding to the nucleus piriformis of Ramon y Cajal and of Craigie, and to the inferior part of the dorsal nucleus of Deiters, as termed by Bartels; (2) a central region, corresponding to the medial part of Bartels's dorsal nucleus of Deiters, and consisting of medium-sized cells and, probably, of scattered cells between the piriform and bigeminal nuclei of Ramon y Cajal and perhaps a small group called the nucleus vestibularis minor by Craigie; (3) a dorsal subdivision of the medial division, corresponding to the medial part of the bigeminal nucleus of Ramon y Cajal, part of the nucleus gemelli of Bartels, and the nucleus gemelli of Craigie.

The intermediate division of the dorsolateral nucleus, according to Sanders, corresponds to the lateral part of the bigeminal nucleus (noyau jumeaux) of Ramon y Cajal, and of the nucleus gemelli of Bartels. It consists of large angular cells and is well demarcated from other cell masses.

The lateral division of the dorsolateral nucleus includes the nucleus quadrangularis and nucleus vestibulocerebellaris of Ramon y Cajal and of Craigie. It may also include the nucleus vestibulo-floccularis of Craigie. Sanders retains the term nucleus quadrangularis for a relatively distinct subdivision of the lateral division which extends farther forward than the medial or intermediate divisions of the dorsolateral nucleus. The vestibulo-cerebellar nucleus, according to Sanders, is a small, triangular cell mass situated ventromedial of diffuse cells scattered ventralward and lateralward along the vestibular fibers and lying lateral of the ventral part of the intermediate division of the dorsolateral nuclear group. In the sparrow its cells are no larger than those of the piriform nucleus, which is part of the medial division.

The superior vestibular nucleus, Sanders (1929) states, extends caudally just above the descending nucleus. Followed anteriorly it forms an elongated mass which extends dorsalward to the small-celled ventral part of the dorsolateral vestibular nucleus. The superior nucleus of Sanders corresponds to the nucleus oralis of Bartels (1925) and Craigie (1928).

In the virtually wingless Apteryx australis, according to Craigie (1930), the vestibular nuclei are poorly defined and the numerous centers, described by Ramon y Cajal, and by himself in the hummingbird, cannot be distinguished. The triangular nucleus, corresponding to the nucleus ventromedialis of Sanders, is small and not clearly differentiated from the central gray substance. Near the anterior end of the acoustic angular nucleus scattered large cells of the type characteristic of Deiters's nucleus make their appearance. Farther rostrally these form definite dorsal and ventral groups, the dorsal group less extensive and consisting of larger cells than the ventral aggregation. The scattered cells of the dorsal group disappear among the transverse fibers of the vestibular root, but the ventral group extends farther and spreads out just anterior of the dorsal division, merging anteriorly with the oral nucleus (superior of Sanders).

The oral nucleus of Apteryx, regarded by Craigie as homologous with the nucleus of Bechterew in mammals, is described as difficult to differentiate from the lateral cerebellar nucleus with which it is continuous. Its cells, however, are a little larger, in general, and more deeply stained. The relatively simple pattern of the vestibular centers in Apteryx, in contrast with the complex pattern which Craigie (1928) had found in the hummingbird, Craigie linked with the loss of the power of flight in the Kiwi.

Bartels (1925) had called attention to great differences in the size, form, and degree of differentiation of the vestibular nuclei among the birds. Grouping the species he studied into songbirds and non-songbirds, this author states that the songbirds have the more highly differentiated vestibular nuclei. Most of the songbirds are good flyers but no better than many species without song, among which the hummingbirds are included, as Craigie notes. When the vestibular nuclei of the hummingbird are compared with those of the Kiwi Craigie's conclusion is plausible, but relative size and, perhaps, other factors must be taken into account. Adjacent nuclei, in general, tend to merge in larger species. Whether or not the vestibular nuclei of the larger flying birds are as distinct as in the sparrow and hummingbird remains unknown.

Comparison of the vestibular nuclei and their subdivisions in birds with those of reptiles and mammals is of interest. It is noteworthy that the vestibular nuclei of the turtle, most completely analyzed by Weston (1936), correspond to the six nuclei of Sanders (1929) in the sparrow, except the nucleus vestibularis ventromedialis. This nucleus, however, Weston regards as homologous with the avian nucleus vestibularis dorsomedialis of Sanders, the difference being chiefly topographical. The number of primary vestibular nuclei in the sparrow does not, therefore, appear to be related to the greater importance of the vestibular system in birds. The subdivision of some of these nuclei into secondary and tertiary cell masses in the sparrow and many other birds, however, probably is so related. Nevertheless, a comparison of the vestibular nuclei of the larger reptiles, such as varanids and crocodilians, with those of large flying birds must be made before conclusions can be drawn regarding the relative differentiation into secondary and further subdivisions, or their apparent reduction to a smaller number, as in Apteryx.

The nucleus vestibularis superior of Weston was found only in turtles in a position corresponding to the similarly named nucleus in the sparrow. Even in turtles it appeared to be a direct rostroventral continuation of the nucleus vestibularis dorsolateralis and to correspond to the most anterior part of the nucleus vestibularis superior of Beccari (1912), Ariens Kappers (1921), and Larsell (1926, 1932b). The superior vestibular nucleus of these authors and of Papez (1929) corresponds, on the whole, to Weston's dorsolateral vestibular nucleus and to van Hoevell's (1916) anterior vestibular nucleus in the caiman. The nucleus vestibularis superior of Sanders, or oralis of Bartels and of Craigie, in birds, was regarded by Sanders, Bartels, and Craigie as homologous with the nucleus of Bechterew in mammals, as already noted. The dorsolateral and superior vestibular nuclei of Sanders, in birds, apparently represent a further differentiation of the reptilian nuclei to which Weston gave the same names.

In mammals various subdivisions of one or another of the four nuclei (lateral or Deiters's, medial or Schwalbe's, superior or Bechterew's, and inferior or descending), usually recognized, or cell groups within or apparently related to them, have been described by a number of authors, e.g., Lewy (1910), Fuse (1912), Winkler and Potter (1914), Meessen and Olszewski (1949), Olszewski and Baxter (1954), Brodal and Pompeiano (1957), and others.

Brodal and Pompeiano refined the definition of the four principal nuclei in the cat and described smaller cell groups topographically related to them. These authors also differentiated the interstitial nucleus of the vestibular nerve, described by Ramon y Cajal (1909) and observed by Fuse (1912), Klossowsky (1933), and others in mammals. This nucleus was regarded by Ramon y Cajal as probably homologous with the nucleus tangentialis of birds and reptiles, although the terminals of vestibular root fibers on its cells differ from the spoon-like endings in birds and most lower vertebrates. Brodal and Pompeiano regard the interstitial nucleus in the cat as an aberrant part of Deiters's nucleus. We shall return to the question of homologies of the interstitial nucleus of the vestibular root of mammals.

Study of the fiber connections of the vestibular nuclei of the cat by the newer silver degeneration methods has demonstrated that the organization of these nuclei is far more complex than has previously been assumed. The terminations of the primary vestibular fibers are usually considered distributed throughout the four classical nuclei. Walberg, Bowsher, and Brodal (1958), however, have shown that only certain regions of the nuclei receive vestibular root fibers, while other regions are free of them. Pompeiano and Brodal (1957b) demonstrated that the terminations of spino-vestibular fibers are limited to certain parts of some of the vestibular nuclei, and other studies have shown similar limitations in the distribution of other tracts that enter the nuclear complex.

Attempts to homologize the secondary and tertiary subdivisions of the avian vestibular nuclei, as described by Sanders (1929), with subdivisions or cell groups in mammals lead, however, to confusion. The dorsolateral nucleus of Sanders and the vestibulo-cerebellar nucleus of Ramon y Cajal (included in the lateral division of the dorsolateral nucleus by Sanders) are difficult to compare with mammalian nuclei. More or less distinct cell groups (nucleus of Onofrowicz, 1885; nucleus supremus acustici of Lewandowsky, 1904; nucleus of Kohnstamm, 1910) have been described dorsolateral of Deiters's nucleus, in the region of the superior vestibular nucleus of mammals. Fuse (1912) and Brodal and Pompeiano (1957) were unable to confirm them and, on the basis of cytoarchitectonic uniformity, the latter authors regarded the superior vestibular nucleus of the cat as a single unit of the vestibular nuclear complex.

If one considers the interstitial nucleus of the vestibular root of mammals as homologous with the tangential nucleus of birds, at least five of the six avian vestibular nuclei appear to correspond to the principal vestibular nuclei of mammals, although there are discrepancies with respect to the secondary connections of some. Whether and to what extent the subdivisions in birds of the dorsolateral nucleus and other small cell groups of various authors correspond to the cell groups described by Brodal and Pompeiano (1957) within or adjacent to the principal nuclei of the cat only future research can determine.

The connections of the vestibular nuclei. The central relations of the vestibular root of birds have been described by Wallenberg (1898, 1900), Winkler (1907), Ramon y Cajal (1908b), Bartels (1925), Craigie (1928), Sanders (1929), Ariens Kappers, Huber, and Crosby (1936), Ariens Kappers (1947) and others. The various accounts are in general accord but there are differences in some respects.

Coarse fibers of the anterior root form spoon-like terminations, already mentioned, on the cells of the tangential nucleus soon after entering the medulla oblongata, the fibers continuing in reduced size beyond this nucleus, as illustrated by Ramon y Cajal (1908a). These are fibers from the anterior and lateral cristae ampullares, according to Ariens Kappers (1947). Fibers from the posterior ampulla and the macula neglecta that enter the posterior root of the VIII nerve, separate from the cochlear fibers, according to both Winkler and Sanders, and terminate in the dorsal part of the tangential nucleus. Sanders traced some of the posterior root vestibular fibers to synaptic endings around the nuclear cells, but said most of them merely traverse the nucleus. Wallenberg (1900) and Ramon y Cajal (1908b) believed that all the posterior root vestibular fibers pass through the nucleus. According to Ariens Kappers (1947), however, coarse fibers from the posterior ampulla and the papilla neglecta end in the tangential nucleus in the same manner as those from the anterior and lateral ampullae.

Root fibers of medium size from the macula utriculi, entering through the anterior root, and similar fibers from the macula sacculi, entering by the posterior root in most birds, bifurcate into ascending and descending branches. Utricular fibers end in the ventrolateral (Deiters's) nucleus. Ascending root fibers reach all divisions of the dorsolateral nucleus, the superior nucleus and the dorsomedial (triangular) nucleus, Sanders says. Such fibers also continue to the cerebellum, as found by Wallenberg (1900), Sanders (1929), and Whitlock (1952).

The ascending fibers to the dorsolateral and superior nuclei are utricular, Ariens Kappers states. The fascicle to the cerebellum includes both utricular and saccular fibers. The fibers to the dorsomedial nucleus may be collaterals of the sacculo-cerebellar fibers, but this is uncertain. Vestibular root fibers, not identified as to source, but many of them small, cross the midline to the contralateral vestibular region, according to Sanders (1929) and Winkler (1907).

Descending utricular fibers apparently end in part by collaterals in the nucleus inferior (descendens) and continue as the descending vestibular root to the cord; these appear to be augmented by descending saccular fibers.

Secondary connections of the vestibular nuclei have been described by Wallenberg (1900), Bartels (1925), Sanders (1929), Ariens Kappers, Huber, and Crosby (1936), Ariens Kappers (1947), and others. The tangential nucleus gives rise to fibers that enter the contralateral medial longitudinal fascicle. Ascending fibers pass to the nuclei of the III and IV nerves, and descending fibers continue into the spinal cord. The tangential nucleus apparently has no cerebellar connections. According to Ariens Kappers (1947) this nucleus, with its large afferent fibers from the ampullary cristae and its central connections through the fasciculus longitudinalis medialis, constitutes the primary center for dynamic labyrinthine reflexes.

The ventrolateral (Deiters's) nucleus gives rise to an ipsilateral vestibulo-spinal tract, and also contributes to the fasciculus longitudinalis medialis. Descending fibers in the medial longitudinal fascicle pass to the spinal cord, while ascending fibers reach the midbrain and the post optic hypothalamic region, those to the latter region forming the vestibulo-hypothalamic tract of Wallenberg (1900). Ascending branches of utricular fibers ending in Deiters's nucleus accompany utricular and saccular root fibers to the cerebellum.

The nucleus inferior (descendens), which receives descending branches or their collaterals of utricular fibers, and collaterals from the secondary, the descending, vestibular tract, apparently contributes to the direct vestibulospinal tract. This tract continues in the ventrolateral funiculus of the cord to the lumbar region. It is regarded by Groebbels (1928) as the principal pathway serving static tonicity of the neck, body, and extremities.

According to Shimazono (1912) the "internal vestibular nucleus," apparently corresponding to the dorsomedial nucleus of Sanders, gives rise to fibers that end in the "flocculus," apparently the "avian auricle." Craigie

(1928) describes fibers from the lower part of the dorsomedial nucleus, which he calls nucleus triangularis, as entering the vestibular decussation.

The dorsolateral vestibular nucleus, which lies in the path of the ascending vestibular branches, is complex both in organization and in its efferent fibers. Sanders says that large cells of the medial and intermediate divisions of this nucleus are so oriented that their dendrites extend across the field and come into relation with vestibular root fibers and the ascending tract to the cerebellum, on the one hand, and with efferent cerebellar fibers on the other. The axons of these cells are said to join the descending cerebellar efferent system. Smaller dendrites of the nucleus quadrangularis (a part of the lateral division of the dorsolateral nucleus) come into relation with the spino-cerebellar system. There is some evidence, Sanders believes, that the dorsolateral nuclear group contributes to the medial longitudinal fascicle by way of the cerebellifugal system. According to Ramon y Cajal (1908b) the vestibulo-cerebellar nucleus (included by Sanders in the lateral division of the dorsolateral nucleus) is a special part of the vestibular nuclear complex which receives vestibular root fibers and gives origin to a system of large, branching fibers that reach the cerebellum. Bartels (1925), as above noted, included the dorsolateral nucleus with the Deiters's nucleus complex, stating that the fiber connections indicate that it is an efferent rather than afferent nucleus. According to Ariens Kappers (1947) the axons arising in the dorsolateral nucleus pass to the cerebellum.

The confusing and more or less contradictory descriptions of the fiber connections of the dorsolateral nucleus and its subdivisions leave the impression that it is a precerebellar center of correlation of vestibular and spinal impulses. The efferent fibers from the large cells of the medial and intermediate divisions, described by Sanders, apparently carry correlated vestibular and cerebellipetal impulses that would appear related to the complex reflexes of flying.

The superior vestibular nucleus (the nucleus oralis of Bartels, and the nucleus of Bechterew of Ariens Kappers) contributes fibers to the medial longitudinal fascicle that end in the eye muscle nuclei of the midbrain. Ascending fibers are also said to enter the cerebellum, ending in the fastigial nucleus and possibly also in the flocculus and vermis (Ariens Kappers, 1947). Whitlock (1952) observed chromatolytic changes in cells of the superior nucleus of the pigeon following extirpation of the "auricle."

Vestibular fibers to the cerebellum, Whitlock states, include both ascending VIII root fibers and secondary fibers from vestibular nuclei. Except the superior nucleus, already mentioned, none of the vestibular nuclei are specifically named by this author. In silver and Bodian preparations of chick and duck embryo the fibers enter the caudal part of the cerebellum, following its posterior margin and many crossing the midline as a vestibular commissure. Marchi preparations of adult pigeons, according to Whitlock, show similar origins and terminations of vestibulo-cerebellar fibers. We shall return to their distribution in the cerebellum.

The specific nuclei of origin of the vestibulo-cerebellar fibers of birds have been variously assigned, as already indicated. Voris and Hoerr (1932), in the opossum, and Brodal and Pompeiano (1957), in the cat, as above noted, found fibers to the cerebellum only from the medial and inferior (descending) vestibular nuclei. Restudy of the avian nuclei by the more modern degeneration methods should clarify any differences between avian and mammalian connections or remove the discrepancies of present descriptions.

The cochlear nuclei. The nucleus angularis is situated in the dorsolateral angle of the medulla oblongata, at the level of entrance of the cochlear root of the VIII nerve. The root fibers enter the ventromedial part of the nucleus, which lies lateral of the incoming fibers. According to Sanders (1929) the cells are multipolar, medium-sized elements of somewhat angular form.

The nucleus magnocellularis lies medially and caudally with reference to the angular nucleus and is the principal terminus of the cochlear root. According to Ramon y Cajal (1908b) the cells are small laterally, gradually increasing in size medialward. Sanders describes all the cells as approximately equal in size, except ventrolaterally in the caudal part of the nucleus where they are smaller, more irregular, and stain more lightly than in the remainder of the cell mass.

The nucleus laminaris is sickle-shaped in birds and partly surrounds the magnocellular nucleus. It extends farther rostrally than any of the other cochlear nuclei. The cells of the dorsal third of the caudal part of the nucleus are smaller and stain more deeply than those of the remainder, according to Sanders. The cells of approximately the ventral two thirds are larger, more fusiform, and oriented parallel with fascicles of fibers that pass among them. In the more rostral part of the nucleus the cells are said to be rounded, more diffuse, and more homogeneous. According to Ramon y Cajal (1908b), large cells are found in the dorsal part, and small cells in the ventral part of the nucleus. The apparent difference between the descriptions of Ramon y Cajal and Sanders with respect to the sizes of cells may be due to the plane of the sections, Sanders believes. Ramon y Cajal suggested that the laminar nucleus is homologous with the

accessory superior olive of mammals. In experimental-anatomical preparations of the pigeon, Stotler (1951) demonstrated that in morphology and connections it corresponds to the medial accessory superior olive of mammals.

A superior olive is closely associated with the cochlear centers. Schepman (1918) and Ariens Kappers (1921) state that it consists of dorsal and ventral parts. The dorsal part is usually the larger and is evidently the superior olive as described by Sanders in the sparrow. The ventral part, according to Ariens Kappers, Huber, and Crosby (1936), is thinner and may be distinct from the other. Sanders describes the superior olive as consisting of closely packed small cells, many of them spindle-shaped. In cross section the nucleus is rounded, the outer cells forming somewhat concentric rings around a central core. Larger scattered cells near the origin of the ascending tract of the cochlear system (the lateral lemniscus) are sometimes considered part of the superior olive (Ariens Kappers, Huber, and Crosby).

The central relations of the cochlear fibers of birds are similar, in general, to those of reptiles. The cochlear division of the posterior VIII root ends in the nucleus angularis and nucleus magnocellularis. The nucleus laminaris also receives auditory impulses, but whether through cochlear root fibers or by secondary connections from the other two nuclei is controversial. Wallenberg (1900) believed that the fibers are secondary, and Ramon y Cajal (1908b) describes them as uncrossed collaterals of the lateral lemniscus. According to Sanders (1929), direct cochlear fibers that pass through the laminar nucleus to reach the medial and posterior parts of the magnocellular nucleus give off fine unmyelinated collaterals that form pericellular synaptic connections with the cells of the laminar nucleus. Bok (1915) mentions cochlear root fibers to the superior olive and Sanders says that a few direct cochlear fibers may enter the ventral arcuate system.

Secondary fibers, taking origin in the angular and magnocellular nuclei, joined by fibers from the laminar nucleus, arch ventrally and medially to form the lemniscus lateralis, many passing beneath the medial longitudinal fascicle to decussate across the midline. The lemniscus sends collaterals into the ipsilateral and contralateral superior olives, Wallenberg (1898, 1900) states, and is augmented by fibers from the ipsilateral olive (Ariens Kappers, 1947). After giving off collaterals to the semilunar nucleus (homologous with the mammalian nucleus of the lateral lemniscus), the lemniscus terminates in the nucleus isthmi and, especially, in the dorsal part of the lateral mesencephalic nucleus of Ariens Kappers, Huber, and Crosby (1936) or lateral tegmental nucleus of Ariens Kappers (1947). This nucleus is homologous with the inferior colliculus of mammals. Some cells that accompany the lemniscus fibers before they decussate, observed by Bok (1915), probably represent cellular elements of a primitive trapezoid body.

According to Mesdag (1909) the laminar nucleus has connections with the cerebellum, and Bok (1915) describes a "cochleo-cerebellar" tract ending in the cerebellar nuclei. This tract, he says, is formed of fibers from the magnocellular nucleus that cross in a dorsal cochlear commissure, situated beneath the floor of the fourth ventricle. After decussating, the fibers come into contact with the dendrites of large cells in front of the cerebellum. Sanders (1929) describes fibers from the laminar nucleus that join the cochleo-cerebellar tract, but Stotler (1951), who considers the laminar nucleus the homologue of the medial accessory superior olive of mammals, as already noted, regards a cerebellar connection as unlikely. Degeneration experiments on the pigeon by Whitlock (1952) yielded no evidence of connections from any of the cochlear nuclei to the cerebellum.

Developmental aspects of the vestibular and cochlear nuclei. The experimental results of Levi-Montalcino (1949) on chick embryos are of interest with reference to the differentiation and connections of the vestibular and cochlear nuclei. This author removed the otocyst in embryos at the 40 hour stage of incubation, with the result that the inner ear and the vestibular and cochlear ganglia failed to develop.

Differentiation of the cochlear centers, however, was not affected by absence of the root fibers up to 11 days of incubation. In later stages the three cochlear nuclei showed different degrees of hypoplasia. The nucleus angularis was most severely affected, the nucleus magnocellularis was atrophied to a lesser degree, and the nucleus laminaris showed only slight effects.

Among the vestibular nuclei only the nucleus tangentialis was appreciably affected. This nucleus normally is differentiated in a medial position and migrates to its lateral site after entrance of the large vestibular root fibers that make synaptic connections with its cells. The nucleus failed to differentiate and migrate when these fibers were absent. The other vestibular nuclei developed normally until the end of the embryonic period. Extirpation of different parts of the brain had no effect on the development of either the vestibular or the cochlear centers.

Levi-Montalcino suggests that a quantitative relation exists between the degree of hypoplasia and the number of synaptic connections that these nuclei receive. It is not improbable that the crossed vestibular root fibers of Sanders (1929) and of Winkler (1907) provide some con-

nections. The spino-cerebellar tract and the dendritic contacts of some of the nuclei, above mentioned, provide others. The dorsolateral and ventrolateral vestibular nuclei, two of the largest of the group, although they receive ipsilateral vestibular root fibers, are apparently efferent nuclei that seem to be little affected by absence of the vestibular roots. The tangential nucleus which, like the magnocellular and angular nuclei of the cochlear group, receives only ipsilateral root fibers, is the only one of the vestibular group to be seriously affected by the absence of such fibers. Presumably secondary connections to the others, and contralateral connections, provide the stimuli necessary for further growth and differentiation after the initial embryonic period.

CUTANEOUS RECEPTORS, PROPRIOCEPTORS, AND RELATED NERVES

Sensory nerve endings, some of highly specialized type, have long been known in the feathered skin of birds. Herbst corpuscles occur near the follicles of the feathers and in the beak. Similar nerve endings are found in clusters about the joints and between the bones of the lower leg. Other types of specialized nerve endings occur in the beak of ducks, geese, and similar aquatic birds.

Neuromuscular spindles in birds, as described by Huber and De Witt (1897) and Regaud and Favre (1904–05), have two to eight intrafusal fibers among which sensory nerve fibers branch and terminate. The spindles have a capsule but no lymphatic space. A motor innervation was described by Cipollone (1897) and small ventral root fibers of the spinal nerves, similar to those of Häggqvist (1938) in mammals, were found by Graf (1956).

The trigeminal nerve is less developed in most birds than in reptiles. The sensory root ends in a superior sensory nucleus which is divided into dorsal and ventral parts. This root conducts cutaneous and proprioceptive sensibility, relayed to the cerebellum by a trigemino-cerebellar tract which arises in the dorsal superior V nucleus (Biondi, 1913; Craigie, 1928). It is well developed in birds.

The mesencephalic V root emerges with the motor root, distributing to the muscles of the beak where they presumably end in neuromuscular spindles. Some mesencephalic V fibers are said to enter the nuclei of the III and IV nerves, and collaterals to the medial nucleus of the cerebellum are mentioned by Ariens Kappers (1947). These collaterals are branches of axons whose cells are situated in the mesencephalic V nucleus. Most of the axons of these cells, according to Wallenberg (1900), reach the motor V and, perhaps, the motor VII and motor IX nuclei.

The Development of the Cerebellum

Returning to the cerebellum, the rudiment of the organ appears in the chick embryo at 4½ days' incubation, Mesdag (1909) says. Earlier developmental stages of the brains of several species of birds, illustrated from wax models by Krabbe (1952), show the rhombencephalon as a trough-like structure, the ventricular cavity of which is covered by an ependymal roof. The rostral end of the trough turns dorsalward and broadens, differentiating into the metencephalon. Ingvar (1918) found a lateral swelling on either side of the rhombencephalon of 5 day chick embryos but these swellings were not yet fused across the midline of the roof of the ventricular space. I have confirmed these expansions in the 5 day chick embryo and believe that they correspond to the cerebellar part of the columna dorsalis of Bergquist and Källen. They continue to expand and also increase in thickness.

In chick embryos at 8 days of incubation the cerebellum is tilted caudalward and presents bilateral rounded dorsal surfaces separated by a median sagittal furrow which penetrates to the ependymal layer (fig. 185). A

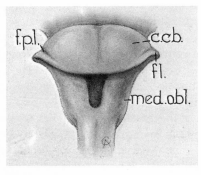

Figure 185. Dorsal view of cerebellum of chick embryo, Gallus domesticus, incubated 8 days. (Larsell, 1948.)

groove parallel with the cerebellar margin, on either side, delimits a slightly enlarged lateral projection of the margin from the larger medial mass. This groove is the lateral segment of the posterolateral fissure, the lateral projection is the rudiment of the flocculus, and the still paired cell masses medial of the fissure, on either side, are the rudiments of the corpus cerebelli (fig. 185). Saetersdal (1956a) describes the lateral segment of the posterolateral fissure in the 7 day chick embryo and Ingvar (1918) mentions a slight depression in a similar position in the 5 day chick embryo.

Ascending V root and, possibly, secondary trigeminal fibers and also spino-cerebellar fibers enter the base of the developing cerebellum. In chick embryos of 9 days incubation some of these fibers decussate across the mid-

line of the anterior part of the cerebellum. These decussating fibers form a commissura cerebelli which is related to the future corpus cerebelli. Vestibular root fibers, possibly accompanied by secondary vestibular fibers, follow the lateral and posterior margins of the cerebellum. A small fascicle of these fibers decussates across the midline near the posterodorsal tip of the cerebellum, forming a vestibular commissure which corresponds to the vestibulolateral commissure of Ichthyopsida but lacks fibers related to the lateral-line system. Between the two commissures a thin zone of incipient cortex covers the ependymal layer at the midline. Laterally this zone is separated from the ependyma by a cellular layer which represents the lateral cell mass already mentioned in earlier stages. An external granular layer appears at a later stage of incubation; its growth and variation in thickness have been described by Saetersdal (1956b) in chick embryos of 11 days incubation to hatching, and in young chicks to 25 days after the beginning of incubation. This author also studied the external granular layer in Columba, Anas, Phaseanus, and Turdus.

According to Murphy (1900) and Ingvar (1918) no fissures have appeared in the cerebellum of the 9 day chick embryo. My own observations are in accord with reference to fissures that cross the midline; the posterolateral fissure, already mentioned at earlier stages, extends farther medially, however, than in the 8 day embryo but does not yet reach the midline.

In the 9½ day chick embryo the bilateral rudiments of the corpus cerebelli have fused and the external sagittal furrow has disappeared (fig. 186). The marginal zone, extending posteromedially from the flocculus and delimited from the corpus cerebelli by the posterolateral fissure, is more prominent and shows an enlargement on either side of the midline. These two enlargements are the paired rudiments of the nodulus. In subsequent develop-

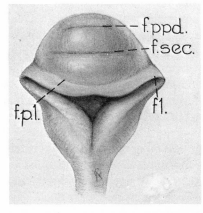

Figure 186. Dorsoposterior view of cerebellum of chick embryo incubated 9½ days. (Larsell, 1948.)

ment they fuse across the midline, forming an unpaired cortical fold. In the 9½ day embryo they are delimited from the corpus cerebelli by the further medial extension of the posterolateral fissure which, at this stage, reaches the midline. The differentiation of the flocculonodular lobe from the corpus cerebelli is now complete (figs. 186, 187).

The corpus cerebelli of the 9½ day chick embryo has four transverse furrows. These and the posterolateral fissure correspond to the five cerebellar fissures described by Saetersdal (1956a) at this stage of the chick embryo. Ingvar (1918) found only three, which he called fissures *x, y,* and *un,* at a corresponding age. The difference in number is probably due to varying rates of development in individual embryos or to factors related to incubation. The fissures in our embryos and in those of Saetersdal

are the posterolateral (*un* of Ingvar), secunda (*y* of Ingvar), and the prepyramidal, prima (*x* of Ingvar), and intraculminate. An additional fissure, the posterior superior, appears in the 10 day embryo and in some, at this stage, a furrow considered secondary, as will appear, and called uvular sulcus 1, is also found. This furrow corresponds to Ingvar's fissure *z.* A cormorant embryo of 65 mm C.R. length shows all these fissures (fig. 189).

Duck embryos show the cerebellar and vestibular commissures by the 10th day of incubation (fig. 188A). The vermal segment of the posterolateral fissure, the fissura secunda, prepyramidalis, and prima are represented in the 11 day embryo (figs. 190, 191). In 11½ days incubation the posterior superior fissure and uvular sulcus 1 have appeared, but no indication of the intraculminate or preculminate fissures is yet visible. The anterior lobe of

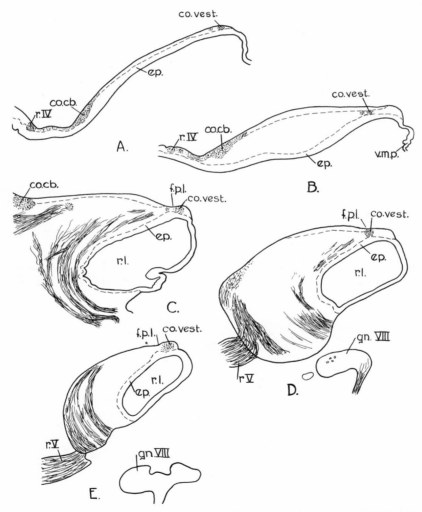

Figure 187. Sagittal sections through cerebellum of chick embryo incubated 9 days. A. Midsagittal section. B, C, D, E. Sections at successive lateral sagittal planes. Bodian method. ×45. (Larsell, 1948.)

the duck differentiates more slowly than in the chick or cormorant or in the species described by Saetersdal in developmental stages corresponding to those of chick, cormorant, and duck above mentioned. An indication of retarded development of the anterior lobe of the duck is also represented by a vertical groove which extends ventralward, in the median sagittal plane, from the fissura prima in the 11 day embryo. The 11½ day stage of the duck, however, has several fissures (fig. 189A). At the 13 day stage the preculminate fissure is developed. Its depth indicates that it appeared later than the intraculminate fissure (fig. 192). In the chick embryo the preculminate fissure appears during the 11th day of incubation, as also found by Saetersdal.

Ventral of the preculminate fissure two fissures are formed during the 11th day of incubation in the chick and during the 13th day in the duck embryo (fig. 193). The more ventral of these I called the precentral fissure in my 1948 contribution but did not name the other. On

the grounds of the relations of the corresponding fissures and their immediately adjacent lobules in the higher primates and man, described in a later section, and because the names of all the fissures in birds are transferred from fissures in man and mammals that appear to correspond, the previously unnamed furrow, next beneath the preculminate, will be called the precentral fissure and the more ventral one precentral fissure *a* (fig. 194).

Saetersdal (1956a) found all the above-named fissures not only in the chick embryo but also in the developing cerebellum of the pigeon and pheasant. Only the posterolateral fissure and fissura secunda had appeared

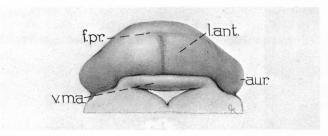

Figure 190. Anterior view of cerebellum of duck embryo, Anas domesticus, incubated 11 days. ×8. (Larsell, 1948.)

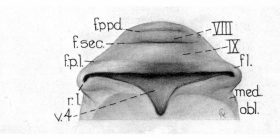

Figure 191. Posterior view of cerebellum of duck embryo incubated 11 days. ×8. (Larsell, 1948.)

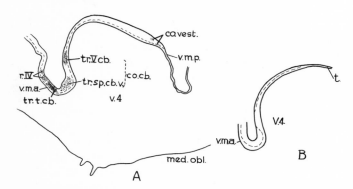

Figure 188. Midsagittal sections of cerebellum. A. Duck embryo incubated 10 days. Bodian method. ×53. B. Cormorant embryo, 27 mm long. Hematoxylin and orange G stain. ×21. (Larsell, 1948.)

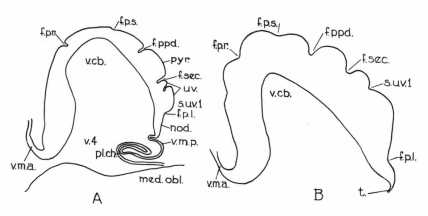

Figure 189. Midsagittal sections of cerebellum. A. Duck embryo incubated 11½ days. Dissection. Surface stain with carmine. Camera lucida. ×20. B. Cormorant embryo, 65 mm long. Hematoxylin and orange G stain. ×42. (Larsell, 1948.)

in the pigeon at the 10th day of incubation; the intraculminate appeared next, followed by the prepyramidal and uvular sulcus 1 in the 11 day embryo. The fissura prima is fairly prominent in the 13 day stage, and shallow posterior superior and preculminate fissures have also appeared. The precentral fissure and precentral fissure *a* of my revised terminology are shown in the 15 day chick embryo (fig. 199).

The sequence of appearance of the fissures is roughly the same in the different species but there are variations.

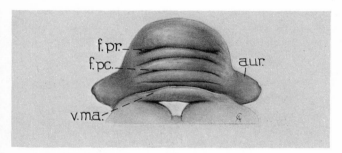

Figure 192. Anterior view of cerebellum of duck embryo incubated 13 days. Intraculminate fissure between f. prima and f. preculminata. ×8. (Larsell, 1948.)

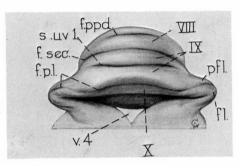

Figure 193. Posterior view of cerebellum of duck embryo incubated 13 days. ×8. (Larsell, 1948.)

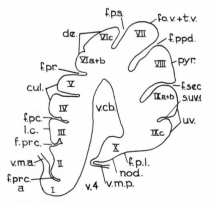

Figure 194. Midsagittal section of cerebellum of duck embryo incubated 13 days. ×20. (Larsell, 1948.)

Whether or not the posterolateral fissure is completed by reaching the midline before the fissura secunda is formed has not been determined, but this seems doubtful. The fissura secunda, not the fissura prima as in most mammals, is the first fissure in the corpus cerebelli of birds. In the chick embryo the prepyramidal fissure seems to appear at about the same stage as the prima, and in the 65 mm cormorant these fissures have approximately the same depth (fig. 189B). Saetersdal's pigeon embryos show no indication of the fissura prima until after the prepyramidal, intraculminate, and even uvular sulcus 1 have appeared. The retarded formation of the fissura prima seems due to its position at the anterodorsal part of the strongly arched cerebellum. As the cortex develops and thickens sufficiently to become folded elsewhere, the tensions of rapid growth in this strongly arched part of the organ apparently prevent folding along the line where the fissura prima is eventually formed. As the tempo of growth of the cortex increases the tension factor is apparently overcome and a furrow appears.

The relative size eventually attained by the folia adjacent to a given fissure appears to be another of the factors that determine the order of appearance and the relative depth of individual fissures. In the 13 day duck embryo all the fissures of the posterior part of the corpus cerebelli are much deeper than those of the anterior part and the folds between them are larger and higher (fig. 194). The same holds true at corresponding stages of development of other birds. In the later stages of development and in most adult birds the corresponding posterior fissures are made deeper than those of the anterior part of the organ and cortical folds, which become the folia, are considerably larger. This anticipatory early development, especially prominent in the rudiment of folium IX (uvula), seems to account for the early appearance of uvular sulcus 1, which is regarded as a secondary furrow.

In most mammals the fissura prima is the first to appear in the corpus cerebelli. Usually it also becomes the deepest. Aciron (1950), however, believed that this fissure appears later than the preculminate in the white rat and, according to Jansen (1954), it makes its appearance in the fin whale later than the prepyramidal fissure. In some mammals the fissura prima is also shallower than certain other fissures, as is nearly always true in birds.

The fissura prima of adult birds, as identified by following it from the embryonic to the adult stage in the chicken and duck, and confirmed by its prominence in the adult cerebellum of some species or established in others by comparison of adjacent folia, is less prominent in nearly all birds than the fissura secunda (figs. 197, 211, 225). The terms fissura prima and fissura secunda obviously are inappropriate with reference to the order of development of the two furrows in birds. But for the sake of more ready comparison with the fissures so named, and with their adjacent lobules in mammals, the terms are retained.

The deep fissura prima of mammals divides the corpus cerebelli into two large lobes, the anterior and the posterior. The relatively shallow fissura prima of most adult birds makes such a division less obvious. The homologies of the fissures and of the folia delimited by them with corresponding features in mammals, as described below, makes it evident that the fissura prima of birds divides the avian corpus cerebelli into anterior and posterior lobes that correspond to those of mammals. They also roughly correspond, respectively, to the anterior and posterior vermis of Shimazono (1912), who, however, includes the nodulus in the posterior vermis. The anterior and posterior lobes are more evident in the adult than in the embryonic bird cerebellum, but the terms are introduced at this point to facilitate further description.

Considering uvular sulcus 1 as a secondary furrow, the nine remaining fissures above described divide the developing cortex into ten primary folds that represent the rudiments of folia I–X of the adult cerebellum. All of these, except folium IX, are shown in simple, undivided form in the 11 day chick and 13 day duck embryos (fig. 194). Saetersdal (1956a) illustrates them in simple form in 11 day chick, 15 day pigeon, and 15 day pheasant embryos. Folia I–V form the anterior lobe of the corpus cerebelli, folia VI–IX represent the vermal part of the posterior lobe of the corpus, and folium X is the nodulus of the flocculonodular lobe.

At early stages of folding there are no distinct medullary rays. As the folia take form diffuse fibers from the developing medullary sheet enter their bases and spread toward the differentiating cortex. Along with lengthening of the folia and further differentiation of the cortex the medullary fibers become collected into compact sheets, represented by the rays in sagittal sections. The rays branch into the subfolia as these develop, fraying at their apices. The rays are augmented by descending axons of Purkinje and other cells, as these elements become differentiated in the cortex. It should be emphasized that formation of the medullary rays follows, rather than precedes, the development of the folia and their subdivisions as in mammals.

Folium I, continuous with the anterior medullary velum, elongates rostralward and extends laterally beneath the remainder of the anterior lobe. It forms a broad plate which gradually becomes dish-like, only the dorsal surface being formed of cortex; the deep part of the folium is a medullary layer facing the ventricular cavity. By the

18 day stage of the duck embryo (fig. 196) the anterior part of the cortical layer has arched ventrally in such a manner that it hooks around the medullary layer and the velum has its attachment to the ventral surface of the folium. Subsequent growth results in increasingly greater recurving of the rostral part of the folium (figs. 197, 198). In the chick and cormorant such recurving does not occur. It is more pronounced in the adult mallard and a similarly recurved folium I is illustrated in the turkey (Meleagris) by Turner (1891). It also occurs in some other species. Further folding in the duck would result in a central medullary core similar to that in folium X of the grouse (p. 245). Such complete folding of folium I has not been encountered in any species, but were it to

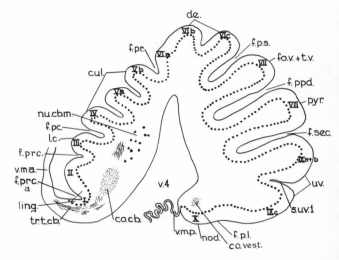

Figure 195. Midsagittal section of cerebellum of duck embryo incubated 15 days. Bodian method. ×26½. (Larsell, 1948.)

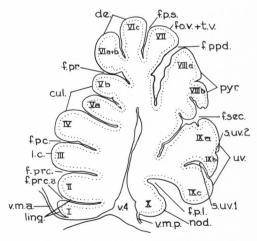

Figure 196. Midsagittal section of cerebellum of duck embryo incubated 18 days. Dissection. Camera lucida. ×12. (Larsell, 1948.)

occur folium I would resemble lobule I of the rat and other small mammals.

Folia II and III are distinct individual folds at the 11th day of incubation of the chick and at the 13th day of the duck (fig. 194). With growth they become well-defined subdivisions of the anterior lobe that correspond to lobules II and III, respectively, of the rat and other mammals. Many authors have included these two lobules in the so-called central lobule of mammals and I applied this term to the two folia in birds (1948). My subsequent reanalysis of the lobules of mammals (1952, 1953a, 1954) and in man has made it clear that the term central lobule, transferred from the older terminology of the human cerebellum, is properly applicable only to lobule III. Lobule II is variable in the higher primates and man, although quite constant in most other mammals, as is folium II in birds. Folium III, homologous with lobule III, can be considered the central lobule, but folium II is a distinct morphological entity which corresponds to part of the lingula of the classical terminology of the human cerebellum, folium I also being included.

Folia IV and V, situated between the preculminate fissure and the fissura prima, corresponds to the culmen of mammals. Both are undivided in the 13 day duck embryo but in the 15 day and later stages of incubation folium V is deeply divided into subfolia Va and Vb (figs. 195–198). In the 15 day chick embryo folium V is slightly divided and folium IV is divided more deeply (fig. 199). The 4-day-old chick (fig. 200) and young adult chickens show an undivided folium IV and a rather deeply divided folium V (fig. 210), indicating variations in these two folia, which are functionally related.

Folium VI, of the posterior lobe, is divided by a shallow furrow into VIa + b and VIc in the 13 day duck embryo. At the 15 day stage of incubation subfolia VIa and VIb are initially separated (fig. 195) and in the newly hatched duckling they are quite distinct from one another (fig. 198). Subfolium VIc and the basal part of folium VI have elongated dorsalward so greatly that the apex of the cerebellum of the duck from this stage on lies far dorsal of the fissura prima. In chick embryos subfolia VIa + b and VIc remain small and poorly delimited from each other.

Folium VII is divided by a slight superficial furrow in the 20 day duck (fig. 197) and the young duckling (fig. 204), but in the latter the medullary ray distinctly divides distally. In chick embryos, young chicks, and young adult chickens folium VII remains undivided. The posterior superior fissure becomes very deep in the duck (fig. 198), owing to the dorsal expansion of folia VI and VII, but in the chicken this fissure is relatively shallow.

Folium VIII is slightly divided, distally, in the 18 day and older duck embryo and in 15 day and older chick embryos and young chicks (figs. 196–200).

Folium IX is divided into a small dorsal subfolium and

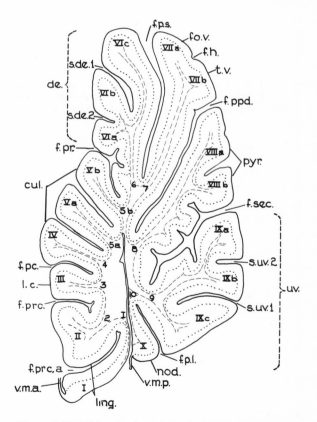

Figure 198. Midsagittal section of cerebellum of newly hatched duck. Bodian method. ×14. (Larsell, 1948.)

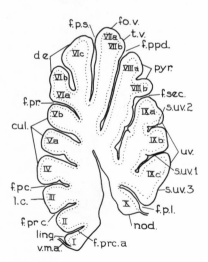

Figure 197. Midsagittal section of cerebellum of duck embryo incubated 20 days. Dissection. Camera lucida. ×12. (Larsell, 1948.)

a larger ventral one by uvular sulcus 1 in the 11½ day embryo, as already noted. The dorsal subdivision expands rapidly, forming subfolium IXa + b at the 13 day stage of incubation (fig. 194). The ventral subdivision represents subfolium IXc. By the 18 day stage of incubation subfolia IXa and IXb are separated by uvular sulcus 2 (figs. 196, 203). The differentiation of subfolia in folium IX of the chick embryo is similar.

Folium X, the nodulus of the flocculonodular lobe, remains as a simple fold (figs. 197, 206), to the margin of

which the choroid tela is attached. In the later embryonic stages of the duck it hooks forward into the ventral part of the cerebellar ventricle, in which the tenial margin becomes hidden.

The variations of the individual folia and their subdivisions are more pronounced in adult specimens of different species. They are further considered in the cerebella of the species described in the following section.

Embryonic stages of the duck and chick show the steps by which the intimate relations of the two components of the "avian auricle" are attained. As already mentioned, the flocculus and the lateral segment of the posterolateral fissure are clear early in cerebellar development, as in crocodilian and mammalian embryos.

In the duck embryo of 11 days' incubation a rounded projection extends laterally from each side of the cerebellar base (fig. 191). The anterior part of this projection is an extension of the caudal part of the flocculus, delimited from the anterior part by a superficial furrow which represents the lateral segment of the posterolateral fissure. By the 13th day of incubation the anterior part of the projection stands out distinctly from the remainder of the corpus cerebelli (figs. 192, 193). Caudomedially it is continuous with folium IX, the uvula, but more specifically with subfolium IXc. In my earlier (1948) description of the "avian auricle" I called the component

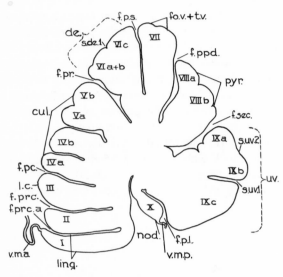

Figure 199. Sagittal section, slightly to one side of the midplane, of cerebellum of chick embryo incubated 15 days. Dissection. Camera lucida. ×20. (Larsell, 1948.)

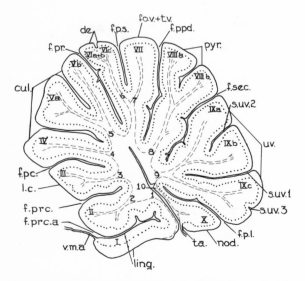

Figure 200. Midsagittal section of cerebellum of chick 4 days after hatching. Dissection. Camera lucida. ×12. (Larsell, 1948.)

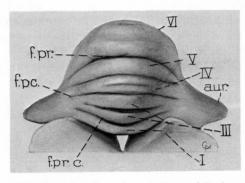

Figure 201. Anterior view of cerebellum of duck embryo incubated 15 days. ×8. (Larsell, 1948.)

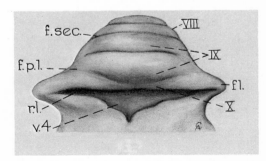

Figure 202. Posterior view of cerebellum of duck embryo incubated 15 days. ×8. (Larsell, 1948.)

related to folium IX the "avian paraflocculus" and suggested that it corresponds to the accessory paraflocculus of mammals.

The relation of the flocculus to the "avian paraflocculus" is illustrated in figures 202 to 205 of the cerebellum of duck embryos and 1-day-old duckling, and in figure 206 of the cerebellum of a chick 4 days after hatching. At these stages the posterolateral fissure delimits the flocculus from the "avian paraflocculus" and continues around the tip of the "auricle," defined as the lateral projection formed by the "avian paraflocculus" and the flocculus, to the dorsolateral surface of the medulla oblongata. Medially the fissure deepens and separates folium X from subfolium IXc. In the 15 day duck embryo the "avian auricle" forms a conical lateral projection with broad base and rounded apex, the flocculus being more prominent than the paraflocculus in posterior view (fig. 202). In 1-day-old duckling the parafloccular component has increased in relative size so that in posterodorsal view it arches in front of the flocculus and covers it laterally (figs. 204, 205). The medial continuity of the "avian paraflocculus" with subfolium IXc is well shown at these stages of development. In the 18 day duck embryo uvular sulcus 1 continues laterorostrally and ven-

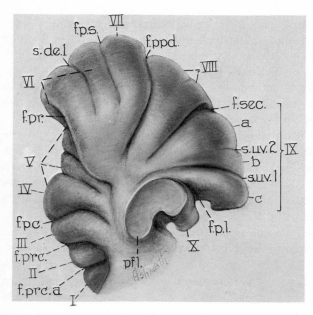

Figure 203. Lateral view of cerebellum of duck embryo incubated 18 days, with paraflocculus and flocculus dissected away. ×13. (Larsell, 1948.)

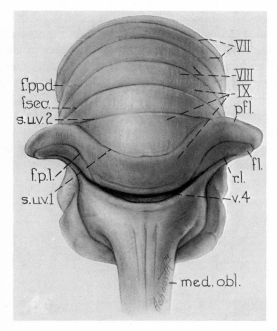

Figure 204. Posterodorsal view of cerebellum of duck one day after hatching. ×8. (Larsell, 1948.)

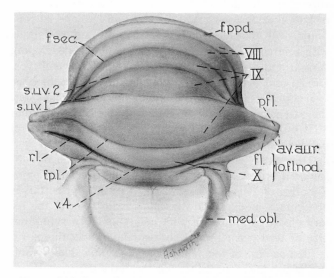

Figure 205. Posterior view of cerebellum of duck one day after hatching. ×8. (Larsell, 1948.)

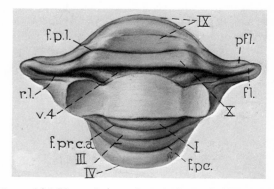

Figure 206. Ventral view of cerebellum of chick 4 days after hatching. ×8. (Larsell, 1948.)

trally as a faint furrow between the anterodorsal part of the base of the "auricle" and unfoliated cortex in front of the base (fig. 203).

Restudy of the "auricle" and of the lateral surface of the avian cerebellum, and closer comparison of folia VIII and IX with the corresponding lobules of mammalian embryos, have shed additional light on the homologies of this region of the avian cerebellum. The mammalian lobules which I described subsequently (1952, 1953, 1953a, 1953b, 1954) to the folia of birds, are further elaborated and those of additional species are included in later sections of this volume.

In the 18 day duck embryo subfolia IXa and IXb converge laterally into a tapering cortical fold which is continuous, by a low ridge around the end of the fissura secunda, with a similarly tapering lateral continuation of folium VIII, the pyramis (fig. 203). Indications of similar continuity are evident in the adult cerebellum of some species but are difficult to recognize in others. The ventrolateral extension of subfolia IXa and IXb and its continuity with that of folium VIII have the same relations with reference to the fissura secunda as the developing ventral and dorsal paraflocculi of mammalian embryos. Dorsal and ventral paraflocculi are not represented as lateral projections in birds, as they are in mammals, but the extensions of subfolia IXa and IXb and of folium VIII may be considered rudimentary ventral and dorsal paraflocculi respectively.

The "avian paraflocculus," as a continuation of subfolium IXc, clearly corresponds to the accessory paraflocculus of Jansen in mammals. As will appear, this is continuous medially, in mammals, with folia of the inferior part of lobule IX that corresponds to subfolium IXc of birds; usually the accessory paraflocculus is regarded as part of the ventral paraflocculus. The homology of the "avian paraflocculus" with the accessory paraflocculus is most evident when the uvula and parafloccular complex of the spiny anteater, Echidna aculeata, is compared with folium IX and the "avian paraflocculus" as most simply shown in duck embryos. It also is evident, however, in other mammals, including man.

The "avian auricle" is less prominent in the chick embryo and young chick than in the duck at corresponding stages of general development of the cerebellum. As in the duck, however, it comprises floccular and parafloccular components which are distinctly separable by the posterolateral fissure as in duck embryos. The medial relations of the two are identical with those in the duck embryo (fig. 206). In both duck and chick embryos the flocculus, although clearly constituting the lateral part of the flocculonodular lobe, is more closely associated with the parafloccular component than is true of the usual relations between flocculus and accessory paraflocculus in mammalian embryos. Sometimes, in mammals, the two are closely associated with one another.

The flocculus gradually is covered anteriorly by the lateral growth of the "avian paraflocculus" both in chick and duck, the two components merging distally to such an extent that the posterolateral fissure almost disappears between them. It can be followed, however, in the adult duck and the pigeon to the dorsolateral surface of the medulla oblongata (fig. 207B). In the horned owl and cormorant it ends against the cerebellar peduncle (figs. 212A, 226) and in other species faint traces of the lateral part of the fissure are recognizable. We shall return to the "auricle" and its subdivisions in adult birds, in which the fiber connections also will be considered. The embryonic history of the projection clearly shows its double origin and the relation of the parafloccular part to the corpus cerebelli, whereas the flocculus is part of the flocculonodular lobe.

Rostral of the base of the "auricle" and ventral of the extremities of the folia of the posterior lobe an area of unfoliated cortex is demonstrable in gross specimens of embryonic cerebella by light surface staining, as well as in sections stained by the customary techniques. This area constitutes the incipient cerebellar hemisphere already mentioned in the chicken and other species.

Variations of the "avian auricle," rudimentary hemisphere, and folia I–X in the adult stage of various species are described in the following sections.

AVES II

The Adult Cerebellum

THE number of families and orders of birds is so great that a close study of the cerebellum must be limited to a relatively small number of species. The cerebella of many of the species described, however, have distinctive characteristics that appear to be ordinal. So far as possible two or more species of the same order were studied. The form of the organ differs and, in general, the larger species have more numerous cortical folds than the smaller ones, as noted by Leuret and Gratiolet (1839–57) and Brandis (1894). The increased number, however, is owing to subfoliation of one or another of primary folds described in my 1948 contribution and named folia I–X.

As shown in embryonic stages of chick and duck (Larsell, 1948) and in a number of other species representing several orders described by Saetersdal (1956a), the primary folia are constant in number although differing in relative size when one species is compared with another. This difference is more evident in later developmental stages and in adult birds. The secondary foliation which individual folia undergo in later stages of development also varies from species to species. The cerebellum of hummingbirds appears to be an exception with respect to the number of primary folia. In this group of small and highly specialized birds some of the folia of the anterior lobe are so atrophic that they do not form typical cortical folds, while others are so enlarged that they also are atypical. The folia of the posterior lobe are more typical and folia VI and IX are subfoliated. As will appear, the hummingbird cerebellum falls within the pattern common to all species investigated.

The secondary foliation in adult birds may differ in individual folia of different species whose body weight is approximately equal but which vary in other characteristics. Folium VI, for example, is much larger and more subfoliated in the duck than in the chicken and the grouse. Also, the depth of the fissures delimiting secondary folia varies from species to species. Consideration of the fiber tract connections of individual folia, described below, and of the locomotor habits and sensory equipment of individual species, leads to the conclusion that functional factors are closely associated with the relative size and subfoliation of the primary folia. One of these factors is the relative importance, in different species, of afferent impulses to individual folia. The cerebellar cortical areas activated by stimulation of the nerves to the feathers, in various parts of the body, and of the retina and cochlea, have been investigated by Whitlock (1952), to whose results we shall return.

The early differentiation of folium X, the nodulus, and its continuation with the flocculi, forming the flocculonodular lobe, has already been described. The posterolateral fissure, delimiting this lobe from the corpus cerebelli, deepens medially in the adult cerebellum, but laterally it becomes so shallow in the "avian auricle" that the boundary between the components of the auricle, related respectively to the flocculonodular lobe and corpus cerebelli, is often nearly obliterated although distinct in embryonic stages. The floccular and parafloccular components of the "auricle" were recognized by Ingvar (1918) in the chicken although not ascribed, respectively, to the two fundamental divisions of the cerebellum.

As already noted in embryonic stages, the corpus cerebelli is divided by the fissura prima into anterior and posterior lobes, the anterior lobe comprising folia I–V and the posterior lobe folia VI–IX. Corresponding divisions of the cerebellum of mammals were described and named lobules I–V in the anterior lobe and lobules VI–IX in the posterior lobe; the nodulus of the flocculonodular lobe corresponding to folium X of birds was called lobule X (Larsell, 1952, 1953a, 1954). In the further description of the folia close comparisons with the lobules of mammals will be made. This will include not only the morphological features but also the fiber tract connections demonstrated by experimental-anatomical methods in birds, in comparison with the distribution of corresponding tracts in mammals. In addition, the results of electrophysiological studies in birds and mammals with reference to cerebellar subdivisions that are activated by stimulation of various parts of the body and of sensory organs will be compared. Such comparisons must anticipate some of the results in mammals presented in greater detail in the following volume, but duplication to this extent is deemed necessary in order to establish homologies on a firm basis.

On the grounds of its position with reference to the fissura prima and the anterior medullary velum and of its fiber tract connections, described below, the anterior lobe of birds corresponds to the relatively much smaller anterior lobe of Ingvar in Crocodilia. It also corresponds to the anterior lobe of Elliot Smith, Ingvar, and others in mammals, in which it is subdivided into lobules I–V.

As described in the section on the mammalian cerebellum, the anterior lobe of mammals is divided into dorsal and ventral segments by the early-appearing fissura preculminata. The ventral segment is divided a little later by the fissura praecentralis into the rudiment of lobule III and a subdivision which represents the common rudiment of lobules II and I. As a rule this rudiment subsequently divides into the individual lobules, but lobule I is small in the adult stage of some species (e.g., pig and some primates), while in others it attains considerable size and is divided from lobule II by a relatively deep fissure. The two lobules are closely related in development irrespective of the size of lobule I in the adult stage. A reanalysis of the human lingula and lobulus centralis (Larsell, 1953b) makes it clear that the lingula of classical terminology comprises two atrophic and more or less merged subdivisions corresponding to lobules I and II of mammals, and that the human lobulus centralis corresponds to lobule III.

In my 1948 contribution on the avian cerebellum, folium I was regarded as corresponding to the lingula of mammals, as this term has been used by many authors to designate lobule I of the Roman numeral terminology. Folia II and III were regarded as homologous with the lobulus centralis of mammals, in which some authors include two subdivisions that correspond to lobules II and III. Folia I and II of adult birds (except the hummingbirds) are more deeply separated one from the other than are lobules I and II in mammals; also folium II is relatively larger, as a rule, than lobule II of mammals. The developmental history of the two folia in the duck embryo and in embryos of other birds described by Saetersdal (1956a) appears to make them homologous with lobules I and II of mammals and therefore with the human lingula. They are well differentiated one from the other in the duck embryo, beginning with the second half of the incubation period. In the 13 day embryo of the duck and in approximately corresponding developmental stages of the cerebellum of the chick and the species described by Saetersdal the two folia are separated by a shallower furrow than that which separates folium II from folium III. As folia I and II elongate rostralward this furrow deepens so that in the adult cerebellum it is approximately as deep as the fissure between folia II and III which has also deepened as its adjacent lobules have expanded rostralward. The furrow between folia II and III corresponds to the precentral fissure of mammals and the one between folia I and II to precentral fissure a.

Folium III corresponds morphologically to lobule III (centralis) and folia IV and V to lobules IV and V (culmen) of mammals. The dorsal and ventral segments of the anterior lobe which differentiate into lobules IV and V and lobules I, II, and III, respectively, in mammals, are not recognizable in embryonic or adult birds. The preculminate fissure, which separates them and is the deepest in the anterior lobe of mammals, is no deeper than the precentral in birds. Both are exceeded in depth by the intraculminate fissure between folia IV and V beginning in embryonic stages as noted by Saetersdal (1956a).

Comparison of the folia of the anterior lobe, as interpreted on morphological grounds, with the subdivisions of the lobe in which Whitlock (1952) demonstrated spino-cerebellar fibers in Marchi preparations of the pigeon cerebellum, and with the corresponding morphological mammalian lobules in which such fibers terminate, reveals a remarkable similarity. Degenerating spino-cerebellar fibers, following lesions of the cord at various levels including cervical to lower lumbar segments, were found in folia II, III, IV, and V. A ventrally directed continuation of degenerated fibers tapered toward folium I but disappeared short of its base. In sagittal sections of the chicken cerebellum, stained by the Weigert method, a thin sheet of fibers continues from the region corresponding to that where the Marchi degeneration disappears in the pigeon and forms a layer immediately beneath the ventricular surface of folium I. Transverse Weigert sections of the cerebellum of the chicken and the horned owl show a similar layer in the lateral part of the folium. This is continuous with the lateral part of the sheet of fibers extending into folium II and, apparently, also with the ventral spino-cerebellar tract in the base of the cerebellum. Degenerated spino-cerebellar fibers were also found by Whitlock in folium VI and in other folia of the posterior lobe, to which we shall return.

Anderson (1943), who included in his "lingula" of the rat only the subdivision which I subsequently (1952) called lobule I, found degenerating fibers of both the dorsal and ventral spino-cerebellar tracts in this lobule, in his "lobulus centralis" (lobule II and III) and in the "culmen" (lobules IV and V) following lesions in the lower cervical and thoracic segments of the cord. He also found degenerated fibers in various vermal lobules of the posterior lobe, to which we shall return, and in hemispheral lobules not differentiated in birds.

The conclusions of a number of other authors with reference to the distribution of the spino-cerebellar tracts within the cerebellum of mammals are considered in a subsequent section. Here only those of Vachananda (1959), who employed the Roman numeral terminology of the vermal lobules in the rhesus monkey, and those of Chang and Ruch (1949), who described the distribution of spino-cerebellar fibers from the tail region of the cord in the spider monkey, Ateles, will be compared further with those of Whitlock in birds.

Vachananda made lesions in the cords of a series of monkeys at various levels from the second cervical to the first sacral segments. He employed the Swank-Davenport modification of the Marchi method to demonstrate the resulting degeneration of the spino-cerebellar tracts. Following section of the cord at the second cervical level, degeneration of ventral and dorsal spino-cerebellar fibers, according to Vachananda, was found in all lobules of the vermis except I, VII, and X. The largest numbers for both tracts are said to have ended in lobules II and III. Without considering here the relative number ending in other lobules, we see that the distribution confirms the observations of Anderson in the rat, except that Vachananda did not include lobule I. In one of his monkeys, however, he found a few degenerated fibers to this lobule which, in the light of the observations of Anderson on the rat, Chang and Ruch on Ateles (see below), and those on folium I of birds, above noted, suggest a distribution to lobule I also. This instance, evidently considered aberrant and omitted from Vachananda's summary of distribution of the spino-cerebellar tract, suggests that such fibers to lobule I in the remaining animals may not have responded to the not always certain Marchi techniques, as appears also to have been true in Whitlock's pigeons. Possibly they were greatly reduced in number or absent, owing to reduction of the distal part of the tail in the rhesus monkey.

In Marchi preparations of the spider monkey, Ateles, following section of the cord at the level of the first caudal segment, Chang and Ruch (1949) found degenerated ventral spino-cerebellar tract fibers to the "lingula" and the "lobulus centralis," a few passing toward the culmen and the walls of the fissura secunda in the posterior lobe. As will appear later, the lingula and central lobule of these authors in Ateles correspond respectively to lobules I and II of other mammals and also of Ateles as I interpret them (1953a, other studies). The degenerated spino-cerebellar fibers were regarded as functionally related to the tail, the innervation of which was described by Chang and Ruch (1947). According to these authors (1949) the tail muscles of Ateles comprise basal and intrinsic groups. The basal muscles have their origin from various bones of the pelvis and their attachment to the basal part of the tail, whereas the intrinsic muscles have both origin and insertion on the caudal vertebrae. The spino-cerebellar fibers to lobules I and II presumably include at least some that are functionally related to proprioceptors and exteroceptors of the base of the tail. Others probably relay proprioceptive impulses from the intrinsic tail muscles and exteroceptive impulses from the distal part of the tail, especially the tail pad. Differentiation of degenerating fibers related to the basal and the distal parts of the tail, respectively, was precluded by the level of section of the cord. The degenerated fibers, however, terminated chiefly, as already noted, in the two ventral lobules of the anterior lobe.

In addition to afferent fibers of the spino-cerebellar tracts to lobules I, II, or both, as seen in Marchi preparations, efferent effects on the tail, resulting from electrical stimulation of the cortex of the "lingula" (evidently lobules I and II) were recorded by Hampson, Harrison, and Woolsey (1952). These authors did not subdivide the tail.

Comparison of the tail muscles of birds with those of Ateles brings to light similarities that are suggestive with reference to the functional relations to them of folia I and II. These muscles have been described in various species by Shufeldt (1890), Porta (1908), Fisher and Goodman (1955), and others. They are more complex than in mammals.

Some, having their origin in various units of the pelvic girdle, attach to rectrices or other large feathers. Others from the pelvic girdle insert on processes of the caudal vertebrae. A levator cloacae, whose origin is not indicated, attaches to the cloaca (Fisher and Goodman). It appears justifiable to consider the muscles of the pelvic girdle that attach to caudal vertebrae as corresponding to the basal tail muscles of mammals. In addition, birds have interspinal muscles between successive free caudal vertebrae and between the last of these and the pygostyle (Fisher and Goodman). These may be regarded as corresponding to the intrinsic tail muscles of mammals. All the tail muscles presumably have proprioceptors in addition to motor terminations, and the mixed motor and sensory nerves leading to them include sensory fibers to feathers related to the tail region.

The most caudal of Whitlock's lesions of the cord, namely the lower lumbar segments, was too high to permit any conclusions regarding the origin of spino-cerebellar fibers that reached folium II and extended toward folium I in his Marchi preparations. In this author's electrophysiological experiments stimulation of a mixed motor and sensory nerve to the tail region activated folia III and IV ipsilaterally. No records of activation of folia I and II were obtained, however, owing to difficulties of approach to these two folia. The distribution of spino-cerebellar fibers to both, as above described, makes it probable that they too were activated. If it be assumed that the fibers to them are from the tail region, as are the fibers to lobules I and II of Ateles, activation of folia III and IV by stimuli from the tail must mean that in birds a greater proportion of the tail fibers of the spino-cerebellar tracts continues upward in the anterior lobe farther than in mammals as represented by Ateles.

Suggestive evidence, presented in the section on mammals, points to a functional relation of lobule II to the basal tail muscles and their derivatives (e.g., in anthropoids) and probably to the exteroceptors connected with nerves of the body segments from which these muscles derive. Lobule I is probably related to the distal part of the tail, including its intrinsic muscles and its exteroceptors. In the pig, for example, lobule I is very small compared with lobule II. The small size of lobule I appears to be correlated with the reduction of the distal part of the tail, and the larger size of lobule II with the greater importance of the basal tail muscles and segmentally related cutaneous areas. The movements of the tail in the pig appear to be dependent on the basal tail muscles. The contrast between the small lobule I of the pig and the large corresponding lobule in Ateles which in addition has a hemispheral extension on either side is the most striking illustration of correlation between this lobule and the functional importance of the distal part of the tail. In Ateles the elongated and prehensile tail serves as a fifth limb, of great importance in this animal's activities both as a motor and as a sensory organ. The basal muscles appear to serve the movements of the tail as a whole, whereas the distal muscles are concerned with its more refined activities in grasping and related movements. Many other examples of apparent correlation of lobule I with the distal, and of lobule II with the basal part of the tail are found among mammals (see the next volume), although experimental confirmation is lacking.

Similar indications of the relations of folia I and II of

birds to the distal and basal parts, respectively, of the tail are less apparent. Possibly the relatively reduced folium I of the penguins is correlated with a reduced distal part of the tail. The tail of the penguins is of great importance in maintaining an upright posture of its body, but the relations of the muscles and feathers involved are unknown to me.

Stimulation of the sciatic nerve, according to Whitlock, activated folium III and also folia IV and V. No response to tactile stimulation of the leg area could be recorded from folium III. Whitlock, however, regarded the tactile leg area as probably coextensive with the anterior lobe area which responds to stimulation of the sciatic nerve and probably extends into folium III. The activation of folia IV and V by stimulation of the sciatic nerve, as well as of leg feathers, again indicates less localized distribution of spino-cerebellar fibers from the lower extremity than in mammals. Although folium III apparently is not so richly or specifically related to the lower extremity by its spino-cerebellar connections as is lobule III of mammals, the developmental history and morphological relations of the two subdivisions appear to make them homologous.

Stimulation of the radial nerve to the wing, or movements of wing feathers, activated folia IV, Va, Vb, and VIa. These correspond to the folia in which most of the remaining spino-cerebellar fibers were distributed in Whitlock's Marchi preparations. Except for a greater representation of degenerated spino-cerebellar fibers in folium VI than in lobule VI of mammals as shown in Anderson's Marchi preparations of the rat, the three folia correspond to the three mammalian lobules. In the electrophysiological studies of Adrian (1943) and Snider and Stowell (1942, 1944) stimulation of the upper extremity activated loci of the anterior lobe and in the lobulus simplex (lobule VI) of the posterior lobe (Snider and Stowell). The loci correspond in general to the ipsilateral fields of the avian folia that respond to tactile or appropriate nerve stimulation. The areas of response were more discrete in mammals and also included areas in hemispheral lobules not differentiated in birds. The apparently greater distribution of loci activated by stimulation of the tail region in folia IV and V, and of those activated from both leg and wing in folium VIa, in addition to folia IV and V, appears to indicate a greater overlap of fibers representing the lower part of the body in birds. Folium VIa also responded to stimulation of the trigeminal nerve and of face feathers, as did the anterior part of lobule VI to impulses from corresponding sources in mammals.

The posterior lobe, comprising folia VI–IX, the unfoliated cortex of the lower lateral cerebellar surface, and the parafloccular part of the "avian auricle," has more prominent folia and more elongated fissures than in late embryonic stages. It differs from Ingvar's posterior lobe by excluding the nodulus and flocculi but including the uvula and pyramis, as Ingvar defined these subdivisions, and also all of his medial lobe. The fissura secunda, between folia VIII and IX, is usually deeper and its walls more foliated than any other fissure of the corpus cerebelli. The relative depth of the fissures, however, does not always indicate either their order of appearance in the embryo or their significance as boundaries of major subdivisions of the adult cerebellum. This depth is governed by the form of the cerebellum in individual species and the size attained by the folia immediately adjacent to individual fissures. The depth of the fissura secunda results from the large size of folium IX in all birds. Except in Apteryx, as illustrated by Craigie (1930), this folium is divided into three secondary folia which, especially in the larger species, may subfoliate. Most frequently the medullary rays to the secondary folia are trident-like branches of a short primary ray, as in duck and chick embryos. In some other species the ventralmost of the three folia has a separate ray, but this is believed to be a modification of the more usual pattern. Folium VI, immediately behind the fissura prima, is the most variable in relative size and in the number of subfolia into which it is divided in different species.

In Marchi preparations, following destruction of the superior sensory nucleus of the trigeminus or the region just dorsal of it, Whitlock found degenerated fibers distributed to folia V, VI, and sometimes VII. Removal of cortex from the dorsal surfaces of folia VI and VII was followed by chromatolysis of cells in the dorsolateral part of the superior sensory trigeminal nucleus, as shown in Nissl preparations. Stimulation of the trigeminal nerve, however, activated only subfolia VIa and VIb in the pigeon and VIb in the duck, while stimulation of the feathers of the face area in pigeon and owl activated VIa, VIb, and VIc. It therefore appears probable that the Marchi degeneration to folia V and VII resulted from injury to other than trigeminal fibers and that the trigeminal distribution is confined to folium VI. In the cat and monkey, according to Adrian (1943), activation of cerebellar cortex by stimulation of the face area was limited to the lobulus simplex (lobule VI).

According to Whitlock, folium VI also receives tecto-cerebellar fibers and such fibers also distribute to folia VII, VIII, and possibly IX. Distribution to these folia was indicated by degenerated fibers following destruction of the tectal gray substance or of the anterior medullary velum. Other than tecto-cerebellar fibers may also have been involved, but removal of the cortex of folia VI and

VII resulted in chromatolytic changes in the cells of the tectal region and of the nucleus isthmi. Electrical stimulation of the tectum and photic stimulation of the retina in the horned owl activated folia VII and VIII, while stimulation of the cochlea by sound activated folia VIc, VII, and VIII. In the pigeon folia VII and VIII were activated by impulses from the cochlea and retina, and in the duck subfolia VIIa, VIIIa, and VIIIb responded to impulses from the cochlea and subfolia VIb and VIIb to photic stimulation of the retina.

Snider and Stowell (1944) and Snider (1945) reported responses in the lobulus simplex (lobule VI and HVI), folium and tuber vermis (lobule VII), and pyramis (lobule VIII) of the cat to photic impulses. Fadiga, Pupilli, and von Berger (1956) found activation in lobules VI and VII by photic stimuli in the unanesthetized cat. In Snider and Stowell's experiments with cochlear stimulation in the cat, responses to chicks were recorded from the lobulus simplex (lobule VI), the folium and tuber vermis (lobule VII), and the pyramis (lobule VIII). The projection from the tectum to these lobules was believed to involve the tecto-cerebellar tract, as Whitlock (1952) also concluded with reference to the corresponding folia of birds.

As demonstrated by Marchi degeneration following destruction of the inferior olive, fibers from these nuclei reach all parts of the cerebellar cortex (Whitlock). Brodal (1940b) had shown a similar distribution from the inferior olive of the cat by the Brodal-Gudden method.

Ponto-cerebellar fibers reaching the rudimentary cerebellar hemispheres, the "avian paraflocculus," and, in smaller numbers, folia VI–VIII and the dorsal subfolium of IX were demonstrated by Brodal, Kristiansen, and Jansen (1950). These authors employed the method of retrograde degeneration for the determination of the origin and distribution of the avian pontocerebellar fibers.

The flocculonodular lobe, comprising folium X and the two flocculi, receives vestibular fibers apparently to the exclusion of other connections, except olivo-cerebellar fibers. After experimental lesions of the vestibular nerve and the vestibular nuclei in the pigeon, Whitlock found degenerated fibers, in Marchi preparations, to folium X, folium IX, and the lateral extensions of these two folia which form the "avian auricle." The auricle varies in relative size in different species and also in the direction, lateral or laterocaudal, of its projection. It also varies in the distinctness of demarcation of its component parts, one from the other, by the posterolateral fissure. The variation in the depth of the lateral segment of the posterolateral fissure appears to be related to the number of vestibular fibers, probably secondary, that pass beneath it into the parafloccular part of the auricle. As already noted, the "avian paraflocculus" corresponds to the accessory paraflocculus of mammals. The floccular part of the auricle is reduced as compared with the flocculus of mammals.

The somatotopic pattern of the cerebellar areas activated from the various body regions and sensory organs of birds corresponds in general to that of mammals as determined by Snider and Stowell (1942, 1944) and Adrian (1943) and recently reviewed by Dow and Moruzzi (1958). In birds, however, there appears to be more overlap of the areas of activation by tactile stimulation, especially in the anterior lobe, than in mammals.

Recently Goodman, Horel, and Freemon (1963) have demonstrated three longitudinal zones in the cerebellar cortex of young ducks, with implanted electrodes. These zones correspond to the vermal, intermediate, and lateral zones of Jansen and Brodal in mammals. Responses to electrical stimulation were very similar to those obtained in the rat with the same method by Goodman and Simpson (1961).

The cerebellum of the pigeon is the most generalized of those studied in birds, all the morphological features above described being present in relatively simple form. Comparison of the organ in the various species will therefore begin with that of the pigeon.

Pigeon (Columba Livia)

The numerous varieties of domesticated pigeons are descendants of the wild rock pigeon, Columba livia, of the order Columbiformes. All specimens used in my investigations were from ordinary unspecialized stock but unfortunately no data about age, weight, or sex were obtained.

The pigeon is a strong and swift flier, the homing or carrier pigeon being capable of sustained flight for long distances at speeds as great as sixty miles per hour. Pigeons are also at home on the ground, moving about on short, active legs. Their vision is acute and their hearing excellent.

The cerebellum of the pigeon is well developed with respect to the primary folia, depth of intervening fissures, and size of "avian auricle" (fig. 207), but retains a relatively simple form and pattern, as pointed out by Brouwer (1913). The ten primary folia seen in chick and duck embryos are represented in similar pattern, although some that are undivided in the smaller and apparently immature cerebella have secondary folia in larger specimens.

The posterolateral fissure is relatively shallow in the pigeon but can be followed from the rhombic lip of one side of the medulla oblongata to the other, thus forming

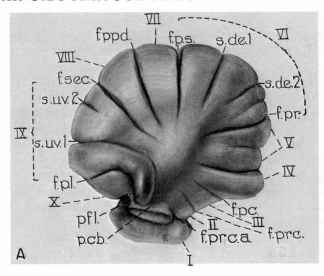

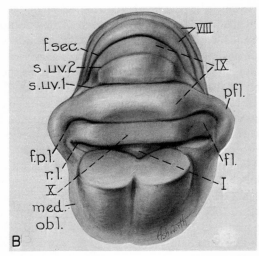

Figure 207. Cerebellum of adult pigeon, Columba livia. A. Lateral view; B. Posterior view. ×6½. (Larsell, 1948.)

a complete boundary between flocculondular lobe and corpus cerebelli (fig. 207B).

The cerebellar ventricle is a thin cleft in some specimens; in others it is wider, anteroposteriorly, and has a slight posterior recess above the base of lobule X (fig. 208).

THE CORPUS CEREBELLI

The anterior lobe of the corpus cerebelli is smaller than the posterior lobe (fig. 207A). The fissura prima, in some specimens, is the deepest of the cerebellar fissures; in larger cerebella the fissura secunda is deeper and more prominent. The five primary folia of the anterior lobe are delimited by relatively deep fissures. Individual folia show differences of subfoliation in large specimens as compared with smaller ones.

Folium I is situated between the cerebellar peduncles as a relatively large, dish-like fold which tapers at its rostral end and is continuous with the anterior medullary velum (fig. 208). The molecular layer faces the dorsal surface of the folium, this surface forming the floor of the concavity. The granular layer faces the fourth ventricle, but a thin fibrous layer, continuous with the medullary sheet of the anterior wall of the cerebellar ventricle, separates it posteriorly from the ventricular surface. The fibers of this layer, however, spread among the granules and the layer disappears on the ventral surface.

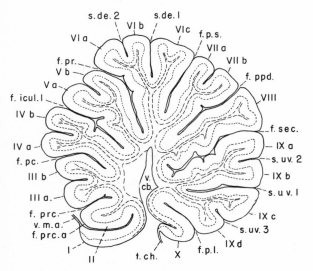

Figure 208. Midsagittal section of cerebellum of adult pigeon. ×8. (Larsell and Whitlock, 1952.)

Folium II is situated dorsal of folium I, dipping somewhat into the concavity. Its medullary ray fans out, with a suggestion of bifurcation in some specimens.

Folium III forms an elongated simple fold with rounded anterior surface in some cerebella; in others it is divided into two subfolia (fig. 208).

Folium IV is large and extends rostrally beyond the general anterior surface of the cerebellum (fig. 207A). It is subdivided in the larger specimens.

Folium V is large and is divided into subfolia Va and Vb (fig. 208). A second shallow furrow also divides its ventral surface, which faces the intraculminate fissure. Folia IV and V together correspond to the culmen of mammals. A furrow considered homologous with the mammalian preculminate fissure, although it is not so deep in Columba as the fissure between folia IV and V, separates folia III and IV.

In the posterior lobe, folium VI, delimited anteriorly by the fissura prima, is divided into subfolia VIa, VIb, and VIc, as in duck embryos and, partially, in the 15 day chick embryo. Secondary folium VIc is delimited from VIb by a relatively deep furrow which may be called declival sulcus 1, and subfolia VIa and VIb are separated by a shallower declival sulcus 2 (fig. 208). The lower portion of the posterior wall of the fissura prima probably corresponds to the small folia in a similar position in the newly hatched duck.

Folium VII is undivided in some specimens but in others it has a shallow furrow dividing it into subfolia VIIa and VIIb (fig. 208). The furrow which delimits the folium from VIc is regarded as homologous with the posterior superior fissure of mammals.

Folium VIII is undivided in the pigeon but in some specimens the medullary ray bifurcates at its tip and the surface of the folium facing the fissura secunda is slightly foliated (fig. 208). The furrow between folia VII and VIII corresponds to the prepyramidal fissure of mammals. Folium VIII, as already noted, is homologous with the mammalian pyramis.

Folium IX, the uvula, is divided into subfolia IXa, IXb, and IXc by uvular sulci 1 and 2 (fig. 207). The furrow between folia VIII and IX corresponds to fissure *y* of Brouwer (1913) and Ingvar (1918) and to the fissura secunda, above described, in chick, duck, and cormorant embryos. Uvular sulcus 1, corresponds to Ingvar's sulcus *z*, which the Swedish author considered homologous with the fissura secunda of Elliot Smith in mammals. The large subdivision between this sulcus and the fissura secunda, as above defined, which was regarded as the pyramis by Ingvar, comprises subfolia IXa and IXb, the two being separated by a shallow uvular sulcus 2. In the larger cerebella subfolium IXc is divided into two folia of the third order.

THE FLOCCULONODULAR LOBE

Folium X, the nodulus of the flocculonodular lobe, constitutes the caudal wall of the lower part of the cerebellar ventricle (fig. 208). The surface directed toward the ventricle is formed of a thin medullary sheet with a subjacent granular layer, but a molecular layer covers its caudal and ventral surfaces as far rostrally as the tenia of the choroid plexus. The band of white substance is delimited from the main medullary mass of the cerebellum by the small posterior recess of the cerebellar ventricle, but an arching band of fibers connects the nodulus and subfolium IXc. The nodulus, including both granular and molecular layers, is continuous laterally, on either side, with the flocculus (fig. 207B). The two flocculi and the nodulus thus constitute the flocculonodular lobe as in mammals. The posterolateral fissure arches around the end of each flocculus, becoming very shallow laterally but continuing, as a faint furrow, for a short distance onto the surface of the medulla oblongata, where it forms the lateral boundary of the rostral part of the rhombic lip.

The lateral part of the "avian auricle," as seen from lateral and anterior views, surrounds the end of the flocculus and tilts slightly caudalward. This part of the auricle, the "avian paraflocculus," is continuous medially with subfolium IXc, as figures 208A,B illustrate and as shown in embryos of chick and duck. It is attached rostromedially, however, to the main mass of the cerebellar base by a somewhat conical elevation which widens gradually as it approaches this mass.

A rudimentary lateral hemisphere is formed by unfoliated cerebellar cortex which extends as far ventrally as the curved dark margin indicated in figure 207A. This is visible, beneath the "avian paraflocculus," and as far as the posterior border of folium I. Uvular sulcus 1 ends on the rostral surface of the "avian auricle," as in the duck embryos, and does not reach the margin of the rudimentary hemisphere; accordingly there is continuity of unfoliated cortex from the parafloccular to the rostral part of the lateral ventral region of the cerebellum.

Hummingbirds (Lampornis Sp., Chrysolampis Mosquitos, and Cyanolaemus Elemanciae)

As is generally known, the hummingbirds, which belong to the order Micropodiformes, depend entirely on their wings for locomotion, their legs apparently serving only as a landing gear. The beat of the wings is extremely rapid and the birds poise themselves in the air by wing and tail-feather action. The tail feathers also apparently play an important role in flight. The muscles of flight and the related skeletal structures are relatively more developed in the hummingbirds than in any other avian species, according to Marshall (1920).

The cerebellum of the hummingbirds is of unusual relatively large size, as noted by Craigie (1928). Its pattern is simple but shows some striking variations from the generalized organ of the pigeon. As already noted, the cerebellar ventricle extends but a short distance into the base of the cerebellum (fig. 209); it is reduced to a narrow cleft between the two medial cerebellar nuclei. The medullary mass, instead of forming a sheet beneath the anterior and posterior walls of the ventricle, as in the pigeon and other species, constitutes a large medullary body in which the cerebellar nuclei are embedded and from which the medullary rays radiate into the folia.

The "avian auricle," called the lobus floccularis by Craigie, is an unusually large, rounded projection from the posterior base of the cerebellum. The posterolateral fissure, to which we shall return, is continuous from side to side of the cerebellum by a faint groove in each "auri-

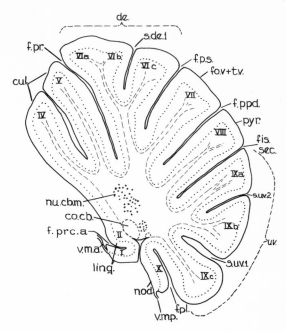

Figure 209. Midsagittal section of cerebellum of hummingbird (Lampornis). Cresyl violet stain. ×20. (Larsell, 1948.)

cle," so that it divides the cerebellum into corpus cerebelli and flocculonodular lobe.

THE CORPUS CEREBELLI

The anterior part of the corpus cerebelli differs strikingly from the corresponding portion of other avian cerebella. Instead of five primary folia ventral of the fissura prima (fissure *x* of Craigie), only two large and two very small folds of cortex are found in the hummingbird. The ventralmost small fold is folium I. It extends forward from the anterior cerebellar base and is characteristically continuous with the anterior medullary velum. The granular layer faces the fourth ventricle and the molecular layer is typically dorsal in position. The small cortical fold dorsal of folium I and delimited from it by a shallow fissure appears to correspond to folium II of the pigeon. Probably the stretch of unfolded cortex dorsal of folium II, as labeled in figure 209, corresponds to folium III of the pigeon. The two large folia, separated by a deep interculminate fissure, are regarded as folia IV and V. The fissura prima, behind folium V, is the deepest furrow in the hummingbird cerebellum, corresponding in this respect to the fissura prima of small mammals; it divides the anterior lobe, with its greatly modified folia, from the posterior lobe.

The posterior lobe typically comprises folia VI–IX (fig. 209). Folium VI consists of two secondary folds, subfolia VIa+b and VIc. Subfolia VIa and VIb show only a suggestion of differentiation from each other and they are served by branches of a single primary medullary ray. A deep furrow, corresponding to the posterior superior fissure of the embryonic chick and duck and the adult pigeon cerebellum, separates folium VI from primary folium VII.

Folium VII is undivided and is delimited by the prepyramidal fissure from folium VIII, the caudal boundary of which is the fissura secunda (which Craigie calls fissure *y*).

The remaining three folds of the corpus cerebelli subfolia IXa, IXb, and IXc, are subdivisions of primary folium IX, the uvula. They are separated from one another by uvular sulci 2 and 1, respectively. As in other species, the branches of one primary medullary ray lead to all three subfolia, but this primary ray is very broad at its base in the hummingbird.

THE FLOCCULONODULAR LOBE

The posterolateral fissure, delimiting the flocculonodular lobe from the corpus cerebelli, can be followed from one side to the other in sagittal sections. Medially, where it forms the posterior boundary of folium X, it is relatively deep (fig. 209); laterally, however, where flocculus and "avian paraflocculus" appear to merge, it is a shallow groove. This groove can be traced onto the surface of the medulla oblongata.

The "avian auricle" typically comprises an "avian paraflocculus" and a flocculus. The flocculus extends laterally beneath the parafloccular portion of the "auricle." Uvular sulcus 1 becomes very broad, laterally, so that the lower subfolium (IXc) of the uvula is widely separated from the intermediate subfolium, IXb. It is the lower uvular subfolium, IXc, which continues laterally into the parafloccular portion of the "auricle."

Cerebellar cortex extends below the projecting mass of the "auricle" onto the bulbar surface, as Craigie notes, and continues forward to the base of folium I. This cortex is unfoliated and is regarded as the incipient lateral hemisphere.

Chicken (Gallus Domesticus)

The domestic chicken, of the order Galliformes, though capable of flying short distances, is a relatively poor flier but a good walker and scratcher. Since its cerebellum, including the "avian auricles," has been described developmentally only up to the young chick stage, the folia will be considered briefly in the adult. Nearly mature bantam roosters were selected as showing the folial pattern most simply for this type of bird. A sagittal section near the median plane is illustrated in figure 210.

THE CORPUS CEREBELLI

In the anterior lobe folium I, as seen in sagittal section, forms a tongue-like rostral projection from the base of the cerebellum, tapering toward the anterior medullary velum. The folium as a whole has the form of a shallow dish. Precentral fissure *a*, separating it from folium II, is slightly bifurcated at its deep extremity so that a small swelling, regarded as part of the base of folium I, is present between the two rami (fig. 210).

Folia II–V do not differ greatly from the corresponding divisions in the pigeon. Folium II is somewhat ovoid in form, with a broad base. Folium III is broad dorsoventrally and has a thickening of the molecular layer, which indicates the position of a furrow in some other species, but no surface furrow is present in the bantam fowl. The preculminate fissure is relatively shallow. Folium IV is elongated rostralward but shows no sign of subdivision. Folium V, however, is divided into subfolia Va and Vb by a furrow which extends about halfway to the base of the primary folium.

In the posterior lobe folium VI is a simple undivided fold of cortex but has a thickening of the molecular layer in the region corresponding to the position of declival sulcus 1 in species that show this furrow. The fissura prima, separating folia V and VI, is deep and its external lips are situated very high on the rostral surface of the cerebellum (fig. 210).

Folium VIII is divided into subfolia VIIIa and VIIIb. The prepyramidal fissure which delimits it from folium VII is deep but its walls are unfoliated.

Folium IX is divided by uvular sulci 1 and 2 into subfolia IXa, IXb, and IXc, the last named being subdivided

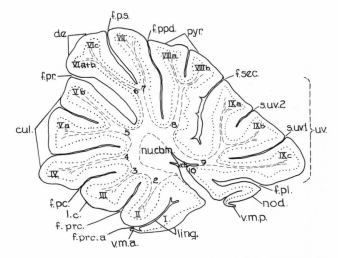

Figure 210. Outlines of midsagittal section of cerebellum of young adult bantam chicken. Weigert stain. ×20. (Larsell, 1948.)

into subfolia by uvular sulcus 3 in young chicks of the larger common hen, as already noted. In the bantam fowl there is only a thickening of the molecular layer at the position of this furrow.

THE FLOCCULONODULAR LOBE

Folium X bends forward on itself so that its ventral surface is formed of molecular layer (fig. 210). A thin sheet of medullary substance extends into the folium along the posterior wall of the cerebellar ventricle and turns caudally into the folded portion of the folium, forming a slender medullary ray. The posterolateral fissure is deep and relatively wide between folia IX and X. Laterally it becomes shallow between the floccular and parafloccular parts of the "avian auricle," but has the typical relations.

Grouse (Dendragapus Fuliginosus)

The sooty grouse, also a gallinaceous bird, can fly rapidly for short distances, raising its weight from the ground, when flushed, with a great whir of wings and swerving sharply upward into a tree. When flushed from a tree "the bird pitches straight downward . . . at almost bullet speed, to land in another tree far below"

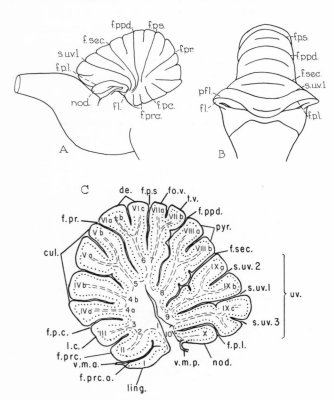

Figure 211. Cerebellum of sooty grouse, Dendragapus fuliginosus. A. Lateral view. B. Posterior view. C. Midsagittal section. (Larsell, 1948.)

(Gabrielson and Jewett, 1940). On the ground it walks about, seeking food. It is not a migratory bird in the usual sense but changes its habitat, with the seasons, between the open ridges of the mountains and heavy timber and the borders of meadows at lower altitudes.

The cerebellum of this species is rounded, in lateral profile, the posterior portion projecting caudally beyond the outline of the greater part of the organ (fig. 211A). The posterior aspect presents a helmet-like shape, the "avian auricles" forming the rim (fig. 211B). In median sagittal section the ten primary folia can be recognized, but with several deviations from the pattern represented in the pigeon.

THE CORPUS CEREBELLI

In the anterior lobe folium I is elongated and extends rostrally from its base toward the anterior medullary velum with only a slight upward tilt of its anterior half. Precentral fissure *a*, separating it from folium II, is bifurcated at its deep end, as in the bantam fowl; a small secondary folium is formed between the two branches. The entire folium I thus first extends ventrally and then turns rostrally almost at right angles (fig. 211C).

Folia II and III are rounded in outline, folium III having a more flattened anterior surface. The deep furrow above folium III is interpreted as the fissura preculminata.

Folium IV is divided by a deep fissure into subfolia IVa and IVb, the two being served by a common primary medullary ray. This ray has a short, broad base before bifurcating into the secondary rays.

Folium V is also divided into subfolia (Va and Vb), but by a shallower furrow than that in folium IV. Considered together folia IV and V of the grouse form a relatively larger part of the anterior lobe than in the bantam fowl or the common chicken.

In the posterior lobe folium VI shows only two secondary folia, namely, VIa + b and VIc (fig. 211C). They are relatively narrow, rostrocaudally, as in the chicken. Because of this feature, together with the large size of folia IV and V, the mouth of the fissura prima has been pushed to a position near the rostrodorsal border of the cerebellum, as in the chicken. The posterior superior fissure, dividing folium VI from folium VII, is deeper than in the bantam chicken but not so deep as the other principal furrows. These two folia are small in both species and their individual medullary rays arise from a continuation of the main medullary sheet between the deep ends of the fissura prima and the prepyramidal fissure in a pattern which is approached in the hummingbird and pigeon, but not in the other species studied.

Folium VII of the grouse is divided by a shallow sulcus

into subfolia VIIa and VIIb. Corresponding subfolia are prominent in the eagle but extremely variable in other species, even the larger ones. The posterior surface of folium VII of the grouse is somewhat foliated. The pre-pyramidal fissure, which separates folia VII and VIII, is considerably curved as seen in sagittal section of the cerebellum, with suggestions of foliation of its walls (fig. 211C).

Folium VIII is more deeply divided into subfolia VIIIa and VIIIb at the surface, and also has several low folia in the anterior wall of the fissura secunda.

Folium IX is divided by an unusually deep uvular sulcus 1 into a pattern which corresponds to that of the uvula in the embryonic chick and duck. Subfolia IXa and IXb, separated from each other by uvular sulcus 2, together with their common base, appear to form a unit independent of subfolium IXc. Comparison with the developmental pattern in duck and chick, and with the adult pattern of folium IX in these and other species, however, appears to justify the interpretation that they are subdivisions of the larger unit. In the grouse uvular sulcus 3 divides the folium ventral of uvular sulcus 1 into two definite subfolia as in some pigeons, the eagle, cormorant, and penguin. A less definite corresponding subfoliation is found in some of the other species but was not observed in the owls, irrespective of size.

THE FLOCCULONODULAR LOBE

Folium X is so strongly folded on itself that the extensive ventricular surface which the nodulus shows in the developing duck and chick and in adults of some species is greatly reduced in the grouse (fig. 211C); the folding has resulted in a central core of medullary substance. As in other species, folium X continues laterally with the flocculus, the flocculonodular lobe formed by the paired flocculi and the nodulus being delimited from the corpus cerebelli by the medially prominent posterolateral fissure.

The "avian auricle" of the grouse has a broad base and tapers gradually, as seen from behind, to a small rounded extremity (fig. 211B). The lateral portion comprises the flocculus and "avian paraflocculus," both of which have typical medial connections with folia X and IXc, respectively. Uvular sulcus 1 continues onto the rostral surface of the base of the "auricle." The posterolateral fissure can be followed around the auricular tip to the dorsal lateral surface of the medulla oblongata (fig. 211A).

Dusky Horned Owl (Bubo Virginiatus Saturatus)

The owls, constituting the order Strigiformes, are nocturnal birds of prey, the numerous species varying greatly in size. Most owls are little given to migration, but they have well-developed wings and strong legs with taloned feet adapted to grasping. They descend swiftly and silently on their prey. Their visual acuity is unique (Walls, 1942) and the large eyes are so placed that vision is binocular. The auditory system is well developed (Whitlock, 1952) and the opening to the ear is larger in some species than in other birds; the feathers surrounding this opening are often thin and bristle-like, apparently facilitating the passage of sound waves.

The dusky horned owl is one of the largest species, the skin length measuring 19 to 24 inches, the wings 14 to 15 inches, and the tail about 8 to 9½ inches. It is fierce and powerful and can kill other birds as large as turkeys, and also squirrels, rabbits, and even skunks (Gabrielson and Jewett, 1940). The cerebellum of this owl will be described in considerable detail because this species was used in some of the experimental studies of Whitlock (1952), already mentioned.

THE CORPUS CEREBELLI

As seen in lateral profile the cerebellum of the horned owl is nearly oval in outline (fig. 212A). Anterior and posterior views show the "avian auricle" jutting out from the inferior part of either side (figs. 212B, 213). The ten primary folia, corresponding to folia I–X of other birds, are most readily identifiable in the hemisected cerebellum by following them from the medial surface onto the external surface. Most of these have secondary folds but the pattern varies from that of the pigeon and other species already described.

The cerebellar ventricle is an elongated cleft which expands anteroposteriorly some distance above its opening into the fourth ventricle, a short posterior recess extending above the base of folium X (fig. 214).

A furrow which extends from the dorsolateral surface of the cerebellum almost to the dorsal tip of the ventricle is identified as the fissura prima on the basis of its correspondence in position and folial relationships to this fissure in the duck and chicken, in which it has been followed from embryonic stages. It delimits a group of six large cortical folds which together constitute the anterior lobe. The folds represent folia I–V, folium V being deeply divided into two subfolia (fig. 214).

Folium I is relatively short and thin in median sagittal section but dips deeply into the fourth ventricle. Its anterior tip is directly continuous with a short anterior medullary velum. Anterior and posterior views show folium I, when exposed by dissection, as a rounded mass lying between the bilateral cerebellar peduncles. Actually it is a deeply concave fold into the concavity of which the deeper part of folium II projects and is covered laterally,

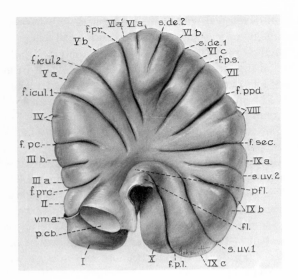

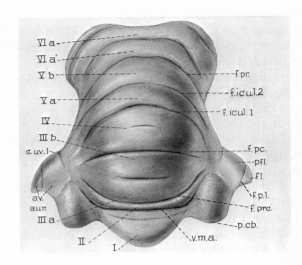

Figure 212. Cerebellum of dusky horned owl. Left, lateral
view. Right, anterior view. (Larsell and Whitlock, 1952.)

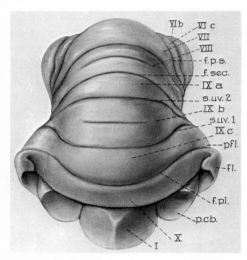

Figure 213. Posterior view of cerebellum of dusky
horned owl. (Larsell and Whitlock, 1952.)

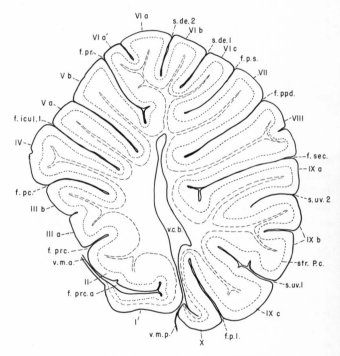

Figure 214. Midsagittal section of cerebellum of dusky
horned owl. ×7. (Larsell and Whitlock, 1952.)

on each side, by the high lateral walls of folium I (fig.
212A).

Folium II is large, as seen in sagittal section, and its
rostroventral surface is indented by a shallow furrow. In
anterior view the folium is shown as a broad band which
curves posteriorly, on either side, to disappear in unfoliated cortex anterior of the "auricle" (fig. 212B). A
broad-based medullary ray enters the folium from the
periventricular medullary sheet and bifurcates, a smaller
ray continuing into each of the subdivisions delimited by
the shallow furrow mentioned above.

Folium III also forms a broad band on the lower rostral cerebellar surface, tapering on each side toward the

unfoliated cortex. It is divided, by a short and shallow
furrow, into subfolia IIIa and IIIb (fig. 212B). The precentral fissure delimits it from folium II but the preculminate fissure which separates folia III and IV is much
deeper. The lateral extent of the two fissures, however,
is about equal, both disappearing at the border of the unfoliated cortex.

246

Folium IV forms a broad band which projects farther rostrally than the other folia of the anterior lobe, as in other birds. In the horned owl a slight furrow gives the only external indication of subdivision of this folium, but in sagittal section the medullary ray is seen to divide distally, one branch passing dorsally and one ventrally into the expanded distal swelling of the folium. The cortex also is thickened under the shallow furrow (fig. 214).

Folium V is divided into subfolia Va and Vb, the two being about equal in size and lateral extent (fig. 212A, B). Comparison with corresponding sagittal sections of the cerebellum of chick and duck embryos, and of adult pigeon, chicken, eagle, and other birds, substantiates the interpretation that these two folds in the owl are subdivisions of folium V.

In the posterior lobe folium VI is difficult to delimit from folium VII because of uncertainty regarding the identity of the posterior superior fissure in the horned owl. Close comparison with the cerebella of the two other species of owls, described below, and with those of other birds, especially the eagle and penguins, appears to justify the interpretation as labeled in figures 212, 213, and 214. The furrow interpreted as the posterior superior fissure also extends slightly farther lateroventrally than that which lies immediately anterior of it. With this as the posterior boundary, folium VI comprises four subfolia. The most anterior one, however, which is delimited posteriorly by a shallow furrow, is interpreted as a subdivision of VIa. In the smaller short-eared owl, described below, subfolium VIa is large but not subdivided. Both VIa and VIb are subfoliated in the eagle but the furrow in VIa is shallower than in the horned owl.

Folium VII forms a simple surface band, in the horned owl, which extends ventrolaterally and rostrally between the posterior superior and the prepyramidal fissures, the latter penetrating deeply into the cerebellum (fig. 214).

Folium VIII is divided by a shallow furrow extending but a short distance from the midline on either side (fig. 213). The fissura secunda, which delimits the folium posteriorly, bifurcates near its deep end, as in the eagle and some other large species described below. Its walls, however, are not foliated as in several other large birds. The fissure extends rostrolaterally to the unfoliated cortex of the ventrolateral surface of the cerebellum (fig. 212A).

Folium IX has four secondary folia (figs. 213, 214), but the two intermediate folds appear to be subdivisions of IXb. The depth of the furrow between subfolia IXb and IXc in the owl corresponds to that of uvular sulcus 1 in the duck, chicken and other species. Secondary folia IXa and IXc are not subfoliated in the horned owl although both are divided into tertiary folds in the eagle,

and IXc is so divided in several other species. Uvular sulcus 1, followed superficially in the owl, arches rostrally and ventrally around the dorsal surface of the base of the auricle and delimits the "avian paraflocculus" from the unfoliated hemispheral cortex. The "avian paraflocculus," as is well shown in figure 212A, is the lateral continuation of subfolium IXc.

THE FLOCCULONODULAR LOBE

Folium X, delimited from subfolium IXc by the posterolateral fissure, is narrow at its base. Distally it hooks forward so that it presents a considerable surface which, however, is hidden by subfolium IXc when the cerebellum is viewed posteriorly, unless tilted forward as illustrated in figure 213. Folium X is continuous with the flocculus on either side. The posterolateral fissure extends onto the "avian auricle," delimiting the floccular from the parafloccular portion of this lateral projection (fig. 212A). In surface views of the "auricle" the lateral extremities of this fissure are recognizable as shallow grooves extending well onto the rostral surfaces of the two "auricles." The fissure cannot be followed to the medulla oblongata in the horned owl, as is possible in embryos of chick and duck and in the adult barn owl, described below. Apparently this is because the cortex of the lateral part of the "auricle" is thin and a great mass of fibers immediately beneath the cortex obliterates surface markings.

Short-Eared Owl (Asio Flammeus)

The short-eared owl belongs to the same family, the Strigidae, as the horned owl but is smaller. Skin length ranges from about 14 inches to 17 inches, wing length from 12 to 13 inches, and length of tail about 6 inches. This species flies slowly by day, with steady, vigorous sweeps of the long wings. It sees well by daylight and is said to find its way about, without great difficulty, even in bright sunlight (Gabrielson and Jewett, 1940). Its prey consists chiefly of small animals such as mice.

The cerebellum of the short-eared owl has a primary folial pattern very similar to that of the horned owl, but in the anterior lobe only folia II and V are subfoliated. As shown in figure 215, folium II is divided into two secondary folds of quite unequal size. Subfolia Va and Vb are very similar to their counterparts in the horned owl except that they are smaller. Folium VI, of the posterior lobe, is clearly divided into three subfolia, VIa, VIb, and VIc. The posterior superior fissure, delimiting subfolium VIc from folium VII, cannot be mistaken. Folium VII is not divided. Folium VIII, which is partly divided in the horned owl, forms a simple but large surface band in the short-eared owl. Folium IX shows uvular sulci 1 and 2, dividing it into subfolia IXa, IXb, and IXc, similar to those of most other species of birds described. In the short-eared owl subfolium IXb, however, shows a thickening of the cortex and a bifurcation of its medullary ray suggestive of the subfoliation above described for the corresponding fold in the horned owl.

Folium X, the nodulus, is narrow at its base in sagittal section (fig. 215); distally it is hooked forward so that

lium VIII, which is partly subfoliated in the horned owl, shows no indication of subdivision in the barn owl and in the short-eared owl. Folium IX is divided into subfolia IXa, IXb, and IXc. The fissura secunda is the deepest furrow of the cerebellum and uvular sulcus 1 can be followed on the lateral cerebellar surface as the boundary between the "avian paraflocculus" and the unfoliated cortex (fig. 216).

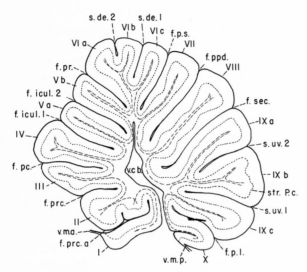

Figure 215. Midsagittal section of cerebellum of short-eared owl. Weigert series. ×7. (Larsell and Whitlock, 1952.)

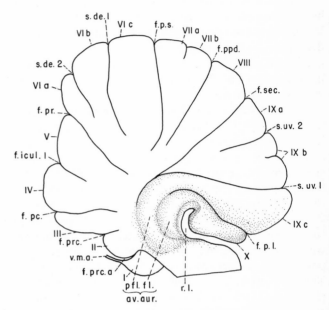

Figure 216. Lateral view of cerebellum of barn owl. ×6. (Larsell and Whitlock, 1952.)

the entire folium is relatively larger than in the horned owl. The posterolateral fissure, followed in sagittal sections of this species, clearly extends onto the lateral surface of the "avian auricle" and arches ventrally and caudally to the surface of the medulla oblongata. It completely delimits the two components of the "auricle" superficially.

Barn Owl (Tyto Alba Pratincola)

The barn owl belongs to the family Tytonidae. Skin length ranges from about 15 to 18 inches, wing 12½ to 14 inches, and tail 5½ to 7½ inches. It feeds on small animals such as mice and gophers.

The folial pattern of the cerebellum of this species is simple, only folia VI, VII, and IX having secondary surface folds (figs. 216, 217). Folium V is slightly folded in the floor of the fissura prima. Folium VI is divided into subfolia VIa, VIb, and VIc, but the fissure between VIa and VIb is deep so that VIa is much more prominent, as seen in sagittal section (fig. 218), than in the horned and short-eared owls. The subfoliation of folium VII is very slight but contrasts with the complete absence of subdivision of this folium in the other two species of owls. Fo-

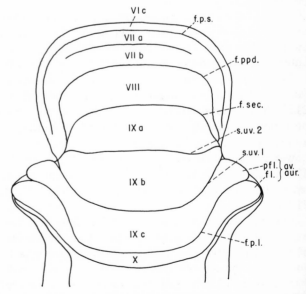

Figure 217. Posterior view of cerebellum of barn owl. ×6. (Larsell and Whitlock, 1952.)

Folium X, the nodulus of the flocculonodular lobe, forms a ventrocaudally directed plate which is not turned forward, distally, as in the other two owls, but the molecular layer arches forward beneath the ventral surface. The folium is continuous, by a broad band of cortex, with the flocculus on each side. The posterolateral fissure is prominent as far laterally as the dorsorostral surface of the "avian auricle" (fig. 217). From this point it forms a faint but definite groove which arches ventrally to the rhombic lip of the medulla oblongata, distinctly delimiting the flocculus from the "avian paraflocculus" (fig. 216).

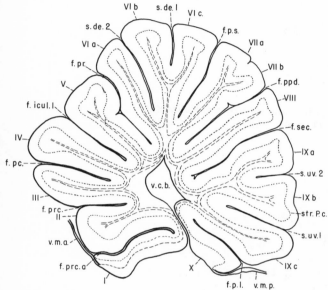

Figure 218. Midsagittal section of cerebellum of barn owl. (Larsell and Whitlock, 1952.)

Bald Eagle (Haliaeetus Leucocephalus)

The eagles belong to the order Falconiformes and, as is well known, are powerful fliers and also have great strength of legs, talons and beak. Their powers of vision are proverbial. The bald eagle has a skin length of 34½ to 43 inches, wing length of 22½ to 27 inches and tail length about 11½ to 14½ inches.

The cerebellum of the bald eagle closely resembles that of the golden eagle, Aquila, illustrated by Herrick (1893), but the "avian paraflocculus" appears to be larger in Aquila. None of the fissures or cerebellar subdivisions, however, are labeled in Herrick's figures. Brouwer (1913) briefly described and illustrated the cerebellum of Haliaeetus melanocephalus.

THE CORPUS CEREBELLI

The fissura prima is somewhat difficult to identify in the eagle. The fissure so labeled in figures 219 and 220, however, appears to correspond to the fissura prima of other species of birds and to fissure *x* of most of Brouwer's and Ingvar's illustrations in which it is labeled, including that of Haliaeetus melanocephalus, illustrated by Brouwer. The large cerebellum of the buzzard, Gyps fulvus, as illustrated by Ingvar, somewhat resembles that of the eagle but fissure *x* is not labeled.

The fissura secunda is readily identified both by its subfoliated walls and because it is the anterior boundary of folium IX which is characterized by its trident-like medullary ray and typical subdivisions. Fissure *y*, as labeled in Brouwer's (1913) figures of the cerebellum of Haliaeetus melanocephalus appears to correspond to uvular sulcus 2 of figures 219 and 220. In the bald eagle this furrow is deep, but the arrangement of medullary ray 9, as shown in these figures, leaves no doubt regarding the relation to folium IX of the secondary folium dorsal of uvular sulcus 2. The deeper fissure, with foliated walls, of the bald eagle is the fissura secunda. With the three principal fissures — the posterolateral, the prima, and the secunda — established, we may consider the folia and their subdivisions of the corpus cerebelli.

Folium I presents a rounded lateral surface which tapers caudalward beneath the nodulus before turning dorsorostrally as the surface of a nearly vertical segment of the folium. The caudal surface of this segment is separated from the nodulus by a narrow ventricular space representing the inferior part of the cerebellar ventricle. As illustrated in figure 221, the lobule is situated between the cerebellar peduncles and, as in other species of birds, forms the transversely narrowest subdivision of the cerebellum. The horizontal segment of the folium turns dorsalward on either side, forming a cup-like space into which the ventral subfolium of folium II extends and is hidden. A deep and curved precentral fissure *a* delimits folium I from folium II (fig. 219). The lingular surface of this fissure is divided by two shallow furrows into three low folds of cortex, the ventralmost being continuous with the anterior medullary velum. Most of the ventricular surface of the folium is formed by the granular layer, but a thin medullary sheet extends ventralward from the principal medullary layer, forming the upper part of the ventricular surface of the folium (fig. 220). The fibers of this sheet spread diffusely in the granular layer so that a distinct fibrous band soon disappears.

Folium II is short and rounded and is divided into subfolia IIa and IIb by a shallow furrow. It is separated from folium III by a relatively shallow precentral fissure.

Folium III is divided into subfolia IIIa and IIIb. Its medullary ray is distinct from that to folium II (fig. 222).

Folium IV is elongated rostrally and is divided into small subfolia, IVa and IVb. The preculminate fissure,

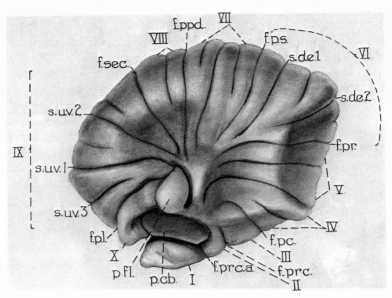

Figure 219. Lateral view of cerebellum of immature bald eagle, Haliaeetus leucocephalus ×3½ . (Larsell, 1948.)

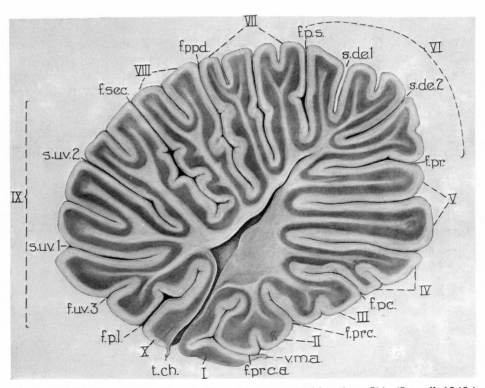

Figure 220. Median section of cerebellum of immature bald eagle. ×5¼ . (Larsell, 1948.)

which separates it from folium III, is relatively shallow owing to the thickened anterior wall of the cerebellar ventricle behind folia III and IV. This thickening of the wall is due largely to a cellular mass which probably represents fusion across the midline, as in the hummingbird, of the medial cerebellar nuclei. This apparent fusion, however, requires confirmation in appropriately prepared material.

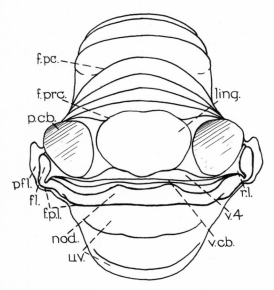

Figure 221. Ventral view of cerebellum of bald eagle, Haliaeetus leucocephalus. ×4. (Larsell, 1948.)

Folium V is separated from folium IV by a much deeper intraculminate fissure. It is divided into subfolia Va and Vb by a furrow of nearly equal depth. The intraculminate fissure extends farther on the lateral cerebellar surface, however, than the secondary furrow (fig. 219). Each subfolium has a separate medullary ray, a feature which, together with the deep fissure between them, suggests that they are primary folia. The corresponding region in embryos of the chick and duck, however, shows only one primary cortical fold. In the 15 day chick embryo a shallow furrow has appeared which, in the 4-day-old chick, extends about midway from the surface to the base of medullary ray 5. Late stages of the duck embryo and adult ducks show a deep fissure, as in the eagle. The pigeon, grouse, and other birds have relatively shallow corresponding furrows, the two subfolia divided by them obviously being subdivisions of the primary folium. These considerations appear to justify the interpretation that folia Va and Vb of the eagle are secondary folds.

In the posterior lobe, folium VI, situated between the fissura prima and the posterior superior fissure, is di-

vided into subfolia VIa, VIb and VIc. Declival sulcus 1 is shallower than declival sulcus 2 but extends farther ventrally on the lateral cerebellar surface (fig. 219). Subfolia VIa and VIb are both divided by shallow furrows into subfolia of the third order (fig. 222). The posterior superior fissure separating folia VI and VII is relatively shallow but extends well ventrally on the lateral cerebellar surface.

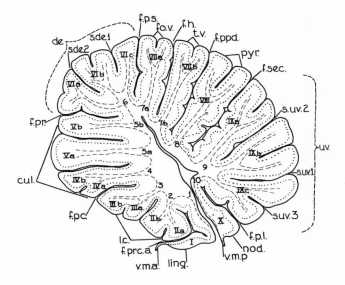

Figure 222. Sagittal section of cerebellum of bald eagle. ×4. (Larsell, 1948.)

Folium VII is divided by a deep fissure into subfolia VIIa and VIIb, each provided with a medullary ray which arises independently from the deep medullary layer. Comparison of the development of folium VII in chick and duck embryos, and of the various degrees of subfoliation in adult cerebella of other species, appears to justify the interpretation that in the eagle the two prominent folds represent subfolia rather than primary folia. The increased size and more pronounced subdivision of folium VII in the eagle, as compared with other species, is perhaps correlated with the visual power of this bird. Whitlock (1952) has demonstrated that activation of the cerebellar cortex of the pigeon, duck, and owl by optic and auditory stimuli and by stimulation of the tectum is localized in folia VII and VIII.

Folium VIII is separated from folium VII by the prepyramidal fissure, the walls of which are slightly foliated in the eagle. The folium is divided by a shallow furrow into two superficial subfolia, and two low subfolia in the deep part of the folium face the fissura secunda (fig. 222).

Folium IX is divided into large subfolia IXa, IXb, and

251

IXc. Uvular sulcus 1, separating IXb and IXc, is relatively shallow in sagittal section, but there can be no doubt of its identity when followed on the surface. It extends to the rostral surface of the "auricle." Uvular sulcus 2 is deeper and ends just dorsal of the tip of the "avian paraflocculus" (fig. 219). Folia IXa and IXb, which it separates, are very large in the eagle, giving the uvula of this species the largest size, in proportion to the remainder of the cerebellum, of any species investigated. Both are subdivided into tertiary folia. Folium IXc also is divided by a shallow furrow into tertiary subfolia, as in the duck and several other species. There also is a small subfolium on the caudal surface of the deep part of the posterolateral fissure. As in other species, folium IXc is continuous laterally with the "avian paraflocculus."

THE FLOCCULONODULAR LOBE

The posterolateral fissure can be followed from the cerebellar peduncle of one side to the cerebellar peduncle of the other in the eagle. It is deep in median sagittal section, separating a relatively thin folium X, the nodulus, from subfolium IXc (fig. 222). Although narrow in the sagittal plane, folium X has considerable volume, owing to the length of its dorsoventral axis. The posterior surface of the folium is formed by the molecular layer which also turns rostralward at the ventral border to form the ventral surface. The anterior surface, constituting the lower posterior wall of the cerebellar ventricle, is formed by a thin sheet of medullary substance that gradually tapers and disappears, as its fibers distribute in the granular layer, a short distance above the attachment of the choroid tela (fig. 220). Folium X tapers lateralward but is continuous with the flocculus proper by a continuous fold of cortex.

As in other birds, the flocculus is closely associated with the "avian paraflocculus," the two forming the "avian auricle." The paraflocculus component turns sharply caudalward around the end of the flocculus, hiding it from lateral view (fig. 219). The flocculus and the remainder of the flocculonodular lobe, however, are well exposed from the ventral aspect (fig. 221).

The area of unfoliated cortex is relatively small in the eagle. But the principal fissures of the corpus cerebelli are more elongated on the lateral cerebellar surface than in other species examined except the penguins. The folia which they delimit extend into the rudimentary hemisphere, producing a slight foliation of the hemispheral cortex (fig. 219).

Duck (Anas Platyrhynchus)

According to Amadon and Gilliard (1952) all varieties of domestic ducks except the Muscovy are descend-

ants of the wild mallard, belonging to the order Anseriformes. Embryos of the domestic duck were used in the study of development of the cerebellum, but some of the folia and their subdivisions of the adult domestic duck are less developed than in the wild mallard. The description of the adult cerebellum, therefore, is based primarily on the organ in the wild Anas platyrhynchus.

The skin length of the wild mallard varies from 20 to 25 inches, wing length is about 10 to 12 inches, tail is short, and bill length is 2 to 2½ inches. This species is migratory and is said to attain a speed of fifty-five miles an hour or more. The power of flight is greatly reduced in the domestic duck, but both it and the wild duck are at home in the water.

Externally the duck cerebellum differs greatly in appearance from that of the pigeon. The contour, as viewed from one side, is heart-shaped (fig. 223), the apex being directed upward and forward. Viewed from behind the posterolateral surface is deeply depressed on both sides between a broad base and the rounded dorsal part of the organ (fig. 224). The constriction of the posterior portion so produced emphasizes the lateral projection, on each side, from the posterior basal part. A conspicuous vertical ridge on each side divides the rostrolateral surface of the cerebellum from the more strictly lateral surface, in the lower part of which a concavity is formed. The greater part of the broad posterior base and all of

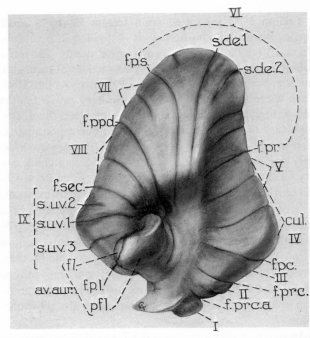

Figure 223. Lateral view of adult mallard duck, Anas platyrhynchus. ×5. (Larsell, 1948.)

the dorsally and rostrally extending part of the organ are included in the corpus cerebelli. The prominent lateral projections are the "avian auricles" (fig. 224). A pear-shaped swelling in the posterior surface of each auricle is the flocculus; the two flocculi are connected across the midline by a continuous fold of cortex, the nodulus, which is delimited from the corpus cerebelli by the median segment of the posterolateral fissure. A shallow continuation of this fissure extends around each flocculus which, with the nodulus, forms the flocculonodular lobe. The fissures and the ten primary folia, as described in the duck embryo, are readily recognizable in the adult duck.

Folium IV is relatively small in median sagittal section but laterally it expands to greater size than in the pigeon. The preculminate fissure, separating it from folium III, is deeper than in the pigeon.

Folium V is divided into subfolia Va and Vb by a fissure deeper than that which separates Va from folium IV. This feature and the distinct medullary ray to each make them appear to be primary folia. Folium V of the 13 day duck embryo, however, is undivided; in the 15 day embryo two subfolia are seen, as also in subsequent stages of development. The pigeon and most other species show a shallower furrow between the subfolia of fo-

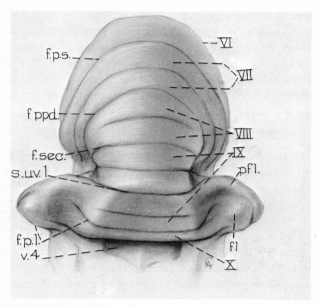

Figure 224. Posterior view of cerebellum of wild mallard duck. ×5. (Larsell, 1948.)

THE CORPUS CEREBELLI

Folium I, in the anterior lobe, is relatively large. Its rostral portion folds ventrocaudally, the recurved tip extending approximately halfway to the base of the folium before it becomes continuous with the anterior medullary velum. The dorsal and anterior surfaces of the folium are formed by its molecular layer; the granular layer also hooks ventrocaudally, but only the anterior recurved part has a ventricular surface, the more caudal part being separated from the ventricle by a thin medullary layer (fig. 225).

Folium II is divided into two subfolia, IIa and IIb; the latter is separated from folium I by precentral fissure *a*.

Folium III is undivided in the duck as in the small pigeon, in contrast with the two subfolia of the larger pigeons. This difference may be related to the presence of two subfolia of folium II in the duck.

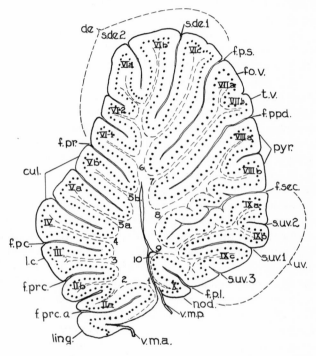

Figure 225. Midsagittal section of cerebellum of wild mallard duck. Dissection. ×7. (Larsell, 1948.)

lium V and a single medullary ray leading to them. In the eagle, however, the two folds are as completely divided as in the adult duck and have separate medullary rays. On the basis of their development in the duck and the subfoliation of folium V in some degree in all other species except in the smaller birds and in Apteryx, as the corresponding folium is illustrated by Craigie (1930), it appears justifiable to consider the two folds in the duck as subfolia Va and Vb. The fissura prima, between subfolium Vb and folium VI, is relatively shallow in the adult duck (fig. 225). Its developmental history leaves no doubt as to its identity.

In the posterior lobe folium VI of the adult duck shows secondary folia VIa, VIb, and VIc all more expanded than in the newly hatched duckling but with no further subdivisions. Two small folia, described in the young duck as located in the posterodorsal wall of the fissura prima, also are found in the adult domestic duck but they do not reach the external cerebellar surface. In the wild mallard two relatively large folds (VI-1 and VI-2, fig. 225), interposed between subfolia Vb and VIa, appear to represent enlarged versions of the small folia of the domestic duck. Folium VI of the wild duck, accordingly, is considerably larger than in the domestic variety. Declival sulcus 1, which separates subfolia VIb and VIc, is quite deep in the median sagittal plane of the mallard and extends well down on the lateral surface of the cerebellum (fig. 223).

Folium VII is large and is divided by a shallow and, superficially, short furrow into subfolia VIIa and VIIb. The posterior superior fissure, between folia VI and VII, is also quite deep and extends to the concavity on the lower part of the lateral cerebellar surface.

Folium VIII also has a large external surface, but is narrower from side to side than the folia already described. It is divided into subfolia VIIIa and VIIIb by a shallow fissure. The posterior surface of the folium, hidden as the anterodorsal wall of the fissura secunda, has two low cortical folds (fig. 225).

Folium IX is large in the duck, as in other birds, but appears to be exceeded in surface area by folium VI. The uvular wall of the fissura secunda, which separates folia VIII and IX, is also foliated (fig. 225). The two secondary folia, IXa + b and IXc, which appear in the 11½ day duck embryo and are prominent at the 15 day stage of incubation, are increased by differentiation of subfolium IXb, beginning in the 18 day embryo, and of two subfolia of IXc at a later stage of development, to four superficial subfolia in the adult. Subfolium IXc, which is delimited from IXb by uvular sulcus 1, is continuous laterally with the "avian paraflocculus" of the auricle, described below. Subfolium IXb ends laterally on the base of the auricle, and IXa disappears in the depression above the base of the auricle. Uvular sulcus 1 continues, above and in front of the base of the auricle, delimiting this base from the unfoliated cortex of the rudimentary hemisphere (fig. 223). The fissura secunda ends dorsal of this base between the lateral extremity of subfolium IXa + IXb and the corresponding part of folium VIII, the two cortical folds being continuous with one another around the end of the fissure, as more clearly shown in the 18 day embryo than in the adult duck. The relations of the fissura secunda to the pyramis (folium VIII) and the uvula (folium IX) and their lateral continuations, accordingly, are entirely similar to those in mammalian embryos, as described in the next volume.

The "avian auricle" is prominent in the duck, its lateral projection being emphasized, as already noted, by the narrow posterior part of the cerebellum and the concavity in its lower lateral surface. Viewed from above the auricle appears pedunculated, but seen posteriorly or anteriorly it has a broad base. The lateralmost part of the auricle is the "avian paraflocculus" which, as already noted, is continuous medially with subfolium IXc (fig. 224). Laterally the paraflocculus arches in front of and around a pear-shaped swelling which is continuous medially with folium X, the nodulus. This swelling is the flocculus. The "avian paraflocculus," as already mentioned, appears to correspond to the accessory paraflocculus of Jansen (the Nebenflocke of Henle or the accessory flocculus of some other authors) in mammals. Its medial relations are entirely similar to those of the accessory paraflocculus. In some stages of the human embryo the accessory paraflocculus and the flocculus are so intimately related that, as in birds, they are difficult to differentiate one from the other.

THE FLOCCULONODULAR LOBE

Folium X, the nodulus, separated from subfolium IXc by the posterolateral fissure, is sharply folded forward, distally, so that its tip forms the posterior wall of the lower part of the cerebellar ventricle, a narrow cleft separating the infolded part of the folium from the ventrocaudally directed major part (fig. 225). The choroid tela is attached to the infolded tip. A thin medullary layer forms the ventricular surface of the major part of the folium. The nodulus continues laterally to the flocculus on either side.

The flocculus is delimited from the "avian paraflocculus" by the shallow lateral continuation of the posterolateral fissure already mentioned (fig. 224). This arches around the floccular swelling and reaches the rhombic lip of the medulla oblongata as a faint groove, more apparent in the embryonic than in the adult brain.

Cormorant (Phalacrocorax Penicillatus)

The cormorants belong to the order Pelecaniformes. Brandt's cormorant, here described, has a skin length of 28 to 33 inches, wing length of 10½ to nearly 12 inches, tail of 5½ to 6½ inches, and bill slightly more than 2½ to nearly 3 inches. The neck is long and the feet very large. The cormorant is a swimmer and diver but is also capable of sustained flight which, however, is slow and clumsy. The wings are not used in swimming, as in some other birds, the motive power for this form of propulsion being supplied entirely by the legs and feet, Gabrielson and Jewett (1940) state. The stiff tail feathers, in addition to their function in flight, appear to serve as props in maintaining a nearly erect position on land.

The cerebellum of the adult cormorant differs greatly from that of the duck and owls. Instead of forming a dorsorostral or dorsal peak the dorsal surface is flattened and the entire cerebellum is elongated anteroposteriorly (fig. 226). The cerebellar ventricle is a triangular cavity whose apex extends forward and upward, rather than dorsalward, but the enlarged space is continuous with the fourth ventricle by a narrow canal (fig. 227).

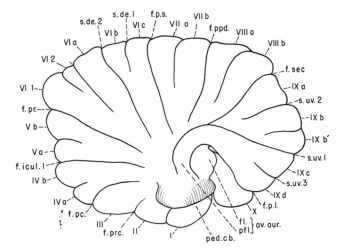

Figure 226. Lateral view of cerebellum of Brandt's cormorant. ×4.5. (Larsell and Whitlock, 1952.)

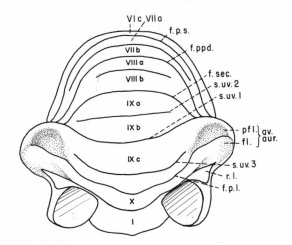

Figure 227. Posterior view of Brandt's cormorant. ×4.5. (Larsell and Whitlock, 1952.)

THE CORPUS CEREBELLI

The folia of the anterior part of the corpus cerebelli and the fissura prima are difficult to interpret in the cormorant. In our earlier description of the cerebellum of this species (Larsell and Whitlock, 1952), the interpre-

tation, for which I was responsible, made the entire anterior part of the organ the anterior lobe and the deep fissure opening farthest anteriorly on the dorsal cerebellar surface was regarded as the fissura prima. On this basis the anterior lobe would comprise five folia, having separate medullary rays, in addition to folium I. The two folds immediately dorsal of folium I, however, were regarded as subdivisions of folium II because in the 126 mm cormorant embryo the cortical segment immediately rostral of folium I is only partly divided by a furrow which does not reach the lateral surfaces. In the adult cerebellum the corresponding furrow is shallower than the one next above it and is also shorter on the lateral surfaces.

Further consideration of the cormorant cerebellum and comparison with additional other species leads to the conclusion that the cortical folds earlier regarded as subfolia IIa and IIb are, instead, folium II and folium III respectively (fig. 228). The medullary ray of folium II, so interpreted, is slightly bifurcated, distally, as in some other species in which this folium is not externally divisible. The relative size of both II and III also would correspond more closely to that of other species, as would the distinctly separated bases of their medullary rays.

With this interpretation of folia II and III, folia III and IV of the earlier description would become folia IV and V, respectively. They also have a greater resemblance to folia IV and V of other species. Both are subfoliated by relatively shallow furrows, as in the larger pigeons and some other birds, and subfolium IVa is smaller than IVb, as in the eagle and penguins. Both project farther rostralward than folium III, as in all species (fig. 228).

The fissura prima, on the basis of the revised interpretation, is represented by the fissure opening farthest dorsally on the anterior cerebellar surface and extending toward the rostrodorsally directed apex of the cerebellar ventricle. In both these respects it corresponds to the fissura prima of most other species. Confirmation of these

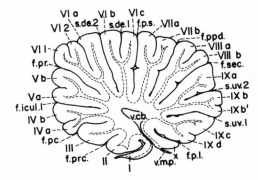

Figure 228. Midsagittal section of cerebellum of Brandt's cormorant. ×3. (Larsell and Whitlock, 1952.)

interpretations is dependent on additional embryonic material, but they clarify the subdivisions of the posterior lobe as well as those of the anterior lobe, when compared with most other species.

Folium I is relatively small in median sagittal section but is broad between the cerebellar peduncles and has a large ventricular surface (fig. 228). Folium II rests in the concavity of the dorsal surface of folium I. The remaining folia of the anterior lobe have already been sufficiently described and are shown in figures 226 and 228.

The folia of the dorsal part of the posterior lobe do not easily fall into the pattern of most species. The fissura secunda is identified by its position with respect to folium IX, which is characterized by its three large secondary folia and the medullary rays leading to them (fig. 228). Rostral of this fissure, however, three apparently primary folia are so similar and are separated by fissures so nearly equal in depth that they are difficult to identify with individual folia of other species. Between the most anterior of these and the fissura prima lies an apparently primary folium with three subfolia. Rather arbitrarily these three subfolia may be regarded as VI-1, VI-2, and VIa; the two subfolia of the apparently primary fold behind VIa are VIb and VIc. These subdivisions are based on the presence of subfolia VI-1 and VI-2 in the duck and penguins, which are also water birds, and the absence of any corresponding cortical folds in other species studied. So interpreted, declival sulcus 2 is unusually deep, but the corresponding furrow in the eagle, barn owl and emperor penguin is also deeper than declival sulcus 1. It is questionable how much significance should be attached to the relative depth of the declival furrows, either in individuals of the same species or in different species. The small number of specimens available from each species, only one of the adult cormorant, does not permit any general conclusions, since there is variation among related species and also in individuals of the same species in subfolia VIa, VIb, and VIc.

Considering the large segment anteriorly delimited by the deep fissure of the cormorant as including subfolia VIb, and VIc, the furrow behind this segment would be the posterior superior fissure and the fold of cortex folium VII (fig. 228). The next caudal furrow is interpreted as the prepyramidal fissure and the segment of cortex between it and the fissura secunda as folium VIII, the pyramis. Folia VII and VIII are both subfoliated by a shallow furrow (fig. 227).

Folium IX is subfoliated by uvular sulci 1 and 2, into IXa, IXb, and IXc, already mentioned; IXb and IXc are slightly subfoliated. Folium IXc is continuous laterally, as in other species, with the "avian parafloc-culus" of the auricle (fig. 227).

THE FLOCCULONODULAR LOBE

Folium X, the nodulus, is narrow, anteroposteriorly, in median sagittal section. It is continuous with the flocculus on both sides (fig. 227). The posterolateral fissure is prominent except on the lateral and ventral surfaces of the "auricle," where only a faint furrow, representing its continuation, is visible (fig. 227). A lateral recess of the fourth ventricle forms a space beneath and behind the flocculus.

In a 126 mm total length cormorant embryo the floccular part of the auricle is relatively more prominent than the parafloccular component (fig. 229). As seen from beneath, the lateral recess distinctly separates the two parts except at the tip of the auricle (fig. 230). By the adult stage the parafloccular component has enlarged to such an extent that the flocculus is displaced posteriorly and ventrally.

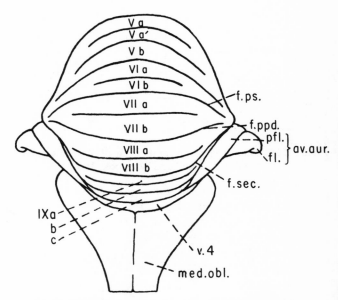

Figure 229. Dorsal view of cerebellum of 126 mm long cormorant embryo. ×5. (Larsell and Whitlock, 1952.)

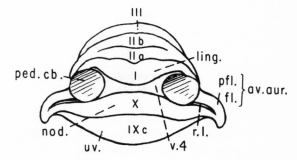

Figure 230. Ventral view of cerebellum of 126 mm long cormorant embryo. ×4. (Larsell and Whitlock, 1952.)

AVES III

Penguins

THE penguins belong to the order Sphenisciformes. Their wings are modified to flippers which are powerful swimming organs and are used exclusively for propulsion when the birds are submerged in the water. Although incapable of flight in the air, penguins "fly in the water" at speeds estimated to exceed twenty-five miles an hour (Austin, 1961). The legs are short and sturdy, serving as paddles for surface swimming and for locomotion on land. Most species have a waddling gait but the crested penguins hop. The tail is short and helps to maintain an erect position in standing. The bodies are plump and heavy.

Three species have been available for study of the cerebellum: the emperor penguin (Aptenodytes forsteri), the adelie penguin (Pygosceles adeliae), and the rockhopper (Eudyptes crestatus). The emperor penguin attains an erect height of 36 to 42 inches and a weight of 90 pounds; the adelie is 24 inches tall; and the rockhopper about 25 inches (Austin).

The cerebellum of the penguins is relatively large but is typically avian in form. Anteriorly it is broad and tilts forward. The posterior part of the corpus cerebelli is constricted, as in the duck, and the "avian auricle" extends laterally beyond the cerebellar peduncle (fig. 231C).

The fissures and folia are well shown superficially as well as in sagittal sections. The pattern is very similar in the three species, but the secondary fissures are deeper in the emperor penguin. The posterolateral fissure is shallower than the principal fissures of the corpus cerebelli, but clearly divides the corpus from the flocculonodular lobe.

THE CORPUS CEREBELLI

The principal fissure of the anterior part of the corpus cerebelli is deep and extends farther on the lateral surfaces than any of the other furrows. In the rockhopper, it is relatively deeper and its walls are more foliated than in the other two species (fig. 231A). There can be no question that this furrow is the fissura prima, dividing the corpus cerebelli into anterior and posterior lobes. The anterior lobe of the rockhopper is relatively somewhat larger than in the other two species, this larger size and the more prominent fissura prima appearing to be related to the adaptation of the legs for the hopping method of progression.

Folia I–V of the rockhopper have the general pattern found in the larger pigeons with respect to relative size and secondary foliation, but there are some variations (fig. 231A). Folium I projects more deeply into the fourth ventricle by a vertical, descending segment. This is continuous, after a sharp turn, with a horizontal segment whose anterior tip is attached to the anterior medullary velum. A shallow furrow divides the upper surface of the folium into two low secondary folia. The entire folium is goblet-shaped, as in the eagle, and the ventral part of folium II projects into the cavity. Folium I is similar in the emperor and adelie penguins.

Folium II is undivided in the single rockhopper cerebellum available. Several specimens of the adelie penguin show superficial subfolia, and in the emperor penguin two large subfolia sometimes have separate medullary rays from the deep medullary sheet.

Folium III is divided into two subfolia in all three species but is relatively somewhat larger in the rockhopper. The larger size of this folium may be related to the smaller size of folium II in this cerebellum.

Folium IV is subfoliated in all three species, the rays to the secondary folia bifurcating from the primary ray.

Folium V is separated by a deep fissure into two large subfolia in some emperor penguins, but in others the fissure is relatively shallow (fig. 233); in the adelie there may be a relatively shallow furrow or the folium may not be divided; the one rockhopper cerebellum shows two terminal subfolia, separated by a rather shallow fissure, and four low folds of cortex facing the fissura prima (fig. 231A).

The posterior lobe, comprising folia VI–IX, is relatively large in the penguins. Folium VI of the rockhopper is divided into three subfolia that appear to correspond to VIa, VIb, and VIc of the pigeon, eagle, and owls; in addition, however, an elongated fold between folium V and subfolium VIa corresponds to subfolium VI–1, or perhaps to VI–1+VI–2, of the duck (fig. 231A). A similar folium occurs in some cerebella of the

emperor penguin in which folium V is deeply subdivided, as well as in others having smaller subfolia Va and Vb. It also occurs in the adelie. One emperor penguin cerebellum presented only two elongated and deeply separated folia between folium IV and the base of folium VI. Possibly these should be considered as subfolia Va and Vb, and the anterior subfolium of VI as corresponding to VI–1, but if so folium VI of this cerebellum was much smaller than in others or in the rockhopper and adelie.

Folium VII is divided into two superficial folia in all three species by a relatively shallow furrow. The walls of the posterior superior and prepyramidal fissures which, respectively, separate folium VII from folia VI and VIII, are slightly foliated (figs. 231A, 232B, 233). It will be

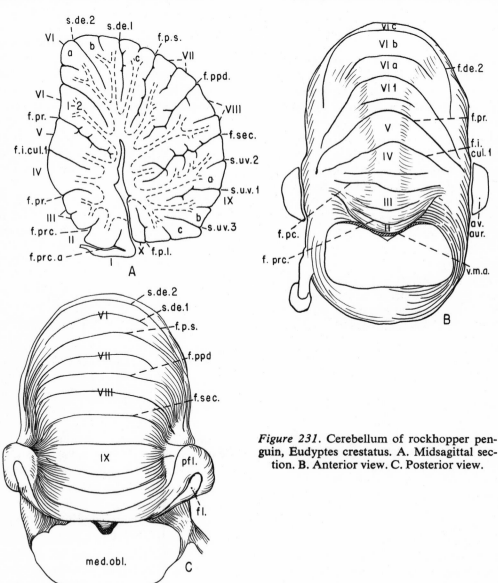

Figure 231. Cerebellum of rockhopper penguin, Eudyptes crestatus. A. Midsagittal section. B. Anterior view. C. Posterior view.

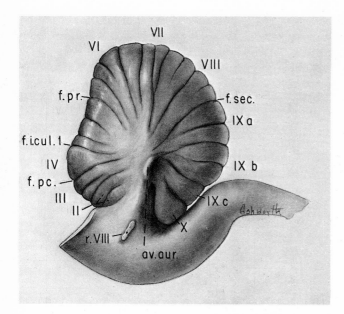
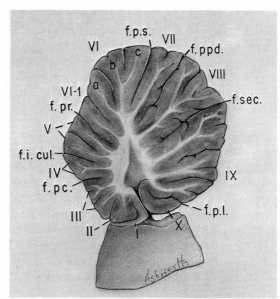

Figure 232. Cerebellum of adelie penguin, Pygosceles adeline. Left, lateral view. Right, midsagittal section.

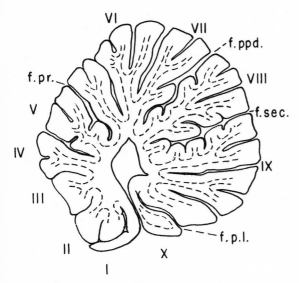

Figure 233. Median section of cerebellum of emperor penguin, Aptenodytes forsteri.

recalled that in the eagle folium VII is divided by a deep fissure into two large subfolia, VIIa and VIIb, which together constitute a large segment of the posterior lobe.

Since Whitlock (1952) found that folium VII of the pigeon, owl, and duck is activated somewhat preponderantly by stimulation of the retina, one might foresee a larger folium VII in the large-eyed penguins. Perhaps the greater depth of the fissures that delimit it compensate for the smaller surface exposure of the folium, as compared with the eagle.

Folium VIII is large and subfoliated in all three species of penguins (figs. 231A, 232B, 233). Two, sometimes three subfolia reach the surface in the emperor penguin. When only two do so these are more deeply separated from one another than the two in the adelies and the rockhopper. The dorsal wall of the fissura secunda, which separates folium VIII from folium IX, is folded into four or five small subfolia. Folium VIII also was activated by photic stimuli in Whitlock's experiments, but a little preponderantly by impulses of auditory origin.

Folium IX is large, as in other birds, and is typically divided into three secondary folia by two rather deep fissures. These secondary folia are more subfoliated than in any other birds investigated. Compared with folium IX of the eagle, the large secondary folium immediately behind the fissura secunda appears to represent IXa; the remaining two are IXb and IXc. Uvular sulcus 1, although shallower in the median sagittal plane than uvular sulcus 2, continues laterally as the boundary of the "avian paraflocculus," as in the eagle and other species (fig. 231C).

THE FLOCCULONODULAR LOBE

Folium X, the nodulus, is elongated dorsoventrally, in median sagittal section (fig. 231A), and also expands distally, as in the eagle; a shallow furrow on the posterior surface delimits a thicker terminal subfolium. The choroid tela is attached at the ventral anterior margin of the nodulus, where the canal of the cerebellar ventricle opens into the fourth ventricle (fig. 231A).

259

A rounded expansion behind the caudally curved "avian paraflocculus" represents the flocculus. It is intimately related with the paraflocculus, but a shallow lateral continuation of the posterolateral fissure forms a boundary between the two. The flocculus tapers medialward to become continuous with the more expanded lateral part of the nodulus.

Cursorial Birds

No strictly cursorial birds have been included in my own investigations, but the cerebellum of the ratite South American ostrich, Rhea americana, was briefly described, and some figures of the organ in the emu, Dromacus novaehollandia, were published by Ingvar (1918). A short description of the kiwi (Apteryx australis) cerebellum is given by Craigie (1930). These three species represent, respectively, the orders Rheiformes, Casuariformes, and Apteriformes of the Ratitae. All have rudimentary wings but are incapable of flight. Rhea americana is about 4 feet tall, has a heavy body, long neck and large, strong legs; it runs rapidly with neck and wings extended. Its sight is keen. The emu attains a height of 5 feet and is exceeded in size, among living birds, only by the African ostrich. It is said to be a powerful swimmer as well as runner. The kiwi is about the size of the domestic fowl but somewhat heavier. It is a nocturnal species with rudimentary or absent vision but its hearing is acute. Its nostrils are situated near the end of the long beak, which is used to test the ground before the bird, partly by touch and partly by smell. Rudimentary wings, not more than three inches long when fully extended, are concealed beneath the feathers.

The cerebellum of Apteryx, according to Craigie (1930), is relatively small. The anterior part is entirely concealed by the cerebral hemispheres. The "auricular or floccular lobes" are notably small. Presumably these are divisible into flocculus proper and "avian paraflocculus," as in other birds, but Craigie does not indicate such subdivisions. The cerebellar ventricle is a short median vertical cleft which extends anteriorly and posteriorly beyond the opening into the fourth ventricle. Craigie divides the body of the cerebellum into the anterior, medial, and posterior lobes of Ingvar in birds by fissures x and y of Brouwer; he is not certain, however, if fissure x, the fissura prima, is the furrow between the fifth and sixth cortical folds of the anterior surface or the shallower one next behind it.

A tentative interpretation of the Apteryx cerebellum, based on Craigie's description and illustrations, in terms of the fissures and folia above described in other birds, includes the five folia labeled I–V in figure 234 in the anterior lobe. All except folium II are undivided. The fissura prima is represented by the more dorsal of the two furrows, whose identity was regarded as uncertain by Craigie.

Behind the fissura prima, so interpreted, folium VI is recognizable by two subfolia which can be considered VIa and VIb+c, or possibly only subfolia VIa and VIb,

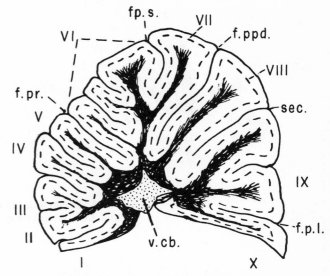

Figure 234. Sagittal section of cerebellum of the kiwi, Apteryx Australis. (Modified from Craigie, 1930.)

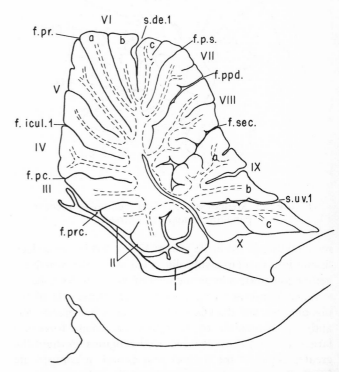

Figure 235. Midsagittal section of the cerebellum of ostrich. (Modified from Ingvar, 1918.)

in view of the reduced or absent vision of this species, while the tactile trigeminal connections apparently are important. Folium VII is small but folium VIII is large, reflecting the reduced vision and the probably acute auditory sense. Folium IX is divided into two subfolia that probably correspond to IXa + b and IXc of other species (fig. 234).

A tentative interpretation of the folia in Ingvar's figure of a sagittal section of Rhea is indicated by the labels in figure 235. The anterior lobe of this species is relatively large and folium IX of the posterior lobe has the typical three, instead of only two, secondary folia. The fissura secunda is prominent and its walls are considerably foliated, as in other large species. Folia VI, VII, and VIII are very similar to the corresponding folia of other large birds.

It should be emphasized that although the tentative interpretations of the folia, both in Apteryx and Rhea, appear to conform to the folia of other species, they lack the assurance which firsthand study of embryonic and adult material could supply, or the modifications such study might necessitate.

Summary

As the preceding descriptions indicate, the corpus cerebelli is constant in general pattern in all species. Variations of individual folia, as between species, appear to be correlated with differences in sensory or motor equipment. The most striking variation, that of the anterior lobe in the hummingbird, is owing to absence of folium III as a distinct cortical fold, and the reduction of folia I and II. The relatively large size of folia IV and V, and of folium VI of the posterior lobe, appears to be correlated with the great importance of the wings in the hummingbirds. Whitlock (1952), as already noted, found degenerating fibers of the spino-cerebellar tracts to all three of the corresponding folia, by the Marchi method in the pigeon, and obtained responses in folia IV, V, and the anterior part of VI, upon stimulation of wing feathers or nerves in pigeons, horned owl, and duck. In strong fliers, such as the wild mallard duck and the eagle, folia V and VI are well developed. The large size of folium VI of the duck probably is correlated, in part, with the greater extent of the trigeminal sensory area in the beak of this species. The large size of folium V in the bantam chicken, a relatively poor flier, appears anomalous in relation to the size of its wings. The relative development of folium III (possibly folia III and IV) in all but the hummingbird appears to be correlated with the walking or swimming ability of individual species, or with the strength of the legs for other purposes. The stimulation of feathers of the leg or of nerves leading to it in the pigeon and owl acti-

vated both folia, but this was also true when the tail feathers were stimulated (Whitlock, 1952). Folia I and II vary considerably in different species. Except for evidence that folium II receives spino-cerebellar fibers and folium I probably does so, as already described, there is no experimental indication of their functional relations in birds.

Some of the folia of the posterior lobe present considerable variation from species to species, folium VI having the widest range. In addition to activation from the wings this folium also responded, in Whitlock's experiments, to impulses from the face; its posterior subdivision, subfolium VIc, responded in the owl to auditory stimuli. It is relatively small in the chicken, grouse, cormorant, and owls, but large in the hummingbird, duck, and penguin. Folium VII is unusually large in the eagle, apparently in correlation with the visual power of this species. Folium VIII appears to be relatively larger than average in the chicken, grouse, duck, and penguin. Folium IX, as already noted, is the largest in all species and its lateral continuations, especially the "avian paraflocculus," are the most prominent.

The homology of the pars interposita and pars lateralis of reptiles with the vermis, in the restricted sense, and the pars intermedia, respectively, of mammals would lead one to expect corresponding longitudinal zones in the avian cerebellum. As above noted, such zones and a lateral zone corresponding to the lateral zone in mammals have recently been demonstrated by Goodman, Horel, and Freemon (1963) in ducklings. The rudimentary hemisphere, unfoliated in the smaller species, becomes increasingly foliated in the larger birds by lateral continuation of the vermal folds.

The flocculonodular lobe of adult birds is less readily recognized than in many mammals owing to the intimate relations of the flocculus and the "avian paraflocculus." The posterolateral fissure is deep between the nodulus and uvula, but because it is so shallow on each side its lateral relations remained obscure until elucidated in embryonic stages. The fissure can be followed onto the "avian auricle" of the adult, however, as described in the preceding pages, and in some species to the medulla oblongata. The developmental history of this fissure and of the flocculus and nodulus in birds appears to leave no question regarding the morphological significance of the fissure and of the entity of the flocculonodular lobe in the avian cerebellum.

Takeda (1960), who uses the Roman numeral terminology for the ten principal folia of the cerebellum, divides the organ into lobus anterior, lobus medius, and lobus posterior. The lobus anterior comprises folia I–V, the lobus medius segments VI–VIII, and the lobus posterior folia IX and X.

THE CEREBELLAR NUCLEI

The cerebellar nuclei of birds are larger and more complex than in crocodilians. They are situated lateral of the inferior part of the cerebellar ventricle. Brandis (1894) and Shimazono (1912) divided the deep gray substance of the avian cerebellum into medial and lateral nuclei. Van Hoevell (1916) subdivided the medial nucleus into a dorsally situated pars magnocellularis and a ventral pars parvocellularis. In the kiwi, Apteryx australis, Craigie (1930) describes the cerebellar nuclei as large but simple in form, comprising a medial and a lateral nucleus on each side of the cerebellar ventricle. For birds in general Ariens Kappers (1947) distinguishes a medial and a lateral nucleus.

Ramon y Cajal (1908a), who based his study of the cerebellar nuclei on silver preparations of late embryos and newly hatched birds, divides the nuclear gray substance into internal, intercalated, intermediate, and lateral nuclei, the last being subdivided into superior and inferior parts. In his *Histologie du Système Nerveux* Ramon y Cajal (1909–11) groups these subdivisions into a large internal nucleus, an intermediate nucleus of smaller size, and a still smaller lateral nucleus, the last being situated near a "minuscule hemisphere cerebellaux." From Golgi and reduced silver preparations the nuclear cells are described as multipolar, their dendrites extending from the cell body in all directions. The axons collect to form the efferent cerebellar tracts.

Craigie (1928) found in hummingbirds the medial cell mass, which he called the fastigial nucleus, so large that it nearly obliterates the cerebellar ventricle. The posteroventral part of this nucleus is formed of small cells; the anterior part is described as extending further rostrally than the other nuclei, its anterior connections being largely with the cortex of the anterior lobe. Craigie describes the intermediate nucleus of Ramon y Cajal as a rounded or roughly triangular cell mass having a ventromedially directed hilus. It extends much farther posteriorly than the fastigial nucleus and also toward the base of the "floccular lobe," i.e., the "avian auricle," as above defined. A group of cells situated farther laterally and caudally in the medullary substance connecting the "auricle" with the vestibular region was regarded as probably corresponding to Ramon y Cajal's (1908b) inferior part of the lateral nucleus. The superior lateral nucleus of Ramon y Cajal was not identified with certainty, but possibly was represented by a cell mass which extends farther laterally from the ventrolateral connection between the fastigial and intermediate nuclei. I have confirmed Craigie's description from this author's serial sections of the cerebellum of several species of hummingbirds. The nucleus intercalatus of Cajal, not mentioned by Craigie, is probably represented by the small-celled part of his fastigial nucleus.

In the sparrow, Sanders (1929) recognized five nuclear masses corresponding to those of Ramon y Cajal (1908b), whose terminology she adopted. The internal nucleus is described as comprising medial and lateral divisions, separated by fiber bundles. It corresponds to the internal nucleus of Ramon y Cajal and the fastigial nucleus of Craigie. The intermediate nucleus is said to extend farther forward than the other four cell masses. Its cells are somewhat larger, in general, than those of the internal nucleus, but smaller, closely arranged cells are included in the lateral part of the nucleus. The ventral part is formed of definitely smaller cells than elsewhere in the nucleus or in the internal nucleus. Farther caudally the intermediate nucleus has a large-celled dorsomedial zone and a ventrolateral zone of small cells; a ventrocaudal projection of small cells extends toward the lateral nuclear mass. The lateral cerebellar nucleus, divided into superior and inferior parts, is said to extend farther ventralward and caudalward than the other cell groups; it is situated lateral of the small-celled part of the intermediate nucleus and dorsal of the superior vestibular nucleus. The cells are mostly of medium size, some smaller cells occurring in the caudal part of the nucleus. The nucleus intercalatus is small and its cells are of small size.

The descriptions of the authors above cited, based on serial sections stained by various methods, indicate the nuclei as discrete cell masses which vary in appearance from one section to another. Brandis (1894) and Shimazono (1912), as pointed out by Doty (1946), apparently did not see, or at least did not identify, all the nuclear groups, but Brandis recognized bridges of cells among the fiber bundles that connect the major groups. A wax plate model of the cerebellar nuclei of the sparrow, prepared by Doty, is interpreted by Ariens Kappers, Huber, and Crosby (1936) as showing that the entire deep gray of the sparrow cerebellum constitutes a continuous nuclear mass. This has folds and thickened zones that, in section, give a variety of pictures of nuclear form and relations according to the plane and level of individual sections. On the basis of this model and study of thick sections stained with toluidine blue, Doty confirmed the observations of Sanders. He concluded, however, that the nuclei she described are merely the more dominant collections of cells in a continuous sheet which enlarges medially and laterally into major subdivisions. Other parts of the folded sheet are said to be relatively thin, probably favoring functional localizations. Fields in the sheet that differ in cytological structure were believed to indicate specific functional areas by Ariens Kappers, Huber, and Crosby (1936) and Doty (1946).

Yamamoto, Ohkawa, and Lee (1957) differentiated the cerebellar nuclei into nucleus medialis, nucleus interpositus, and nucleus lateralis, named according to the terminology of Brunner (1919) in mammals. These masses are said never to divide into subnuclei but to be continuous one with another; the cerebellar nuclei are described as continuous with the superior vestibular nucleus. According to Takeda (1960), four nuclei were described by Takeda, Nakamura, and Yamadori. These authors included Ramon y Cajal's internal and intercalated nuclei in one nuclear mass which they call the medial nucleus; an intermediate nuclear mass is divided into anterior and posterior interpositus nuclei; and a lateral nuclear mass is considered homologous with the lateral nucleus of Cajal. The medial nucleus is continuous with the smaller interpositus nuclei and these with the lateral nucleus. Except for differences in relative size, the four nuclei of these authors correspond to the four nuclei of mammals.

Rüdeberg (1961), who adopted the terminology of Ramon y Cajal, identified all the nuclei of the Spanish author in the adult chicken, except for the nucleus intercalatus which could not be differentiated with certainty. In his morphogenetic studies on avian cerebellar nuclei Rüdeberg found a cell mass called A_2B, in chick and pigeon embryos, which is apparently formed by a contribution of cells from migration B to migration A. At a later stage of development continuity between the dorsal part of migration A with this cell mass is broken. Still later, the rostral part of A_2B divides into a lateral mass called N_1 and a medial mass N_2; the caudal part divides into a dorsal mass N_3, and a ventral N_4. In the newly hatched chick N_1 corresponds approximately to the nucleus intermedius, and N_2 to the nucleus internus. Masses N_3 and N_4, respectively, form the nucleus lateralis superior and the nucleus lateralis inferior.

My own observations have been made chiefly on the cerebellar nuclei of hummingbirds and penguins. The small hummingbirds and the emperor penguin represent the extremes in body size and in methods of propulsion of the species investigated. The nuclei of the smaller adelie penguin were compared with those of the emperor. As already stated, my observations on these nuclei in hummingbirds are in accord with Craigie's description. Myelin- and protargol-stained sections of the penguin cerebellum show two principal masses of cells, much obscured as to outlines by the fibers that permeate them. Sections stained with toluidine blue, however, show a large nucleus medialis, corresponding to the nucleus in-

ternus of Ramon y Cajal, and, farther laterally, more scattered and smaller cells that I regard as the nucleus intercalatus; the latter and the nucleus internus together appear to correspond to the fastigial nucleus of Craigie in the hummingbird, including the small cells mentioned above. The two nuclei appear also to correspond to the fastigial nucleus of mammals, which considerable evidence indicated is formed of two parts. Dorsally and laterally two smaller cell masses appear to correspond, respectively, to Ramon y Cajal's intermediate and dorsal lateral nuclei; they are in continuity one with the other by more loosely arranged cells. Probably they correspond to the anterior and posterior interpositus nuclei of Takeda, but are relatively larger. Lateroventrally a compact cell mass with a tapering projection toward the "avian auricle" corresponds to Ramon y Cajal's ventral lateral nucleus and, apparently, to the lateral nucleus of Yamamoto and his coworkers and of Takeda and his. The position and ventrolateral projection of this nucleus suggest that it is related to the rudimentary hemisphere and the "avian paraflocculus," which is relatively large in penguins. Such a relation would correspond to that of the lateral nucleus of mammals. The confusion of this nucleus in mammals with the lateral cerebellar nucleus of reptiles, already described, will be avoided by designating the mammalian nuclear mass the nucleus lateralis (dentatus), since it develops into the dentate nucleus proper of anthropoid apes and man. The lateroventrally situated nucleus in birds is the precursor of this hemispherally related nuclear mass.

The demonstration of longitudinal cortical zone in birds (Goodman, Horel, and Freemon, 1963) corresponding to the vermis proper, the intermediate zone, and the lateral zones of mammals suggests cortico-nuclear connections similar to those in mammals.

THE FIBER CONNECTIONS

The afferent tracts. The distribution of afferent tracts to individual folia of the cerebellum has already been described. A review of the contributions of earlier authors and further consideration of the sources and course of individual tracts will complement the description of their terminations.

Various afferent fiber systems of the avian cerebellum were described by Friedländer (1898), Wallenberg (1898, 1900), Frenkel (1909), Kuhn, and Trendelenburg (1911), Shimazono (1912), Ingvar (1918), and others, chiefly from Marchi preparations. Additional observations, based on myelin- and silver-stained preparations, were reported by Ramon y Cajal (1908a), Craigie (1928, 1930), and Sanders (1929). The intracerebellar distribution of most of the tracts, however, remained obscure, as pointed out by Brodal, Kristiansen, and Jansen (1950). Whitlock (1952) classified this aspect of the subject, as above described.

Wallenberg (1900) described vestibular root fibers to the cerebellar cortex and the deep cerebellar nuclei in Marchi preparations of the pigeon. He stated, however, that the lesion made did not exclude the restiform body and the angular nucleus as possible sources of the degenerated fibers. Vestibular root fibers to the cerebellum of the sparrow were described by Ramon y Cajal (1908b), but Frenkel (1909) did not find such fibers in the pigeon. Sanders (1929) described root fibers to the cerebellar nuclei of the sparrow. According to Ariens Kappers (1947), ascending vestibular root fibers terminate in the nucleus medialis (internus of Ramon y Cajal) and perhaps in the cortex of the flocculus and "vermis."

Secondary vestibulo-cerebellar fibers were established by various authors, but with differences in the descriptions of nuclei of origin and of termination in the cerebellum. According to Ramon y Cajal (1908b) such fibers reach the roof nuclei. Shimazono (1912) described a tractus octavoflocularis from the "internal" vestibular nucleus. According to Sanders (1929) the ventrolateral vestibular nucleus sends fibers to the cerebellum and the superior vestibular nucleus has connections with the inferior lateral cerebellar nucleus, some of the fibers possibly reaching other parts of the cerebellar nuclear complex. Groebbels (1927, 1928) describes connections from the vestibular nuclei to the lateral cerebellar nucleus and cerebellar cortex.

More recent conceptions of the morphology of the bird cerebellum and renewed efforts at analysis of its fiber tracts have clarified the distribution of the vestibular fibers in the organ (Larsell, 1948; Whitlock, 1952). Primary and secondary vestibular fibers to the cerebellum and their relation to the vestibular commissure (called the lateral commissure in our earlier publications) have already been described in chick and duck embryos. Both root and secondary fibers pass to the "avian auricle" and also toward the midline (figs. 187, 236). The medially directed fibers run parallel with the posterolateral fissure, the secondary fibers appearing to outnumber the root fibers. Fibers that do not continue into the vestibular commissure terminate in the cortex adjacent to the fissure. At the midline the commissure comprises two small fascicles and some scattered fibers. The fascicles may represent root fibers and secondary fibers, respectively, but this is uncertain. Both primary and secondary fibers continue forward from the larger lateral vestibular fascicles and appear to enter the cerebellar nuclei.

In Marchi preparations of adult pigeons Whitlock (1952), as above noted, found both vestibular root and

secondary fibers to the cerebellum (fig. 238), as had Wallenberg (1900). The root fibers were followed to folium X, some possibly ending in folium IX, and also to the "auricle." Secondary vestibular fibers were followed to the "auricle," as also indicated by Shimazono (1912). Since such fibers were traced into the vestibular commissure of embryonic stages of the duck and chick (figs. 187, 236), distributing, in part, to the cortex adjacent to the posterolateral fissure, it is probable that secondary fibers to folium IX end in its ventral part in the adult cerebellum. Secondary fibers end in both components of the "auricle," but whether root fibers end in the flocculus only or also in the "avian paraflocculus" is uncertain. Both root fibers and secondary fibers appeared to enter the cerebellar nuclei, according to Whitlock, as Sanders (1929) had found in the normal sparrow cerebellum.

Aside from reference to chromatolytic cells in the superior vestibular nucleus following extirpation of the "auricle," Whitlock does not mention individual nuclei of origin of the secondary vestibular fibers to the cerebel-

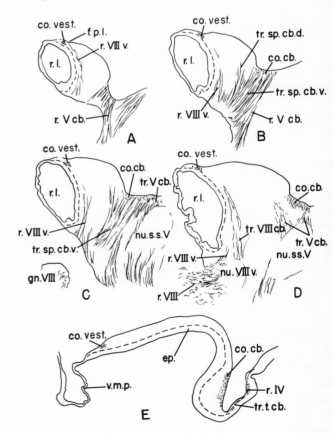

Figure 236. Cerebellum of duck embryo incubated 12 days. A. Sagittal section through the auricle. B, C, D, E. Sagittal sections at successively medial planes, showing cerebellar commissures and the fiber pathways contributing to them. Silver gelatin method. ×27. (Whitlock, 1952.)

lum. As already noted, the secondary vestibulo-cerebellar connections of mammals appear to be derived only from the medial and inferior vestibular nuclei (Voris and Hoerr, 1932; Brodal and Pompeiano, 1957). Cerebellar fibers from the superior nucleus (Sanders; Whitlock) and from the ventrolateral nucleus (Sanders) are therefore not in accord with the mammalian connections, as most recently described. Shimazono's (1912) fibers to the "auricle" from the "internal" (probably dorsomedial vestibular) nucleus, however, appear to correspond in part to mammalian connections.

The distribution of vestibular fibers chiefly to the flocculonodular lobe (although some reach the uvula as in mammals) corresponds to that in mammals. Vestibular fibers to the accessory paraflocculus of mammals, corresponding to the "avian paraflocculus," have not been demonstrated. If they exist, as appears possible on the grounds of anatomical relations of accessory paraflocculus and flocculus in mammalian embryos another similarity is presented.

Mesdag (1909), Bok (1915), and Sanders (1929) described connections between various nuclei of the acoustic system and the cerebellum. Ariens Kappers (1947) states that there is a cerebellar projection from the cochlear nuclei, illustrating it in a diagram as arising from the magnocellular acoustic nucleus. In an experiment in which the cochlear nuclei were destroyed, in addition to the vestibular region, Whitlock (1952) was unable to find degenerated fibers between any part of the cochlear group of nuclei and either the cortex or the deep nuclei of the cerebellum in Marchi preparations. Additional experiments, involving lesions of some or all of the folia of the posterior lobe of the corpus cerebelli, failed to produce chromatolytic changes in the laminar or magnocellular nuclei of the cochlear nuclear complex.

The spino-cerebellar system is large in birds. It was first described by Friedländer (1898), who differentiated dorsal and ventral spino-cerebellar tracts, some of the fibers originating as far caudally as the lumbar segments of the cord. Frenkel (1909) and Kuhn and Trendelenburg (1911) made additional experimental observations. The latter authors described a spino-cerebellar commissure in the cerebellum and traced fibers to the cerebellar cortex, especially that of the anterior folia. Shimazono (1912) also found spinal fibers distributed chiefly to the frontal part of the cerebellum but some were scattered in the caudal region. The distribution of the spino-cerebellar tracts, as described by Ingvar (1918) from Marchi preparations is in good accord, in general, with the observations of Whitlock (1952) already reviewed, but some differences should be noted.

In silver preparations of 15 and 20 day duck embryos

Whitlock traced both dorsal and ventral spino-cerebellar tracts from the superficial region of the lateral funiculus of the cord upward through the medulla oblongata and into the cerebellum. The dorsal tract, after passing through the roots of the vestibular nerve, arches abruptly dorsalward before entering the cerebellum. The ventral tract continues rostralward as far as the roots of the trigeminus and then curves upward to enter the rostral part of the cerebellar base. In adult birds including pigeon, chicken, hummingbird, and two species of owl, a similar course was observed in material stained by silver and/or myelin sheath methods.

Experimental lesions in the cord of the pigeon, confined to the spino-cerebellar system, resulted in degeneration of fibers in the superficial zone of the dorsal part of the lateral funiculus of the cord, as Whitlock demonstrated by the Marchi method. After entering the cerebellar peduncle the dorsal spino-cerebellar tract turns upward into the cerebellum farther caudally than the ventral tract. Both tracts undergo partial decussation in the deep part of the cerebellum. Their distribution, according to Whitlock, is entirely to the cortex; no spinocerebellar tract degeneration could be followed to the deep nuclei. Since other authors who have employed the Marchi method likewise failed to observe such fibers to the deep nuclei it is probable that the spino-cerebellar fibers, regarded by Sanders (1929) as terminating in these nuclei, belong instead to the adjacent cerebellar commissure.

In Marchi preparations of the pigeon both Ingvar and Whitlock (fig. 237) found spino-cerebellar fibers to folia II–V of the anterior lobe, and in the anterior part of folium VI, and to folium IX. Ingvar called folium II the lingula, folium III the lobulus centralis, folia IV and V the culmen, folium VI the dorsal principal process of his medial lobe, and the two principal divisions of folium IX the pyramis and uvula, respectively, of his posterior lobe. The number of degenerating fibers to his lingula is much smaller than Whitlock represents to folium II. Folium I, although represented in Ingvar's illustration of the cerebellum in median sagittal section, is unlabeled and no degenerated fibers are indicated to it. Nor are any shown to folium VIII, in which Whitlock found a small number. This folium, not specifically labeled by Ingvar, he considered part of his medial lobe. As above indicated, I regard it as corresponding to the pyramis (lobule VIII) of mammals.

Neither Ingvar nor Whitlock was able to differentiate the dorsal and ventral spino-cerebellar tracts in their cerebellar distribution, and little is known of the cells of origin of either tract in the spinal cord of birds.

Trigemino-cerebellar connections have been described

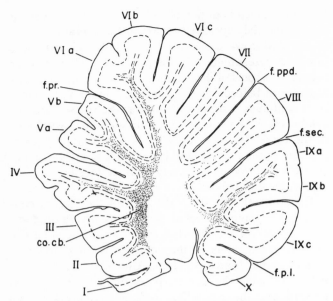

Figure 237. Cerebellum of adult pigeon. Midsagittal section showing the terminal distribution of the degenerating spino-cerebellar tracts in the spinal cord. Marchi method. ×9. (Whitlock, 1952.)

in the adult bird cerebellum by a number of investigators. Biondi (1913) observed fibers extending from the superior sensory V nucleus to the same side of the cerebellum, and Craigie (1928) described a corresponding tract in the hummingbird. According to Sanders (1929) and Woodburne (1936), direct trigeminal sensory root fibers reach the cerebellum, and also a large trigemino-cerebellar tract originates in the superior V nucleus. Many of the fibers decussate, some of them, according to Woodburne, in the ventral part of the anterior lobe — that is, the commissura cerebelli. Ariens Kappers (1947) believed that the secondary fibers take origin in a trigemino-cerebellar nucleus, distinct from the chief sensory trigeminal nucleus in most birds, and are distributed to the anterior lobe. In Marchi preparations of the pigeon Whitlock followed fibers, apparently originating in the superior trigeminal nucleus, to folia V, VI, and VII (fig. 238), but stimulation of feathers of the face region activated only folium VI, as already noted (fig. 239).

A projection from the nuclei of the dorsal funiculus is mentioned by Brandis (1894), Frenkel (1909), and Shimazono (1912). The so-called nucleo-cerebellar path of mammals, with which these authors compare it, has been shown to have its origin in the lateral cuneate nucleus, which nucleus has not been demonstrated in birds. Ariens Kappers (1947) points out that the nuclei of the dorsal funiculus of birds are but slightly developed.

The tecto-cerebellar tract was described in birds by Münzer and Wiener (1898) and by Wallenberg (1900).

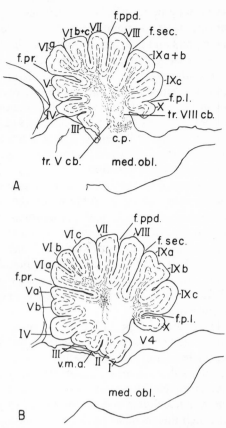

Figure 238. Cerebellum of adult pigeon. A. Paramedian, B. Midsagittal section, showing terminal distribution (black dots) of the degenerating fibers of the trigemino-cerebellar tract (folia V, VI, VII) and the vestibulo-cerebellar tract (folia IX, X), following a lesion of the vestibular and trigeminal regions. Marchi method. ×5. (Whitlock, 1952.)

Degeneration of the tract after injury to the medial part of the optic tectum, beneath the ventricle, was observed by Frenkel (1909). Shimazono (1912), who made fairly deep lesions in the optic lobe, describes the tract as taking a caudal course, first in a ventromedial and then in a dorsomedial direction, and entering the cerebellum behind the spino-cerebellar tract. Within the cerebellum it is said to divide into three parts; the most lateral fascicles, however, decussate before distributing to the cortex. According to Münzer and Wiener the tract ends in the middle region of the cerebellum, but Shimazono found more degeneration in the "vermis posterior"; this was more pronounced on the side of the lesion than contralaterally. In the hummingbird Craigie (1928) found fibers from the ventral magno-cellular part of the nucleus isthmi which he calls collectively the semilunar-cerebellar tract. According to Sanders (1929), tecto-cerebellar fibers swing medialward from the dorsal part of the tectum, in the sparrow, and are joined by fibers from the nucleus isthmi pars principalis, and perhaps by a fascicle which Craigie called the semilunar-cerebellar tract. Some of the fibers are described as decussating and others as reaching the ipsilateral side of the cerebellum. According to Craigie (1928) and Ariens Kappers (1947), the nucleus isthmi receives fibers from the lateral lemniscus and may constitute part of a cochleo-cerebellar connection.

In silver preparations of chick and duck embryos (figs. 188A, 195) the tecto-cerebellar tract was found to extend from the superior and medial regions of the tectum through the anterior medullary velum and into the cerebellum (Larsell, 1948). Its distribution, as seen in Marchi preparations of the adult pigeon, and the folia activated by stimulation of the tectum, retina, and cochlea (see fig. 239A,B,C), have already been described. The observation by Craigie that the nucleus isthmi, which contributes fibers to the tecto-cerebellar tract, receives afferents from the lateral lemniscus is of interest with reference to possible cochleo-cerebellar connections.

Olivo-cerebellar connections were demonstrated by Yoshimura (1910) and Shimazono (1912); following extirpation of part of the cerebellum these authors observed degeneration in the inferior olive. In normal fiber preparations Williams (1909), Sinn (1913), Craigie (1928, 1930), and Sanders (1929) followed fibers from the olive into the cerebellum. Kooy (1917) also confirmed such connections and Ariens Kappers (1947) believed that olivary fibers reach all parts of the vermis. In our silver preparations of chick and duck embryos and in Weigert series of adult cerebella of several species, olivo-cerebellar fibers are well shown. In Marchi preparations, after unilateral destruction of the inferior olive in the pigeon, Whitlock (1952) found degenerated fibers that cross the midline and are distributed to all the folia of the cerebellum, as above mentioned. Chromatolytic changes were limited to the contralateral inferior olive, following ablation of the cerebellar cortex of one side.

The inferior olive of birds is divided into dorsal and ventral lamellae by Kooy (1917), Vogt-Nilsen (1954), and others. It is derived from the caudal part of the rhombic lip by cell migrations in a ventromedial direction, according to Harkmark (1954a), who studied the early development of the olive in chick embryos. A deep migration gives rise to the entire dorsal lamella and a superficial migration to the ventral lamella. The dorsal lamella is the larger of the two in adult birds and is divided into medial and lateral parts. The medial part is regarded by Kooy as homologous with the medial accessory olive of mammals, and the lateral part with the dorsal accessory olive. Vogt-Nilsen subdivides the medial part in

birds, which he calls medial accessory olive, into dorsal, middle, and ventral portions. The dorsal margin of the dorsal portion is usually bent somewhat laterally, forming the dorsal cap of Kooy. The dorsal and middle portions often are more or less interconnected, fusing in many places. The lateral part of the dorsal lamella (dorsal accessory olive) is larger than the medial part and is

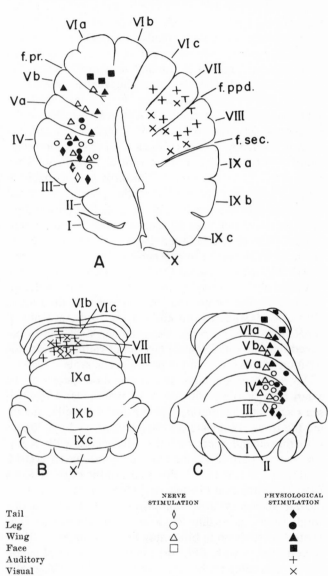

	NERVE STIMULATION	PHYSIOLOGICAL STIMULATION
Tail	◊	◆
Leg	○	●
Wing	△	▲
Face	□	■
Auditory		+
Visual		×
Tectal	T	

Figure 239. Composite diagrams of total number of active points located in cerebellum of adult owl as plotted on midsagittal (A), posterior (B) and anterior (C) views. The stimulation of a peripheral nerve or of a tactile receptor or of various parts of the body, as well as auditory and visual receptors, are indicated. The active points are projected to the surface of the folium from which they were recorded in the anterior and posterior views. (Whitlock, 1952.)

divided into medial and lateral portions. These are completely separated at the middle levels of the olive but are interconnected at caudal levels. Rostrally they often merge, but the medial portion usually extends farther forward than the lateral portion.

The ventral lamella, according to Kooy, is homologous with the mammalian principal olive. It is divided into lateral and medial parts. The lateral part is the larger and extends farther caudally. Its cells are more closely arranged than those of the medial part. The medial part is said to extend farther forward and often is connected with the ventral part of the medial accessory olive.

Yoshimura (1910) describes the ventral lamella of the African ostrich, Struthio camelus, as very small, as did Craigie (1930) in the kiwi, Apteryx australis. In the cassowary, Cassuaris australis, it is relatively small, according to Kooy (1917); Ziehen (1934a), however, found a very broad but short ventral lamella in Rhea americana. These and other ratite birds are incapable of flight. Yoshimura believed that the poorly developed ventral lamella of the ostrich is correlated with its inability to fly. Kooy and Vogt-Nilsen, however, found no indication of correlation between flying capacity and the size of the ventral lamella in present-day Neognathae. Kooy (1917, 1918), Mareschal (1934), and others regard the principal olive as a phylogenetically recent part of the inferior olive. On the grounds of evidence that the ratites, although descended from early flying birds, are phylogenetically older than the Neognathae, Vogt-Nilsen believed that the small ventral lamella of ratites reflects the position of this group in the phylogenetic scale.

To return to a comparison of the subdivisions of the avian inferior olive with those of mammals: Vogt-Nilsen regards the medial part of the dorsal lamella, including the three subdivisions above named, as homologous with the medial accessory olive, in accord with Kooy. The rostral part of the medial accessory olive is considered the phylogenetically oldest part of the olive by Kooy (1917), Mareschal (1934), and others. In mammals the medial accessory olive comprises ventral and medial subdivisions, according to Kooy and Mareschal. The ventral subdivision in birds may be homologous with the rostral part or with all of the mammalian ventral subdivision, according to the tentative suggestion of Vogt-Nilsen, and the middle and dorsal portions may be homologous with the medial subdivisions of mammals.

A possible homology of the dorsal portion of the avian medial accessory olive with nucleus β of Brodal (1940b) in mammals is also suggested tentatively by Vogt-Nilsen. Nucleus β is more or less intimately connected with the dorsal cap of mammals. In birds the dorsal cap is said to be an outgrowth of the dorsal portion of the medial accessory olive. The homology of the ventral lamella with the principal olive of mammals has already been mentioned.

In mammals all parts of the cerebellar cortex receive olivo-cerebellar fibers as found by Dow (1939) and Brodal (1940b). The studies of Brodal on the cat and rabbit led him to conclude that all cells of the inferior olive project fibers to the cerebellar cortex or the deep nuclei, and that the projections to the cortex, at least, are predominantly contralateral. The flocculus and nodulus receive fibers from the rostral part of the medial accessory olive, the vermis receives all its fibers from the medial and dorsal accessory olives, and the paraflocculus and hemisphere receive projections from the principal olive. Brodal gives additional details, to which we shall return.

Since the paraflocculus, including the accessory paraflocculus, of the cat and rabbit, receives fibers from the contralateral principal olive, which is homologous with the ventral lamella of birds, there is reason to believe, as Vogt-Nilsen (1954) suggests, that the parafloccular part of the "avian auricle" is supplied with crossed fibers from the ventral lamella. In normal avian material stained with thionin, Vogt-Nilsen found a possible correlation between the ventral lamella and the "auricle," both of which are small in most ratite birds. Presumably the parafloccular component of the auricle is reduced in correlation with the ventral lamella. No mention is made of the flocculus and medial part of the dorsal lamella in this connection, although he recognized the two components of the "auricle," and that the parafloccular component receives fibers from the pons as well as from the ventral lamella of the olivary nucleus. The flocculus of birds, apparently like that of mammals, probably receives no pontine fibers. Olivary fibers to the cerebellar nuclei, found in mammals, are presumably also present in birds.

The cells of the avian inferior olive are described by Vogt-Nilsen as predominantly polygonal in form but including numerous round, elongated, or fusiform elements. They contain rather coarse Nissl granules and have round or oval nuclei with one, sometimes two, nucleoli. Dendrites radiate from many of the cell bodies. The largest olives are said often to have the largest cells, while in smaller olives the cells are smaller. According to Kooy, large birds have larger cells than small birds. Vogt-Nilsen states that the great majority of cells are about the same size in individual birds, but small variations in cell size occur in all parts of the olive. In some birds the largest cells are more abundant in specific regions such as the dorsal cap of the medial accessory olive and the most lateral part of the ventral lamella. Cells of definitely small size, and transitional sizes between them and the larger cells, are found. The small cells tend to form clusters among which elongated and spindle-shaped cells are said to be more numerous than among the larger elements.

The cells of the inferior olive of mammals, as seen in Golgi preparations, are of several types, according to Scheibel and Scheibel (1955). These are distinguishable by differences in the size of the cell body and the extent and pattern of their dendritic branches. Within the olive there are at least four types of synaptic endings of the afferent fibers leading to the olivary nuclear masses. Comparable studies in birds, however, are lacking.

As already mentioned, Brodal, Kristiansen, and Jansen (1950) demonstrated pontine nuclei, a lateral and a medial, in the chicken, and showed that they project fibers to the rudimentary cerebellar hemisphere, the "avian paraflocculus," folia VI–VIII, and the dorsal part of IX. Whitlock (1952) confirmed the pontine nuclei in the adult pigeon and demonstrated experimentally that they project to the cerebellar cortex. In penguins I find an externally visible and relatively large brachium pontis which connects the pontine nuclei with the cerebellum. The specific distribution of the ponto-cerebellar fibers has not been determined in the penguins.

Transversely directed fibers on the ventral surface of the rostral part of the medulla oblongata were first described by Wallenberg (1903, 1904), who regarded them as an interfloccular commissure. Shimazono (1912) followed these fibers, in the pigeon, from the cerebellar peduncle into the lateral cortex of the cerebellum, a few passing to the "flocculus" (undoubtedly the "avian auricle" of my terminology). These fibers were regarded as an efferent cerebellar tract, but Shimazono reached no conclusion respecting their origin. Craigie (1928) mentions similar fibers in the hummingbird and, in the kiwi he (1930) describes them as an extensive system of superficial arcuate fibers, a large proportion being cerebellar. Their distribution, subsequently described by Brodal, Kristiansen, and Jansen (1950), was not recognized.

The presence of an incipient pontine nucleus in birds was suggested by Papez (1929) and by Ariens Kappers, Huber, and Crosby (1936). Ariens Kappers (1947) suggests, however, that the grey substance between the levels of the trigeminal and acoustic nerve roots, which he called prepontine nuclei, may form part of a more archaic tecto-ponto-cerebellar system upon which the cortico-ponto-cerebellar system may develop. It remained for Brodal, Kristiansen, and Jansen (1950) to demonstrate the pontine nuclei and their connections, as already noted.

A strio-cerebellar tract was described in birds by K. Schroeder (1911), Craigie (1928), and Huber and Crosby (1929). According to Ariens Kappers (1927),

this tract appears to arise in the paleostriatum and to accompany the ventral peduncle of the lateral forebrain bundle through the diencephalon and mesencephalon, thereafter turning dorsally into the cerebellum. Ariens Kappers, Huber, and Crosby (1936) suggest that, in part at least, it may represent a cerebello-striate tract.

The efferent tracts. The cerebellar efferent fibers of birds may be grouped into those having cerebello-tegmental, cerebello-thalamic, and cerebello-spinal connections and those that end in relation to the vestibular nuclei. Both groups form more clearly defined tracts than in reptiles. The confusion which has prevailed regarding the cerebellar nuclei of birds makes it difficult to interpret the origin of some of the tracts, as described by various authors, in terms of the nuclei of Ramon y Cajal. It is therefore necessary to indicate the nucleus of origin as given by individual authors.

A cerebello-bulbar and cerebello-spinal tract which, according to Shimazono (1912), arises entirely in the "medial cerebellar nucleus," decussates in the inferior part of the cerebellum and then passes caudalward into the medulla oblongata and the spinal cord. Shimazono describes it as occupying the same region of the lateral funiculus of the cord as the spino-cerebellar tracts, but its fibers are scattered. In its course through the medulla oblongata it is said to give off fibers to the motor trigeminal and facial nuclei. According to Friedländer (1898) cerebello-spinal fibers reach the lumbar cord. Ariens Kappers (1947) describes fibers from the cerebellar nuclei that join the fasciculus longitudinalis medialis, accompanied by similar fibers from the vestibular nuclei, as a very archaic descending system. Shimazono (1912) states that he was never able to follow cerebellar fibers into the medial longitudinal fascicle, but Groebbels (1927, 1928) describes fibers from the "lateral cerebellar nucleus" to this fascicle on both sides that continue into the spinal cord. It appears very unlikely that the lateral nucleus of Groebbels corresponds to the nucleus so designated by Ramon y Cajal. A descending system that has its origin in the ipsilateral "flocculus" (probably the true flocculus) and its termination in the vestibular nuclei, is also described by Groebbels. This system apparently corresponds to the flocculo-vestibular path found by Dow (1936) and others in mammals, and probably consists of axons of Purkinje cells rather than of fibers originating in cerebellar nuclei. Fibers from the "medial nucleus" and the "lateral nucleus" are described as uniting into a cerebello-vestibular tract which, according to Ariens Kappers, Huber and Crosby (1936), distributes to the vestibular nuclei.

According to various authors, cerebellar fibers reach the oculomotor (Wallenberg, 1900; Sanders, 1929, "probably"), trochlear, and abducens nuclei (Sanders). In view of the relatively large size of the eye-muscle nuclei in birds cerebellar connections with them should be, and apparently are, much more evident than in reptiles or mammals. Cerebelloreticular fibers, ending in the reticular formation of the medulla oblongata and of the midbrain, are also described by Sanders.

The brachium conjunctivum in the sense of an ascending cerebellipetal tract apparently has its origin in all three nuclear groups, as Jansen and Jansen (1955) have demonstrated in the cat. According to most authors who have investigated this tract in birds, it decussates completely in the midbrain and terminates in the red nucleus. Frenkel (1909) and Muskens (1930), however, state that some of the fibers continue as a cerebello-diencephalic tract to the thalamus. Muskens describes this tract as originating in the "nucleus medianus cerebelli," crossing in the ventral cerebellar commissure between the medial nuclei, and continuing to the nucleus anterior thalami.

It is evident from the above review that the relations of most of the efferent cerebellar tracts with the subdivisions of the cerebellar nuclear mass, as well as their distribution, remain in a state of confusion. Recourse to the newer degeneration methods so successfully employed on the mammalian cerebellum by Jansen and Brodal no doubt will clarify their relations in birds also.

THE HISTOLOGY

The minute anatomy of the avian cerebellum was described by Stieda (1864) and, more completely, by Ramon y Cajal (1888b, 1904, 1908a, 1909–11), Falcone (1893), and Dogiel (1896). Additional observations were published by Craigie (1926), Hirako (1935, 1940), and others to whom reference is made below.

The cerebellar cortex consists of molecular, Purkinje cell, and granular layers. In the embryos and young birds there is an external granular layer, as in mammals. This has been studied most recently by Saetersdal (1956b) with especial reference to rate of growth and its significance in the growth of the molecular and internal granular layers.

The internal or definitive granular layer rests, in general, on the medullary substance of the cerebellum. In folia I and X of some species, however, the fibers that constitute the medullary layer fray out among the granules, especially distally, without forming a distinct band; the granular layer, accordingly, is separated from the ventricular surface only by ependyma. There are many variations of the pattern, ranging from that in the hummingbird in which all of the granular layer of both these folia reaches the ventricular surface, to the horned owl and cormorant in which both folia have a fairly thick

medullary layer throughout their length. The largest cerebella, those of the eagle and the penguin, show a thinner medullary layer in both folia I and X than do the owls and cormorant. The granular layer of the remaining folia varies somewhat in thickness, but no pattern characteristic of individual folds in the different species is apparent except perhaps at the junction of folia IX and X; here this layer is, as a rule, thin.

The molecular layer is thin in the flocculus and immediately adjacent portion of the "avian paraflocculus." Elsewhere it forms a uniformly thick external layer in all the folia but is thinner beneath the deep parts of the fissures.

The medullary substance, except for variations in folia I and X, as described, forms a relatively uniform stratum between the granular layer and the cerebellar ventricle. In the lower part of the anterior lobe it divides into two more or less distinct sheets, as already noted, between which the cerebellar nuclei and related fibers are situated.

The cellular and fibrous elements of the avian cerebellar cortex, as pointed out by Ramon y Cajal (1911), are very similar to those of mammals. The Purkinje cells of birds have a rounded or pear-shaped body and, usually, a single radially elongated primary dendrite which arborizes less freely than in mammals (fig. 240). Dogiel (1896), who stained the cerebellar cortex with methylene blue, illustrates Purkinje cells with one or two primary dendrites, and Hirako (1935) describes them (from Golgi preparations) as possessing one, two, or three such dendrites. Those with two or three dendritic processes are less numerous and occur beneath the deep parts of the fissures. The primary dendrites divide at some distance from the cell body, the secondary processes diverging from each other at a wide angle. Tertiary terminal dendrites arise from the secondary branches and, for the most part, take a course perpendicular to the cortical surface, but some of the lower tertiary branches spread horizontally or even toward the granular layer. They are less numerous and thicker, as shown in Golgi preparations, in the young chick (fig. 241) than in the adult pigeon, and in the latter than in the corresponding branches of mammals. The gemmules or spines with which they are studded are smaller and farther apart in birds. Hirako (1935) describes the Purkinje cells of the chicken, when stained by a modified Weigert-Pal technique, as showing very slender tertiary dendritic branches having sharp contours and a punctilinear appearance.

The axons of the Purkinje cells penetrate the granular layer to enter the medullary rays. Usually they have but two collaterals, in contrast with three or four in mammals, these recurving toward the zone immediately above the Purkinje cell bodies. Ramon y Cajal (1908a, 1909–11) concluded that the Purkinje cell axons of birds, as of mammals, terminate in the deep cerebellar nuclei, there forming synaptic connections with the nuclear neurons. Experimental evidence that the axons end in the cerebellar nuclei was presented by Shimazono (1912). In one experiment, however, he found degeneration granules extending from the Purkinje cell layer not only to

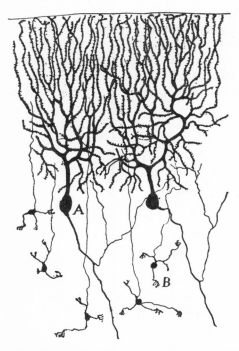

Figure 240. Purkinje cells (A) and granular cells (B) from cerebellum of adult pigeon. Golgi method.
(Ramon y Cajal, 1909–11.)

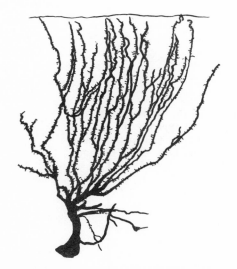

Figure 241. Purkinje cell from cerebellum of chick. Golgi method. (Hirako, 1935.)

the medial and lateral nuclei, but also descending through the cerebellar peduncle to the region of Deiters's nucleus. The cortical area destroyed in this experiment is described only as "den mittleren Teil der Kleinhirnrinde," the folia involved being uncertain. The fibers observed probably correspond to long corticifugal fibers such as found by Bender (1932) and others in mammals, and experimentally demonstrated by Jansen and Brodal (1940, 1942) as reaching the vestibular nuclei from the cortex of the entire vermis. It is probable that they included fibers from the flocculonodular lobe to these nuclei, like those demonstrated in mammals by Dow (1936).

A plexus of fibers lies beneath and around the bodies of the Purkinje cells, corresponding to the periganglionic plexus of mammals. It has been less thoroughly studied in birds, but Shimazono (1912) states that degenerated fibers can be followed to this plexus as a result of lesions involving the afferent cerebellar paths, whether placed in the spinal cord, the medulla oblongata, or the optic lobe. He also followed many fibers from this plexus directly to the dendrites of the Purkinje cells, around which they twine.

The granular layer includes both granule cells and star or Golgi type II neurons. According to Ramon y Cajal (1909–11), who described them more fully in 1888, the granules of birds have fewer, shorter, and smaller terminal dendritic branches than are found in mammals. These processes end in cerebellar islets or glomeruli, discovered in birds by Ramon y Cajal (1898), but earlier described in mammals by Denissenko (1877). The axons of the granule cells ascend into the molecular layer and bifurcate in typical fashion to form the parallel fibers (fig. 240).

The star or Golgi type II cells, according to Ramon y Cajal, differ but little from those of mammals. In 1890 he described the axons of the large star cells of the granular layer as branching into innumerable twigs, ending as short, fine arborizations, identically with those in mammals. The dendrites of the large Golgi cells pass into the molecular layer, there dividing into branches whose course is perpendicular to the surface of the folium. Dogiel (1896) describes large Golgi type II cells as scattered throughout the granular layer. Their dendrites ascend into the molecular layer, usually with no branches until they reach it, but occasionally one or two small twigs pass into the granular layer. Near the folial surface the dendritic branches break up into a mass of fine, varicosed threads which, with corresponding processes of similar dendrites, form a dense network. Dogiel also describes Golgi cells whose dendrites and axons are confined entirely to the granular layer. Basket cells constitute the most specialized type of several varieties of star cells found in the molecular layer. These varieties correspond quite closely to those of mammals, as described by Ramon y Cajal (1888b, 1909–11), Dogiel (1896), and others.

The basket cells are numerous in birds. They are usually triangular or spindle-shaped and give off two or three dendritic processes from opposite poles of the cell body (fig. 242A). These dendrites, at first large, soon branch into long, slender, varicosed fibers that divide many times into finer branches. Some branch at various levels of the molecular layer, but a few processes and their branches take a radial course toward the folial surface, dividing just beneath it into very fine twigs (Dogiel, 1896). Some

branches pass toward the layer of Purkinje cells and divide into numerous terminal twigs that interlace above the Purkinje cells. The axon of the basket cell emerges from the cell body or from a dendrite and is soon reduced to a very thin thread. After a short course it thickens and continues as a varicosed fiber which runs at right angles to the major axis of the folium, finally becoming reduced in size and arching toward a Purkinje cell, on the body of which it breaks up into very fine terminal twigs (fig. 242). In its course the axon gives off numerous collaterals, some of which pass to the Purkinje cell bodies to form pericellular baskets while others pass into the molecular layer, there ramifying into very slender threads. According to Ramon y Cajal (1889), the pericellular basket

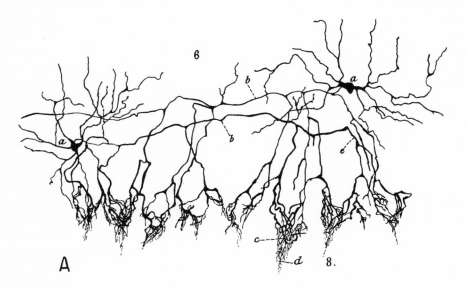

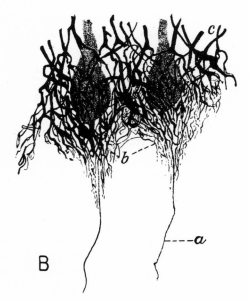

Figure 242. A. Basket cells from cerebellum of sparrow. B. Purkinje cells of sparrow. Cell perikarya inclosed by baskets. Golgi method. (Ramon y Cajal, 1909–11.)

(fig. 242B) is applied intimately to the body of the Purkinje cell and also forms a large terminal fringe beneath the cell body; from this fringe fine fibers continue in a pincer-like formation onto the proximal part of the Purkinje cell axon. The pincer is much exaggerated in birds as compared with mammals.

In the outer zone of the molecular layer small superficial cortical or horizontal cells, occurring in large numbers, form a distinctive cellular element. Ramon y Cajal (1888b, 1909–11) has shown them in the pigeon by the Golgi method and Dogiel (1896) with the methylene blue stain. Many lie close to the pia. These cells are spindle-shaped, oval, or triangular in outline. Two or three dendrites issue from the cell body and usually run at right angles to the major axis of the folium, sometimes turning downward toward the inner part of the molecular layer and sometimes toward its surface. They branch many times and finally disappear as very fine varicosed threads. These cells are subdivided by Dogiel into two types: those with ascending axons and those whose axons run at right angles to the major axis of the folium. Other star cells, whose structural pattern shows various gradations between the basket cells and the superficial cortical cells, occur in the zone between the deep and the superficial portions of the molecular layer.

Mossy fibers were first demonstrated in the avian cerebellum and were subsequently found in mammals by Ramon y Cajal (1888b, 1889), using the Golgi method. Dogiel (1896) described them as they appear in the bird cerebellum when stained with methylene blue, and Ramon y Cajal (1909–11) states that they are very similar in birds and mammals. They enter the granular layer as large myelinated fibers which give off short, varicosed branches at intervals. Those branches form rosettes of terminal twigs, the latter being fewer and less complex in birds than in mammals. Craigie (1926), who compared the mossy fibers in a number of species of birds and mammals, found variations of structure in different species. Among the birds the simplest were encountered in the blackbird, Turdus morulus, the strongest flier of the five species studied.

Climbing fibers in birds twine about the dendrites or the Purkinje cells, according to Ramon y Cajal, as far as those of the third order. Renewed studies by recently introduced techniques might well reveal further details much like those found by Scheibel and Scheibel (1954) in mammals. Recent experimental evidence that the climbing fibers of the mammalian cerebellum derive from the inferior olive (Szentágothai and Rajkovits, 1959) suggests a similar origin of these fibers in birds.

Shimazono (1912) obtained experimental evidence of association fibers from one side of a folium to the other. Following circumscribed lesions of the cerebellar cortex small degeneration granules were shown, by the Marchi method, extending transversely along the Purkinje cell layer to the opposite side of the injured folium. No connections between adjacent folia or between the folia of the two sides, other than the intrafolial association fibers, were observed.

Synarmotic cells, such as were found in mammals by Landau (1928) connecting the granular layer on one side of a medullary ray with that of the other side, are described in birds by Löwenberg (1938, 1939). They are largely localized in the medullary substance and give rise to associative fibers that connect different parts of the same folium. This author also regards as associative neurons the Golgi or star cells whose dendrites extend from the granular layer into the molecular layer. These cells are said to be more numerous in birds than in mammals.

Abbreviations, Bibliography, and Index

ABBREVIATIONS USED IN THE FIGURES

a.ac., acousticolateral area
af.fi., afferent fibers
al., alba
aq.cer., cerebral aqueduct
aq.s., aqueduct of Sylvius
a.r.l., anterior wall of lateral recess
a.s., sensory area
aur., auricle
ax., axon

b.c., basket cells
bl.v., blood vessel
br.conj., brachium conjunctivum
bu.olf., olfactory bulb

ca.cb., cerebellar cavity
cal.scr., calamus scriptorius
cb., cerebellum
cb.c., cerebellar cells
cb.v.pl., cerebellovelar plate
c.c., central canal
c.cb., corpus cerebelli
c.cb.,p.d.(p.dors.), dorsal part of corpus cerebelli
c.cb.,p.ven., ventral part of corpus cerebelli
cer.h., cerebral hemisphere
cl.fi., climbing fibers
c.n.mgc., cells of nucleus magnocellularis
co.ac.lat., acousticolateral commissure
co.ac.lat.p.nuc.dors., dorsal nucleus component of acousticolateral commissure
co.cb., cerebellar commissure
co.lat., lateral commissure
col.d., dorsal column
col.d.l., dorsolateral column
col.mot., motor cell column
col.v., ventral column
col.v.l., ventrolateral column
co.nuc.gust.sec., commissure of secondary gustatory nucleus
co.post., posterior commissure
co.p.t., posterior tectal commissure
co.v., velar commissure
co.ven., ventral commissure
co.vest., vestibular commissure
co.v.lat., vestibulolateral commissure

c.quad.post., corpus quadrigeminum posterius
cr.cav., cranial cavity
cr.cb., cerebellar crest
c.t., caudal tongue of pars interposita
cul., culmen

d.a., anterior diverticulum
d.a.r.l., anterior diverticulum of lateral recess
de., declive
dec.r.IV, decussation of IVth root
dec.v., decussatio veli
dien., diencephalon

em.V., trigeminal eminence
em.cb.v., ventral cerebellar eminence
em.gr., eminentia granularis
em.gr.,c.cb., eminentia granularis of cerebellar corpus
em.gr.d., dorsal granular eminence of cerebellar corpus
em.gr.lo.v.lat., eminentia granularis of vestibulolateral lobe
em.gr.v., ventral granular eminence of cerebellar corpus
em.s.t., subcerebellar eminence of tegmentum
em.v., ventral cerebellar eminence
ep., ependyma
ep.c., ependymal cells

f.arc.d., dorsal arcuate fibers
f.arc.ex.d., dorsal external arcuate fibers
f.arc.int., internal arcuate fibers
fas.l.l.as., ascending lateral-line fascicles
fas.l.l.as. + V.as., ascending lateral-line and trigeminal fascicles
f.ex.arc., external arcuate fibers
f.h., horizontal fissure
fi., fibers
fi.VII.l.l., lateral-line VII fibers
fi.arc., arcuate fibers
fi.arc.int., internal arcuate fibers
fi.r.VII.l.l.v., fiber of ventral lateral-line VII root
f.isth., fovea isthmi

f.l.m., medial longitudinal fasciculus
f.pc., preculminate fissure
f.pfl., parafloccular fissure
f.p.l., posterolateral fissure
f.post., posterior fissure
f.ppd., prepyramidal fissure
f.pr., fissura prima
f.prc., precentral fissure
f.p.s., posterior superior fissure
f.rh.mes., rhomb-mesencephalic fissure
f.sec., fissura secunda

G.c., Golgi II cell
gl., glomeruli
gn.V., ganglion of V nerve
gn.VII., ganglion of VII nerve
gn.VIII., ganglion of VIII nerve
gn.VIII.ac., acoustic ganglion of VIII nerve
gn.max.mand., maxillo-mandibular ganglion
gn.oph.prof., deep ophthalmic ganglion
gn.sac., saccular ganglion
gn.utr., utricular ganglion
gr., granular layer
gran.ext.nuc.dors., external granular layer of dorsal nucleus
gr.c., granule cells
gris.periv., periventricular gray
gr.p.v., periventricular gray
gust.VII., gustatory component of VII nerve

hab., habenula
hyp., hypophysis

i.a.gr.bd., interauricular granular band
i.em.c.m., intereminential cellular mass
i.f.aur., inferior fold of auricle
i.l.gr.bd., interlobular granular band

k.valv., keel of valvula cerebelli

l.ant., anterior lobe of corpus cerebelli
l.c., central lobule
l.inf.dien., inferior lobule of diencephalon
ling., lingula

l.lat.,l.lat.cb., lateral lobule of cerebellum
lm., lemniscus
lm.b., lemniscus bulbaris
lm.sp., lemniscus spinalis
lo.ac.lat., acousticolateral lobe or area
lo.ant.c.cb., anterior lobe of corpus cerebelli
lo.fac.,lo.VII., facial lobe
lo.fl.nod., flocculonodular lobe
lo.l.l.ant., anterior lateral-line lobe
lo.olf., olfactory lobe
lo.opt., optic lobe
lo.post.c.cb., posterior lobe of corpus cerebelli
lo.vag.,lo.X., vagal lobe
lo.visc., visceral lobe
lo.v.lat., vestibulolateral lobe
l.post., posterior lobe of cerebellum
l.vest., vestibular lobe

M.c., Müller cell
med.cb.ri., median cerebellar ridge
med.obl., medulla oblongata
mes., mesencephalon
mes.V.c., cells of mesencephalic V root
m.t., mesencephalic tectum

n.I., olfactory nerve
n.II., optic nerve
n.IV., trochlear nerve
n.V., trigeminal nerve
n.VII., facial nerve
n.VIII., acoustic nerve
n.IX., glossopharyngeal nerve
n.X., vagus nerve
nb., neuroblast
nod., nodulus
n.sp.1., first spinal nerve
n.ter., nervus terminalis
nuc.III., oculomotor nucleus
nuc.IV., nucleus of IV nerve
nuc.V.m., motor nucleus of V nerve
nuc.V.s., sensory V nucleus
nuc.VIII.m.ant., anterior motor VIII nucleus
nuc.cb., cerebellar nucleus
nuc.cb.1., lateral cerebellar nucleus
nuc.cb.m., medial cerebellar nucleus
nuc.coch., cochlear nucleus
nuc.dors., dorsal nucleus of acousticolateral lobe
nuc.gust.sec., secondary gustatory nucleus
nuc.hab.d., right habenular nucleus
nuc.hab.si., left habenular nucleus
nuc.isth., nucleus isthmi
nuc.lat.cb., lateral cerebellar nucleus
nuc.lat.valv., nucleus lateralis valvulae
nuc.med., medial nucleus of acousticolateral lobe
nuc.med.cb., medial cerebellar nucleus
nuc.tang., tangential nucleus
nuc.tr.sol., nucleus tractus solitarii
nuc.vent., ventral nucleus of acousticolateral lobe
nuc.vest., nucleus vestibularis
nuc.vest.dors.lat., dorsolateral vestibular nucleus
nuc.vest.l., lateral vestibular nucleus

nuc.vest.sup., superior vestibular nucleus
nuc.vest.v(ent.), ventral vestibular nucleus
nuc.vis.sec., secondary vestibular nucleus

ot., otocyst

par.fi., parallel fibers
p.aur., auricular part of cerebellum
p.dors.c.cb., dorsal part of corpus cerebelli
ped.cb., cerebellar peduncle
pfl., paraflocculus
p.g.c., primitive granule cell
pgt., pigment
p.int.cb., pars interposita cerebelli
p.lat.cb., pars lateralis cerebelli
pl.ch., choroid plexus
pli.enc., plica encephali
p.med.lo.v.lat., medial part of vestibulolateral lobe
p.olf., olfactory peduncle
p.P.c., primitive Purkinje cell
pr.em.gran., primitive eminentia granularis
p.st., pineal stalk
Pur.c., Purkinje cell
p.vent.c.cb., ventral part of corpus cerebelli
pyr., pyramis

r.III., root of III nerve
r.IV., root of IV nerve
r.V., root of V nerve
r.V.asc., ascending trigeminal root
r.V.de., descending root of V nerve
r.V.m., motor root of V nerve
r.V.s., sensory root of V nerve
r.V.sp., spinal V nerve
r.VII, root of VII nerve
r.VII.l.l., lateral-line root of VII nerve
r.VII.l.l.ant., anterior lateral-line VII root
r.VII.l.l.d., dorsal lateral-line VII root
r.VII.l.l.d'., dorsomedial lateral-line VII root
r.VII.l.l.m., medial lateral-line VII root
r.VII.l.l.v., ventral lateral-line VII root
r.VII.m., motor VII root
r.VII.mot., motor VII root
r.VIII., vestibular root
r.VIII.ant., anterior root of VIII nerve
r.VIII.as., ascending root of VIII nerve
r.VIII.d., cochlear nerve
r.VIII.post., posterior root of VIII nerve
r.VIII.v., vestibular root
r.IX + X., roots of IX and X nerves
r.X., roots of vagus nerve
r.X.l.l., lateral line root of vagus nerve
r.X.l.l.d., dorsal lateral-line X root
r.X.l.l.v., ventral lateral-line X root
r.d.l.l.VII., dorsal root of lateral-line VII nerve
rh.l., rhombic lip
r.l., lateral recess of fourth ventricle
r.mes.V., mesencephalic V root
r.mot.V., radix motorius trigemini
r.v.l.l.VII., ventral root of lateral-line VII nerve

s.a., anterior sulcus of cerebellum

s.de.1., declival sulcus 1
s.de.2., declival sulcus 2
s.ext., external sulcus
s.f.aur., superior fold of auricle
s.fl.int.d., dorsal internal floccular sulcus
s.fl.int.v., ventral internal floccular sulcus
s.l., sulcus limitans
s.lat., lateral sulcus
sp.c., spinal cord
s.pr.tr., primary transverse fissure
st.c., stellate cell
st.ep., epiphyseal stalk
str.fibr.c.cb., fibrous layer of cerebellar corpus
str.gr(an)., stratum granulosum, granular layer
str.gr.cb., cerebellar gray layer
str.gris.p.v., stratum griseum periventriculare
str.mol., molecular layer
str.mol.cb., stratum moleculare cerebelli
str.Pur., layer of Purkinje cells
s.uv.1., uvular sulcus 1
s.uv.2., uvular sulcus 2
s.uv.3., uvular sulcus 3
s.v.cb., sulcus ventralis cerebelli

t.ch., tela choroidea
teg., tegmentum
teg.b., tegmentum of bulb
teg.c., tegmental cells
teg.mes., tegmentum of midbrain
tel., telencephalon
tela a., anterior tela of fourth ventricle
ter.l.l.fi., terminals of lateral-line fibers
thal., thalamus
t.opt., optic tectum
tor.s.c., torus semicircularis
tr.V.de., tr.V.sp., descending or spinal V tract
tr.VII.l.l.d.as., ascending lateral-line VII tract
tr.VII.l.l.d.de., descending lateral-line VII tract
tr.VIII.as., ascending VIII tract
tr.X.l.l.as., ascending lateral-line X tract
tr.a., dorsal longitudinal tract of acousticolateral area
tr.b., ventral longitudinal tract of acousticolateral area
tr.b.cb., bulbo-cerebellar tract
tr.b.t., bulbo-tectal tract
tr.cb.b., cerebello-bulbar tract
tr.cb.teg., cerebello-tegmental tract
tr.cb.teg.cr., crossed cerebello-tegmental tract
tr.gust.sec., secondary gustatory tract
tr.l.l.valv., lateral-line tract to valvula
tr.lo.cb., lobo-cerebellar tract
tr.mam.cb., mammillo-cerebellar tract
tr.mes.V., mesencephalic V tract
tr.mes.cb., mesencephalo-cerebellar tract
tr.mes.cb.ant., anterior mesencephalocerebellar tract
tr.mes.cb.post., posterior mesencephalocerebellar tract

ABBREVIATIONS

tr.mes.cb.v., ventral mesencephalo-cerebellar tract
tr.ol.cb., olfacto-cerebellar tract
tr.sac.cb., tractus sacculo-cerebellaris
tr.sol., solitary tract
tr.sp.cb., spino-cerebellar tract
tr.sp.cb.d., dorsal spino-cerebellar tract
tr.sp.cb. + ol.cb., spino-cerebellar and
olivo-cerebellar tracts
tr.sp.cb.v., ventral spino-cerebellar tract
tr.sp.t., spino-tectal tract
tr.t.cb., tr.tec.cb., tecto-cerebellar tract

tr.teg.cr., crossed cerebello-tegmental tract
tr.t.isth., tractus tecto-isthmi
tr.trig.cb., tr.V.cb., trigemino-cerebellar
tract
tr.t.v. + t.cb., tecto-velar and tecto-cerebellar tract
tr.utr.cb., utriculo-cerebellar tract
tr.v.a., tractus visceralis ascendens
tr.vest.cb., tractus vestibulo-cerebellaris
tr.vest.d., direct vestibulo-cerebellar tract
tr.vis.as., tractus visceralis ascendens
tr.vis.tert., tertiary visceral tract

t.v., tuber vermis

uv., uvula

V.3., third ventricle
V.4., fourth ventricle
valv.cb., valvula cerebelli
v.cb., cerebellar ventricle
v.m.a., anterior medullary velum
v.mes., mesencephalic ventricle
v.m.p., posterior medullary velum

z.tr., transitional zone

BIBLIOGRAPHY

Aciron, E. E., 1950. Fissuracion del cerebelo en la rata blanca (Epimys norvegicus). Arch. Anat. Antrop. (Lisboa), 27:215–261.

Addens, J. L., 1928. The eye muscle nerves of petromyzonts, especially in their general morphological significance. Proc. kon. ned. Akad. Wet., Sect. Sci., 31:433–748.

Addison, W. H. F., 1923. A comparison of the cerebellar tracts in three teleosts. J. comp. Neurol., 36:1–35.

Adrian, E. D., 1943. Afferent areas in the cerebellum connected with the limbs. Brain, 66:289–315.

Ahlborn, F., 1883. Untersuchungen über das Gehirn der Petromyzonten. Z. wiss. Zool., 39:191–196.

Alcock, R., 1899. The peripheral distribution of the cranial nerves of ammocaetes. J. Anat. (Lond.), 33:131–153.

Allis, E. P., Jr., 1889. The anatomy and development of the lateral line system in Amia calva. J. Morph., 2:463–568.

———, 1900. The lateral sensory canals of Polypterus bichir. Anat. Anz., 17:433–451.

———, 1901. The lateral sensory canals, the eye-muscles, and the peripheral distribution of certain of the cranial nerves of Mustelus laevis. Quart. J. micr. Sci., 45:87–236.

———, 1904. The latero-sensory canals and related bones in fishes. Int. Mschr. Anat. Physiol., 21:401–503.

———, 1922. On certain features of the latero-sensory canals of the Plagiostomi. J. comp. Neurol., 35:1–14.

Amadon, D., and E. T. Gilliard, 1952. The illustrated encyclopedia of animal life. Vol. 8, Greystone Press, New York.

Anderson, R. F., 1943. Cerebellar distribution of the dorsal and ventral spino-cerebellar tracts in the white rat. J. comp. Neurol., 79:415–423.

Ariens Kappers, C. U., 1906. The structure of the teleostean and selachian brain. J. comp. Neurol., 16:1–109.

———, 1907. Untersuchungen über das Gehirn der Ganoiden, Amia calva und Lepidosteus osseus. Abh. Senckenberg nat. Ges. Frankfurt-a.M., 30:449–500.

———, 1920–21. Die vergleichende Anatomie des Nervensystems der Wirbeltiere und des Menschen. De Erven F. Bohn, Haarlem.

———, 1927. The relation of cerebellum weight to the total brain weight in human races and in some animals. J. nerv. ment. Dis., 65:113–124.

———, 1934. The phylogenetic development of cerebellum. Psychiat. neurol. Bl. (Amst.), 38:788–796.

———, 1947. Anatomie comparée du Système Nerveux. De Erven F. Bohn, Haarlem; Masson & Cie, Paris.

———, and E. Hammer, 1918. Das Zentralnervensystem des Ochsenfrosches (Rana catesbyana). Psychiat. neurol. Bl. (Amst.), 22:368–415.

Ariens Kappers, C. U., G. C. Huber, and E. C. Crosby, 1936. The comparative anatomy of the nervous system of vertebrates, including man. Macmillan Co., New York.

Aristoteles, 1878. Trans. by Richard Cresswell. Aristotle's History of Animals. 10 books, G. Ball and Sons, London.

Arnold, F., 1838. Bemerkungen über den Bau des Hirns und Rückenmarkes. Zurich.

———, 1851. Handbuch der Anatomie des Menschen. 2. Band. 2. Abthl. Freiburg.

Aronson, L. R., and G. K. Noble, 1945. The sexual behaviour of Anura. II. Neural mechanisms controlling mating in the male leopard frog, Rana pipiens. Bull. Amer. Mus. Nat. Hist., 86:83–140.

Ashcroft, D. W., and C. S. Hallpike, 1934. On the function of the saccule. J. Laryng., 49:450–460.

Ayers, H., and J. Worthington, 1907. The skin end-organs of the trigeminus and lateralis nerves of Bdellostoma dombeyi. Amer. J. Anat., 7:329–336.

———, 1908. The finer anatomy of the brain of Bdellostoma dombeyi. I. The acoustico-lateral system. Amer. J. Anat., 8:1–16.

Baker, R. C., and G. O. Graves, 1932. The development of the brain of Amblystoma (3 to 17 mm. body length). J. comp. Neurol., 54:501–559.

Banchi, A., 1903. Sulle vie di connessione del cervelletto. Arch. ital. Anat. Embriol., 2:426–517.

Barnard, J. W., 1936. A phylogenetic study of the visceral afferent areas associated with the facial, glossopharyngeal, and vagus nerves, and their fiber connections. The efferent facial nucleus. J. comp. Neurol., 65:503–602.

Bartelmez, G. W., 1915. Mauthner's cell and the nucleus motorius tegmenti. J. comp. Neurol., 25:87–128.

Bartels, M., 1925. Über die Gegend des Deiters- und Bechterewskernes bei Vögeln. Z. Anat. Entwickl.-Gesch., 77:726–784.

Bartholin, T., 1655. Anatomica reformata. Hagæ.

Beccari, N., 1908. Ricerche sulle cellule e fibre del Mauthner e sulle loro connessioni in pesci ed anfibii (Salmo fario, S. irideus, e Salamandrina perspicillata). Arch. ital. Anat. Embriol., 6:660–705.

———, 1912. La costituzione, i nuclei terminali e le vie di connessione del nervo acustico nella Lacerta muralis, Merr. Arch. ital. Anat. Embriol., 10:646–698.

———, 1930. Differenze di grandezza e di forma in rapporto con l'età nelle terminazioni a coppa del nucleo del nervo oculomotore nei Pesci Teleostei. Monit. zool. ital., 41:132–138.

———, 1931. Studi comparativi sopra i nuclei terminali del nervo acustico nei Pesci. Arch. zool. ital., 16:732–739.

Beck, G. M., 1927. The cerebellar terminations of the spino-cerebellar fibres of the lower lumbar and sacral segments of the cat. Brain, 50:60–98.

Bender, L., 1932. Corticofugal and association fibers arising from the cortex of the vermis of the cerebellum. Arch. Neurol. Psychiat. (Chic.), 28:1–25.

Bengmark, S., R. Hugosson, and B. Källén, 1953. Studien über Kernanlagen in Mesencephalon sowie im Rostralteil des Rhombencephalon von Mus musculus. Z. Anat. Entwickl.-Gesch., 117:73–91.

Benjamins, C. E., 1913. Beitrag zur Kenntnis des häutigen Labyrinthes. Über eine vierte Crista acustica. Z. Ohrenheilk., 68:101–124.

Bergquist, H., and B. Källén, 1953. Studies on the topography of the migration areas in the vertebrate brain. Acta anat. (Basel), 17:353–369.

———, 1954. Notes on the early histogenesis and morphogenesis of the central nervous system in vertebrates. J. comp. Neurol., 100:627–659.

———, 1955. The archencephalic neuromery in Ambystoma punctatum. An experimental study. Acta anat. (Basel), 24:208–214.

Berkelbach van der Sprenkel, H., 1915. The central relations of the cranial nerves in Silurus glanis and Mormyrus caschive. J. comp. Neurol., 25:5–63.

Bielschowsky, M., and M. Wolff, 1904. Zur Histologie der Kleinhirnrinde. J. Psychol. Neurol. (Lpz.), 4:1–23.

Bindewald, C., 1911. Eine Commissura intertrigemina im Amphibiengehirn. Anat. Anz., 40:243–247.

Biondi, G., 1913. I nuclei d'origine e terminali del nervo trigemino nel pollo. Riv. ital. neuropat. psichiat. ed elettroterapia, 6:50, 117. (Cit. Craigie, 1928.)

Bok, S. T., 1915. Die Entwicklung der Hirnnerven und ihrer zentralen Bahnen. Die stimulogene Fibrillation. Folia Neurobiol., 9:475–565.

Bolk, L., 1906. Das Cerebellum der Säugetiere. De Erven F. Bohn, Haarlem; G. Fischer, Jena.

Bradley, O. C., 1903. On the development and homology of the mammalian cerebellar fissures. J. Anat. (Lond.), 37:112–130, 221–240.

———, 1904. The mammalian cerebellum; its lobes and fissures. J. Anat. (Lond.), 38:448–475.

———, 1905. The mammalian cerebellum; its lobes and fissures. Part II. The cerebellum in primates. J. Anat. (Lond.), 39:99–117.

Brand, A. R., and P. P. Kellogg, 1939. Auditory responses of starlings, English sparrows and domestic pigeons. Wilson Bull., 51:38–41.

Brandis, F., 1894. Untersuchungen über das Gehirn der Vögel. II Theil: Das Kleinhirn. Arch. mikr. Anat., 43:787–813.

Brickner, R. M., 1929. A description and interpretation of certain parts of the teleostean midbrain and thalamus. J. comp. Neurol., 47:225–282.

Brodal, A., 1940a. Modification of Gudden method for study of cerebral localization. Arch. Neurol. Psychiat. (Chic.), 43:46–58.

———, 1940b. Experimentelle Untersuchungen über die olivocerebellare Lokalisation. Z. ges. Neurol. Psychiat., 169:1–153.

———, and J. Jansen, 1941. Beitrag zur Kenntnis der spinocerebellaren Bahnen beim Menschen. Anat. Anz., 91:185–195.

———, 1954. Structural organization of the cerebellum with particular reference to problems of cerebellar function and localization. In J. Jansen, and A. Brodal, Aspects of cerebellar anatomy, pp. 285–395. Johan Grundt Tanum, Oslo.

Brodal, A., K. Kristiansen, and J. Jansen, 1950. Experimental demonstration of a pontine homologue in birds. J. comp. Neurol., 92:23–69.

Brodal, A., and O. Pompeiano, 1957. The vestibular nuclei in the cat. J. Anat. (Lond.), 91:438–454.

Brouwer, B., 1913. Über Hemiatrophia neocerebellaris. Arch. Psychiat. Nervenkr., 51:539–577.

Brunner, H., 1919. Die zentralen Kleinhirnkerne bei den Säugetieren. Arb. neurol. Inst. Univ. Wien, 22:200–277.

Burckhardt, R., 1897. Beitrag zur Morphologie des Kleinhirns der Fische. Arch. Anat. Physiol., Anat. Abt. (Suppl.):111–136.

Burdach, K. Fr., 1822. Vom Baue und Leben des Gehirns. 2 Bde. Leipzig.

Burlet, H. M. de, 1928. Über die Papilla neglecta. Anat. Anz., 66:199–209.

———, 1929. Zur vergleichenden Anatomie der Labyrinthinnervation. J. comp. Neurol., 47:155–169.

———, 1934. Vergleichende Anatomie des stato-akustischen Organs. In L. Bolk, E. Goppert, E. Kallius, and W. Lubosch, Handbuch der vergleichenden Anatomie der Wirbeltiere, Bd. 2, pp. 1293–1432. Urban & Schwarzenberg, Berlin and Wien.

Burr, H. S., 1928. The central nervous system of Orthagoriscus mola. J. comp. Neurol., 45:33–128.

Byrnes, C. M., 1929. The comparative morphology of the proprioceptors. Res. Publ. Ass. nerv. ment. Dis., 6:281–296.

Cajal. See Ramon y Cajal.

Carus, C. G., 1814. Versuch einer Darstellung des Nervensystems und insbesondre des Gehirns nach ihrer Bedeutung, Entwickelung und Vollendung im thierischen Organismus. Breitkopf & Härtel, Leipzig.

Catois, E. M., 1899. Sur l'histologie et l'anatomie microscopique de l'encéphale chez les poissons. Caen. (Cit. Ramon y Cajal, 1909–11.)

———, 1901. Recherches sur l'histologie et l'anatomie microscopique de l'encéphale chez les poissons. Bull. Sci. France et Belgique, 36:1–165. (Cit. Ramon y Cajal, 1909–11.)

Chambers, W. W., and J. M. Sprague, 1955a. Functional localization in the cerebellum. I. Organization in longitudinal cortico-nuclear zones and their contribution to the control of posture, both extrapyramidal and pyramidal. J. comp. Neurol., 103:105–129.

———, 1955b. Functional localization in the cerebellum. II. Somatotopic organization in cortex and nuclei. Arch. Neurol. Psychiat. (Chic.), 74:653–680.

Chang, H.-T., and T. C. Ruch, 1946–47. Morphology of the spinal cord, spinal nerves, and caudal musculature of the spider monkey. Yale Z. Biol. Med., 19:345–377.

———, 1949. The projection of the caudal segments of the spinal cord to the lingula in the spider monkey. J. Anat. (Lond.), 83:303–307.

Charlton, H. H., 1933. The optic tectum and its related fiber tracts in blind fishes. J. comp. Neurol., 57:285–325.

Cipollone, L. T., 1897. Ricerche sull' anatomia normale e patologica delle terminazioni nervose nei muscoli striati. Suppl. Ann. med. nav., Berlero, Roma.

Clark, S. L., 1939. Responses following electrical stimulation of the cerebellar cortex in the normal cat. J. Neurophysiol., 2:19–35.

Clark, W. B., 1906. The cerebellum of Petromyzon fluviatilis. J. Anat. (Lond.), 40:318–325.

Clark, W. E. Le Gros, 1928. On the brain of the Macroscelididae (Macroscelides and Elephantulus). J. Anat. (Lond.), 62:245–275.

———, 1932. The brain of Insectivora. Proc. zool. Soc. (Lond.), 2:975–1013.

Coghill, G. E., 1902. The cranial nerves of Amblystoma tigrinum. J. comp. Neurol., 12:205–289.

———, 1906. The cranial nerves of Triton taeniatus. J. comp. Neurol., 16:247–264.

———, 1924. Correlated anatomical and physiological studies of the growth of the nervous system in Amphibia. J. comp. Neurol., 37:37–122.

———, 1929. Anatomy and the problem of behaviour. Cambridge University Press, Cambridge.

Conel, J. L., 1929. The development of the brain of Bdellostoma stouti. I. External growth changes. J. comp. Neurol., 47:343–403.

———, 1931. The development of the brain of Bdellostoma stouti. II. Internal growth changes. J. comp. Neurol., 52:365–499.

Craigie, E. H., 1920. On the relative vascularity of various parts of the central nervous system of the albino rat. J. comp. Neurol., 31:429–464.

———, 1926. Notes on the morphology of the mossy fibres in some birds and mammals. Trav. Lab. Rech. biol. Madrid, 24:319–331.

———, 1928. Observations on the brain of the humming bird (Chrysolampis mosquitus Linn. and Chlorostilbon caribaeus Lawr.). J. comp. Neurol., 45:377–481.

———, 1930. Studies on the brain of the kiwi (Apteryx australis). J. comp. Neurol., 49:223–357.

Deganello, U., 1906. Degenerazioni nel nevrasse della Rana consecutive all' asportazione del labirinto dell' orecchio. Atti. Ist. Veneto Sci., 65:829–849.

Dejerine, J., 1901. Anatomie des centres nerveux. 2 vols., T. J. Rueff, Paris.

Demole, V., 1927. Structure et connexions des noyaux dentelés du cervelet. Schweiz. Arch. Neurol. Psychiat., 20:271–294; 21:73–110.

Denissenko, G., 1877. Zur Frage über den Bau der Kleinhirnrinde bei verschiedenen Klassen von Wirbelthieren. Arch. mikr. Anat., 14:203–242.

Detwiler, S. R., 1945. The results of unilateral and bilateral extirpation of the forebrain of Amblystoma. J. exp. Zool., 100:103–107.

Dijkgraaf, S., 1934. Untersuchungen über die Funktion der Seitenorgane an Fischen. Z. vergl. Physiol., 20:162–214.

———, 1947a. Über die Reizung des Ferntastsinnes bei Fischen und Amphibien. Experientia (Basel), 3:206–208.

———, 1947b. Ein Töneerzeugender Fisch im Neapler Aquarium. Experientia (Basel), 3:493–494.

———, 1950. Über die Auslösung des Gasspuckreflexes bei Fischen. Experientia (Basel), 6:188–190.

———, 1952. Bau und Funktionen der Seitenorgane und des Ohrlabyrinths bei Fischen. Experientia (Basel), 8:205–216.

———, 1960. Hearing in bony fishes. Proc. roy. Soc. B, 152:51–54.

Ditmars, R. L., 1910. Reptiles of the world. Macmillan Co., New York.

———, 1944. Reptiles of the world. Rev. ed., Macmillan Co., New York.

Dogiel, A. S., 1896. Die Nervenelemente im Kleinhirne der Vögel und Säugethiere. Arch. mikr. Anat., 47:707–719.

Doty, E. J., 1946. The cerebellar nuclear gray in the sparrow (Passer domesticus). J. comp. Neurol., 84:17–30.

Dow, R. S., 1935. The relation of the paraflocculus to the movement of the eyes. Amer. J. Physiol., 113:296–298.

———, 1936. The fiber connections of the posterior parts of the cerebellum in the rat and cat. J. comp. Neurol., 63:527–548.

———, 1939. Cerebellar action potentials in response to stimulation of various afferent connections. J. Neurophysiol., 2:543–555.

———, 1942a. Cerebellar action potentials in response to stimulation of the cerebral cortex in monkeys and cats. J. Neurophysiol., 5:121–136.

———, 1942b. The evolution and anatomy of the cerebellum. Biol. Rev., 17:179–220.

———, and G. Moruzzi, 1958. The physiology and pathology of the cerebellum. University of Minnesota Press, Minneapolis.

Dudok van Heel, W. H., 1956. Pitch discrimination in the minnow (Phoxinus laevis) at different temperature levels. Experientia (Basel), 12:75–77.

Edinger, L., 1901. Das Cerebellum von Scyllium canicula. Arch. mikr. Anat., 58:661–678.

———, 1906. A preliminary note on the comparative anatomy of the cerebellum. Brain, 29:483–486.

———, 1908. The relations of comparative anatomy to comparative psychology. J. comp. Neurol., 18:437–457.

———, 1909. Ueber die Einteilung des Cerebellums. Anat. Anz., 35:319–338.

Elliot Smith. See Smith.

Ewart, J. C., 1889. On the cranial nerves of Elasmobranch fishes. Proc. roy. Soc. Lond., 45:524–537.

———, 1892. The lateral sense organs of elasmobranchs. I. The sensory canals of Laemargus. Trans. roy. Soc. Edinb., 37:59–85.

Fadiga, E., G. C. Pupilli, and G. P. von Berger, 1956. Le risposte della corteccia cerebellare a impulsi trasmessi per le vie ottiche. Arch. Sci. biol. (Bologna), 40:541–601.

Falcone C., 1893. La corticcia del cerveletto. Napoli.

Federici, F., 1926. Über die peripherische Ausbreitung des VIII. Schädelnervenpaares bei den Vögeln und über die Bedeutung der Lagena. Anat. Anz., 61:449–465.

Ferrier, D., 1876. The functions of the brain. Smith-Elder and Co., London.

Flatau, E., and L. Jacobsohn, 1899. Handbuch der Anatomie und vergleichenden Anatomie des Centralnervensystems der Säugetiere. S. Karger, Berlin.

Flourens, P., 1844. Mémoires d'anatomie et de physiologie comparées. J.-B. Baillière et fils, Paris.

Franz, V., 1911a. Über das Kleinhirn in der vergleichenden Anatomie. Biol. Zbl., 31:434–445.

———, 1911b. Das Kleinhirn der Knochenfische. Zool. Jb., Abt. Anat. Ontog., 32:401–464.

Frederikse, A., 1931. The lizard's brain. An investigation of the histological structure of the brain of Lacerta vivipara. C. C. Callenbach, Nijkerk, Holland.

Frenkel, B., 1909. Die Kleinhirnbahnen der Taube. Bull. int. Acad. Cracovie, Cl. Med., 2:123–147. (Cit. Ariens Kappers, Huber, and Crosby, 1936.)

Friedländer, A., 1898. Untersuchungen über das Rückenmark und das Kleinhirn der Vögel. Neurol. Zentralbl., 17:351–379, 397–409.

Frisch, K. von, 1936. Über den Gehörsinn der Fische. Biol. Rev., 11:210–246.

———, 1938. The sense of hearing in fish. Nature (Lond.), 141:8–11.

———, and H. Stetter, 1932. Untersuchungen über den Sitz des Gehörsinnes bei der Elritze. Z. vergl. Physiol., 17:686–801.

Fritsch, G., 1878. Untersuchungen über den feineren Bau des Fischgehirns. Berlin.

Fusari, R., 1887. Untersuchungen über die feinere Anatomie des Gehirnes des Teleostier. Int. Mschr. Anat. Physiol., 4:275–300.

Fuse, G., 1912. Die innere Abteilung des Kleinhirnstiels (Meynert, IAK.) und der Deiterssche Kern. Arb. hirnanat. Inst. Zurich, 6:29–267.

———, 1920. Studien über die Kleinhirnrinde der Wirbeltiere. I. Die japanische Schildkröte. Arb. anat. Inst. Sendai, 5:92–131.

Gabrielson, I. N., and S. G. Jewett, 1940. Birds of Oregon. Oregon State College, Corvallis.

Gadow, H., 1901. Amphibia and reptiles. Macmillan, London.

Giacomini, E., 1898a. Sulla maniera onde i nervi si terminano nei miocommi e nelle estremità delle fibre muscolari dei miomeri negli Anfibii urodeli. Monit. zool. ital., 9:92–95.

————, 1898b. Sulla maniera onde i nervi si terminano nei tendini e nelle estremità delle fibre muscolari degli arti negli Anfibii urodeli. Monit. zool. ital., 9:105–110.

Glees, P., C. Pearson, and A. G. Smith, 1958. Synapses on the Purkinje cells of the frog. Quart. J. exp. Physiol., 43:52–60.

Goldstein, K., 1905. Untersuchungen über das Vorderhirn und Zwischenhirn einiger Knochenfische (nebst einiger Beiträgen über Mittelhirn und Kleinhirn derselben). Arch. mikr. Anat., 66:135–219.

Goodman, D. C., 1958. Cerebellar stimulation in the unanesthetized bullfrog. J. comp. Neurol., 110:321–335.

Goodman, D. C., J. A. Horel, and F. R. Freemon, 1963. Functional localization in the cerebellum of the bird (Anas domesticus). Anat. Rec., 145:233–234.

Goodman, D. C., and J. T. Simpson, Jr., 1959. Functional localization in the cerebellum of the white rat. Anat. Rec., 133:280.

————, 1960. Cerebellar stimulation in the unrestrained and unanesthetized alligator. J. comp. Neurol., 114:127–135.

————, 1961. Functional localization in the cerebellum of the albino rat. Exp. Neurol., 3:174–188.

Gordon, J., 1815. A system of human anatomy. W. Blackwood and J. Anderson & Co., Edinburgh.

Goronowitsch, N., 1888. Das Gehirn und die Cranialnerven von Acipenser ruthenus. Morph. Jb., 13:515–574.

Graf, W., 1956. Caliber spectra of nerve fibers in the pigeon (Columba domestica). J. comp. Neurol., 105:355–363.

Gray, L. P., 1926. Some experimental evidence on the connections of the vestibular mechanism in the cat. J. comp. Neurol., 41:319–364.

Griffin, D. R., 1950. Underwater sounds and the orientation of marine animals, a preliminary survey. Tech. Rept. no. 3, Project NR 162-429, O. N. R. and Cornell Univ., 1–26.

————, 1958. Listening in the dark. Yale University Press, New Haven.

Groebbels, F., 1923. Die untere Olive der Vögel. Anat. Anz., 56:296–301.

————, 1927. Die Lage- und Bewegungsreflexe der Vögel. V. Mitteilung. Die physiologische Gruppierung der Lage- und Bewegungsreflexe der Haustaube und ihre weitere Analyse durch Labyrinthentfernung und galvanische Reizung nach Entfernung des Labyrinths und seiner Teile. Pflügers Arch. ges. Physiol., 217:631–654.

————, 1928. Die Lage- und Bewegungsreflexe der Vögel. VI. Mitteilung. Degenerationsbefunde im Zentralnervensystem der Taube nach Entfernung des Labyrinths und seiner Teile. Pflügers Arch. ges. Physiol., 218:89–97.

Grundfest, H., and B. Campbell, 1942. Origin, conduction and termination of impulses in the dorsal spino-cerebellar tract of cats. J. Neurophysiol., 5:275–294.

Häggquist, G., 1938. Zur Kenntnis einer doppelten cerebrospinalen Innervation der Skeletmuskeln. Z. mikr.-anat. Forsch., 43:491–508.

Haller, A. von, 1777. Bibliotheca Anatomica. II. Tiguri, Bern.

Haller, B., 1898. Von Bau Wirbelthier-gehirns. I. Salmo und Scyllium. Morph. Jb., 26:345–641.

Hampson, J. L., C. R. Harrison, and C. N. Woolsey, 1952. Cerebrocerebellar projections and the somatotopic localization of motor function in the cerebellum. Res. Publ. Ass. nerv. ment. Dis., 30:299–333.

Harkmark, W., 1954a. Cell migrations from the rhombic lip to the inferior olive, the nucleus raphe and the pons. A morphological and experimental investigation on chick embryos. J. comp. Neurol., 100:115–209.

————, 1954b. The rhombic lip and its derivatives in relation to the theory of neurobiotaxis. In J. Jansen and A. Brodal, Aspects of cerebellar anatomy, pp. 264–284. Johan Grundt Tanum, Oslo.

Hausman, L., 1929. The comparative morphology of the cerebellar vermis, the cerebellar nuclei, and the vestibular mass. Res. Publ. Ass. nerv. ment. Dis., 6:193–237.

Hawkes, O. A. M., 1906. The cranial and spinal nerves of Chlamydoselachus anguineus. Proc. zool. Soc. Lond., 2:959–991.

Heier, P., 1948. Fundamental principles in the structure of the brain. A study of the brain of Petromyzon fluviatilis. Acta Anat. (Suppl. VI):1–213.

Heister, L., 1717. De adienrandi cerebelli structura Ephemer. Acad. Cass. Leop. Car.

Henle, J., 1879. Handbuch der Nervenlehre des Menschen. 2 Aufl. Braunschweig.

Hensel, H., 1955. Über die Funktion der Lorenzinischen Ampullen der Selachier. Experientia (Basel), 11:325–327.

Herrick, C. J., 1893. Illustrations of the surface anatomy of the brain of certain birds. J. comp. Neurol., 3:171–176.

————, 1899. The cranial and first spinal nerves of Menidia: A contribution upon the nerve components of the bony fishes. J. comp. Neurol., 9:153–455.

————, 1901. The cranial nerves and cutaneous sense organs of the North American Siluroid fishes. J. comp. Neurol., 11:177–249.

————, 1905. The central gustatory paths in the brain of bony fishes. J. comp. Neurol., 15:375–456.

————, 1907. The tactile centers in the spinal cord and brain of the sea robin, Prionotus carolinus. L. J. comp. Neurol., 17:307–327.

————, 1908. On the commissura infima and its nuclei in the brains of fishes. J. comp. Neurol., 18:409–431.

————, 1914a. The cerebellum of Necturus and other urodele Amphibia. J. comp. Neurol., 24:1–29.

————, 1914b. The medulla oblongata of larval Amblystoma. J. comp. Neurol., 24:343–427.

————, 1924. Origin and evolution of the cerebellum. Arch. Neurol. Psychiat. (Chic.), 11:621–652.

————, 1925. Morphogenetic factors in the differentiation of the nervous system. Physiol. Rev., 5:112–130.

————, 1927. The amphibian forebrain. IV. The cerebral hemispheres of Amblystoma. J. comp. Neurol., 43:231–325.

————, 1930. The medulla oblongata of Necturus. J. comp. Neurol., 50:1–96.

————, 1933a. Morphogenesis of the brain. J. Morph., 54:233–258.

————, 1933b. The amphibian forebrain. VI. Necturus. J. comp. Neurol., 58:1–288.

————, 1933c. The amphibian forebrain. VII. The architectural plan of the brain. J. comp. Neurol., 58:481–505.

————, 1944. The fasciculus solitarius and its connections in amphibians and fishes. J. comp. Neurol., 81:307–331.

————, 1948. The brain of the tiger salamander. University of Chicago Press, Chicago.

————, and J. B. Obenchain, 1913. Notes on the anatomy of a cyclostome brain: Ichthyomyzon concolor. J. comp. Neurol., 23:635–675.

Herrick, C. L., 1891. Contributions to the comparative morphology of the central nervous system. J. comp. Neurol., 1:5–37.

Hindenach, J. C. R., 1931. The cerebellum of Sphenodon punctatum. J. Anat. (Lond.), 65:283–318.

Hirako, G., 1935. Beiträge zur wissenschaftlichen Anatomie des Nervensystems. Demonstration der Purkinjeschen Zellen des Kleinhirns, die durch Weigert-Palsche Markscheidenfärbung dargestellt sind. Folia anat. jap., 13:561–566.

————, 1940. Differenzierung, Entwicklung und Formveränderung der Purkinjeschen Zellen beim Hühnerkleinhirn. Jap. J. med. Sci., 8:97–110.

Hirsch-Tabor, O., 1908. Über das Gehirn von Proteus anguineus. Arch. mikr. Anat., 72:719–730.

Hoagland, H., 1933a. Electrical responses from the lateral-line nerves of catfish. J. gen. Physiol., 16:695–714.

———, 1933b. Quantitative analysis of responses from lateral-line nerves of fishes. J. gen. Physiol., 16:715–732.

———, 1935. Pacemakers in relation to aspects of behavior. Macmillan Co., New York.

Hochstetter, F., 1919. Beiträge zur Entwicklungsgeschichte des menschlichen Gehirns, I. F. Deuticke, Wien and Leipzig.

———, 1929. Die Entwicklung des Mittel- und Rautenhirns. In Beiträge zur Entwicklungsgeschichte des menschlichen Gehirns, II, pp. 83–200. F. Deuticke, Wien and Leipzig.

Hocke Hoogenboom, K. J., 1929. Das Gehirn von Polyodon folium Lacép. Z. mikr.-anat. Forsch., 18:311–392.

Hoevell, J. J. L. D. van, 1916. The phylogenetic development of the cerebellar nuclei. Proc. kon. ned. Akad. Wet., Sect. Sci., 18:1421–1434.

Hofer, B., 1908. Studien über die Hautsinnesorgane der Fische. I. Die Funktion der Seitenorgane bei den Fischen. Ber. kgl. Bayer biol. Versuchsstation. München, 1:115–164. (Cit. Löwenstein, 1957.)

Holm, J., 1901. The finer anatomy of the nervous system of Myxine glutinosa. Morph. Jb., 29:365–401.

Holmes, G., 1903. On the comparative anatomy of the nervus acusticus. Trans. roy. irish Acad., 32:101–144.

Holmgren, N., 1919. Zur Anatomie des Gehirns von Myxine. Kungl. Svenska Vetenskapsakad. Handl., 60:1–96.

———, 1922. Points of view concerning forebrain morphology in lower vertebrates. J. comp. Neurol., 34:391–459.

———, 1925. Points of view concerning forebrain morphology in higher vertebrates. Acta zool., 6:413.

———, 1946. On two embryos of Myxine glutinosa. Acta zool., 27:2–90.

———, and C. J. van der Horst, 1925. Contribution to the morphology of the brain of Ceratodus. Acta zool., 6:59–165.

Hoogenboom. See Hocke Hoogenboom.

Horst, C. J. van der, 1919. Das Kleinhirn der Crossopterygii. Bijdr. Dierk., 21:113–118.

———, 1925. The cerebellum of fishes. I. General morphology of the cerebellum. Proc. kon. ned. Akad. Wet., Sect. Sci., 28:735–746.

———, 1926. The cerebellum of fishes. II. The cerebellum of Megalops cyprinoides (Brouse) and its connections. Proc. kon. ned. Akad. Wet., Sect. Sci., 29:44–53.

Houser, G. L., 1901. The neurones and supporting elements of the brain of a selachian. J. comp. Neurol., 11:6–175.

Huber, G. C., and E. C. Crosby, 1926. On thalamic and tectal nuclei and fiber paths in the brain of the American alligator. J. comp. Neurol., 40:97–227.

———, 1929. The nuclei and fiber paths of the avian diencephalon, with consideration of telencephalic and certain mesencephalic centers and connections. J. comp. Neurol., 48:1–225.

———, 1933. The reptilian optic tectum. J. comp. Neurol., 57:57–163.

Huber, G. C., and Lydia De Witt, 1897. A contribution on the motor nerve-endings and the nerve-endings in the muscle-spindles. J. comp. Neurol., 7:169–230.

———, 1900. A contribution on the nerve terminations in neuro-tendinous end-organs. J. comp. Neurol., 10:159–208.

Hugosson, R., 1957. Morphologic and experimental studies on the development and significance of the rhombencephalic longitudinal cell columns. H. Ohlsson, Lund.

Ingvar, S., 1918. Zur Phylo- und Ontogenese des Kleinhirns. Folia neuro-biol. (Lpz.), 11:205–495.

Jahn, U., 1959. Morphological observations on living neuromuscular spindles. Acta Anat., 39:341–350.

Jakob, A., 1928. Das Kleinhirn. In von Möllendorff's Handbuch des mikroskopischen Anatomie des Menschen, Vol. 4, pp. 674–916. J. Springer, Berlin.

Jansen, J., 1930. The brain of Myxine glutinosa. J. comp. Neurol., 49:359–507.

———, 1954. On the morphogenesis and morphology of the mammalian cerebellum. In J. Jansen and A. Brodal, Aspects of cerebellar anatomy, pp. 13–81. Johan Grundt Tanum, Oslo.

———, and A. Brodal, 1940. Experimental studies on the intrinsic fibers of the cerebellum. II. The cortico-nuclear projection. J. comp. Neurol., 73:267–321.

———, 1942. Experimental studies on the intrinsic fibers of the cerebellum. The cortico-nuclear projection in the rabbit and the monkey (Macacus rhesus). Skr. norske Vidensk.-Akad., I. Mat.-nat. Kl., No. 3, pp. 1–50.

———, 1954. Aspects of cerebellar anatomy. Johan Grundt Tanum, Oslo.

Jansen, J., and J. Jansen, Jr., 1955. On the efferent fibers of the cerebellar nuclei in the cat. J. comp. Neurol., 102:607–632.

Jeleneff, A., 1879. Histologische Untersuchung des kleinen Gehirnes der Neunauge (Petromyzon fluviatilis). Bull. Acad. Imper. Sci., St. Petersburg, T.25:334–345.

Johnson, S. E., 1917. Structure and development of the sense organs of the lateral canal system of selachians (Mustelus canis and Squalus acanthias). J. comp. Neurol., 28:1–74.

———, 1918. The peripheral terminations of the nervus lateralis in Squalus sucklii. J. comp. Neurol., 29:279–289.

Johnston, J. B., 1898. Hind brain and cranial nerves of Acipenser. Anat. Anz., 14:580–602.

———, 1901. The brain of Acipenser. Zool. Jb. Anat. Abt., 15:59–260.

———, 1902. The brain of Petromyzon. J. comp. Neurol., 12:1–86.

———, 1905. The radix mesencephalica trigemini. The ganglion isthmi. Anat. Anz., 27:364–379.

———, 1906. The nervous system of vertebrates. P. Blakiston's Son and Co., Philadelphia.

———, 1908. Additional notes on the cranial nerves of petromyzonts. J. comp. Neurol., 18:569–608.

———, 1918. The history of the nucleus caudatus and the stria terminalis in vertebrates. Proc. Am. A. Anat., 1917. Anat. Rec., 14:41.

Juh Shen Shyu, 1939. On fiber connections of reptilian cerebellum. J. Orient. Med., 31:79–103.

Kappers. See Ariens Kappers.

Kashiwamura, T., 1955. Contributions to the comparative anatomy of the tractus tecto-cerebellaris in the brains of some lower vertebrates. Hiroshima J. med. Sci., 3:217–238.

Katz, B., 1948. The efferent regulation of the muscle spindle in the frog. J. exp. Biol., 26:201–217.

Kawakami, M., 1954. Contributions to the comparative anatomy of the cerebellar fiber connections in the reptiles. Hiroshima J. med. Sci., 2:295–317.

Kingsbury, B. F., 1895a. On the brain of Necturus maculatus. J. comp. Neurol., 5:139–205.

———, 1895b. The lateral line system of sense organs in some American Amphibia, and comparison with the Dipnoans. Trans. Amer. micr. Soc., 17:115–154.

———, 1897. The encephalic evaginations in ganoids. J. comp. Neurol., 7:1–36.

Kleerekoper, H., and K. Sibabin, 1959. A study of hearing in frogs (Rana pipiens and Rana clamitans). Z. vergl. Physiol., 41:490–499.

Koelliker, A., 1862. Untersuchungen über die letzten Endigungen der Nerven. Z. wiss. Zool., 12:149–164.

Kohnstamm, O., 1900. Ueber die gekreuzt-aufsteigende Spinalbahn und ihre Beziehung zum Gowers'schen Strang. Neurol. Cbl., 19:242–249.

———, 1910. Studien zur physiologischen Anatomie des Hirnstammes. III. J. Psychol. Neurol. (Lpz.), 17:33–57.

Kooy, F. H., 1917. The inferior olive in vertebrates. Folia neurobiol. (Lpz.), 10:205–369.

———, 1918. The inferior olive in Cetacea. Folia neuro-biol. (Lpz.), 11:647–664.

Krabbe, K. H., 1939. Studies on the morphogenesis of the brain in reptiles. Einar Munksgaard, Copenhagen.

———, 1952. Studies on the morphogenesis of the brain in birds. Einar Munksgaard, Copenhagen.

Kreht, H., 1930. Ueber die Faserzüge im Zentralnervensystem von Salamandra maculosa, L. Z. mikr.-anat. Forsch., 23:239–320.

———, 1931. Ueber die Faserzüge im Zentralnervensystem von Proteus anguineus Laur. Z. mikr.-anat. Forsch., 25:376–427.

Kudo, K., 1923. Über den Torus longitudinalis der Knochenfische. Anat. Anz., 56:359–367.

———, 1924. Beiträge zur Anatomie des Zwischen- und Mittelhirns der Knochenfische. III. Eine frontale Verbindung des Torus longitudinalis. Anat. Anz., 57:271–275.

Kühn, A., and W. Trendelenburg, 1911. Die exogenen und endogenen Bahnen des Rückenmarks der Taube mit der Degenerationsmethode untersucht. Arch. Anat. Physiol., Anat. Abt., 35–48.

Kuffler, S. W., and C. C. Hunt, 1952. The mammalian small-nerve fibers: a system for efferent nervous regulation of muscle spindle discharge. Res. Publ. Ass. nerv. ment. Dis., 30:24–47.

Kuhlenbeck, H., 1956. Die Formbestandteile der Regio praetectalis des Anamnier-Gehirns und ihre Beziehungen zum Hirnbauplan. Okajimas Folia anat. jap., 28:23–44.

Kuhne, W., 1863a. Ueber die Endigung der Nerven in den Muskeln. Virchows Arch. Path. Anat., 27:508–533.

———, 1863b. Die Muskelspindeln. Virchows Arch. Path. Anat., 28:528–538.

Kuithan, W., 1895. Die Entwicklung des Kleinhirns bei Säugetieren. Münch. med. Abh., 7:1–40.

Kulchitsky, N., 1924. Nerve endings in muscles. J. Anat. (Lond.), 58:152–169.

Kupffer, A. von, 1899. Zur Kopfentwicklung von Bdellostoma. S.-B. Ges. Morphol. Physiol. München, Heft 1.

———, 1906. Die Morphogenie des Centralnervensystems. In O. Hertwig's Handbuch der vergleichenden und experimentellen Entwicklungslehre der Wirbeltiere, Vol. 2, Teil 3. G. Fischer, Jena.

Landau, E., 1928. Zweiter Beitrag zur Kenntnis der Körnerschicht des Kleinhirns. Anat. Anz., 65:89–93.

Lange, S. J. de, 1917. Das Hinterhirn, das Nachhirn und das Rückenmark der Reptilien. Folia neuro-biol. (Lpz.), 10:385–422.

Langelaan, J. W., 1919. On the development of the external form of the human cerebellum. Brain, 42:130–170.

Larsell, O., 1920. The cerebellum of Amblystoma. J. comp. Neurol., 31:259–282.

———, 1923. The cerebellum of the frog. J. comp. Neurol., 36:89–112.

———, 1925. The development of the cerebellum in the frog (Hyla regilla) in relation to the vestibular and lateral-line systems. J. comp. Neurol., 39:249–289.

———, 1926. The cerebellum of reptiles: lizards and snake. J. comp. Neurol., 41:59–94.

———, 1931. The cerebellum of Triturus torosus. J. comp. Neurol., 53:1–54.

———, 1932a. The development of the cerebellum in Amblystoma. J. comp. Neurol., 54:357–435.

———, 1932b. The cerebellum of reptiles: chelonians and alligator. J. comp. Neurol., 56:299–345.

———, 1934a. The differentiation of the peripheral and central acoustic apparatus in the frog. J. comp. Neurol., 60:473–527.

———, 1934b. Morphogenesis and evolution of the cerebellum. Arch. Neurol. Psychiat. (Chic.), 31:373–395.

———, 1935. The development and morphology of the cerebellum in the opossum. Part I. Early development. J. comp. Neurol., 63:65–94.

———, 1936a. The development and morphology of the cerebellum in the opossum. Part II. Later development and adult. J. comp. Neurol., 63:251–291.

———, 1936b. Cerebellum and corpus pontobulbare of the bat (Myotis). J. comp. Neurol., 64:275–302.

———, 1937. The cerebellum: a review and interpretation. Arch. Neurol. Psychiat. (Chic.), 38:580–607.

———, 1945. Comparative neurology and present knowledge of the cerebellum. Bull. Minn. med. Found., 5:73–85.

———, 1947a. The cerebellum of myxinoids and petromyzonts, including developmental stages in the lampreys. J. comp. Neurol., 86:395–445.

———, 1947b. The development of the cerebellum in man in relation to its comparative anatomy. J. comp. Neurol., 87:85–129.

———, 1948. The development and subdivisions of the cerebellum of birds. J. comp. Neurol., 89:123–189.

———, 1952. The morphogenesis and adult pattern of the lobules and fissures of the cerebellum of the white rat. J. comp. Neurol., 97:281–356.

———, 1953a. The cerebellum of the cat and the monkey. J. comp. Neurol., 99:135–199.

———, 1953b. The anterior lobe of the mammalian and the human cerebellum. Anat. Rec., 115:341.

———, 1954. The development of the cerebellum of the pig. Anat. Rec., 118:73–107.

———, and D. G. Whitlock, 1952. Further observations on the cerebellum of birds. J. comp. Neurol., 97:545–566.

Leuret, F., and P. Gratiolet, 1839–57. Anatomie comparés du système nerveux. J.-B. Baillière et fils, Paris.

Levi-Montalcino, R., 1949. The development of the acustico-vestibular centers in the chick embryo in the absence of the afferent root fibers and descending fiber tracts. J. comp. Neurol., 91:209–241.

Lewandowsky, M., 1904. Untersuchungen über die Leitungsbahnen des Truncus cerebri und ihren Zusammenhang mit denen der Medulla spinalis und des Cortex cerebri. Neurobiol. Arb. II, Ser. 1, 63–147. G. Fischer, Jena.

Lewy, R. H., 1910. Der Deiterssche Kern und das Deiterospinale Bündel. Arb. hirnanat. Inst. Zurich, 4:227–244.

Leydig, F., 1851. Über die Nervenknöpfe in den Schleimkanälen von Lepidoleprus, Umbrina und Corvina. Müll. Arch. Anat. Physiol., 235–240.

Lindström, T., 1949. On the cranial nerves of the Cyclostomes with special reference to N. trigeminus. Acta. zool., 30:315–458.

Liu, Hin-Ching, and R. B. Maneely, 1962. Some cutaneous nerve endings in the soft-shelled turtle of South China. J. comp. Neurol., 119:381–389.

Löwenberg, H., 1938. The presence of the synarmotical cell in the cerebellum of birds. Bio-Morphosis, 7:273–280.

———, 1939. Études sur les cellules de Golgi, les cellules interstitielles et les voies d'association intracérébelleuses chez les mammifères et les oiseaux. Arch. int. Méd. exp., 14:51–102.

Löwenstein, O., 1957. The sense organs: the acoustico-lateralis system. In M. E. Brown, The physiology of fishes, Chapt. 2, Part 2, pp. 155–186. Academic Press, New York.

Luciani, L., 1891. Il cervelletto: Nuovi studi di fisiologia normale e patologica. Le Monnier, Firenze.

Lundberg, A., and O. Oscarsson, 1962. Functional organization of the ventral spino-cerebellar tract in the cat. IV. Identification of units by antidromic activation from the cerebellar cortex. Acta physiol. scand., 54:252–269.

McNally, W. J., 1929, 1930. Five lectures on the physiology of the ear. Ann. Otol. (St. Louis), 38:1163–1196; 39:248–290.

Malacarne, M. V. G., 1776. Nuova esposizione della vera struttura del cerveletto umano. G. M. Briolo, Torino. (Cit. Ziehen, 1934a.)

———, 1780. Encefalotomia universale. G. M. Briolo, Torino.

Malme, A. N., 1892. Studien über das Gehirn der Knochenfische. Stockholm.

Mangold, E., 1913. Gehörssinn und statischer Sinn. B. Gehörssinn und statischer Sinn bei Wirbeltieren. I. Allgemeine anatomische Vorbemerkungen. H. Winterstein's Handbuch der vergleichenden Physiologie, 4:907–908. G. Fischer, Jena.

Manning, F. B., 1924. Hearing in the goldfish in relation to the structure of its ear. J. exp. Zool., 41:5–20.

Mareschal, P., 1934. L'olive bulbaire. Anatomie, ontogénèse, phylogénèse, physiologie et physio-pathologie. G. Doin et Cie, Paris.

Marie, P., and C. Guillain, 1903. Le faisceau de Türck (faisceau externe du pied de peduncle). Sem. méd. (Paris), 23:229–233.

Marshall, N. B., 1951. Bathypelagic fish as sound scatterers in the ocean. J. Marine Res., 10:1–17.

Marshall, W., 1920. Brehm's Tierleben. Die Vögel, Bd. 3.

Mather, V., and M. Hines, 1934. Studies on the innervation of skeletal muscle. V. The limb muscles of the newt, Triturus torosus. Amer. J. Anat., 54:177–201.

May, R. M., 1954. The innervation of the skin of the lizard A. roquet. Bull. Soc. Zool. (France), 79:176–183.

Mayser, P., 1881. Vergleichend anatomische Studien über das Gehirn der Knochenfische mit besonderer Berücksichtigung der Cyprinoiden. Z. wiss. Zool., 36:259–366.

Meckel, J. F., 1817. Handbuch der menschlichen Anatomie. 3. Ed. Halle and Berlin.

Meessen, E., and J. Olszewski, 1949. A cytoarchitectonic atlas of the rhombencephalon of the rabbit. S. Karger, Basel and New York.

Merkel, F., 1880. Über die Endigungen der sensiblen Nerven in der Haut der Wirbelthiere. H. Schmidt, Rostock.

Mesdag, T. M., 1909. Bijdrage tot de ontwikkelingsgeschiedens van de structuur der hersenen bij het kip-embryo. (Diss.), Groeningen. (Cit. Ingvar, 1918.)

Meynert, T., 1872. The brain of mammals. In Stricker's Manual of histology. Wm. Wood and Co., New York.

Müller, Johannes, 1837. Die vergleichende Anatomie der Wirbeltiere. Abh. kon. Akad. Wiss., Berlin.

———, 1838. Die vergleichende Neurologie der Myxinoiden. Abh. kon. Akad. Wiss., Berlin. (Cit. Ariens Kappers, 1906.)

Münzer, E., and H. Wiener, 1898. Beiträge zur Anatomie und Physiologie des Centralnervensystems der Taube. Mschr. Psychiat. Neurol., 3:379–406.

Murphy, C. C., 1900. Die morphologische und histologische Entwicklung des Kleinhirns der Vögel. (Diss.), Berlin. (Cit. Brouwer, 1913.)

Murray, R. W., 1956. The thermal sensitivity of the lateralis organs of Xenopus. J. exp. Biol., 33:798–805.

———, 1957. Evidence for a mechanoreceptive function of the ampullae of Lorenzini. Nature (Lond.), 179:106–107.

———, 1959. The response of the ampullae of Lorenzini to combined stimulation by temperature change and weak direct currents. J. Physiol., 145:1–13.

Muskens, L. J. J., 1930. On tracts and centers involved in the upward and downward associated movements of the eyes after experiments in birds. J. comp. Neurol., 50:289–331.

Nachtrieb, H. F., 1910. The primitive pores of Polyodon spathula (Walbaum). J. exp. Zool., 9:455–468.

Nicholls, G. E., 1912a. An experimental investigation on the function of Reissner's fibre. Anat. Anz., 40:409–432.

———, 1912b. The structure and development of Reissner's fiber and the sub-commissural organ. Part I. Quart. J. micr. Sci., 58:1–116.

Noble, G. K., 1931. The biology of the Amphibia. McGraw-Hill Book Co., New York.

Norris, H. W., 1908. The cranial nerves of Amphiuma means. J. comp. Neurol., 18:527–568.

———, 1911. The rank of Necturus among the tailed amphibians as indicated by the distribution of its cranial nerves. Proc. Iowa Acad. Sci., 18:37.

———, 1913. The cranial nerves of Siren lacertina. J. Morph., 24:245–338.

———, 1925. Observations upon the peripheral distribution of the cranial nerves of certain ganoid fishes (Amia lepidosteus, Polyodon, Scaphirhynchus and Acipenser). J. comp. Neurol., 39:345–432.

Norris, H. W., and S. P. Hughes, 1920. The cranial, occipital, and anterior spinal nerves of the dogfish, Squalus acanthias. J. comp. Neurol., 31:293–402.

Ochoterena, I., 1932. Histologia del cerebelo del Tepayaxin (Phrynosoma orbiculare, Wieg.). An. Inst. Biol. (Méx.), 3:81–94.

Olszewski, J., and D. Baxter, 1954. Cytoarchitecture of the human brain stem. New York.

Onufrowicz, B., 1885. Experimenteller Beitrag zur Kenntniss des Ursprungs des Nervus acusticus des Kaninchens. Arch. Psychiat. Nervenkr., 16:711–742.

Palmgren, A., 1921. Embryological and morphological studies on the midbrain and cerebellum of vertebrates. Acta zool., 2:1–94.

Pansini, S., 1889. Des terminations des nerfs sur les tendons des vertebres. Arch. ital. Biol., 11:225.

Papez, J. W., 1929. Comparative neurology. T. Y. Crowell Co., New York.

Parker, G. H., 1904. The function of the lateral-line organs in fishes. Bull. Bur. Fish., 24:183–207.

———, 1908a. The sensory reactions of Amphioxus. Proc. Amer. Acad. Arts Sci., 43:415–455.

———, 1908b. Structure and functions of the ear of the Squeteague. Bull. Bur. Fish., 28:1213–1224.

———, 1908c. The sense of taste in fishes. Science, N. S., 27:453.

———, 1918. A critical survey of the sense of hearing in fishes. Proc. Amer. philos. Soc., 57:69–98.

———, and A. P. van Heusen, 1917a. The responses of the catfish, Amiurus nebulosus, to metallic and non-metallic rods. Amer. J. Physiol., 44:405–420.

———, 1917b. The reception of mechanical stimuli by the skin, lateral-line organs and ears, of fishes, especially in Amiurus. Amer. J. Physiol., 44:463–489.

Pearson, A. A., 1936a. The acoustico-lateral nervous system in fishes. J. comp. Neurol., 64:235–273.

———, 1936b. The acoustico-lateral centers and the cerebellum with fiber connections, of fishes. J. comp. Neurol., 65:201–294.

Perroncito, A., 1901. Sur la terminaison des nerfs dans les fibres musculaires striées. Arch. ital. Biol., 36:245–254.

———, 1902. Etudes ulterieures sur la terminaision des nerfs dans les muscles a fibres striées. Arch. ital. Biol., 38:393.

Piatt, J., 1946. The influence of the peripheral field on the development of the mesencephalic V nucleus in Amblystoma. J. exp. Zool., 102:109–141.

Piper, H., 1906. Aktionsströme von Gehörorgan der Fische bei Schallreizung. Zbl. Physiol., 20:293–297.

Poggendorf, D., 1952. Die absoluten Hörschwellen des Zwergwelses (Amiurus nebulosus) und Beiträge zur Physik des Weberschen Apparates der Ostariophysen. Z. vergl. Physiol., 34:222–257.

Pollard, H. B., 1892. On the anatomy and phylogenetic position of Polypterus. Zool. Jb., Morph. Abt., 5:387–428.

Pompeiano, O., and A. Brodal, 1957a. The origin of vestibulospinal fibres in the cat. An experimental-anatomical study, with comments on the descending medial longitudinal fasciculus. Arch. ital. Biol., 95:166–195.

———. 1957b. Spino-vestibular fibers in the cat. An experimental study. J. comp. Neurol., 108:353–381.

Porta, A., 1908. I muscoli caudali e anali nei generi Pavo e Meleagri. Zool. Anz., 33:116–120.

Ramon y Cajal, P., 1894. Investigaciones micrográficas en el encéfalo de los batracios y reptiles, etc. Zaragoza. (Cit. S. Ramon y Cajal, 1909–11.)

———, 1896. Las células estrelladas de la capa molecular del cerebelo de los reptiles. Rev. Trim. Micrográf. (Cit. S. Ramon y Cajal, 1909–11.)

Ramon y Cajal, S., 1888a. Terminaciones en los husos musculares de la rana. Rev. Trim. Histol. norm. patol., No. 1. (Cit. Ramon y Cajal, 1909–11.)

———, 1888b. Estructura de los centros nerviosus de las aves. I. Cerebelo. Rev. Trim. Histol. norm. patol., No. 1. (Cit. Ramon y Cajal, 1909–11.)

———, 1889. Sur l'origine et la direction des prolongations nerveuses de la couche moléculaire du cervelet. Int. Mschr. Anat. Physiol., 6:158–174.

———, 1890. Sur les fibres nerveuses de la couche granuleuse du cervelet et sur l'évolution des éléments cérébelleux. Int. Mschr. Anat. Physiol., 7:12–31.

———, 1891. La médula espinal de los reptiles. Barcelona.

———, 1894. Notas preventivas sobre la estructura del encéfalo de los teleósteos. An. Soc. españ. Hist. nat., 23. (Cit. Ramon y Cajal, 1909–11).

———, 1898. Centros nerviosos de los aves:cerebelo. Rev. Trim. Histol. norm. patol. (No. 1).

———, 1904. Textura del sistema nervioso del hombre y de los vertebrados. N. Moya, Madrid.

———, 1908a. Los ganglios centrales del cerebelo de las aves. Trav. Lab. Rech. biol. Madrid, 6:177–194.

———, 1908b. Sur un noyau spécial du nerf vestibulaire des poissons et des oiseaux. Trav. Lab. Rech. biol. Madrid, 6:1–20.

———, 1909–11. Histologie du système nerveux de l'homme et des vertébrés. 2 vols. A Maloine, Paris.

Rasmussen, A. T., 1933. Origin and course of the fasciculus uncinatus (Russell) in the cat, with observations on other fiber tracts arising from the cerebellar nuclei. J. comp. Neurol., 57:165–197.

Regaud, C., and M. Favre, 1904–05. Les terminaisons nerveuses et les organs nerveux sensitifs de l'appareil locomoteur. Rev. gén. Hist. Lyon, 1:1–140.

Reil, J. C., 1807–08. Fragmente über die Bildung des kleinen Gehirns im Menschen. Arch. Physiol., 8:1–58.

Retzius, A., 1822. Bidrag till ader- och nerfsystemets anatomie hos Myxine glutinosa. Kungl. Svenska Vetenskapsakad. Handl. (German trans. in Meckel's Arch. Anat. Physiol., Jahrg. 1826.)

Retzius, G., 1881–84. Das Gehörorgan der Wirbelthiere. 2 vols. Samson and Wallin, Stockholm.

———, 1893. Das Gehirn und das Auge von Myxine. Biol. Unters. N. F., 5:55–68.

Rijnberk, G. van, 1908. Die neueren Beiträge zur Anatomie und Physiologie des Kleinhirns der Säuger. Folia neuro-biol. (Lpz.), 1:46–62, 403–419, 535–551.

Riley, H. A., 1929. The mammalian cerebellum. A comparative study of the arbor vitae and folial pattern. Res. Publ. Ass. nerv. ment. Dis., 6:37–192.

Robin, Ch., 1849. Système nerveux des lamproies. Compt. rend. Soc. Biol., Pp. 6–7.

Röthig, P., 1927a. Beiträge zum Studium des Zentralnervensystems der Wirbeltiere. 11. Über die Faserzüge in Mittelhirn, Kleinhirn und der Medulla oblongata der Urodelen und Anuren. Z. mikr.-anat. Forsch., 10:381–472.

———, 1927b. Beiträge zum Studium des Zentralnervensystems der Wirbeltiere. 12. Marchi-Untersuchungen am Ranagehirn. Z. mikr.-anat. Forsch., 11:551–564.

Rohon, V., 1878. Das Centralorgan des Nervensystem des Selachier. Denkschr. kon. Akad. Wiss. Wien. Math-Naturwissensch. Kl., Bd. 37. (Cit. Ariens Kappers, 1906.)

Rolando, L., 1809. Saggio sopra la vera struttura del cervello dell' uomo e degli animali e sopra le funzioni del sistema nervoso. Sassari.

———, 1825. Osservazioni sul cerveletto. Mem. della Reale Accademia delle Science Torino, 29:163–189.

Romer, A. S., 1945. Vertebrate paleontology. University of Chicago Press, Chicago.

Rubin, M. A., 1935. Thermal reception in fishes. J. gen. Physiol., 18:643–647.

Rüdeberg, S. I., 1961. Morphogenetic studies on the cerebellar nuclei and their homologization in different vertebrates including man. (Thesis.) H. Ohlsson, Lund.

———, 1962. Formation of the embryonic migration layers in the cerebellar anlage of the reptile Iguana iguana. Acta Anat., 51:329–337.

Sachs, C., 1874. Physiologische und anatomische Untersuchungen über die sensiblen Nerven der Muskeln. Arch. Anat. Physiol. wiss. Med., 175–195.

Saetersdal, T. A. S., 1956a. On the ontogenesis of the avian cerebellum. Part I. Studies on the formation of fissures. Univ. Bergen. Årb. nat.-vit. R., No. 2, 1–15.

———, 1956b. On the ontogenesis of the avian cerebellum. Part II. Measurements of the cortical layers. Univ. Bergen. Årb. nat.-vit. R., No. 3, 1–53.

Saito, T., 1930. Ueber das Gehirn des japanischen Flussneunauges (Enthosphenus japonicus Martens). Folia anat. jap., 8:189–263.

Samano-Bishop, A., 1946. El sistema acustico cerebelar del Sceloporus microlepidotus. An. Inst. Biol. (Méx.), 17:301–321.

Sand, A. 1937. The mechanism of the lateral sense organs of fishes. Proc. roy. Soc. B, 123:472–495.

———, 1938. The function of the ampullae of Lorenzini, with some observations on the effect of temperature on sensory rhythms. Proc. roy. Soc. B, 125:524–553.

Sanders, A., 1894. Researches on the nervous system of Myxine glutinosa. London.

Sanders, E. B., 1929. A consideration of certain bulbar, midbrain, and cerebellar centers and fiber tracts in birds. J. comp. Neurol., 49:155–222.

Sauerbeck, E., 1896. Beiträge zur Kenntnis vom feineren Bau des Selachierhirns. Anat. Anz., 12:41–52.

Schäfer, E. A., 1893. The spinal cord and brain. In E. A. Schäfer and G. D. Thane, Quain's Elements of Anatomy, Vol. 3, Part 1. Longmans, Green and Co., London and New York.

Schaper, A., 1893. Zur feineren Anatomie des Kleinhirns der Teleostier. Anat. Anz., 8:705–720.

———, 1894a. Die morphologische und histologische Entwicklung des Kleinhirns der Teleostier. Anat. Anz., 9:489–501.

———, 1894b. Die morphologische und histologische Entwicklung des Kleinhirns der Teleostier. Morph. Jb., 24:625–708.

———, 1898. The finer structure of the selachian cerebellum (Mustelus vulgaris) as shown by chrome-silver preparations. J. comp. Neurol., 8:1–20.

———, 1899. Zur Histologie des Kleinhirns der Petromyzonten. Anat. Anz., 16:439–446.

Scharrer, E., 1932. Experiments on the function of the lateral-line organs in the larvae of Amblystoma punctatum. J. exp. Zool., 61:109–114.

————, 1933. Die Erklärung der scheinbar pathologischen Zellbilder im Nucleus supraopticus und Nucleus paraventricularis. Z. ges. Neurol. Psychiat., 145:462–470.

Scheibel, M. E., and A. B. Scheibel, 1954. Observations on the intracortical relations of the climbing fibers of the cerebellum. A Golgi study. J. comp. Neurol., 101:733–763.

————, 1955. The inferior olive. A Golgi study. J. comp. Neurol., 102:77–131.

Schepman, A. M. H., 1918. De octavo-laterale zintuigen en hun verbindungen in de hersenen der vertebraten. (Diss.) J. B. Wolter's U. M., Groningen. (Cit. Ariens Kappers, Huber, and Crosby, 1936.)

Schilling, K., 1907. Über das Gehirn von Petromyzon fluviatilis. Abh. Senckenberg nat. Ges. Frankfurt a. M., 30:425–446.

Schroeder, K., 1911. Der Faseverlauf im Vorderhirn des Huhnes, dargestellt auf Grund von entwicklungsgeschichtlichen (myelogenetischen) Untersuchungen, nebst Beobachtungen über die Bildungsweise und Entwicklungsrichtung der Markscheiden. J. Psychol. Neurol. (Lpz.), 18:115–173.

Schwalbe, G. A., 1881. Lehrbuch der Neurologie. Erlangen.

Shanklin, W. M., 1930. The central nervous system of Chameleon vulgaris. Acta zool., 11:425–490.

————, 1934. The cerebella of three deep sea fish. Acta zool., 15:409–430.

Sheldon, R. E., 1912. The olfactory tracts and centers in teleosts. J. comp. Neurol., 22:177–339.

Sherrington, C. S., 1900. The cerebellum. In E. A. Schäfer, Textbook of physiology, Vol. 2, pp. 893–910. Young J. Pentland, Edinburgh and London.

Shimazono, J., 1912. Das Kleinhirn der Vögel. Arch. mikr. Anat., 80:397–449.

Sihler, Chr., 1900. Neue Untersuchungen über die Nerven der Muskeln mit besonderer Berücksichtigung umstrittener Fragen. Z. wiss. Zool., 68:323–378.

Sinn, R., 1913. Beitrag zur Kenntnis der Medulla oblongata der Vögel. Mschr. Psychiat. Neurol., 33:1–39.

Smith, G. Elliot, 1902. The primary subdivision of the mammalian cerebellum. J. Anat. (Lond.), 36:381–385.

————, 1903a. Notes on the morphology of the cerebellum. J. Anat. (Lond.), 37:329–332.

————, 1903b. Further observations of the natural mode of subdivision of the mammalian cerebellum. Anat. Anz., 23:368–384.

————, 1903c. The morphology of the human cerebellum. Rev. Neurol. Psychiat., 1:629–639.

Smith, K. U., and R. S. Daniel, 1947. Observations of behavioral development in the loggerhead turtle (Caretta caretta). Science, 104:154–156.

Smith, M. C., 1961. The anatomy of the spino-cerebellar fibers in man. II. The distribution of the fibers in the cerebellum. J. comp. Neurol., 117:329–354.

Snider, R. S., 1945. Electro-anatomical studies on a tectocerebellar pathway. Anat. Rec., 91:299.

Snider, R. S., and A. Stowell, 1942. Evidence of a representation of tactile sensibility in the cerebellum of the cat. Fed. Proc., 1:82.

————, 1944. Receiving areas of the tactile, auditory, and visual systems in the cerebellum. J. Neurophysiol., 7:331–357.

van der Sprenkel. See Berkelbach van der Sprenkel.

Stefanelli, A., 1935. Sul valore morfologico del "cervelletto" dei Petromizonti nelle sue relazione col sistema laterale. Monit. zool. ital., 46:175–184.

————, 1937. Il sistema statico dei Petromizonti (sistema laterale, sistema vestibolare, cervelletto). Arch. zool. ital., 24:209–243.

————, 1939. Il cervelletto degli Anamni, Fatti e considerazioni morfologico-comparative. Arch. ital. Anat. Embriol., 17:1–45.

————, 1943. Osservazioni comparative sui nuclei cerebellari dei rettili in relazione al differente modo di locomozione. Monit. zool. ital., 54:65–72.

————, 1953. Il neurone di Mauthner degli Ittiopsidi (Pisces, Amphibia). Experientia (Basel), 9:277–285.

————, and V. Pietrogrande, 1944. Ricerche istologiche comparative sui nuclei cerebellari dei rettili. Ric. Morf., 20–21:351–362.

Steinmann, P., 1914. Über die Bedeutung des Labyrinths und der Seitenorgane für die Rheotaxis und die Beibehaltung der Bewegungsrichtung bei Fischen und Amphibien. Verh. naturf. Ges. Basel, 25:212–243.

Stendell, W., 1914. Die Faseranatomie des Mormyridengehirns. Abh. Senckenberg. nat. Ges. Frankfurt a. M. (Cit. Berkelbach van der Sprenkel, 1915.)

Sterzi, C., 1907–12. Il sistema nervoso centrale dei vertebrati. Cyclostomi; 1909, Pesci, Selaci; 1912, Sviluppo. A Draghi, Padova.

Stetter, H., 1929. Untersuchungen über den Gehörsinn der Fische, besonders von Phoxinus laevis L. und Amiurus nebulosus Ref. Z. vergl. Physiol., 9:339–477.

Stieda, L., 1861. Ueber das Rückenmark und einzelne Theile des Gehirns von Esox Lucius. (Diss.), Dorpat.

————, 1864. Zur vergleichenden Anatomie und Histologie des Cerebellum. Arch. Anat. Physiol., 407–433.

————, 1870. Studien über das centrale Nervensystem der Wirbelthiere. Z. wiss. Zool., 20:273.

————, 1875. Ueber den Bau des centralen Nervensystems der Amphibien und Reptilien. Z. wiss. Zool., 25:1–74.

Stilling, B., 1864. Untersuchungen über den Bau des kleinen Gehirns des Menschen. Bd. 1. Ueber den Bau des Züngelchens und seiner Hemisphären-Theile. Cassel.

Strong, O. S., 1895. The cranial nerves of Amphibia. J. Morph., 10:101–230.

————, 1903. The cranial nerves of Squalus acanthias. Science, 17:254.

Stroud, B. B., 1895. The mammalian cerebellum. J. comp. Neurol., 5:71–118.

Sturkie, P. D., 1954. Avian physiology. Comstock Pub. Ass., Ithaca, N.Y.

Sumi, R., 1926. Über die Morphogenese des Gehirns von Hynobius nebulosus. Folia anat. jap., 4:171–270.

Suzuki, N., 1932. A contribution to the study of the Mormyrid cerebellum. Ann. zool. jap., 13:503–524.

Szentágothai, J., and K. Rajkovits, 1959. Über den Ursprung der Kletterfasern des Kleinhirns. Z. Anat. Entwickl.-Gesch., 121:130–141.

Takeda, H., 1960. Personal communication. Int. Anat. Congr., New York.

Tarin, P., 1750. Adversaria anatomica. Paris.

Tello, F., 1909. Contribución al conocimiento del encéfalo de los teleósteos. Los núcleos bulbares. Trav. Lab. Rech. biol. Madrid, 7:1–29.

Tiegs, O. W., 1932a. A study by degeneration methods of the innervation of the muscles of a lizard (Egernia). J. Anat. (Lond.), 66:300–322.

————, 1932b. The innervation of the striated musculature in Python. Aust. J. exp. Biol. med. Sci., 9:191–201.

————, 1953. Innervation of voluntary muscle. Physiol. Rev., 33:90–144.

Tilney, F., 1923. Genesis of cerebellar functions. Arch. Neurol. Psychiat. (Chic.), 9:137–169.

Tracy, H. C., 1920. The membranous labyrinth and its relation to the precoelomic diverticulum of the swimbladder in clupeoids. J. comp. Neurol., 31:219–257.

Tretjakoff, D., 1909. Das Nervensystem von Ammocoetes. II. Gehirn. Arch. mikr. Anat., 74:636–779.

————, 1927. Das periphere Nervensystem des Flussneunauges. Z. wiss. Zool., 129:359–452.

Tuge, H., 1932. Somatic motor mechanisms in the midbrain and medulla oblongata of Chrysemys elegans (Wied). J. comp. Neurol., 55:185–271.

———, 1934a. Studies on cerebellar function in the teleost. I. Reactions resulting from cerebellar ablation. J. comp. Neurol., 60:201–224.

———, 1934b. Studies on cerebellar function in the teleost. II. Is there a cerebello-tectal path? Marchi method. J. comp. Neurol., 60:225–236.

———, 1935. Studies on cerebellar function in the teleost. III. The mechanisms of the efferent side of the cerebellum. Marchi method. J. comp. Neurol., 61:347–369.

Turner, C. H., 1891. Morphology of the avian brain. I. Taxonomic value of the avian brain and the histology of the cerebrum. J. comp. Neurol., 1:39–92, 265–286.

Vachananda, B., 1958. Experimental and anatomical study of the major spinal afferent systems. (Diss.), Ann Arbor, Michigan.

———, 1959. The major spinal afferent systems to the cerebellum and the cerebellar corticonuclear connections in Macaca mulatta. J. comp. Neurol., 112:303–351.

Versteegh, C., 1927. Ergebnisse partieller Labyrinthextirpation bei Kaninchen. Acta oto-laryng. (Stockh.), 11:393–408.

Vesalius, A., 1543. De Humani Corporis Fabrica. J. Oparin, Basel.

Viault, F., 1876. Recherches histologiques sur la structure des centres nerveux des Plagiostomes. Arch. Zool. exp. gen., T. 5.

Vicq d'Azyr, F., 1786–90. Traite d'anatomie. Paris.

Vieussens, R., 1685. Nevrographia Universalis. Editio Nova. Lugduni, Apud Joannem Certe, in vico Mercatorio sub signo Trinitatis.

Vilstrup, T., 1951. The gelatinous substance of the macula neglecta. Ann. Otol. (St. Louis)., 60:75–91.

Vogt-Nilsen, L., 1954. The inferior olive in birds. A comparative morphological study. J. comp. Neurol., 101:447–481.

Voorhoeve, J. J., 1917. Over den bouw van de kleine hersenen der Plagiostomen. (Diss.), Amsterdam. (Cit. Ariens Kappers, Huber, and Crosby, 1936.)

Voris, H. C., and N. L. Hoerr, 1932. The hindbrain of the opossum, Didelphis virginiana. J. comp. Neurol., 54:277–355.

Vraa-Jensen, G., 1956. On the correlation between the function and structure of nerve cells. Acta psychiat. scand., (Suppl. 109):1–96.

Walberg, F., D. Bowsher, and A. Brodal, 1958. The termination of primary vestibular fibers in the vestibular nuclei in the cat. An experimental study with silver methods. J. comp. Neurol., 110:391–419.

Wallenberg, A., 1898. Die secundäre Acusticusbahn der Taube. Anat. Anz., 14:353–369.

———, 1900. Ueber centrale Endstätten des Nervus octavus der Taube. Anat. Anz., 17:102–108.

———, 1903. Der Ursprung des Tractus isthmo-striatus (oder bulbostriatus) der Taube. Neurol. Cbl., 22:98–101.

———, 1904. Neue untersuchungen über den Hirnstamm der Taube. Anat. Anz., 25:526–528.

———, 1907. Beiträge zur Kenntnis des Gehirns der Teleostier und Selachier. Anat. Anz., 31:369–399.

Walls, G. L., 1942. The vertebrate eye and its adaptive radiation. Cranbrook Press, Bloomfield Hills, Michigan.

Weddell, G., 1941. The pattern of cutaneous innervation in relation to cutaneous sensibility. J. Anat. (Lond.), 75:346–367.

Weidenreich, F., 1899. Zur Anatomie der zentralen Kleinhirnkerne der Säuger. Z. Morphol. Anthropol., 1:259–312.

Weismann, A., 1861. Ueber das Wachsen der quergestreiften Muskeln nach Beobachtungen am Frosch. Z. rat. Med., Ser. 3, 10:263–284.

Westerfield, F., 1922. The ability of mud-minnows to form associations with sounds. J. comp. Psychol., 2:187–190.

Weston, J. K., 1936. The reptilian vestibular and cerebellar gray with fiber connections. J. comp. Neurol., 65:93–200.

———, 1938. Observations on the distribution of ganglion cells and fibers related to the saccule and the basal coil of the cochlea. Acta neerl. Morph., 1:136–150.

———, 1939a. Observations on the comparative anatomy of the VIIIth nerve complex. Acta oto-laryng. (Stockh.), 27:457–498.

———, 1939b. Notes on the comparative anatomy of the sensory areas of the vertebrate inner ear. J. comp. Neurol., 70:355–394.

———, 1939c. Notes on the comparative anatomy of the ganglion cells associated with the vertebrate inner ear sensory areas. J. Anat. (Lond.), 73:263–288.

Wever, E. G., and C. W. Bray, 1936. Hearing in the pigeon as studied by the electrical responses of the inner ear. J. comp. Psychol., 22:353–363.

Whitlock, D. G., 1952. A neurohistological and neurophysiological study of efferent fiber tracts and receptive areas of the avian cerebellum. J. comp. Neurol., 97:567–635.

Williams, E. M., 1909. Vergleichend-anatomische Studien über den Bau und die Bedeutung der Oliva inferior der Säugethiere und Vögel. Arb. neurol. Inst. Univ. Wien, 17:118–149.

Willis, T., 1664. Cerebri Anatome. Cui accesset nervorum descriptic et usus. J. Martyn and J. Allestry, London.

Winkelman, N. W., and J. Eckel, 1929. Origin of the corticocerebellar system as determined in human pathological material. Res. Publ. Ass. nerv. ment. Dis., 6:481–493.

Winkler, C., 1907. The central course of the nervus octavus and its influence on motility. Proc. kon. ned. Akad. Wet., 14:1–202 (Müller, Amsterdam, 1909).

———, and A. Potter, 1914. An anatomical guide to experimental researches on the cat's brain. Amsterdam.

Wlassak, R., 1887. Das Kleinhirn des Frosches. Arch. Anat. Physiol., Physiol. Abt., Suppl. Bd. 109–137.

Woodburne, R. T., 1936. A phylogenetic consideration of the primary and secondary centers and connections of the trigeminal complex in a series of vertebrates. J. comp. Neurol., 65:403–501.

Worthington, J., 1905. The descriptive anatomy of the brain and cranial nerves of Bdellostoma dombeyi. Quart. J. micr. Sci., 49:137–181.

Wunder, W., 1950. Die Seitenlinie, ein besonderes Wassersinnesorgan der Fische. Allgemeine Fischerei-Zeitung, 75:97–99.

Yamamoto, S., K. Ohkawa, and I. Lee, 1957. On the cerebellar nuclei of birds. Arch. histol. jap., 13:129–139.

Yoshimura, K., 1910. Experimentelle und vergleichend anatomische Untersuchungen über die untere Olive der Vögel. Arb. neurol. Inst. Univ. Wien, 18:46–59.

Yoss, R. E., 1952. Studies of the spinal cord. Part I. Topographic localization within the dorsal spino-cerebellar tract in Macaca mulatta. J. comp. Neurol., 97:5–20.

Ziehen, T., 1899. Centralnervensystem. In Bardelebens Handbuch der Anatomie des Menschen. Bd. 1, 1. Abt., pp. 1–576. G. Fischer, Jena.

———, 1903. Centralnervensystem. In Bardelebens Handbuch der Anatomie des Menschen. Bd. 4, 1. Abt., pp. 403–501. G. Fischer, Jena.

———, 1934a. Mikroskopische Anatomie des Kleinhirns. In Bardeleben's Handbuch der Anatomie des Menschen. Bd. 4, 2. Abt. G. Fischer, Jena.

———, 1934b. Beiträge zur vergleichenden Anatomie des Kleinhirns. Anat. Anz., 78:182–187.

INDEX

290